531

LIBRARY, R.A.E. WESTCOTT

REGULATIONS FOR BORROWERS

1. Books are issued on loan for a period of 1 month and must be returned to the Library promptly.

2. Before books are taken from the Library receipts for them must be filled in, signed, and handed to a member of the Library Staff. Receipts for books received through the internal post must be signed and returned to the Library immediately.

3. Readers are responsible for books which they have borrowed, and are required to replace any such books which they lose. In their own interest they are advised not to pass on to other readers books they have borrowed.

4. To enable the Library Staff to deal with urgent requests for books, borrowers who expect to be absent for more than a week are requested either to arrange for borrowed books to be made available to the P.A. or Clerk to the Section, or to return them to the Library for safekeeping during the period of absence.

NON-LINEAR MECHANICS

INTRODUCTION
TO
NON-LINEAR MECHANICS

TOPOLOGICAL METHODS — ANALYTICAL METHODS
NON-LINEAR RESONANCE — RELAXATION OSCILLATIONS

BY

N. MINORSKY, Ph.D.

J. W. EDWARDS   1947   ANN ARBOR

Lithoprinted in U.S.A.
EDWARDS BROTHERS, INC.
Ann Arbor, Michigan
1947

This report aims to bring to the attention of technical personnel, both of the Navy and of other agencies engaged in the war effort, certain new developments in applied mathematical methods. These new methods have come to be called "Non-Linear Mechanics." This new branch of theoretical mechanics does not introduce any new postulates but relies upon the same Newtonian principles commonly used in engineering applications. The only difference between these new methods and the old ones lies in the mathematical methods themselves. The old methods, such as that of small motions, simplify the problem in advance so as to bring it within the scope of linear differential equations. The general theory of these is known, so that approximate solutions are obtained by standard methods. It is the purpose of the new methods to obtain more accurate solutions without recourse to artificial simplification.

A few definitions and examples will be given so that the subject may appear somewhat better defined. The general form of a linear differential equation of the nth order is

$$\frac{d^n x}{dt^n} + p_1(t)\frac{d^{n-1}x}{dt^{n-1}} + p_2(t)\frac{d^{n-2}x}{dt^{n-2}} + \cdots + p_{n-1}(t)\frac{dx}{dt} + p_n(t)x = Q(t)$$

where x, the dependent variable, constitutes the unknown function to be determined by integration, and t is the independent variable, for example, time. In a great majority of dynamical problems x is *a spacial coordinate*. The coefficients $p_1(t) \ldots p_n(t)$ are known functions of t. $Q(t)$, designated sometimes as a *forcing function*, is also a known function of t. According to whether $Q(t) = 0$ or $Q(t) \neq 0$ the linear equation is called homogeneous or non-homogeneous.

In many engineering applications all the functions $p_1(t) \ldots p_n(t)$ are constant; the linear differential equation is then said to have *constant coefficients*. This is the simplest form of a linear differential equation and its solution, as is shown in elementary texts, is reduced to that of solving an algebraic equation. On the other hand, in applications linear differential equations with variable coefficients are often encountered. For instance, the well-known Mathieu equation is

$$\ddot{x} + (a^2 + b^2 \cos pt)x = 0$$

This equation has a great variety of applications, such as oscillations of locomotive mechanisms, theory of modulation in radio circuits, oscillations of membranes with elliptic boundaries, and diffraction of light. Although

the theory of the Mathieu equation is much more difficult than that of equations with constant coefficients, it is still a linear differential equation.

The basic feature of such equations is that they obey the so-called
principle of superposition. Thus, if a system is governed by a linear differential equation and is capable of oscillating in certain modes, the motion
will take place as if each component oscillation with a certain frequency existed alone, not influenced by the presence of oscillations with other frequencies. This constitutes a considerable simplification which permits a
physicist to be guided by intuition without having to rely continuously on
the mathematical methods. In order to be able to proceed in this manner, however, one must be certain that the differential equations are linear. In this
connection there arise frequently serious difficulties as to the limits of
validity of the differential equation describing a certain physical phenomenon. Clearly the only criterion of validity of a certain mathematical law is
its agreement with the observed facts. If this agreement is good, within a
certain range of the phenomena under consideration, it is natural to conclude
that the differential equation correctly describes the phenomena and that the
hypotheses which were made in obtaining the equation are correct. If, however, for some other range the same differential equation ceases to give a
satisfactory agreement with observation this generally indicates that certain
assumptions or *idealizations* which were sufficiently correct for a certain
range cease to be correct when the range of observation is extended. Concepts of constant electric resistance of a conductor, of a constant spring
constant, of a rectilinear characteristic of an electron tube, and so on, appear very often as idealizations valid only in a certain restricted range.
If the problem is investigated within that range the idealized linear differential equations give a reasonably good agreement with observation. If, however, the same phenomenon is studied in a somewhat larger range, in which the
assumed idealizations cease to be true, the departures between the theory and
the observed facts become more and more evident, as the range of the investigation is extended. The reason for such discrepancies is clearly that the
problem has been over-idealized, and a more correct form of differential equation must be employed. In such cases the correct differential equations are
usually non-linear. In some cases, as will appear later, non-linear equations
appear at the **very** outset of the problem. In such cases it is impossible to
describe the phenomenon mathematically by means of linear differential equations for any range, however small.

A few examples which follow illustrate this general situation.

THE PENDULUM

The exact differential equation of the simple pendulum is

$$\ddot{\theta} + \frac{g}{L}\sin\theta = 0 \qquad [1]$$

This is a homogeneous non-linear differential equation of the form

$$\ddot{\theta} + \phi(\theta)\theta = 0$$

with a variable "spring constant"

$$\phi(\theta) = \frac{g}{L}\left(1 - \frac{\theta^2}{6} + \cdots\right)$$

resulting from the expansion of $\sin\theta$ in a power series. If we assume that all terms beginning with $\theta^2/6$ are negligible we obtain the "zero approximation"

$$\phi(\theta) = \frac{g}{L}$$

which gives

$$\ddot{\theta} + \frac{g}{L}\theta = 0 \qquad [2]$$

This is the well-known elementary equation of a "linearized" pendulum having a fixed period $T = 2\pi\sqrt{L/g}$. For the next, or first, approximation we assume $\phi(\theta) = \frac{g}{L}\left(1 - \frac{\theta^2}{6}\right)$. This gives a non-linear differential equation of the form

$$\ddot{\theta} + \left[\frac{g}{L}\left(1 - \frac{\theta^2}{6}\right)\right]\theta = 0 \qquad [3]$$

The spring constant in this case does not remain constant but diminishes with increasing θ. In this manner we obtain a more nearly correct representation of the motion. By retaining a greater number of terms in the power expansion of $\sin\theta$ we obtain still greater accuracy but the problem becomes more complicated. In practice even the first approximation [3] gives an error of less than 1 per cent for angles of the order of 30 degrees.

FROUDE'S DIFFERENTIAL EQUATION OF ROLLING

The oscillations of a ship in still water, according to Froude, are given by the equation

$$I\ddot{\theta} + B_1\dot{\theta} + B_2\dot{\theta}^2 + D\cdot h(\theta) = 0 \qquad [4]$$

in which I is the moment of inertia of the ship about a longitudinal axis through the center of gravity,

B_1, B_2 are the so-called Froude's coefficients of resistance to rolling,

D is the displacement, and

$h(\theta)$ is the variable lever arm of the righting couple.

This equation is non-linear due to the presence of the term $B_2\dot{\theta}^2$ and the term $h(\theta)$ which departs slightly from a linear function of θ. For small angles θ, $h(\theta)$ is approximately of the form $h(\theta) = h_0\theta$, where h_0 is the initial meta-centric height. The linearization of this term is therefore permissible in the range of small angles for which h_0 remains substantially constant. As regards the other non-linear term $B_2\dot{\theta}^2$, it is generally uncertain whether we can "linearize" [4] by dropping this term altogether. In case this can be done for a particular ship, the problem is reduced to a simple linear equation

$$I\ddot{\theta} + B_1\dot{\theta} + Dh_0\theta = 0 \qquad [5]$$

If, however, the experimental evidence is such that the term $B_2\dot{\theta}^2$ is of the same order as $B_1\dot{\theta}$, the differential equation is

$$I\ddot{\theta} + B_1\dot{\theta} + B_2\dot{\theta}^2 + Dh_0\theta = 0 \qquad [6]$$

and the difficulty of dealing with a non-linear differential Equation [6] cannot be avoided.

THE WILLIAMS BLAST GAGE

The differential equation of the Williams gage used for the investigation of explosive blast in air is

$$\ddot{x} + \frac{A}{m}\,p_0\left[\left(\frac{L}{L-x}\right)^\gamma - 1\right] = \frac{1}{m}\,P(t) \qquad [7]$$

where m, A, p_0, L, and γ are constants and $P(t)$ is a known function of time. Introducing the variable $y = x/L$, this equation acquires the form

$$\ddot{y} + k\,\frac{1}{y}\left[\frac{1}{(1-y)^\gamma} - 1\right]y = Q(t) \qquad [7a]$$

This is a non-homogeneous non-linear equation of the form

$$\ddot{y} + \phi(y)y = Q(t) \qquad [7b]$$

where $\phi(y) = \frac{k}{y}\left[\frac{1}{(1-y)^\gamma} - 1\right]$; k is a constant and $0 < y < 1$.

OSCILLATIONS OF A SPHERICAL GAS-FILLED CAVITY IN A FLUID

The differential equation of the phenomenon is

$$\ddot{R} + \frac{3}{2}\,\frac{1}{R}\,\dot{R}^2 + aR^3 - \frac{b}{R^{3(\gamma-1)}} = 0 \qquad [8]$$

where R is the radius of oscillating cavity and a, b, γ are certain constants.

This equation can be written as

$$\ddot{R} + \frac{3\dot{R}}{2R}\,\dot{R} + \phi(R)R = 0 \qquad [9]$$

where the non-linear spring constant $\phi(R) = aR^2 - b/R^{3\gamma-2}$ and the coefficient of damping $b = 3\dot{R}/2R$. Equation [9] is also a homogeneous non-linear differential equation, where the non-linearity is found in both the spring-constant term and in the damping coefficient.

DIRECTIONAL STABILITY OF SHIPS

The differential equation of the initial azimuthal motion of a ship from a straight course with the rudder amidships is

$$J\ddot{\alpha} + C(\dot{\alpha}) - M(\alpha) = 0 \qquad [10]$$

where J is the moment of inertia of the ship about the vertical axis through its center of gravity,

$C(\dot{\alpha})$ is the resistance to turning,

$M(\alpha)$ is the moment of the leeway force, and

α is the angle of the initial deviation.

The function $C(\dot{\alpha})$ is not known at present; it is probably proportional to some power of $\dot{\alpha}$; from physical considerations the linearization of this term by an expression of the form $C(\dot{\alpha}) = C_0\dot{\alpha}$ is not objectionable for small ranges of $\dot{\alpha}$.

As regards the term $M(\alpha)$, its linearization by a term of the form $M_0\alpha$ leads certainly to incorrect results; in fact this would mean that for an increasing α the term $M_0\alpha$, where M_0 is a certain constant, increases indefinitely. Observation shows that for an increasing α the couple $M(\alpha)$ passes through a maximum for a relatively small value of α and becomes zero thereafter, when the line of action of the resultant of the leeway forces recedes toward the center of gravity. This situation can be described more correctly by an approximate expression of the form

$$M(\alpha) = M_0\alpha - M_1\alpha^3$$

Hence a more correct differential equation for the directional stability is of the form

$$J\ddot{\alpha} + C_0\dot{\alpha} - (M_0 - M_1\alpha^2)\alpha = 0 \qquad [11]$$

This is a non-linear differential equation in which the non-linearity is localized in the spring constant $(M_0 - M_1\alpha^2)$ which decreases with the angle α. In this case the spring constant is negative inasmuch as a ship proceeding initially on a straight course is in unstable equilibrium.

PARASITIC OSCILLATIONS OR "HUNTING" IN CONTROL SYSTEMS

Somewhat different non-linear phenomena occur when the damping term of a dynamical system is initially negative and increases with increasing amplitudes so as to become ultimately positive for sufficiently large values of the dependent variable. Phenomena of this kind are amenable to the Van der Pol equation

$$\ddot{x} - \mu(1 - x^2)\dot{x} + x = 0 \qquad [12]$$

The equation of Rayleigh, discovered in connection with acoustic phenomena,

$$\ddot{x} - (A + B\dot{x}^2)\dot{x} + x = 0 \qquad [13]$$

is known to reduce to Van der Pol's equation by a change of variables, so that the two equations have analogous features. These equations have a very extensive field of application in connection with self-excited oscillations in electron-tube circuits.

A few years ago, in connection with a ship stabilization research program, it was discovered that under certain conditions the blade angle on the pump controlling the transfer of ballast between the tanks begins to flutter, interfering seriously with the efficiency of operation. A detailed analysis of this effect is given in Section 31 of this report. It is sufficient to mention here that the non-linear differential equation of this parasitic effect is of the form

$$J\ddot{\phi} - \left[(b - a_1) - a_3\dot{\phi}^2\right]\dot{\phi} + c\phi = 0 \qquad [14]$$

where J is the moment of inertia of the ballast, including tanks and ducts,
a_1 and a_3 are the coefficients in the expression giving the hydrodynamic couple exerted by blades on the ballast,
b is the coefficient of the natural damping (friction), and
c is the coefficient of static stability of the water ballast.

Equation [14] is seen to be Rayleigh's equation mentioned previously.

These few examples show the importance of the methods of non-linear mechanics for the solution of naval problems. As to the question where and how to use these methods, answers can be given only for specific cases. Each problem must be formulated explicitly and then examined to determine whether simplifying assumptions can be introduced to linearize the problem without the loss of any essential features. In cases where this is not possible one must face the situation arising from the essential non-linearity of the phenomenon and apply the more laborious methods of non-linear mechanics. The present report introduces the student who is familiar with standard methods of attack on linear problems to these more advanced methods.

CONTENTS

PART IV - RELAXATION OSCILLATIONS

INTRODUCTION

Practically all differential equations of Mechanics and Physics are non-linear; in the applications linear approximations are frequently used. The Method of Small Motions is a well-known example of the "linearization" of problems which are essentially non-linear. With the discovery of numerous phenomena of self-excitation of circuits containing non-linear conductors of electricity, such as electron tubes, arcs, gaseous discharges, etc., and in many cases of non-linear mechanical vibrations of special types the Method of Small Motions becomes inadequate for their analytical treatment. In fact the very existence of these oscillations in a steady state indicates that there is an element of non-linearity preventing the oscillations from building up indefinitely, which by energy considerations is obviously impossible. In addition to this there is another important difference between these phenomena and those governed by linear equations with constant coefficients, e.g., oscillations of a pendulum with small amplitudes, in that the amplitude of the ultimate stable oscillation seems to be entirely independent of the initial conditions, whereas in oscillations governed by linear differential equations* it depends upon the initial conditions.

Van der Pol (1)** was first to invite attention to these new oscillations and to indicate that their existence is inherent in the non-linearity of the differential equations characterizing the process. This non-linearity appears, thus, as the very essence of these phenomena and, by linearizing the differential equation in the sense of the method of small motions, one simply eliminates the possibility of investigating such problems. Thus, it became necessary to attack the non-linear problems directly instead of evading them by dropping the non-linear terms.

Although the early discoveries of Van der Pol invited the attention of mathematical physicists to these new problems, very little was done theoretically in the following years in the way of further generalizations of Van der Pol's original theory. On the other hand, the accumulation of experimental data continued at a rapid rate and each additional problem had to be treated mainly on its own merits and by methods which were not unified into one central doctrine. The situation was similar in some respects to that which existed in the early

---

* Unless otherwise specified the term "linear differential equations" will be used in the following in referring to those with constant coefficients.

** Numbers in parentheses indicate references on page 131 of this report.

stage of development of the theory of differential equations when, prior to the advent of Cauchy's general theorems of existence, a few isolated methods of direct integration were the only ones available. Later, Cauchy's theorems made it possible to obtain a general theory of linear differential equations.

About fifteen years ago certain Russian scientists directed their attention to a further development of methods of Non-Linear Mechanics with a view toward obtaining a more general basis for a mathematical treatment of numerous experimental facts to which modern electronic circuits and apparatus contributed a large part. A line of approach was soon found in the classical researches of Henri Poincaré who may be considered as a real forerunner of modern Non-Linear Mechanics. In his two treatises "Sur les courbes définies par une équation différentielle" (2) and "Les méthodes nouvelles de la mécanique céleste" (3) the great analyst opened two major avenues of approach to the solution of problems of Non-Linear Mechanics, i.e.,

1.   The topological methods of qualitative integration,
2.   The quantitative methods of approximations by expansions in terms of suitable parameters.

These two trends persist in modern developments of Non-Linear Mechanics, frequently supplementing each other in some respects. The adaptation of these general theories, developed originally for the purposes of Celestial Mechanics, to the problems of applied science in general is the work of Mandelstam, Papalexi, Andronow, Kryloff, Bogoliuboff, and a number of other Russian scientists working jointly in this field during the past fifteen years or so.

The two major trends referred to, the topological method and the quantitative method of successive approximations, have their respective merits as well as limitations. The topological methods are based on the study of the representation of solutions of differential equations in phase space; the latter is mapped by means of point-singularities and certain singular lines so as to obtain certain topological domains in which the form of the integral curves - the phase trajectories - can be investigated by relatively simple geometrical methods.

The main advantage of the topological methods lies in the fact that insofar as they deal with *trajectories*, and not with *laws of motion*, they make it possible to obtain, so to speak, a bird's eye view of the *totality* of all possible motions which may arise in a given system under all possible conditions. Just as a topographic map of a locality gives an idea as to its three-dimensional form - its peaks, valleys, divides, and other features - a topological

picture of a domain of integral curves permits ascertaining at once in
which regions of the domain the motions are periodic and in which they
are either aperiodic or asymptotic. Likewise the critical thresholds
or "divides" which separate the regions of stability and instability
can be easily ascertained by these methods.

The principal limitation of topological methods, as of other
qualitative methods, is that they do not lend themselves readily to
numerical calculations, insofar as they deal with geometrical curves,
the trajectories, and not with the laws of motion which are of interest for numerical calculations.

The quantitative methods, on the other hand, possess the
advantage of leading directly to numerical solutions which are of importance in astronomical as well as in engineering applications. These
quantitative methods, however, inevitably narrow the field of vision
to a relatively limited region of the domain. This frequently limits
the grasp of the situation as a whole, particularly if the system possesses critical thresholds, the separatrices, the branch points of
equilibrium, etc., at which the qualitative features of the phenomena
undergo radical changes; such critical conditions are of common occurrence in Non-Linear Mechanics.

Both methods, however, very frequently supplement each other.
The topological method permits a rapid exploration of the whole field
of integration, and the quantitative method leads to numerical results,
once a particular range of the problem has been selected for study.

Another point of great importance in Non-Linear Mechanics is
the question of stability. The fundamental theorem in this connection
is due to Liapounoff (4). In Non-Linear Mechanics this theorem plays
a role similar to the Routh-Hurwitz theorem for linear systems. Its
formulation is closely related to the question of singularities of differential equations. An interesting feature of this theorem is the
fact that, in a great majority of cases, it permits establishing criteria of stability for a non-linear system from the equations of the
first approximation, which are linear; this fact simplifies the problem appreciably.

This report reviews the progress accomplished in Non-Linear
Mechanics approximately up to 1940; its preparation was greatly facilitated by the availability of the following two works in the Russian
language.

1.   "Theory of Oscillations," by A. Andronow and S. Chaikin,
     Moscow, 1937.
2.   "Introduction to Non-Linear Mechanics," by N. Kryloff and
     N. Bogoliuboff, Kief, 1937.

On a number of questions, particularly those treated in
Part III, the original publications had to be consulted. In view of
the fact that the literature, in Russian alone, comprises more than
2000 pages, to say nothing of the earlier publications of Poincaré,
Liapounoff, Bendixson (5), Birkhoff (6), Van der Pol, and others, no
attempt was made to present a complete account of what has been accomplished in this field. For that reason the report is limited only to
a few selected topics which seem to offer more immediate applications
on the one hand, and which do not require too abstract mathematical
generalizations on the other. It is believed that in its present form
the report is within the grasp of an average reader having a general
knowledge of the theory of ordinary differential equations in the real
domain.

The report as a whole falls into four major subdivisions:

Part I is concerned with the topological methods; its presentation substantially follows the "Theory of Oscillations" (19). The
material is slightly rearranged, the text condensed, and a number of
figures in this report were taken from the book. Chapter V, concerning Liénard's analysis, was added since it constitutes an important
generalization and establishes a connection between the topological
and the analytical methods, which otherwise might appear as somewhat
unrelated.

Part II gives an outline of the three principal analytical
methods, those of Poincaré, Van der Pol, and Kryloff-Bogoliuboff.*

Part III deals with the complicated phenomena of non-linear
resonance with its numerous ramifications such as internal and external subharmonic resonance, entrainment of frequency, parametric excitation, etc. This subject is still in a state of development, and
the classification of the numerous experimental phenomena is far from
being definitely established. Much credit for the experimental discoveries and theoretical studies of these phenomena is due to Mandelstam and Papalexi, and the school of physicists under their leadership.
The first four chapters of Part III represent the application of the
quasi-linear theory of Kryloff and Bogoliuboff to these problems and
the last three concern the developments of Mandelstam, Papalexi,
Andronow, Witt, and others, following the classical theory of Poincaré.

Finally, Part IV reviews the interesting developments of
L. Mandelstam, S. Chaikin, and Lochakow in the theory of relaxation
oscillations for large values of the parameter μ. This theory is
based on the existence of quasi-discontinuous solutions of differential equations at the point of their "degeneration," that is, when
one of the coefficients approaches zero so that the differential

---

* During the preparation of this report there appeared a free translation of extracts of
the Kryloff and Bogoliuboff text by Professor S. Lefschetz, Princeton University Press,
1943.

equation "degenerates" into one of lower order. A considerable number of experimental facts are explained on the basis of this theoretical idealization.

In going over this report the reader will notice that the electrical examples are more numerous than the mechanical ones. The reason for this situation is twofold. First, electrical non-linear oscillations constitute generally *useful* phenomena that are utilized in radio technique, electrical engineering, television, and allied fields, whereas most of the known mechanical non-linear phenomena are of a rather undesirable, parasitic nature. Second, the determination of the parameters and characteristics is generally much easier in electrical than in mechanical problems, particularly when a mechanical system is relatively complicated. This does not mean, of course, that this state of things will always persist; in fact, mechanical engineers are becoming more and more concerned with non-linear problems (7), (8), (9), and the lack of any appreciable progress at present is not due to a lack of interest on their part but rather to the absence of a theory sufficiently broad to cover the various cases encountered in practice.

It is difficult to write a relatively short report on a subject of this scope in a form that will be satisfactory to all readers. A mathematician will undoubtedly find a series of drawbacks in the presentation of purely mathematical matter; the proofs of a number of theorems are omitted. Frequently more rigorous theorems and criteria are replaced by rather intuitive definitions and statements, and so on. It is probable that the mere idea of applying the relatively complicated and laborious methods of Poincaré and Lindstedt for the purpose of explaining the well-known performance of a thermionic generator or of a simple mechanical system with non-linear damping or a non-linear spring constant may appear to an engineer pedantic and hence superfluous. On the other hand, it cannot be denied that in the past theoretical generalizations have been always most fruitful in the long run, although during the initial stages of development, they appeared to contemporaries somewhat laborious and confusing. It is sufficient to mention as an example the modern theory of electronics with its numerous ramifications in the fields of radio technique, television, controls, etc. In this case, between the spectacular experimental discoveries of Hertz, Marconi, Fleming, Lee de Forest, and others, there intervened the less spectacular but not less important theoretical work of Richardson, Langmuir, and Shottky on thermionic emission, which, in turn, was based on the earlier statistical theory of Maxwell and Boltzmann. This permitted later a more rigorous quantitative treatment of these phenomena.

Very likely the present trend toward a codification of theoretical knowledge in the field of non-linear mechanics will bring about a further progress resulting from a more general viewpoint on the whole subject. It must be borne in mind, however, that the period of codification of non-linear mechanics has existed only for about the last fifteen years. Hence, we are witnessing at present only the important initial stages of these studies rather than their final formulation.

It is hoped that this review will attract the active attention of applied mathematicians, physicists, and engineers, for the new methods seem to affect all branches of applied science either by offering more accurate solutions of old problems or by making possible an attack upon new problems beyond the reach of the older mathematical methods.

The preparation of this report was facilitated by valuable discussions and suggestions on the part of a number of mathematicians and mathematical physicists who showed an interest in this work. The writer is indebted to A. Franck and M. Levenson who were most helpful in connection with the critical editorial work and to Professors E. H. Kennard, W. Hurevicz, S. Lefschetz, and J. A. Shohat. The cooperation of the Applied Mathematics Panel of the National Defense Research Committee, Dr. W. W. Weaver, Chairman, and of the Applied Mathematics group at Brown University, Dean R. G. D. Richardson, Chairman is especially acknowledged.

PART I

TOPOLOGICAL METHODS OF NON-LINEAR MECHANICS

CHAPTER I

PHASE TRAJECTORIES OF LINEAR SYSTEMS

1. **PHASE PLANE AND PHASE TRAJECTORIES; LINEAR OSCILLATOR**

Consider the differential equation of a harmonic oscillator

$$m\ddot{x} + cx = 0, \quad (c > 0) \qquad [1.1]$$

where m and c are constants. Its integral is

$$x = A \cos(\omega_0 t + \phi) \qquad [1.2]$$

where A and ϕ are constants of integration determined by the initial conditions at $t = 0$; and $\omega_0 = \sqrt{c/m}$ is the angular frequency.

Since the system is conservative, the integral of energy exists. In fact, multiplying [1.1] by $\dot{x}$ and integrating we get

$$\frac{1}{2}m\dot{x}^2 + \frac{1}{2}cx^2 = h \qquad [1.3]$$

Equation [1.3] expresses the law of conservation of energy: The sum of the kinetic, $\frac{1}{2}m\dot{x}^2$, and of the potential, $\frac{1}{2}cx^2$, energies of the system remains constant throughout the motion. Putting $\dot{x} = y$, [1.3] can be written in the form

$$\frac{x^2}{\alpha^2} + \frac{y^2}{\beta^2} = 1 \qquad [1.4]$$

where $\alpha = \sqrt{2h/c}$, $\beta = \sqrt{2h/m}$. Equation [1.4] represents an ellipse having α and β as semi-axes; see Figure 1.1. The plane of the variables x, y is called the *phase plane*.

The same result is obtained by starting with the integral [1.2] of [1.1]. By differentiating [1.2] we have $\dot{x} = -A\omega_0 \sin(\omega_0 t + \phi)$ and noting that for one single particle the phase angle ϕ can be made equal to zero by a suitable choice of the origin of time, two equations result

$$x = A \cos \omega_0 t; \quad \dot{x} = y = -A\omega_0 \sin \omega_0 t \qquad [1.5]$$

The elimination of t between Equations [1.5] gives

$$\frac{x^2}{A^2} + \frac{y^2}{A^2\omega_0^2} = 1 \qquad [1.6]$$

which is identical with [1.4], provided

$$A = \sqrt{\frac{2h}{c}} = \alpha \quad \text{and} \quad A\omega_0 = \sqrt{\frac{2h}{m}} = \beta.$$

It follows that $\omega_0 = \sqrt{c/m}$.

Although the result is the same, the derivation of [1.4] and [1.6] has been different. Equation [1.6] was obtained from the solution of the dynamical Equation [1.1], whereas [1.4] results from the law of conservation of energy, which is the first integral of the dynamical equation.

In both [1.4] and [1.6] time does not appear explicitly; they express, therefore, a trajectory in the phase plane, the phase trajectory, or simply, *trajectory*, where x and $y = \dot{x}$ are considered as coordinates in that plane.

The uni-dimensional real motion of a particle oscillating along the x-axis according to the sinusoidal law $x = A \cos \omega_0 t$ is thus represented in the two-dimensional phase space, the *phase plane*, by elliptic trajectories, described by the representative point R situated at the extremity of the radius vector r. The projection of R on the x-axis gives the actual position x of the oscillator, and the projection on the y-axis gives its velocity $y = \dot{x}$ at the instant t. In general, if some other initial condition is chosen,* another ellipse E_1 is obtained, concentric with the first one and having the same ratio of semi-axes $\beta/\alpha = \sqrt{c/m} = \omega_0$, inasmuch as this ratio depends only on the constants of the system and not on the initial conditions. Thus, in this case, the phase trajectories representing the motion are a family of concentric ellipses having a constant ratio of semi-axes. These are shown in Figure 1.1.

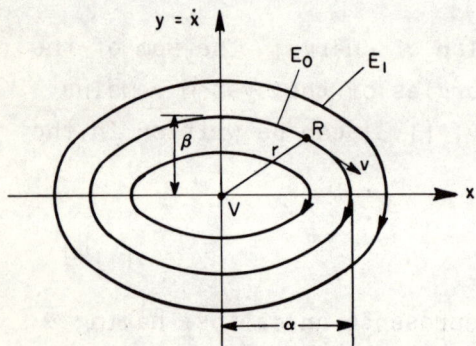

Figure 1.1

This representation frequently offers advantages as compared to the usual plot of coordinates against time in that it gives an idea of the *topology* of trajectories in the phase plane. As we shall see later, it enables one to visualize at once all possible motions which may arise in a system with zones separating motions of one type from those of an entirely different type.**

---

* Such initial conditions which are represented by points situated on the same trajectory are to be excluded inasmuch as they represent the same motion with a different phase; see Section 3.

** The representation of motion by trajectories in the $(x, \dot{x})$ phase plane will be most frequently used in what follows. In some cases, however, different variables may be preferable. Unless specified to the contrary, by the phase plane we shall always mean the plane of variables x and $\dot{x}$.

2. PHASE VELOCITY

The velocity of the point R is called the *phase velocity*. If $\vec{r}$ is the radius vector from V to R, clearly the phase velocity $\vec{v} = d\vec{r}/dt = \vec{i}\dot{x} + \vec{j}\dot{y}$ where $\vec{i}$ and $\vec{j}$ are the unit vectors along the x, y axes of Figure 1.1. With the use of [1.5] we get

$$\vec{v} = i\left[-A\omega_0 \sin\omega_0 t\right] + j\left[-A\omega_0^2 \cos\omega_0 t\right] \qquad [2.1]$$

from which it follows that the phase velocity $\vec{v}$ never becomes zero if $A \neq 0$, inasmuch as $\sin\omega_0 t$ and $\cos\omega_0 t$ cannot be zero simultaneously, the case $\omega_0 = 0$ being excluded. Thus the phase velocity $\vec{v}$ may only vanish when $A = 0$; this is possible only when $h = 0$. In other words, this happens only when the particle is placed initially at $x = 0$ with zero velocity ($\dot{x} = y = 0$). This condition corresponds to the center V of the ellipse. On the other hand, for this point the force kx also vanishes. We are, thus, led to identify the point V with the position of equilibrium of the system. One may surmise that this position of equilibrium is stable although this question needs further consideration.

3. THEOREM OF CAUCHY; SINGULAR POINTS; TRAJECTORIES AND MOTIONS

Cauchy's Theorem of Existence for the solution of a differential equation will play an important role in the following. The proof of this theorem can be found in any textbook of Analysis; for this reason it is sufficient to give here only its formulation.

Consider a differential equation of the nth order

$$x^{(n)} \equiv \frac{d^n x}{dt^n} = f(t, x, \dot{x}, \cdots, x^{(n-1)}) \qquad [3.1]$$

The theorem of Cauchy states: There exists a unique analytic* solution of [3.1] in the neighborhood of $t = t_0$ such that the function x and its $(n - 1)$ derivatives acquire for $t = t_0$ the set of prescribed values $x_0, \dot{x}_0, \cdots, x_0^{(n-1)}$, provided the function $f(t, x, \dot{x}, \cdots, x^{(n-1)})$ is analytic in the neighborhood of this set of values.

It is obvious that [3.1] is equivalent to a system of n equations of the first order

$$\frac{dx}{dt} = y_1; \quad \frac{dy_1}{dt} = y_2; \quad \frac{dy_{n-1}}{dt} = f(t, x, y_1, \cdots, y_{n-1}) \qquad [3.2]$$

---

* Analytic at a given point means admitting a Taylor series about the point.

which is a special case of the system

$$\frac{dy_i}{dt} = f_i(t, y_1, y_2, \cdots, y_n), \; i = 1, 2, \cdots, n \qquad [3.3]$$

In applications, t usually represents time, the other variables representing coordinates of a point in the phase space of a dynamical system. Of particular importance is the case of [3.1] and system [3.2] in which the function f does not depend on time t, and is a function of x, $\dot{x}, \cdots, x^{(n-1)}$, or y_1, y_2, $\cdots$, y_n, alone. From a physical standpoint, this means that the system in question is "autonomous," that is, one in which neither the forces nor the constraints vary in the course of time. This will be assumed in what follows.

Henceforth we shall be concerned mainly with systems with one degree of freedom which are represented in the phase plane by phase trajectories as previously explained. The differential equations are of the form

$$\frac{dx}{dt} = P(x,y); \;\; \frac{dy}{dt} = Q(x,y) \qquad [3.4]$$

A differential equation of the second order

$$\ddot{x} = Q(x, \dot{x})$$

can be reduced to the form [3.4] by putting $y = \dot{x}$, so that one obtains

$$\frac{dx}{dt} = y; \;\; \frac{dy}{dt} = Q(x,y) \qquad [3.4a]$$

It is to be noted that one will frequently encounter dynamical equations of the more general form [3.4].

Upon eliminating the independent variable t between the Equations [3.4] one obtains one equation

$$\frac{dx}{P(x,y)} = \frac{dy}{Q(x,y)} \qquad [3.5]$$

which gives the slope dy/dx of the tangent to the phase trajectory passing through the point (x,y).

We shall often speak of the point $\mathbf{R}(x,y)$, the *representative* point, as moving along the trajectory. By this we mean that the motion of this point is governed by the law expressed by [3.4] or, more particularly, by [3.4a]. Since time does not enter explicitly at the right in [3.4], the general solution of [3.4] can be written as

$$x = \phi(t - t_0, x_0, y_0) \equiv x(t)$$
$$\qquad\qquad\qquad\qquad\qquad\qquad [3.6]$$
$$y = \psi(t - t_0, x_0, y_0) \equiv y(t)$$

so that the trajectory passing through the point (x_0, y_0) at $t = t_0$ may also be obtained from [3.6] by eliminating $(t - t_0)$.

The topological methods studied in Part I will deal with the trajectories [3.5], whereas the analytical methods outlined in Part II will be concerned with the differential equations of motion [3.4]. In some cases it is useful to apply both methods, so as to obtain a more detailed picture of the behavior of a given dynamical system; in such cases [3.5] gives a qualitative idea of the nature of the trajectories in various regions of the phase plane, whereas Equations [3.4] yield the actual motion starting from given initial conditions. Such a procedure is particularly useful when a dynamical system possesses certain critical thresholds or "divides," in which case the application of [3.5] permits a preliminary qualitative study of the nature of the trajectories in various domains of the phase plane before the actual integration of the dynamical Equations [3.4] is undertaken.

In the following, we shall make use of the concept of singularities of differential equations, and therefore we shall find it expedient to make the following definitions.

A.   A point (x_0, y_0) for which $P(x_0, y_0) = Q(x_0, y_0) = 0$ simultaneously is called a *singular point*.

B.   Any other point of the phase plane to which Definition A does not apply is called an *ordinary point*.

From these definitions it follows that an ordinary point is characterized by a definite value of the slope of the tangent to a phase trajectory passing through that point. For a singular point, on the contrary, the direction of the tangent is indeterminate and the trajectory corresponding to [3.4] or [3.4a] degenerates into a single point, the singular point itself.

Using these definitions we can formulate the theorem of Cauchy in the following form: Through every ordinary point of the phase plane there passes one and only one phase trajectory.

One can also consider Equations [3.4] as defining a vector field with components dx/dt, dy/dt which determine a non-vanishing vector for any ordinary point (x, y) of the field. For a singular point (x_0, y_0) we have $P(x_0, y_0) = Q(x_0, y_0) = 0$, hence, both components dx/dt, dy/dt vanish. More specifically, if the vector field is a velocity field, it is clear that a singular point is a point at which the representative point is at rest.

In a number of dynamical problems for which [3.4a] is applicable, an additional interpretation can be given. A singular point in this case occurs when $y = 0$, $dy/dt = 0$, that is, when both the velocity and acceleration of the system are zero; this clearly defines an equilibrium condition. We are thus led to identify the singular points in such a case with the points of equilibrium of a dynamical system.

It follows from the preceding definition that if (x_0, y_0) is a singular point, a trajectory passing through an ordinary point (x, y) at a certain instant will never reach (x_0, y_0) for any finite value of the time parameter t; for the only trajectory passing through the singular point (x_0, y_0) is the *degenerate trajectory* consisting of this point alone. It may happen, however, that a *proper trajectory*, that is, one which consists of more than one point, may approach a singular point either for $t = +\infty$ or $t = -\infty$, which means that $\lim x(t) = x_0$ and $\lim y(t) = y_0$ for $t = +\infty$ or $t = -\infty$. It is to be understood that, when we say that a trajectory "approaches" a point (x_0, y_0), we mean that a representative point following this trajectory in accordance with [3.4] approaches the point (x_0, y_0).

Our main concern will be the study of the behavior of trajectories in the neighborhood of singularities. This question is studied in more detail in the following sections. It may be useful, however, to give at the outset a brief geometrical description of the behavior of trajectories in the neighborhood of the four singularities with which we shall be concerned, leaving a more complete analysis of this subject to a later section.

1. *A vortex point* V is a singularity which is not approached by any trajectory. Point V in Figure 1.1 gives an example of a vortex point. Section 1 illustrates that a vortex point is surrounded by a continuum of closed trajectories such that none approaches it. In this example, the vortex point appears in connection with the elliptic trajectories of the differential equation, $\ddot{x} + \omega_0^2 x = 0$. We shall see later that vortex points may occur in connection with equations of a more general form, in which case the trajectories, while being closed, are not necessarily ellipses. In all cases, however, a vortex point V is characterized by the following two conditions:

a. the trajectories are closed, enclosing the singularity,

b. there is a continuum of these trajectories.

2. *A saddle point* S is a singularity which is approached by four trajectories forming two distinct analytic curves, A_1A_2 and A_3A_4, as shown in Figure 3.1. Two of these trajectories, A_1S and A_2S, approach the saddle point S for $t = +\infty$; two others, A_3S and A_4S, approach S for $t = -\infty$, which is equivalent to saying that the representative points on these trajectories, A_3 and A_4, move away from S. Between these

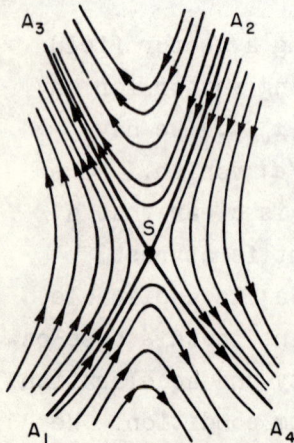

Figure 3.1

four isolated trajectories, there exist four regions containing continua of hyperbolically-shaped
trajectories which do not approach S. The representative point moves along these trajectories in
the direction of the arrows in conformity with the
directions indicated on the asymptotic trajector-
ies A_1, A_2, A_3, A_4, which appear, thus, as "divides"
for the four regions.

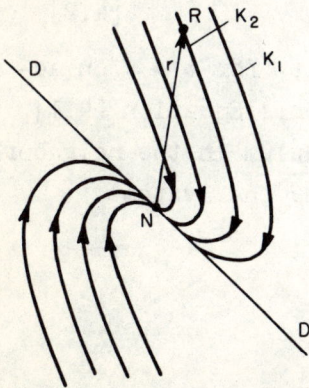

Figure 3.2

    In Section 4 we shall see that this sit-
uation arises, for instance, when one considers
the equation $m\ddot{x} - cx = 0$ of unstable motion. In Section 18 a general criterion for the existence of a saddle point will be given for systems of the
form [3.4].

    3.   *A focal point* F is a singularity which trajectories approach, with-
out any definite direction, in the manner of the spirals K_1 and K_2 shown in
Figure 3.2. The radius vector r of the spirals decreases as R approaches F,
but the direction of approach is indeterminate since a spiral trajectory
winds around a focal point F an infinite number of times as the point R approaches F. There exists an infinity of spiral trajectories one and only one
of which passes through every ordinary point of the phase plane. If the spirals approach F for $t = +\infty$, the point F is called a *stable* focal point. If
the focal point is approached for $t = -\infty$ the direction of motion on the trajectories, as shown by the arrows in Figure 3.2, is reversed so that the trajectories "leave" the focal point. The point F is then called an *unstable
focal point*.

    In Section 5 an example of motion in the neighborhood of a focal
point will be given in connection with the equation $\ddot{x} + 2b\dot{x} + \omega_0^2 x = 0$ of a
damped oscillatory motion ($b^2 - \omega_0^2 < 0$); a more general criterion for the
existence of a focal point in the case of the sys-
tem [3.4] will be given in Section 18.

    4.   *A nodal point* N is a singularity which
is approached by trajectories in the manner of the
curves K_1 and K_2 of Figure 3.3, so that when $r \to 0$
the direction of the tangents to the trajectories
approaches definite limits, e.g., the straight
line DD. According as the point N is approached
for $t = +\infty$ or $t = -\infty$, the nodal point is called
stable or *unstable*; in the latter case the direction of the arrows in Figure 3.3 should be reversed.

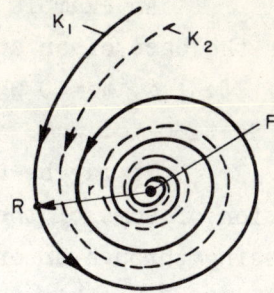

Figure 3.3

An example of trajectories of this kind is given in Section 6 for the case of an aperiodic damped motion corresponding to the equation $\ddot{x} + 2b\dot{x} + \omega_0^2 x = 0$ when $b^2 - \omega_0^2 > 0$; a more general criterion is indicated in Section 18.

It may be useful to add a remark concerning the physical interpretation of some of the preceding definitions. When we speak of a trajectory passing through an ordinary point (x_0, y_0) of the phase plane, we frequently understand by this that we wish to consider the motion as *starting* from given initial conditions x_0, $y_0 = \dot{x}_0$. Furthermore the statement of the theorem of Cauchy, that through every ordinary point (x_0, y_0) of the phase plane there passes one and only one trajectory, is equivalent to saying that if the initial conditions are prescribed, the subsequent motion is uniquely determined.

On the other hand, to a given *trajectory* [3.5], i.e., a geometrical curve in the phase plane, there corresponds an infinity of possible motions [3.5] corresponding to a different selection of the time origin. In fact, if Equations [3.4] are satisfied by solutions [3.6] for a given value of t_0, they are obviously satisfied by [3.6] for any other value of t_0. Geometrically, all solutions [3.6] for the same values of x_0, y_0 are represented by the *same trajectory*, say C, passing through the point (x_0, y_0), although there exists an infinity of possible motions (C) on this trajectory when the arbitrary constant t_0 is varied.*

It can also be stated that the solutions of [3.4] form a two-parameter family, while the trajectories [3.5] form a one-parameter family.

4. PHASE TRAJECTORY OF AN UNSTABLE MOTION; SADDLE POINT

The differential equation

$$m\ddot{x} - cx = 0, \ (c > 0) \tag{4.1}$$

has an exponential solution of the form

$$x = Ae^{rt} + Be^{-rt} \tag{4.2}$$

where $r = + \sqrt{c/m}$. The solution x, thus, tends to infinity for $t \to \infty$ on account of a positive root r of the characteristic equation. Equation [4.1] represents, for instance, the motion of an undamped pendulum in the neighborhood of its unstable equilibrium point. Replace [4.1] by the system

$$\dot{x} = y, \ \dot{y} = \frac{c}{m} x$$

---

* In what follows we shall use consistently this notation, i.e., C will designate a geometrical curve, the trajectory and (C) a motion of the representative point R on the trajectory C.

whence

$$\frac{dy}{dx} = \frac{c}{m}\frac{x}{y} \qquad [4.3]$$

For $x = 0$, $y \neq 0$, the tangent to the
trajectory is horizontal; for $x \neq 0$,
$y = 0$, it is vertical. For $x = 0$,
$y = 0$, the direction of the tangent is
indeterminate; this point is a singular point.

The phase trajectories are
obtained by integrating [4.3] which
gives

$$y^2 - \frac{c}{m}x^2 = C$$

where C is the constant of integration.
The trajectories are thus hyperbolas,
shown in Figure 4.1; the asymptotes are
obtained by putting $C = 0$ which gives

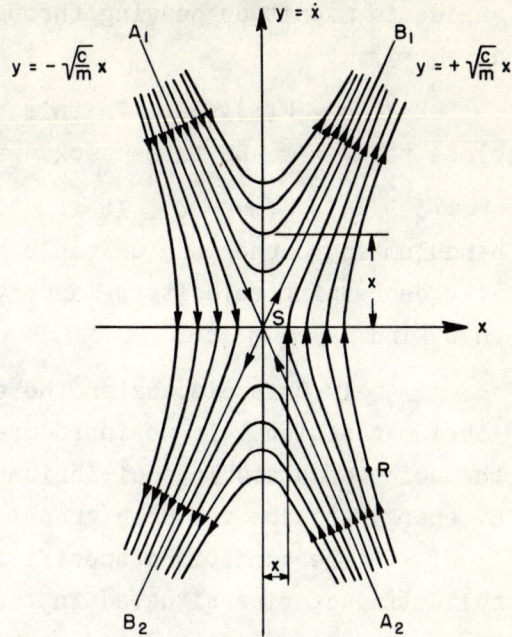

Figure 4.1

$$y = \pm\sqrt{\frac{c}{m}}\ x$$

The representative point R arriving from infinity will approach the origin
$x = y = 0$ and then will depart again into infinity following the direction of
the arrows.

The interpretation of such motion is obtained by considering the
motion of a pendulum in the neighborhood of the point of unstable equilibrium.
Consider the motion of a pendulum having a unit moment of inertia. Let x_1 be
the angle measured from the position of stable equilibrium and $y_1 = \dot{x}_1$ the
angular velocity of the pendulum. The law of conservation of energy gives

$$\frac{1}{2}y_1^2 + V(x_1) = h \qquad [4.4]$$

where $\frac{1}{2}y_1^2$ and $V(x_1)$ are the kinetic and the potential energies respectively;
the constant h is the total energy, communicated, for example, by means of an
impulse at the beginning of the motion.

It is known from Theoretical Mechanics (10) that there are three
typical motions according to $h - V(\pi) \gtreqless 0$. We proceed to consider each case
separately.

1. $h - V(\pi) > 0$. In this case the pendulum goes "over the top" and
continues rotating in the same direction, i.e., y_1 keeps the same sign but

varies in magnitude passing through a maximum at $x_1 = 0$ and through a minimum at $x_1 = \pi$.

2. $h - V(\pi) < 0$. In this case the pendulum reaches a certain angle x_0 close to $x_1 = \pi$ and turns back away from the unstable point $x_1 = \pi$.

3. $h - V(\pi) = 0$. It is shown in Theoretical Mechanics (10) that the pendulum approaches the unstable point $x_1 = \pi$ in infinite time with a gradually decreasing velocity y_1 approaching zero as a limit. We call motion of this kind *asymptotic*.

In this discussion the angle x_1 was measured from the stable equilibrium position. If we introduce now the angle $x = \pi - x_1$, measured from the point of unstable equilibrium S, the results obtained from the equation of energy acquire a simple graphical representation shown in Figure 4.1.

The conditions specified in Case 1 are represented by the hyperbolic trajectories situated in the upper and lower quadrants of Figure 4.1; those corresponding to Case 2 are represented by hyperbolic trajectories in the right and the left quadrants of that figure; and the asymptotic Case 3, in which the total energy h is just equal to the potential energy of the system at the point S of unstable equilibrium, is represented by the asymptotes $A_1 S$ and $A_2 S$ of Figure 4.1 along which the motion of the representative point R is asymptotic.

The inverse process, i.e., the motion of a pendulum placed initially in the unstable position of equilibrium, is also asymptotic; it is represented in the phase plane by asymptotes SB_1 and SB_2.

The singular point $S(0,0)$ of this type is a *saddle point*. It is seen that four asymptotic trajectories approach the saddle point, namely, $A_1 S$ and $A_2 S$ for $t = +\infty$, and $B_1 S$ and $B_2 S$ for $t = -\infty$, inasmuch as the asymptotes are also trajectories. Once again we observe that the point S which is a singular point, is a point of equilibrium which is, however, unstable in this case and a point at which the phase velocity vanishes.

5. PHASE TRAJECTORY OF AN OSCILLATORY DAMPED MOTION; FOCAL POINT

The differential equation of a damped oscillator of unit mass is

$$\ddot{x} + 2b\dot{x} + \omega_0^2 x = 0 \qquad\qquad [5.1]$$

provided $b^2 - \omega_0^2 < 0$. The solution of [5.1] is

$$x = x_0 e^{-bt} \cos(\omega_1 t + \alpha) \qquad\qquad [5.2]$$

where x_0 and α are two constants of integration, b is the decrement,* and $\omega_1 = \sqrt{\omega_0{}^2 - b^2}$ is the damped angular frequency. The system is not conservative in this case. We omit the well-known properties of motion defined by [5.1] and [5.2] and consider the representation of the motion in the phase plane.

The differential Equation [5.1] of second order can be replaced by a system of two differential equations of the first order

$$\frac{dx}{dt} = y; \quad \frac{dy}{dt} = -2by - \omega_0^2 x \qquad [5.3]$$

whence

$$\frac{dy}{dx} = -\frac{2by + \omega_0^2 x}{y} \qquad [5.4]$$

Equation [5.4] is a particular form of [3.5]. It is seen that the origin, $x = y = 0$, is a singular point since the direction of the tangent dy/dx becomes indeterminate at this point. Equation [5.4] is a homogeneous differential equation of the first order and can be integrated by introducing a new variable u defined by the equation $y = ux$. We finally get

$$y^2 + 2bxy + \omega_0^2 x^2 = C e^{2\frac{b}{\omega_1} \tan^{-1} \frac{y + bx}{\omega_1 x}} \qquad [5.5]$$

The phase velocity $\vec{v} = d\vec{r}/dt = \vec{i}\dot{x} + \vec{j}\dot{y}$ is obtained by substituting for x and y their expressions obtained from [5.2]. The absolute value of the phase velocity is

$$|v| = \sqrt{\omega_0^4 x^2 + 4bxy\omega_0^2 + (1 + 4b^2)y^2} \qquad [5.6]$$

The phase velocity is zero only at the origin, $x = y = 0$, of the phase plane, which point coincides with the singular point of the differential equation as seen from [5.4].

Equation [5.5] can be transformed into polar coordinates. The left-hand term can be written as $(y + bx)^2 + (\omega_0{}^2 - b^2)x^2 \equiv (y + bx)^2 + \omega_1^2 x^2$. Introducing new coordinates $u = \omega_1 x$, $v = y + bx$, [5.5] becomes

$$v^2 + u^2 = C e^{2\frac{b}{\omega_1} \tan^{-1} \frac{v}{u}}$$

If we now introduce polar coordinates defined by $u = \rho \cos \psi$, $v = \rho \sin \psi$, the last equation becomes

$$\rho = C_1 e^{\frac{b}{\omega_1} \psi}, \quad C_1 = \sqrt{C} \qquad [5.7]$$

---

* It should be noted that dimensionally, the decrement is b/m, and not b; here however, $m = 1$.

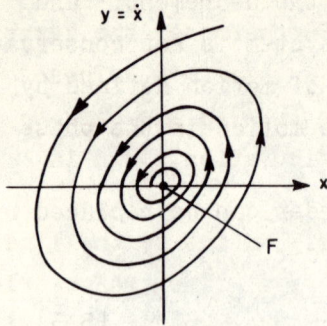

Figure 5.1

where C_1 depends on the initial conditions. The phase trajectory is, thus, a logarithmic spiral in the (u,v)-plane. In view of the transformation of coordinates (from x, y to u, v) the spiral given by [5.7] undergoes a distortion when referred to the original coordinates x, y as shown in Figure 5.1.

For a positive damping, $b > 0$, corresponding to dissipation of energy, the exponent in [5.7] must be negative which can be taken care of by a suitable definition of the positive direction of ψ.

For small values of b/ω_1 the curve in the (u,v)-plane approaches the circle $v^2 + u^2 = C$ which in the (x,y)-plane corresponds to an ellipse given by the equation $y^2 + 2bxy + \omega_0^2 x^2 = C$. One may surmise that the point F towards which the spiral converges is an equilibrium position. We recognize in this singular point the *focal point* defined previously. From physical considerations it is apparent that any trajectory of this kind approaches the focal point for $t = +\infty$; furthermore, the focal point is approached by an infinity of phase trajectories since through every ordinary point of the plane there passes a spiral trajectory.

6. PHASE TRAJECTORY OF AN APERIODIC DAMPED MOTION; NODAL POINT

If in [5.1] $b^2 - \omega_0^2 > 0$, the corresponding characteristic equation has two distinct real roots, $-r_1$ and $-r_2$, of the same sign and the motion is aperiodic of the form $x = Ae^{-r_1 t} + Be^{-r_2 t}$, where A and B are two constants of integration determined by the initial conditions. Differentiating we have $\dot{x} = -Ar_1 e^{-r_1 t} - Br_2 e^{-r_2 t}$. Eliminating time t between x and $\dot{x}$* we obtain the equation of the phase trajectory in the form

$$(xr_1 + y)^{r_1} = C(xr_2 + y)^{r_2} \qquad [6.1]$$

Taking as new variables $v = xr_1 + y$, $u = xr_2 + y$, we get

$$v = Cu^a \qquad [6.2]$$

where $a = r_2/r_1 > 1$, r_2 being the absolute value of the larger root. Equation [6.2] represents parabolic curves tangent to the u-axis at the origin; for $dv/du = Cau^{a-1}$ is zero when $u = 0$ since $a - 1 > 0$ and $v = u = 0$ is a point on the curve.

---

* This elimination is best obtained by solving the system of linear equations with $e^{-r_1 t}$ and $e^{-r_2 t}$ as unknown. By taking logarithms of the solutions thus obtained, the time t is easily eliminated.

For $C = 0$, the curve degenerates into the u-axis, i.e., $v = 0$; for $C \to \infty$ it degenerates into the v-axis, i.e., $u = 0$. Furthermore, the curves [6.2] are convex towards the u-axis since $v''/v = a(a - 1)/u^2 > 0$. These curves are shown in Figure 6.1a. If we transform the (u, v)-plane back to the (x, y)-plane, the phase trajectories have the configuration shown in Figure 6.1b.

The u-axis, $v = 0$, is represented in the (x, y)-plane by the line $y = - x r_1$; the v-axis, $u = 0$, is represented by $y = - x r_2$. The trajectories are tangent to the u-axis at the origin in the (u, v)-plane; hence, they will be tangent to the line $y = - x r_1$ at the origin in the (x, y)-plane as shown in Figure 6.1b. Furthermore, as u increases, the curves in the (u, v)-plane become parallel to the v-axis, hence the asymptotic branches of phase trajectories approach parallelism with the line $y = - x r_2$ in the (x, y)-plane. It is seen that the trajectories cross the x-axis, i.e., the line $y = 0$, at right angles. We also find that the locus of the points in which the trajectories x, y have horizontal tangents lie on the line $y = - \dfrac{r_1 r_2}{r_1 + r_2} x$.

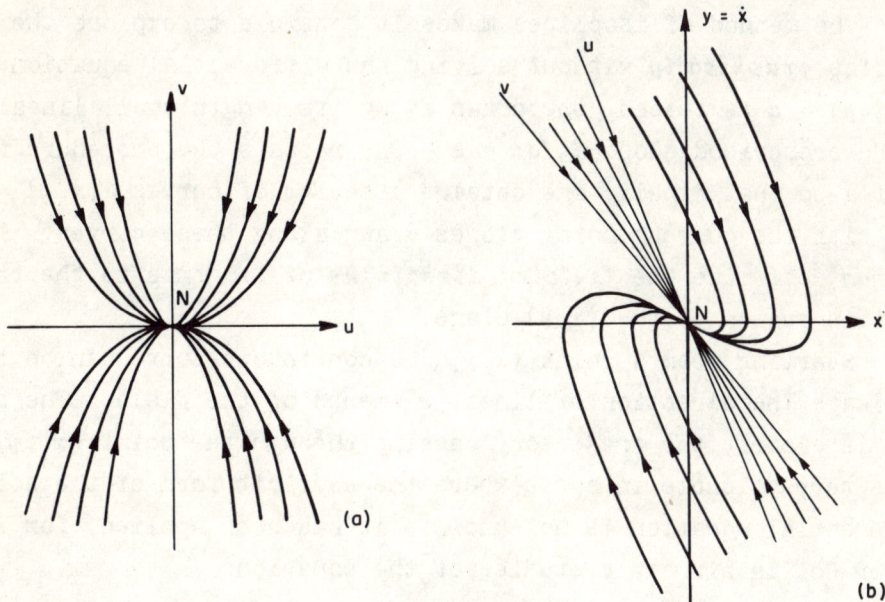

Figure 6.1

These conditions determine the trajectories shown in Figure 6.1b. The origin N, Figure 6.1a is a singular point, a *nodal* point. It is seen that an infinity of trajectories, or integral curves, approaches a nodal point.

7. METHOD OF ISOCLINES

Let

$$\frac{dx}{dt} = P(x,y); \quad \frac{dy}{dt} = Q(x,y)$$

be the differential equations of a dynamical system and

$$\frac{dy}{dx} = \frac{Q(x,y)}{P(x,y)} \equiv F(x,y)$$

that of the trajectories. Suppose that

$$\frac{dy}{dx} = \frac{Q(x,y)}{P(x,y)} \equiv F(x,y) = a = \text{constant} \qquad [7.1]$$

This equation clearly defines a curve in the (x,y)-plane along which the slope, dy/dx, of the trajectories remains constant. Such curves are called *isoclines*. It is apparent that all points of isoclines are necessarily ordinary points since at singular points the slope of trajectories is indeterminate, so that [7.1] has no meaning at such points.

The method of isoclines makes it possible to explore the field of trajectories *graphically* without solving the differential equation. Once the curve $F(x,y) = a$ is traced, one draws along its length small lineal elements having the prescribed slope $dy/dx = a$. One repeats the procedure for other values of a so that finally one obtains a series of curves $F(x,y) = a$, a_1, a_2, $\cdots$, with the corresponding slopes drawn along these curves. These slopes then determine the *field of directions* of tangents to the trajectories in a certain region of the (x,y)-plane.

Starting from a point (x_0, y_0) a continuous curve can be traced following always the direction of lineal elements of the field. The curve so obtained is clearly the trajectory passing through the point (x_0, y_0). The method is very valuable in cases where the explicit form of the solution of the differential equation is not known. It has been applied, for instance, by Van der Pol in his early studies of the equation

$$\ddot{x} - \mu(1 - x^2)\dot{x} + x = 0 \qquad [7.2]$$

This equation can be reduced to the system

$$\dot{x} = y; \quad \dot{y} = \mu(1 - x^2)y - x$$

whose trajectories are given by

$$\frac{dy}{dx} = \frac{\mu(1 - x^2)y - x}{y} \qquad [7.3]$$

The only singularity of [7.2] is clearly the origin, $x = y = 0$; hence the method is applicable everywhere except at that point. Equation [7.1] of the isoclines in this case is

$$y = \frac{x}{(\mu - a) - \mu x^2} \qquad [7.4]$$

For a fixed μ and for a number of different values of the slope a, a series of curves [7.4] are obtained along which the slope of the trajectories is constant.

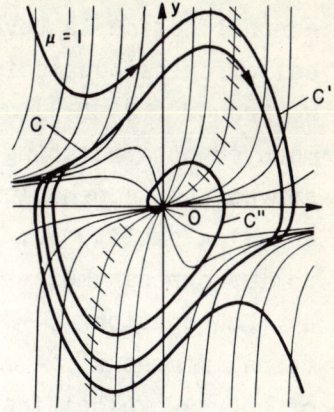

Figure 7.1

      Figure 7.1 shows this construction of Van der Pol (1) for $\mu = 1$ in [7.2] which is self-explanatory. This graphical construction makes it possible to establish the existence of a closed trajectory C to which the non-stationary spiral trajectories C' and C'' approach both from the outside and from the inside of C.

      The reader can easily check, by this method, the principal types of trajectories established previously.

      The principal advantage of the method of isoclines lies in the fact that it always leads to the desired result although its application is tedious and subject to errors inherent in any graphical construction, particularly when the slope of trajectories changes rapidly in certain regions of the phase plane as shown in Figure 7.2. This figure, also taken from Van der Pol's paper, represents the trajectories of [7.2] for $\mu = 10.0$.

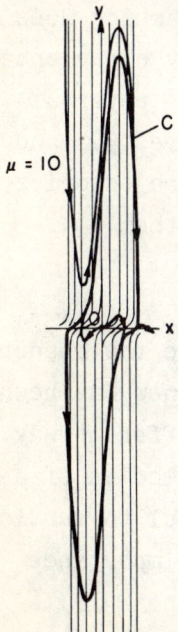

Figure 7.2

8. SYSTEMS WITH NEGATIVE DAMPING; FROUDE'S PENDULUM

      In many branches of applied science one is confronted with problems in which *negative damping* occurs. From a physical standpoint the term is rather unfortunate; its justification lies in the sign of the damping coefficient b. In cases previously considered it was assumed that $b > 0$ corresponds to a *dissipation of energy* from the system. For $b < 0$, on the contrary, there is an *addition* of energy to the system from an external source according to the same law, that is, in proportion to velocity.

      In electrical problems negative damping plays an important role; it is generally associated with circuits containing non-ohmic conductors, which exhibit a decrease in voltage for an increase of current. In many control problems a similar result is observed if the phase of a normally damping control action is reversed (11). Many years before the discovery of electrical circuits possessing negative resistance, or negative damping features, W. Froude (12) (13) discovered a similar effect in the case of a pendulum mounted on a rotating shaft with a certain amount of friction. It was observed that a pendulum of this kind begins to oscillate with gradually increasing amplitudes. The following theory explains this effect: In addition to its own parameters I, b, $mgl = C$ governing the free motion as determined by the equation $I\ddot{\phi} + b\dot{\phi} + C\phi = 0$, the pendulum is also acted upon by an external moment $M(\omega - \dot{\phi})$, due to dry friction, which depends on the difference of angular velocities ω of the shaft and $\dot{\phi}$ of the pendulum. Expanding the function $M(\omega - \dot{\phi})$ in a Taylor series and keeping only the first two terms we have the following differential equation

$$I\ddot{\phi} + b\dot{\phi} + C\dot{\phi} = M(\omega) - \dot{\phi}M'(\omega)$$

that is,

$$I\ddot{\phi} + \left[b + M'(\omega)\right]\dot{\phi} + c\phi = M(\omega) \qquad [8.1]$$

The constant term $M(\omega)$ on the right merely displaces the position of equilibrium and is of no further interest. Thus, interest centers on the coefficient, $[b + M'(\omega)]$, of $\dot{\phi}$. If, in a certain range of ω, the friction is such that $M'(\omega) < 0$, i.e., the friction decreases with ω, the negative term $M'(\omega)$ may outweigh the positive one, b. Thus, the motion of the pendulum occurs as if the coefficient of $\dot{\phi}$ were negative.

From a formal standpoint the introduction of negative damping does not alter the discussion in Sections 5 and 6 appreciably; the only difference in the representation of motion in the phase plane consists in the reversal of the positive direction of the phase trajectories shown in Figures 5.1 and 6.1. Instead of approaching a *stable* focal or nodal point, the trajectories "approach" these points for $t = -\infty$, that is actually depart from them.

9. REMARKS CONCERNING LINEAR SYSTEMS

The above examples are intended primarily to familiarize the reader with the representation of motion by phase trajectories; nothing new has been learned so far, but the known facts were merely presented in a different way. The connection between the singular points and the state of equilibrium of a system will play an important role in what follows and it is useful to mention at this stage that a linear approximation will have considerable importance in establishing the criteria of stability as will be shown in Chapter III. The topology of phase trajectories in the neighborhood of point singularities in non-linear problems remains qualitatively the same as in the simple linear problems studied so far, although quantitatively the relations may be some-what different. Thus, in non-linear conservative systems the trajectories around a vortex point are still *closed curves* but not necessarily ellipses. Likewise the unstable equilibrium in non-linear systems is still character-ized by a saddle point but the asymptotes of the latter are not straight lines as they are in linear cases. We shall investigate these questions in detail in the following chapter but it is worth-while mentioning now that in-sofar as their local properties are concerned, non-linear systems behave not very differently from the linear ones. The important difference lies in the behavior in the large.

It will be shown later that non-linear systems possess under cer-tain conditions closed trajectories of a special type, *the limit cycles*. These new closed trajectories are entirely different from those of linear systems. The most important feature of this new type of trajectory is that it can occur only in a non-conservative system whereas a linear system can possess closed trajectories only when it is conservative. This can be stated as follows: In both linear and non-linear mechanics a similar formulation of conditions for stability is used but the corresponding stationary states of motion are quite different.

A typical pattern of stationary motion in linear mechanics is the motion of a non-dissipative harmonic oscillator, whereas a corresponding pat-tern in a non-linear, non-conservative system is that represented by this special closed trajectory of a new type, the limit cycle, as defined in Chap-ter IV.

The theory of limit cycles and associated phenomena is, thus, a do-main of non-linear mechanics proper for which there exists no counterpart in linear mechanics.

CHAPTER II

PHASE TRAJECTORIES OF NON-LINEAR CONSERVATIVE SYSTEMS

We shall now consider non-linear systems of conservative type, that is, systems in which the dissipation of energy is negligible. The law of conservation of energy is applicable here and leads to a relatively simple topological representation without the necessity for solving the non-linear differential equation. The question of stability of motion in the vicinity of equilibrium points, left open so far, will also be clarified following this line of argument.

10. GENERAL PROPERTIES OF NON-LINEAR CONSERVATIVE SYSTEMS

Consider first a simple motion defined by the differential equation

$$\ddot{x} = f(x) \tag{10.1}$$

in which the restoring force is a certain function of the distance x. It will be assumed that $f(x)$ is analytic for the whole interval $(-\infty, +\infty)$.

Equation [10.1] of the second order is equivalent to the system

$$\dot{x} = y; \quad \dot{y} = f(x) \tag{10.2}$$

Eliminating time we have

$$\frac{dy}{dx} = \frac{f(x)}{y} \tag{10.3}$$

which specifies the field of trajectories in the phase plane. The velocity of motion is given by the ordinate y of the trajectory, and the phase velocity is

$$v = \frac{ds}{dt} = \sqrt{\dot{x}^2 + \dot{y}^2} = y\sqrt{1 + \left(\frac{dy}{dx}\right)^2} \tag{10.4}$$

From [10.3] it follows that the trajectories cross the x-axis ($y = 0$) at right angles and have horizontal tangents at points x_i which are roots of $f(x)$, provided the trajectory does not cross the axis of abscissas ($y = 0$) at these points. We see thus that Cauchy's theorem of uniqueness holds in all cases except at points $(x_i, 0)$ for which $f(x_i) = 0$.

Furthermore, from the fact that at a singular point $y = 0$, $f(x) = 0$, and, in view of relations [10.2], it follows that at singular points $dx/dt = 0$ and $\dot{y} = d^2x/dt^2 = 0$. The latter condition is equivalent to the vanishing of the forces at this point. The last two conditions clearly define a position of equilibrium. Moreover, from [10.4] it follows that at the singular points the phase velocity vanishes.

11. TOPOLOGY OF PHASE TRAJECTORIES IN THE NEIGHBORHOOD OF SINGULAR POINTS

A. GRAPHICAL METHOD

For conservative systems the problem is simplified owing to the existence of the integral of energy. For a system of unit mass we have

$$\frac{1}{2}y^2 + V(x) = h \qquad\qquad [11.1]$$

which expresses that the sum of the kinetic energy, $\frac{1}{2}y^2$, and the potential energy, $V(x)$, remains constant. By definition $V(x) = -\int_0^x f(x)dx$, where $f(x)$ is the restoring force.

For a given value of h, [11.1] represents a curve of constant energy in the phase plane. The motion is impossible if $h - V(x) < 0$ since the value of y is then imaginary. This is ruled out in a physical problem. Equilibrium points are characterized by the relation $f(x) = 0$, that is $V'(x) = 0$. In other words, the potential energy has an extremum value at the point of equilibrium. From [11.1] and the preceding discussion the following conclusions can be formulated:

1. The phase trajectories are symmetrical with respect to the x-axis.

2. The trajectories cross the x-axis at right angles, that is $dy/dx = \infty$; they have a horizontal tangent at the points where $f(x) = 0$, provided y does not vanish at these points.

3. The singular points are situated on the x-axis at points x_i, for which $f(x) = 0$.

The topological picture of the phase trajectories can be best shown in two steps:

a. by drawing an auxiliary diagram giving the representation of the difference $h - V(x)$, and

b. by drawing the phase trajectory $y/\sqrt{2}$ itself, both curves being plotted against x.

Figures 11.1a and b show examples of this representation. Figure 11.1a shows the diagram of the balance of energy $h - V(x)$ for a

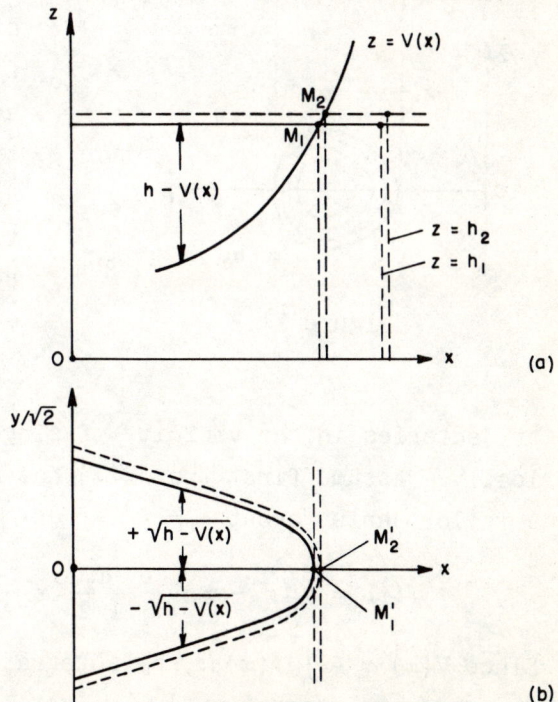

Figure 11.1

given shape of $V(x)$ and assumed value $h = h_1$. The difference $h - V(x)$ is
positive to the left of M_1. Figure 11.1b gives the phase diagram (coordinates x, $y/\sqrt{2}$) corresponding to Figure 11.1a. The phase trajectories are
real to the left of M_1. This case corresponds, for instance, to the trajectories in the right (or left) quadrants of Figure 4.1 representing the motion
in the vicinity of a saddle point when the pendulum does not have enough energy to overcome the "potential barrier" and is thus unable to go over the
upper unstable equilibrium point. In this case, the question of linearity
assumed in connection with Figure 4.1 is waived and the discussion, therefore, can be made general. If the value of h is increased ($h = h_2$), the
point M_1 is shifted to M_2, and the phase trajectory is shifted accordingly
(point M_2').

Figure 11.2 represents an analogous construction when $V(x)$ has a
minimum for $x = x_1$. The only essential difference between this and the preceding case is in that for $x = x_1$; $V(x_1)$ has now an extremum, that is, $f(x) = 0$.
Hence the point $x = x_1$ is a singular point, the vortex point, as previously defined.
The trajectories in the phase space, Figure 11.2b, around the vortex point are obtained
in the same manner as before, that is, for a given value of $h \geqq V(x_1)$ we plot the ordinates $\pm \sqrt{h - V(x)}$ in Figure 11.2a; then for the next curve we change h and plot
another curve, etc. The oval curves which thus appear are enclosed within each other
and the motion is periodic; moreover, in view of non-linearity, these curves depart
somewhat from the elliptic form.

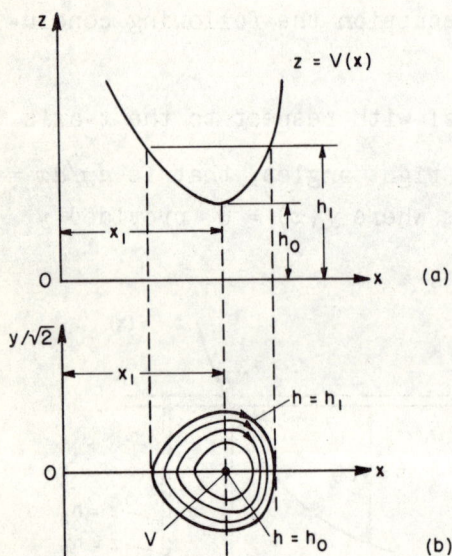

Figure 11.2

B. ANALYTICAL METHOD

The topological picture of the
trajectories in the vicinity of singular points can also be obtained analytically. Assume first that $V(x)$ has a minimum for $x = x_1$, and expand $f(x)$ in
a Taylor series about $x = x_1$

$$f(x) = a_1(x - x_1) + \frac{a_2}{1 \cdot 2}(x - x_1)^2 + \frac{a_3}{1 \cdot 2 \cdot 3}(x - x_1)^3 + \cdots \quad [11.2]$$

Since $V(x) = -\int_0^x f(x)dx$, by integrating [11.2], changing sign, and adding the
constant of integration h_0, we get

$$V(x) = h_0 - \left[\frac{a_1}{1 \cdot 2} (x - x_1)^2 + \frac{a_2}{1 \cdot 2 \cdot 3} (x - x_1)^3 + \cdots \right] \quad [11.3]$$

where

$$a_1 = f'(x_1) = -V''(x_1); \quad a_2 = f''(x_1) = -V'''(x_1) \quad [11.4]$$

Transferring the origin to the singular point, i.e., putting $x = x_1 + \xi$, $y = 0 + \eta$, this gives, upon the substitution of the value of $V(x_1 + \xi)$ as given by [11.3] into the integral of energy $y^2/2 + V(x) = h$, the equation

$$\frac{\eta^2}{2} + h_0 - \left[\frac{a_1 \xi^2}{1 \cdot 2} + \cdots + \frac{a_k \xi^{k+1}}{1 \cdot 2 \cdots (k+1)} + \cdots \right] = h \quad [11.5]$$

Two principal cases can be considered:

1. $a_1 \neq 0$. In this case the curve $V(x)$ and straight line $z = h_0$ have at $x = x_1$ contact of the first order. Since $V(x_1)$ is minimum, $V'(x_1) = 0$ and $V''(x_1) > 0$. Therefore $a_1 = -V''(x_1) < 0$. For $h = h_0$ [11.5] degenerates into an isolated point $\xi = \eta = 0$, which is clearly the vortex point of the phase trajectories. For $h - h_0 = \alpha > 0$, [11.5], to the first order of $f(x)$, is

$$\frac{\eta^2}{2} + \frac{|a_1| \xi^2}{2} = \alpha \quad [11.6]$$

which is of the form

$$\frac{\eta^2}{m^2} + \frac{\xi^2}{n^2} = 1$$

where $m^2 = 2\alpha$; $n^2 = 2\alpha/|a_1|$. The trajectory in the phase plane is thus an ellipse with semi-axes m, n. To the first approximation, for small motions, it is legitimate therefore to consider the motion as a sinusoidal function of time.

2. $a_1 = 0$. For a greater generality assume $a_2 = a_3 = \cdots a_{k-1} = 0$ and $a_k \neq 0$. Then k is necessarily an odd integer and $a_k < 0$, since $z = V(x)$ lies above its tangent in the neighborhood $x = x_1$. For $h = h_0$ the curve [11.5] reduces again to an isolated point $\xi = \eta = 0$, the vortex point of trajectories. For $h - h_0 = \alpha > 0$, [11.6] to the $(k + 1)$ order of k becomes

$$\frac{\eta^2}{2} + \frac{|a_k| \xi^{k+1}}{(k+1)!} = \alpha \quad [11.6]$$

which represents a closed curve differing from an ellipse even for very small oscillations. It would be erroneous, therefore, to "linearize" such a motion even for small oscillations. The topological picture of the trajectories in the phase plane will have the appearance of closed curves surrounding each other around the vortex point **V**, Figure 11.2b, as previously found by the graphical method.

If the potential energy $V(x)$ has a maximum for $x = x_1$ the procedure is similar, with the exception that a_1 (or a_k in the more general case when $a_1 = a_2 = \cdots a_{k-1} = 0$) is now positive, so that the trajectory becomes $\eta^2/2 - a_1 \xi^2/2 = \alpha$ to the first order (case when $a_1 \neq 0$), which is of the form

$$\frac{\eta^2}{m^2} - \frac{\xi^2}{n^2} = 1 \qquad [11.7]$$

with the previous notations. Equation [11.7] represents hyperbolas with $\eta = + \sqrt{a_1}\,\xi$ and $\eta = - \sqrt{a_1}\,\xi$ as asymptotes. The point $\xi = \eta = 0$ is, clearly a saddle point. Thus to the first order, the small motions in the vicinity of the maximum of potential energy are unstable and are represented in the phase plane by hyperbolic trajectories as previously found from a study of linear systems. In the second case ($a_1 = a_2 = \cdots = a_{k-1} = 0$; $a_k \neq 0$), we find by a similar argument that for $a_k > 0$ the trajectories in the phase plane are obtained from [11.5] by neglecting the terms with a_{k+1}, a_{k+2}, $\cdots$; in this case

$$\frac{\eta^2}{2} - \frac{a_k \xi^{k+1}}{(k+1)!} = \alpha \qquad [11.8]$$

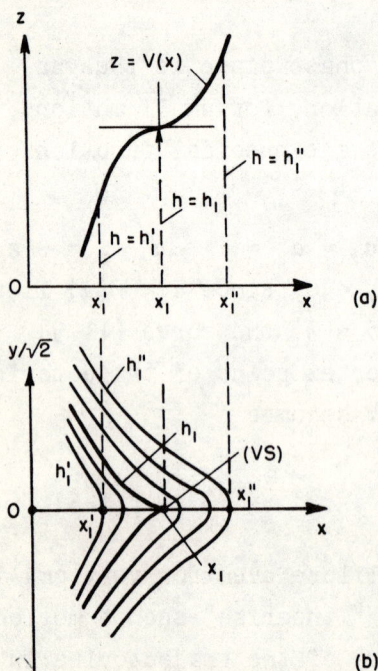

Figure 11.3

The phase trajectories, while still possessing the same general features, such as asymptotic motions, etc., depart from ordinary hyperbolas even for small motions. Furthermore the asymptotes are curvilinear.

3.   The potential energy $V(x)$ has an inflection point at $x = x_1$ with a horizontal tangent, Figure 11.3a. In this case $a_1 = - V''(x_1) = 0$. Furthermore, in the general case, the first term a_k, which is not zero, must be necessarily of *even* order ($k = 2$, 4, $\cdots$) as follows from [11.3] because the potential energy variation changes its sign for $h = h_1 \pm \Delta h$ in this case. In the phase plane, Figure ·11.3b, the trajectory corresponding to the ordinate $h = h_1$ of the inflection point has a singular point VS in the sense of differential geometry, e.g., a

cusp, which represents the coalescence of a vortex point V with a saddle point S. The motion along this singular trajectory is asymptotically approaching the point VS, and reverses the direction of its motion also in an asymptotic manner. The motion is ultimately unstable; this instability is more definite for other trajectories. Everything happens as if the coalescence of a stable vortex point with an unstable saddle point were *contaminating* the process with an ultimate instability. In reality this process of coalescence of singularities means that the singularity at this point is no longer *simple* in character. The complete study of the conditions of equilibrium upon the coalescence of singularities is too complicated, and will not be attempted here.

Summing up the results of this analysis we are led to the following two theorems of which the first is due to Lagrange and the second to Liapounoff.

THEOREM 1. If the potential energy $V(x)$ is minimum at the point $x = x_1$, the equilibrium is stable.

THEOREM 2. If the potential energy $V(x)$ has an extremum at the point x_1, without being a minimum, the equilibrium is unstable.

12. TOPOLOGY OF TRAJECTORIES IN THE PHASE PLANE. SEPARATRIX

The preceding method was applied to the motion occurring in the vicinity of the equilibrium points; it can be extended, however, to the whole phase plane. In this manner we obtain the complete picture, the topology of the phase trajectories with the critical boundaries separating motions of different types. The starting point for this representation is again the energy equation $y^2/2 = -V(x) + h$. The various cases to be discussed are illustrated in Figure 12.1.

1. If $h < V(x)$ for all values of x, clearly no motion is possible. Figure 12.1 exhibits this condition between the points 0 and 1, between point 5 and 7 and to the right of point 13.

2. $h > V(x)$ for all values of x. This case is shown in Figure 12.2. The velocity y never changes sign but varies only in magnitude. At the point x_1 at which $V(x)$ is maximum, the velocity decreases somewhat. This corresponds to the motion of a pendulum having an initial energy h greater than the amount required to carry it to the upper unstable equilibrium point.

3. $V_{max}(x) > h > V_{min}(x)$, assuming that no point of tangency exists between the straight line $z = h$ and the curve $V(x)$ as is shown in Figure 12.1a for $z = h_2$. Between the points a and b, $h - V(x) > 0$; the motion is

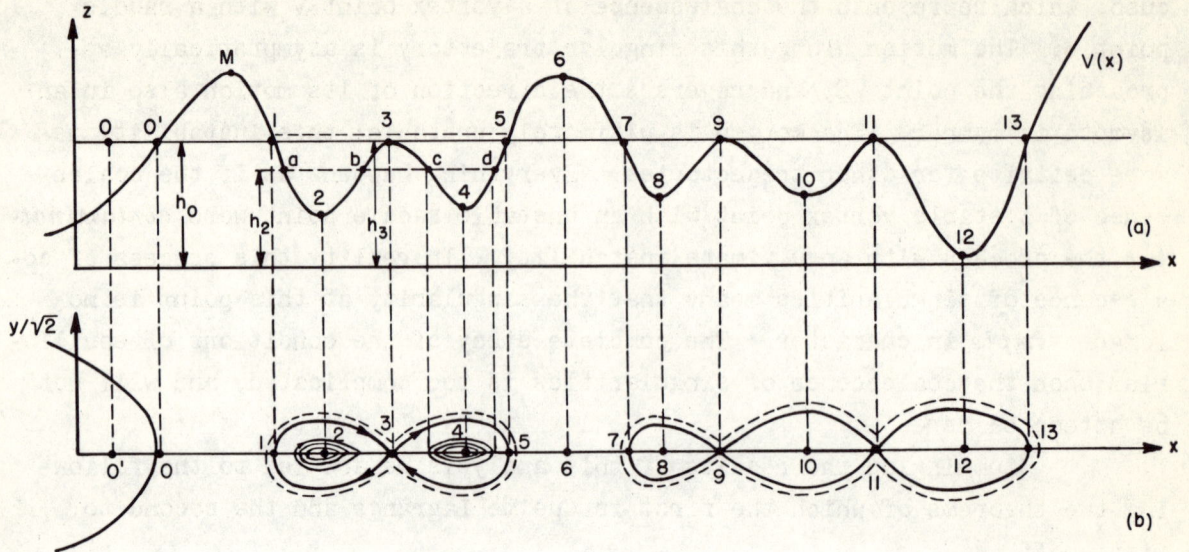

Figure 12.1

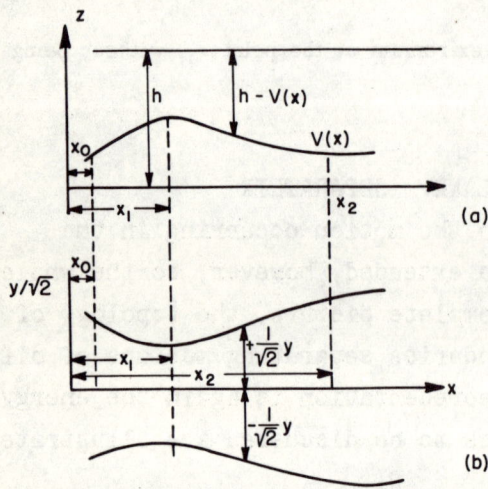

Figure 12.2

thus possible. Point 2 in the interval (a,b) corresponds to the minimum of potential energy, hence, it is a vortex point 2 in the phase diagram. The trajectories surrounding the point 2 are closed curves without points of intersection; by changing h_2 we obtain a family of these trajectories around the point 2 forming an "island" in the phase plane. Similarly, between the points c and d (same value h_2) there appears another "island" of trajectories around the other vortex point 4.

4.   If in a certain region, e.g., to the left of point 0, in Figure 12.1a, the potential energy decreases monotonically, the motion becomes possible again. The trajectory arrives from $x = -\infty$, reaches the point 0 and then turns back. Within a limited range, e.g., between 0, 0' the motion resembles that of a pendulum projected initially with an energy insufficient to carry it over the upper position of unstable equilibrium.

5. $h = V(x_1)$ at a certain $x = x_1$. The line $z = h_3$ is tangent to the curve of energy $V(x)$ at the point 3 of its maximum. Between the points 2 and 3, the motion approaching point 3 becomes asymptotic and point 3 is a saddle point. We note that as the energy constant h_2 approaches the value h_3, the

"island" of trajectories, around the vortex point 2, gradually increases in size, the motion remaining periodic. When the value $z = h_3$ is reached the motion loses its periodic character because the time of approach to the saddle point is infinite. We infer, therefore, that this singular trajectory on which the motion is asymptotic, *the separatrix*, limiting the size of the "islands," is limited by the singular trajectories issuing from the saddle point 3. The same conclusion is also valid for the separatrices issuing from the other two asymptotes of the saddle point 3 and enclosing the vortex point 4 corresponding to another position of stable equilibrium.

If the value of the energy constant h_3 is increased slightly, the saddle point disappears and the phase trajectory encircles the saddle point 3 and the vortex points 2 and 4 as shown by the dotted lines. If, however, the energy constant is decreased slightly, there appear two closed trajectories around the vortex points 2 and 4. We thus find two kinds of trajectories, typified by those in the upper and lower quadrants, Figure 4.1, on the one hand, and those in the left and right quadrants, on the other hand. Furthermore, we are now able to correlate radical changes occurring in the topology of phase trajectories with a critical value of a certain quantity h_3.

When the line $z = h_3$ is tangent to the energy curve at two consecutive maximum points, e.g., points 9 and 11 in Figure 12.1a, the separatrix has the appearance of a chain enclosing three vortex points 8, 10, and 12, and issuing from the asymptotes of two saddle points 9 and 11. For $h = h_3 + \Delta h \ (\Delta h > 0)$ the phase trajectory has the appearance shown in dotted lines, since the saddle points disappear in this case. For $h = h_3 - \Delta h$ three "islands" of periodic trajectories will appear around each of the three vortex points 8, 10, and 12.

We thus meet a situation which will be of great importance in what follows. We shall frequently use the expression "the topological structure of the phase trajectories undergoes a qualitative change" for a critical value of a certain parameter whenever we encounter two entirely different aspects of the trajectories on both sides of this critical value. The value h_3 of the constant of energy h in the above examples illustrates this situation. In these examples the critical or "bifurcation" points at which these changes occur are associated with certain values of the constant of energy appearing in the first integral of a dynamical system. In the following section we shall consider a still more important case when a certain parameter appears in the differential equation itself.

From the elementary considerations developed in this section the following theorem is apparent. Inside a closed phase curve there is always an odd number of singular points, the number of vortex points being greater than the number of saddle points by one unit (2).

Before closing this qualitative study of the topology of trajectories in the phase plane it may be useful to mention the analogy existing between the separatrix and the divide of common topography.* In both cases a small change in the parameter, e.g., small displacement of the source across a theoretical divide, results in an entirely different topographic picture of the ultimate process.

13. BEHAVIOR OF A CONSERVATIVE SYSTEM AS A FUNCTION OF A PARAMETER. CRITICAL VALUES OF A PARAMETER

We propose now to review briefly the theory of Poincaré (14) (15) regarding the dependence of the topological structure of trajectories in the phase plane on a parameter in the differential equation. The qualitative analysis of the trajectories contained in the preceding section has already prepared the ground for a more rigorous quantitative analysis of this question.

Consider a dynamical system described by a differential equation depending on a parameter λ. If the parameter λ is varied, the solutions of the differential equation represented by the trajectories undergo variations. By definition we shall designate as *ordinary values* of λ those values which correspond to trajectories belonging to the same family, as, for instance, was the case of closed trajectories belonging to the same "island" considered in the previous section. Therefore, in an interval of ordinary values of λ a continuous variation of λ corresponds to a continuous variation of the trajectories in the phase plane without any radical changes in their topological features. The values λ_i of the parameter λ, at which the topological structure of the trajectories changes abruptly are called *critical values.***

In dynamical problems it is convenient to introduce a parameter λ in the expression of potential energy $V(x,\lambda)$ and, hence, of the force

$$f(x,\lambda) = -\frac{\partial V(x,\lambda)}{\partial x} \qquad [13.1]$$

As shown in Section 11, the points of equilibrium are given by the extremal values of the potential energy, that is, by equating the expression [13.1] to zero. This equation represents a curve M, in the (x,λ)-plane, Figure 13.1, which, in general, may have points of self-intersection such as F. For a given value λ_0 of the parameter the positions of equilibrium x_1, x_2, x_3 are

---

* The introduction of the *separatrix* and of a parameter in the study of the topology of the phase trajectories is due to Poincaré.

** The term "bifurcation value" is also used.

obtained as points A, B, C of intersec-
tion of M with the straight line $\lambda = \lambda_0$.
If the value of λ is changed the positions of equilibrium change. It was
shown in Section 11 that the stability
of equilibrium depends on the sign of
the derivative $f_x(x,\lambda) = -V_{xx}(x,\lambda)$.*
For a minimum of potential energy
($V_{xx} > 0$; $f_x < 0$), the equilibrium is
stable; hence the point of equilibrium

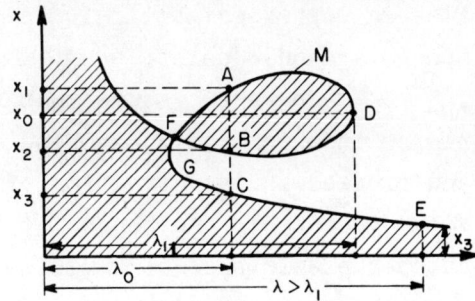

Figure 13.1

is a vortex point. Furthermore for $f_x > 0$ the equilibrium is unstable. Thus
points of equilibrium are given by the equation

$$f(x,\lambda) = 0$$

and the criteria of stability by

$$f_x(x,\lambda) \lessgtr 0 \qquad [13.2]$$

Differentiating the equation $f(x,\lambda) = 0$ with respect to λ we get

$$\frac{dx}{d\lambda} = -\frac{f_\lambda(x,\lambda)}{f_x(x,\lambda)} \qquad [13.3]$$

If by increasing λ we get a value λ_1, at which two points A and B coalesce,
the two positions of equilibrium x_1 and x_2 coalesce into the equilibrium
point x_0, Point D on Curve M. For $\lambda > \lambda_1$ there remains only one point of
equilibrium x_3, Point E on Curve M. When $\lambda = \lambda_1$, [13.1] has a simple root
x_3 and a double root x_0, hence $f_x(x_0,\lambda) = 0$. From [13.3] it follows that
$dx/d\lambda = \infty$, i.e., the tangent at D is vertical.

The value of $\lambda = \lambda_1$ at which both equilibrium points x_1 and x_2
coalesce and then disappear, is the *critical value* of the parameter. For
the point F at which the curve intersects itself, the expression $dx/d\lambda$ is
indeterminate. This implies that both f_x and f_λ vanish. Poincaré gives a
simple rule for ascertaining the stability of motion in the vicinity of a
critical value of the parameter.

POINCARÉ'S THEOREM (14) (15)
If the region in which $f(x,\lambda) > 0$ is *below* the curve $f(x,\lambda) = 0$ for
the positive values for x and λ shown in Figure 13.1 the equilibrium is stable,

---

* In the following the symbol f_x designates the partial derivative of f with respect to x.

34

i.e., a vortex point; if it is *above* the curve the equilibrium is unstable, hence, a saddle point.

In fact, assume that the shaded area in Figure 13.1 represents the region in which $f(x,\lambda) > 0$ and consider a point in the region below the curve and proceed in the direction of increasing x, with λ fixed. In such a case $f(x,\lambda)$ decreases and hence $f_x(x,\lambda) < 0$, that is, $V_{xx}(x,\lambda) > 0$, which indicates the existence of a minimum of potential energy and, hence, stability. The opposite condition occurs when the region of $f(x,\lambda) > 0$ is *above* the curve, i.e., instability. The theorem indicates that the branches FAD and GCE correspond to stability, while the branches GF and FBD correspond to instability.

It is seen thus that the "exchange of stabilities" ("échange des stabilitiés," according to the expression of Poincaré) occurs at the critical values of the parameter. The points of equilibrium in conservative systems always appear and disappear in pairs; the disappearance of equilibrium points in conservative systems always results in the coalescence of a vortex point with a saddle point. As has already been mentioned, after such coalescence no stable equilibrium exists.

A few simple examples illustrating the topological method outlined in this and in the preceding sections are given in the following sections.

14. MOTION OF AN ELASTICALLY CONSTRAINED CURRENT-CARRYING CONDUCTOR

Consider an elastically constrained* conductor of length l and carrying a current i, attracted by a rigidly constrained conductor of infinite length carrying a current I; let a be the distance between the wall W constraining i and the fixed current I, x being the variable distance between W and i. It is assumed that the electrodynamic action exerted on i is limited to the length, i.e., the current i is conveyed through flexible wires pp at right angles to i so that the electrodynamic forces act along the length l only. Furthermore, since the conductors have a finite diameter, $x < a$, the total force acting on the conductor i is

$$f(x,\lambda) = - k\left(x - \frac{\lambda}{a - x}\right) \qquad [14.1]$$

where $\lambda = 2Iil/k$ is a parameter; the first term kx is the force due to the elastic constraint, and the second $k\lambda/(a - x)$ is the electrodynamic force according to the Biot-Savart law.

---

*.As, for example, by the springs ss, Figure 14.1a.

For $\lambda = a^2/4$ one has a critical value of the parameter because both $f(x,\lambda)$ and $f_x(x,\lambda)$ vanish. The differential equation of motion in this case is

$$m\ddot{x} + k\left(x - \frac{\lambda}{a - x}\right) = 0 \qquad [14.2]$$

It is equivalent to the system

$$\dot{x} = y; \;\; \dot{y} = \frac{k}{m} \frac{x^2 - ax + \lambda}{a - x} \qquad [14.3]$$

From [14.3] it follows that

$$\frac{dy}{dx} = \frac{k}{m} \frac{x^2 - ax + \lambda}{y(a - x)} \qquad [14.4]$$

Equation [14.4] establishes the topology of the phase trajectories. There are two singular points, both located on the x-axis ($y = 0$), given by the roots x_1 and x_2 of the equation $x^2 - ax + \lambda = 0$. The coordinates of these points are $(x_1, 0)$ and $(x_2, 0)$ with $x_1 = \frac{a}{2} - b$ and $x_2 = \frac{a}{2} + b$, where $b = \sqrt{\frac{a^2}{4} - \lambda}$. The motion has a different character according as $\lambda \lesseqgtr a^2/4$. The equality $\lambda = a^2/4$ corresponds to the critical value of the parameter.

1. $\lambda < a^2/4$. Both roots x_1 and x_2 are real and positive. Substituting the values of x_1 and x_2 into the expression of $f_x(x,\lambda) = - V_{xx}(x,\lambda)$, we have for $x_1 = \frac{a}{2} - b$, $f_x(x_1,\lambda) < 0$, $V_{xx}(x_1,\lambda) > 0$, and hence the potential energy is minimum; the equilibrium is, therefore, stable and the singular point is a vortex point.

Similarly, for $x_2 = \frac{a}{2} + b$, $f_x(x_2,\lambda) > 0$, $V_{xx}(x_2,\lambda) < 0$, and therefore the equilibrium is unstable; hence, this singular point is a saddle point S.

From [14.4] it follows that as x approaches a, the slope dy/dx of the phase trajectories approaches infinity; hence the trajectories have the vertical line $x = a$ as asymptote.

In order to complete the topological picture we have to determine the separatrix. In this case the integral of energy exists. We obtain its value by integrating the dynamical equation

$$m\ddot{x} - f(x,\lambda) = 0 \qquad [14.5]$$

Multiplying this equation by $\dot{x} = y$ and integrating, we have

$$\frac{1}{2}my^2 + \frac{1}{2}kx^2 + k\lambda \log(a - x) = h \qquad [14.6]$$

The equation of the separatrix is obtained if h is such that the separatrix passes through the saddle point $y = 0$, $x_2 = \frac{a}{2} + b$. Substituting these coordinates into [14.6], the constant of energy becomes

$$h = \frac{1}{2} k \left(\frac{a}{2} + b\right)^2 + k \lambda \log\left(\frac{a}{2} - b\right) \qquad [14.7]$$

Hence, the equation of the separatrix is

$$\frac{1}{2} m y^2 + \frac{k}{2}\left[x^2 - \left(\frac{a}{2} + b\right)^2\right] + k \lambda \log \frac{a - x}{\frac{a}{2} - b} = 0 \qquad [14.8]$$

Figure 14.1b gives the topological picture of the trajectories. It is seen that, if the initial conditions are such that the representative point

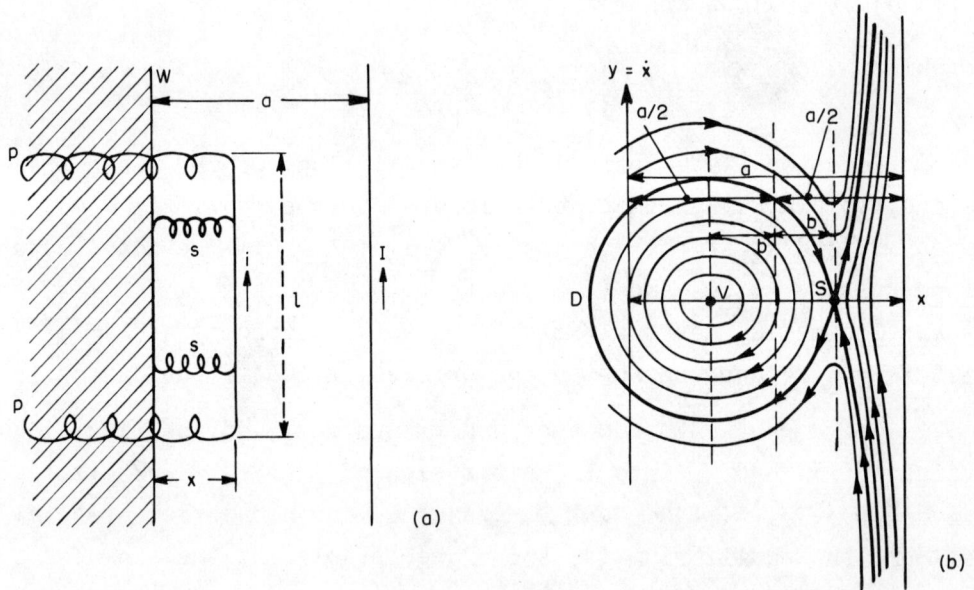

Figure 14.1

for $t = t_0$ is within the area limited by the separatrix D, the motion is periodic around the vortex point V. On the separatrix itself the motion is asymptotic. Outside the separatrix the motion is aperiodic; the phase trajectories exhibit a "dip" above the saddle point and approach the line $x = a$ asymptotically.

2. $\lambda > a^2/4$. In this case there are no singular points, and hence no positions of equilibrium, since the equation $x^2 - ax + \lambda = 0$ has no real roots. The electrodynamic force exceeds the elastic force for all points of the phase plane. The phase trajectories are shown qualitatively on the right side of Figure 14.1b between the separatrix and the line $x = a$.

3. $\lambda = a^2/4$. As λ approaches this value, $b = \sqrt{\frac{a^2}{4} - \lambda}$ approaches zero; both singular points, assuming that the approach takes place from the region where $\lambda < a^2/4$, approach each other and coalesce for $\lambda = a^2/4$. The separatrix

still exists but exhibits a cusp at the point VS of coalescence, Figure 14.2. The motion remains unstable. This case is similar to that considered in Section 11, Case 3, when the potential energy has an extremum value without being either maximum or minimum.

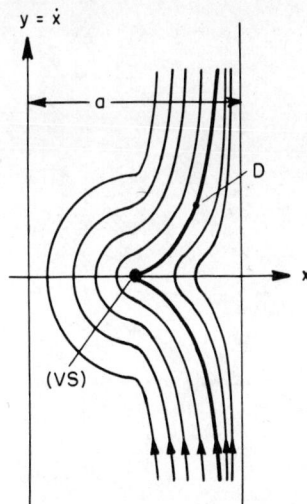

Figure 14.2

15. RELATIVE MOTION OF A ROTATING PENDULUM

This problem may be considered as the generalized study of a centrifugal governor in the absence of friction. Let Ω be the angular velocity of the plane of the pendulum of length a; m the mass of the pendulum, and θ the coordinate angle determining its position on the circle of its relative oscillation, Figure 15.1.

The centrifugal force acting on the particle is $m\Omega^2 a \sin\theta$, and its moment about the axis of the pendulum is $m\Omega^2 a^2 \sin\theta \cos\theta$. The moment due to gravity is $mga\sin\theta$. The resultant total moment is

$$M(\theta,\lambda) = m\Omega^2 a^2(\cos\theta - \lambda)\sin\theta \qquad [15.1]$$

where $\lambda = g/\Omega^2 a$ is a parameter. The signs occurring in [15.1] are apparent from Figure 15.1. For greater generality we may consider negative values of λ; they correspond to a purely theoretical case when $g < 0$.

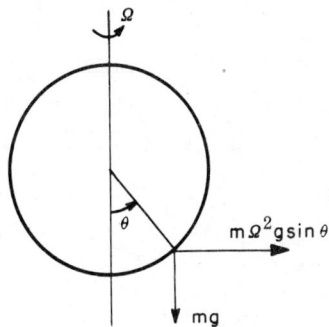

Figure 15.1

The differential equation of relative motion is

$$I\ddot\theta - m\Omega^2 a^2(\cos\theta - \lambda)\sin\theta = 0 \qquad [15.2]$$

where $I = ma^2$ is the moment of inertia of the pendulum. The equivalent system is

$$\dot\theta = \omega; \quad I\dot\omega - m\Omega^2 a^2(\cos\theta - \lambda)\sin\theta = 0 \qquad [15.3]$$

whence

$$\frac{d\omega}{d\theta} = \frac{m\Omega^2 a^2(\cos\theta - \lambda)\sin\theta}{I\omega} \qquad [15.4]$$

Equation [15.4] gives the phase trajectories in the (θ,ω)-plane. The singular points are

$$\omega_1 = 0, \theta = 0; \quad \omega_2 = 0, \theta_2 = \pi; \quad \omega_3 = 0, \theta_3 = \cos^{-1}\lambda \qquad [15.5]$$

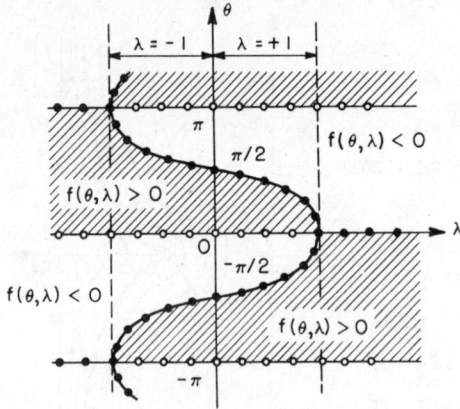

Figure 15.2

The third singular point exists only if $\lambda = g/\Omega^2 a < 1$, that is, for a sufficiently large value of Ω. The force is given by equation

$$f(\theta,\lambda) = m\Omega^2 a^2 (\cos\theta - \lambda)\sin\theta \qquad [15.6]$$

The points of equilibrium are given by $f(\theta,\lambda) = 0$; that is, $\theta = 0$, $\theta = \pi$, $\theta = -\pi$, and $\cos\theta = \lambda$. Figure 15.2 represents the (θ,λ)-diagram for these values. The region in which $f(\theta,\lambda) > 0$ is shaded; the non-shaded regions correspond to $f(\theta,\lambda) < 0$. The branches of the curves $\theta = \cos^{-1}\lambda$, $\theta = 0$, $\theta = \pi$, $\theta = -\pi$, situated above the regions for which $f(\theta,\lambda) > 0$, represent the loci of saddle points shown by circles.* The points $(\theta = 0, \lambda = 1)$, $(\theta = \pi, \lambda = -1)$, $(\theta = -\pi, \lambda = -1)$ are the critical points at which there occurs the "exchange of stabilities" of Poincaré. As regards the curve $\cos\theta = \lambda$, it represents loci of vortex points; this region exists only between the limits $\lambda = \pm 1$.

The integral of energy exists in this case, because the system is conservative by our assumption. Its expression is

$$\frac{I\dot\theta^2}{2} - m\Omega^2 a^2 \left(\frac{\sin^2\theta}{2} + \lambda\cos\theta\right) = h \qquad [15.7]$$

Equation [15.7] expresses the law of conservation of energy. The equation of the separatrix is obtained from the condition that the phase trajectory passes through the saddle point. This condition is satisfied by the points $\theta = \pm\pi$, $\dot\theta = 0$ which gives the equation of the separatrix, Curve A, Figure 15.3,

$$\omega^2 = \frac{m\Omega^2 a^2}{I}\left[\sin^2\theta + 2\lambda(\cos\theta + 1)\right] \qquad [15.8]$$

There exists a second separatrix (B, Figure 15.3) passing through the second saddle point $\theta = 0$, $\dot\theta = 0$, for which $h = -m\lambda\Omega^2 a^2$; its equation is

$$\omega^2 = \frac{m\Omega^2 a^2}{I}\left[\sin^2\theta + 2\lambda(\cos\theta - 1)\right] \qquad [15.9]$$

Figure 15.3 shows the topology of the phase trajectories for $0 < \lambda < 1$. It is observed that the vortex point $\theta = 0$ for $\Omega = 0$ becomes a

---

* The following convention will be used: black points designate the stable singularities and the circles the unstable singularities.

saddle point for $\Omega \neq 0$; at the same
time there appear two vortex points
V_1 and V_2 symmetrically situated with
respect to the point $\theta = \dot{\theta} = 0$ around
which periodic motions are possible.
The oscillations about these vortex
points are asymmetrical with respect
to the point $\theta = \dot{\theta} = 0$; the coordi-
nates of the vortex points are $\theta = \cos^{-1}\lambda$, $\omega = 0$. As soon as the constant of energy reaches the critical
value and the separatrix B is crossed
the motion becomes again periodic and

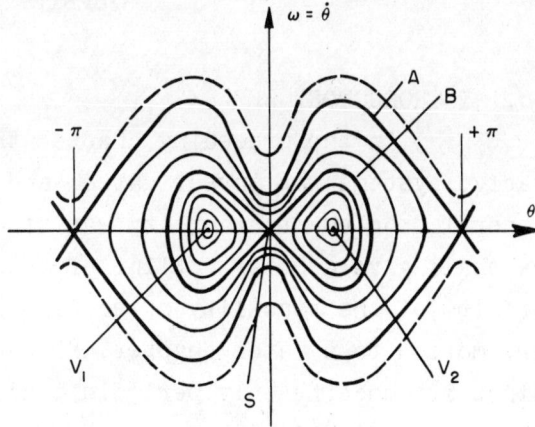

Figure 15.3

symmetrical with respect to $\theta = \dot{\theta} = 0$, but not uniform; the velocity $\omega = \dot{\theta}$
decreases for $\theta = 0$. This range corresponds to the region of the phase plane
situated between the separatrices A and B. When the energy constant reaches
a second critical value at which
the separatrix A is crossed, the
motion becomes rotary, shown by
the broken line in Figure 15.3,
and non-uniform; the phase trajectories pass outside the separatrix
A.

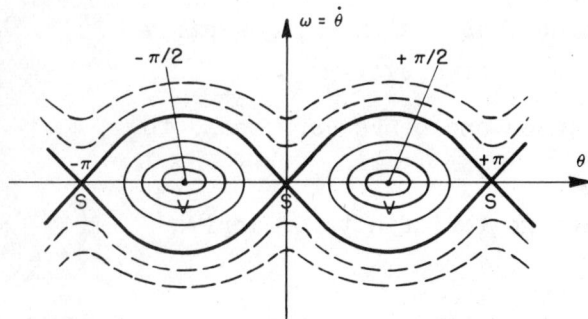

Figure 15.4

To sum up, in the case
$0 < \lambda < 1$ three kinds of motions
are possible:

a., b. Two periodic
oscillatory motions, one around each vortex point (V_1, V_2) and one
around the combination of one saddle point S and two adjoining vortex points V_1, V_2.

c. One periodic motion around the external separatrix A, see
Chapter VII.

For $\lambda = 0$, i.e., $\Omega \to \infty$, both separatrices A and B coalesce, and the
vortex points move to $\theta = \pm \pi/2$ positions. The topological picture of the
trajectories is shown in Figure 15.4. For $|\lambda| > 1$ the topological picture
also changes; there appear vortex points $\theta = 0$, π, $-\pi$, but the intermediate
range disappears entirely. The values $\lambda = -1$, $\lambda = 0$, $\lambda = +1$ are thus the
critical values of the parameter λ.

CHAPTER III

QUESTIONS OF STABILITY

16. INTRODUCTORY REMARKS

In the preceding chapter the question of the equilibrium of conservative systems was investigated, and certain definitions were formulated. The general problem of stability was studied by Liapounoff (4). In this chapter we shall give a brief outline of this study insofar as it is related to the problem of the stability of equilibrium, postponing the question of stationary motion to a later chapter. The study made so far is still incomplete since it concerns only periodic trajectories of a very special type, namely, those occurring in conservative systems. In Chapter IV we shall extend this study in connection with an important class of special periodic trajectories, which arise in non-conservative and non-linear systems.

From the preceding analysis of a few simple motions, it appears that the trajectories of dynamical systems exhibit the following principal properties:

a. They may approach singular points either for $t = + \infty$, or $t = - \infty$, or for both. These points, as was shown, generally correspond to the points of equilibrium of a system.

b. The trajectories may be closed and hence correspond to periodic motions.

c. The trajectories may either go to infinity or arrive from infinity.

We shall be interested primarily in the stationary states of dynamical systems, that is, in the above specified Cases a and b. As regards to Case c, the non-stationary motions, it is of relatively little interest in applications. In fact, when we say that a trajectory "goes to infinity" or "arrives from infinity," we mean that a physical phenomenon is encountered which cannot be studied entirely within the range of observation. The trajectories of Type a characterize motions in the neighborhood of equilibrium, and the problem of stability in this case is that of *equilibrium*. The motions of Type b possess also certain other features of stability which will be defined later.

Insofar as the stability of equilibrium is concerned, the preceding definition of stability for motions occurring in the neighborhood of focal, nodal, and saddle points does not present any difficulty. In fact, the representative point R approaches the focal and nodal points if they are stable and leaves these points (or "approaches" them for $t = -\infty$) if they are unstable. A saddle point is always unstable* in this sense.

The usual definition of stability as an asymptotic approach to the equilibrium position ceases to be convenient, however, if we consider it in connection with motions around a vortex point. In fact, trajectories in this case do not approach this singularity although the potential energy is minimum for that point as required for a stable equilibrium. These considerations led Liapounoff to formulate a definition of stability sufficiently broad so as to be applied to both equilibrium and stationary motions.

17. STABILITY IN THE SENSE OF LIAPOUNOFF

We shall give first an intuitive geometrical definition of stability and supplement it by an analytic definition.

Consider a closed trajectory C. The motion of the representative point R on this trajectory clearly represents a periodic motion. The geometrical formulation of stability of the motion in the sense of Liapounoff can be visualized as follows.

Assume that during the motion of R on C the system has received an impulse translating R abruptly into R', a point which lies on a neighboring closed trajectory, C', as shown in Figure 17.1. Let us consider the "perturbed motion" of R' on C' in relation to the unperturbed one of R on C. If the initial distance $\rho_0 = RR'$, originally small, remains small throughout the subsequent motion, the motion is stable in the sense of Liapounoff; if, however, after a certain finite time, this condition ceases to be fulfilled, the motion is unstable.

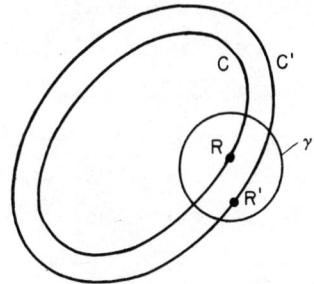

Figure 17.1

It is to be noted that this statement requires that the curves C and C' be close to each other. The proximity of curves C and C' is not sufficient to insure the stability of motion occurring on these curves unless the condition that the distance RR' between the representative points following the trajectories C and C' and considered at the same instant remains small for all value of t, be fulfilled.

---

* Only in a purely theoretical case when the motion of R takes place along the stable separatrix or asymptote, A_1S in Figure 3.1, of a saddle point, the latter may be considered as a *stable* singularity. In Part IV we shall see that under special conditions R may follow a trajectory situated in the neighborhood of a stable separatrix and may give the impression for a limited time that a saddle point is a point of stable equilibrium. Hence one could better describe the stability of a saddle point by introducing the term *almost unstable singularity*.

This can be seen easily from the following example. Assume that the curves C and C′ are two concentric circles whose radii differ by a small quantity Δr. If, for $t = 0$, the points R and R′ are situated on the same radius, the distance RR′ will be small. It follows that, if the motion is to be stable in the above sense, the points R and R′ must remain on the same radius in order that the distance between these points remains small for all values of t. This implies that the two motions must be strictly isochronous.

In this particular instance the motion is clearly that of a conservative system with two slightly different amplitudes. We conclude therefore, that in general the motions of conservative systems may be stable in the sense of Liapounoff only when they are strictly isochronous, that is, when the period of motion of R on C is exactly equal to that of R′ on C′. In general the condition of isochronism is only approximately fulfilled in conservative systems so that such motions are generally unstable in the sense of Liapounoff for all values of t, although they may be considered as temporarily stable if, for a limited time, the motions are almost isochronous in some region. We shall see later that there exist special periodic motions observed in non-linear systems which, on the contrary, exhibit stability in the sense of Liapounoff for all values of t.

After these preliminary remarks we may now formulate the precise analytic definition of stability. Let $x = x(t, x_0, y_0)$ and $y = y(t, x_0, y_0)$ be the coordinates in the (x, y)-plane determining a periodic motion on a trajectory C, with a period T. By this we mean that $x(0) = x(T)$ and $y(0) = y(T)$.

We shall call the motion stable in the sense of Liapounoff if, to any given number $\epsilon > 0$, another number η can be found such that $|\bar{x}_0 - x_0| < \epsilon$, $|\bar{y}_0 - y_0| < \epsilon$ implies $|x(t, x_0, y_0) - x(t, \bar{x}_0, \bar{y}_0)| < \eta$; $|y(t, x_0, y_0) - y(t, \bar{x}_0, \bar{y}_0)| < \eta$ for all t, where $\bar{x}_0, \bar{y}_0$ are the slightly modified initial conditions x_0, y_0.

When the trajectory C reduces to a point, Liapounoff's definition reduces to that of *stability of equilibrium*. This chapter will only deal with the stability of equilibrium.

18. CANONICAL FORMS OF LINEAR EQUATIONS; CHARACTERISTIC EQUATION; CLASSIFICATION OF SINGULARITIES (POINCARÉ); BRANCH POINTS OF EQUILIBRIUM

We shall now investigate the problem of stability of equilibrium more systematically by showing its relation to the nature of the singularities of dynamical equations. Let us consider the system of differential equations

$$\dot{x} = ax + by; \quad \dot{y} = cx + dy \qquad [18.1]$$

where a, b, c, d are constants. In the phase plane this leads to the differential equation of the trajectories

$$\frac{dy}{dx} = \frac{cx + dy}{ax + by} \qquad [18.2]$$

A general non-linear system can be represented by equations

$$\dot{x} = ax + by + P'(x,y); \quad \dot{y} = cx + dy + Q'(x,y) \qquad [18.3]$$

with

$$\frac{dy}{dx} = \frac{cx + dy + Q'(x,y)}{ax + by + P'(x,y)} \qquad [18.4]$$

where $P'(x,y)$, $Q'(x,y)$ are polynomials which have neither constant terms nor linear terms in x and y. Under relatively broad assumptions, it can be shown (16) that in the neighborhood of $x = y = 0$ the investigation of [18.4] can be reduced to that of [18.2].

By means of a linear transformation of variables

$$\xi = \alpha x + \beta y; \quad \eta = \gamma x + \delta y \qquad [18.5]$$

with $\begin{vmatrix} \alpha & \beta \\ \gamma & \delta \end{vmatrix} \neq 0^*$ where α, β, γ, δ are suitable constants, we can reduce the system [18.1] to the canonical form

$$\dot{\xi} = S_1 \xi; \quad \dot{\eta} = S_2 \eta \qquad [18.6]$$

where S_1 and S_2 are constants. In fact, from Equations [18.5] one has

$$\dot{\xi} = \alpha \dot{x} + \beta \dot{y}; \quad \dot{\eta} = \gamma \dot{x} + \delta \dot{y} \qquad [18.7]$$

Substituting $\dot{x}$ and $\dot{y}$ from Equations [18.1] and $\dot{\xi}$ and $\dot{\eta}$ from Equations [18.6] into [18.7], we have identically in x and y

$$S_1(\alpha x + \beta y) = \alpha(ax + by) + \beta(cx + dy)$$

$$S_2(\gamma x + \delta y) = \gamma(ax + by) + \delta(cx + dy) \qquad [18.8]$$

Identifying the coefficients of x and y one obtains

$$\begin{cases} \alpha(a - S_1) + \beta c = 0; \\ \alpha b + \beta(d - S_1) = 0; \end{cases} \qquad \begin{cases} \gamma(a - S_2) + \delta c = 0 \\ \gamma b + \delta(d - S_2) = 0 \end{cases} \qquad [18.9]$$

The first system contains α and β, the second γ and δ considered as the unknowns. Non-trivial solutions exist only when S_1 and S_2 are the roots of the

---

* This implies a one-to-one correspondence of the transformation.

quadratic equation

$$\begin{vmatrix} a - S & c \\ b & d - S \end{vmatrix} = 0 \qquad [18.10]$$

or written explicitly

$$S^2 - S(a + d) + (ad - cb) = 0 \qquad [18.11]$$

Equation [18.11] is called the *characteristic equation* of system [18.1]. The two pairs of equations, [18.9], reduce now to two equations one of which determines the ratio α/β and the other the ratio γ/δ, assuming $S_1 \neq S_2$ and $\alpha/\beta \neq \gamma/\delta$, that is $\begin{vmatrix} \alpha & \beta \\ \gamma & \delta \end{vmatrix} \neq 0$. Conversely, if $\begin{vmatrix} \alpha & \beta \\ \gamma & \delta \end{vmatrix} \neq 0$, then the roots S_1 and S_2 of [18.11] are unequal as seen from [18.9] unless $S_1 = S_2 = a = d$, $b = c = 0$, in which case the original system [18.1] is already in canonical form.

Since we have assumed that $\begin{vmatrix} \alpha & \beta \\ \gamma & \delta \end{vmatrix} \neq 0$, [18.5] can be solved for x and y yielding the set of equations

$$x = \frac{\delta \xi}{\Delta} - \frac{\beta \eta}{\Delta} ; \quad y = - \frac{\gamma \xi}{\Delta} + \frac{\alpha \eta}{\Delta} \qquad [18.12]$$

where $\Delta = \begin{vmatrix} \alpha & \beta \\ \gamma & \delta \end{vmatrix}$. If we choose $\alpha = - c\Delta$, $\beta = (a - S_1)\Delta$, $\gamma = c\Delta$, $\delta = - (a - S_2)\Delta$, Equations [18.9] are satisfied and therefore [18.12] can be written as

$$x = (S_2 - a)\xi + (S_1 - a)\eta ; \quad y = - c\xi - c\eta \qquad [18.13]$$

Equations [18.13] will transform the system [18.1] into the canonical form [18.6].

Thus far the system [18.1] was considered. By a similar procedure it can be shown that the more general system [18.3] can be reduced to a canonical form given by

$$\dot{\xi} = S_1 \xi - \frac{1}{c(S_1 - S_2)} \left[c P'(\xi, \eta) + (S_1 - a) Q'(\xi, \eta) \right]$$

$$[18.14]$$

$$\dot{\eta} = S_2 \eta + \frac{1}{c(S_1 - S_2)} \left[c P'(\xi, \eta) + (S_2 - a) Q'(\xi, \eta) \right]$$

where x and y have been replaced by their expressions [18.13]. If the roots S_1 and S_2 of the characteristic equation are conjugate complex, then it can be shown, see Theorem 3 on page 45, that ξ and η are also conjugate complex. Letting $\xi = u + iv$, $\eta = u - iv$, $S_1 = a_1 + ib_1$, $S_2 = a_1 - ib_1$, and equating real and imaginary parts of [18.14] one gets

$$\dot{u} = a_1 u - b_1 v - \frac{1}{2c} Q'(u,v)$$

[18.15]

$$\dot{v} = b_1 u + a_1 v + \frac{1}{2b_1 c}\left[c P'(u,v) + (a_1 - a) Q'(u,v)\right]$$

These relations, which hold when the roots S_1 and S_2 of [18.11] are conjugate complex, can be obtained directly from [18.3] by an application of the transformation

$$x = 2(a_1 - a)u + 2b_1 v; \quad y = -2cu$$

[18.16]

The latter result is obtained by substituting the values of ξ and η in terms of u and v into [18.13].

Once the possibility of the canonical transformation has been established we can proceed with the analysis of the various cases arising from the nature of the roots of the characteristic Equation [18.11]. We assume hereafter that $S_1 \neq S_2$. We further assume $S_1 S_2 \neq 0$, that is, $\begin{vmatrix} \alpha & \beta \\ \gamma & \delta \end{vmatrix} \neq 0$. When $\begin{vmatrix} \alpha & \beta \\ \gamma & \delta \end{vmatrix} = 0$, [18.2] reduces, if $a \neq 0$, to the simple equation

$$\frac{dy}{dx} = \frac{acx + ady}{a(ax + by)} = \frac{c}{a}$$

THEOREM 1. When the roots S_1 and S_2 are real and of the same sign, the system [18.1] has a *nodal point* at $x = y = 0$.

From the canonical Equations [18.6] we get

$$\frac{d\eta}{d\xi} = \frac{S_2}{S_1}\frac{\eta}{\xi}$$

[18.17]

Separating the variables and integrating we have

$$\eta = C\xi^a$$

[18.18]

where $a = S_2/S_1 > 0$ and C is a constant. The phase trajectories are parabolic curves. For $a > 1$, the curves are tangent to the ξ-axis at the origin of coordinates ($\xi = \eta = 0$) except for the singular curve $\xi = 0$ corresponding to $C \to \infty$. For $a < 1$ the curves are tangent to the η-axis, except for the singular curve $\eta = 0$, corresponding to $C = 0$. If S_1 and S_2 are both negative, it follows from the canonical Equations [18.6] that the representative point in the phase plane approaches asymptotically the point $\xi = \eta = 0$ for $t \to +\infty$. We have then a *stable nodal point*. If S_1 and S_2 are both positive the nodal point is *unstable*. Passing from the (ξ, η) to the (x,y)-coordinates one finds the topological picture of trajectories shown in Figure 6.1, already established by an elementary procedure. There is an infinity of trajectories either approaching or leaving a nodal point.

THEOREM 2. When the roots S_1 and S_2 are real but of opposite signs, the system [18.1] has a *saddle point* at $x = y = 0$.

In this case

$$\frac{d\eta}{d\xi} = - a \frac{\eta}{\xi} \qquad [18.19]$$

where $a = \left| \frac{S_2}{S_1} \right| > 0$. Integrating, we have

$$\eta = C \xi^{-a} \qquad [18.20]$$

The phase trajectories are hyperbolic curves referred to the axes as asymptotes. The representative point (assuming $S_1 > 0$ and $S_2 < 0$) being placed close to the ξ-axis, will move away from the origin as follows from the first Equation [18.6]. However, if it is placed near the η-axis it will first approach the origin, as follows from the second Equation [18.6], and then move away from the origin along the branch approaching the ξ-axis asymptotically as shown in Figure 4.1. The picture is thus typical for a saddle point as previously defined. There are only two singular trajectories, the asymptotes, which pass through a saddle point. In the (x, y)-plane the trajectories in the neighborhood of a saddle point are deformed and the asymptotes are inclined to each other by an angle different from $\pi/2$ in general.

THEOREM 3. When the roots S_1 and S_2 are conjugate complex the system [18.1] has a *focal point* at $x = y = 0$.

For real x and y, we shall show that, when S_1 and S_2 are conjugate complex, ξ and η must be also conjugate complex. Putting $\xi = u + iv$ and $\eta = u - iv$, [18.6] become

$$\frac{du}{dt} + i \frac{dv}{dt} = S_1 \xi = (a_1 + ib_1)(u + iv)$$

$$[18.21]$$

$$\frac{du}{dt} - i \frac{dv}{dt} = S_2 \eta = (a_1 - ib_1)(u - iv)$$

That is

$$\frac{du}{dt} = a_1 u - b_1 v; \quad \frac{dv}{dt} = a_1 v + b_1 u \qquad [18.22]$$

Thus, the velocities $\dot{u}$ and $\dot{v}$ are real in the new coordinates u and v. In the phase plane (u, v) the differential equation of trajectories is

$$\frac{dv}{du} = \frac{b_1 u + a_1 v}{a_1 u - b_1 v} \qquad [18.23]$$

Transforming into polar coordinates, $u = r \cos \phi$, $v = r \sin \phi$, we find

$$\frac{dr}{d\phi} = \frac{a_1}{b_1} r \qquad [18.24]$$

whence $r = C e^{\frac{a_1}{b_1} \phi}$. Thus, in the phase plane (u,v) the trajectories are logarithmic spirals and the point, $u = v = 0$, is an asymptotic point, the *focal point* of trajectories.

Multiplying the first Equation [18.22] by u, the second by v, adding and letting $u^2 + v^2 = \rho$, we find

$$\frac{1}{2} \frac{d\rho}{dt} = a_1 \rho \qquad [18.25]$$

For $a_1 < 0$ the representative point approaches asymptotically the focal point which is thus a *stable* focal point. For $a_1 > 0$ one has an *unstable* focal point. If one now passes from the (u,v)-plane to the original (x,y)-plane, the general nature of motion remains the same but the spirals are distorted in the (x,y)-plane as shown in Figure 5.1.

Summing up these results, the following criteria can be given:

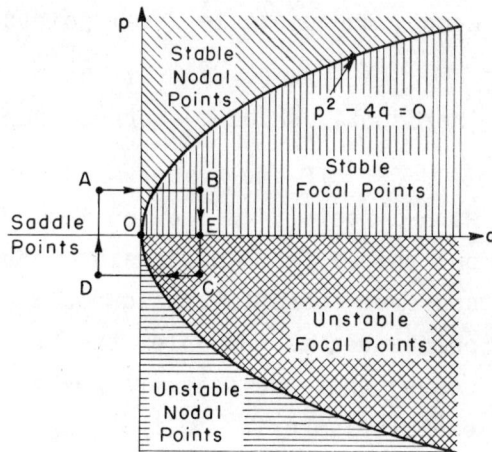

Figure 18.1

1. If S_1 and S_2 are real and negative one has a stable nodal point,

2. If S_1 and S_2 are real and positive one has an unstable nodal point,

3. If S_1 and S_2 are real and of opposite sign one has a saddle point,

4. If S_1 and S_2 are conjugate complex with $R^*[S_{1,2}] < 0$, one has a stable focal point,

5. If S_1 and S_2 are conjugate complex with $R[S_{1,2}] > 0$, one has an unstable focal point.

These various cases can be represented graphically as shown in Figure 18.1 by putting $p = -(a+d)$, $q = \begin{vmatrix} a & b \\ c & d \end{vmatrix}$; the characteristic Equation [18.11] becomes then

$$S^2 + pS + q = 0 \qquad [18.26]$$

---

* R represents the real part of $S_{1,2}$.

If one takes p and q as rectangular coordinates, the zones of distribution of the roots in Cases 1 to 5 are shown in Figure 18.1. For $q < 0$, i.e., $ad - cb < 0$, the roots S_1 and S_2 are real and of opposite signs; hence the region to the left of the axis of ordinates, $q = 0$, represents the zone of saddle points.

The parabola $p^2 - 4q = 0$ separates the half plane, $q > 0$, into four regions:

1. $p > 0$, $p^2 < 4q$; the roots in this case are conjugate complex with $R[S_{1,2}] < 0$, hence this region (vertical shading) corresponds to the stable focal points.

2. $p > 0$, $p^2 > 4q$; the roots are real and negative; this zone (oblique shading) corresponds to the stable nodal points.

3. $p < 0$, $p^2 < 4q$; the roots are conjugate complex with $R[S_{1,2}] > 0$, hence, the unstable focal points (double shading).

4. $p < 0$, $p^2 > 4q$; both roots are real and positive; hence this region (horizontal shading) corresponds to the unstable nodal points.

If one traces a rectangular circuit ABCD surrounding the origin with a positive direction indicated by the arrow and proceeds from A to B, one passes from the domain of saddle points to that of stable nodal points and from there to stable focal points; proceeding along BC the stable focal points become unstable; the branch CD is inverse to AB. The origin O appears, thus, as a *branch point* of equilibrium, insofar as several kinds of equilibrium exist in its neighborhood. It is seen that the nodal points are the singularities intermediate between the saddle points (always unstable) and the focal points. If the latter are stable, the intermediate nodal region is also stable; if the focal points are unstable, the intermediate nodal region is unstable. The threshold $p^2 - 4q = 0$ corresponds to the transition between nodal and focal points, hence between the aperiodic motions and oscillatory damped motions.

19.   STABILITY OF EQUILIBRIUM ACCORDING TO LIAPOUNOFF

Consider a system with one degree of freedom x in the neighborhood of equilibrium $x = x_0$ corresponding to $t = t_0$. According to Liapounoff, the equilibrium is called stable if, for any arbitrary small number ϵ, one can determine another number $\delta = \delta(\epsilon)$ such that

$$|x(t) - x_0| < \epsilon \text{ for } t_0 \leqq t < +\infty \text{ provided } |x(t_0) - x_0| < \delta$$

which means that if the original departure $|x(t_0) - x_0|$ of the system from the position of equilibrium x_0 is small, the subsequent departures $|x(t) - x_0|$

from that position will also remain small in the course of time. We shall apply Liapounoff's criterion to a simple case which will serve to illustrate its physical significance.

Since in this particular case we are interested primarily in *small* deviations from the position of equilibrium, $x = x_0$, let $x = x_0 + \xi$, $|\xi|$ being small. Let the differential equation of motion be

$$\frac{dx}{dt} = f(x) \qquad [19.1]$$

where $f(x)$ is assumed to be analytic at the point $x = x_0$. Substituting for x its value and developing $f(x_0 + \xi)$ in a Taylor series we have

$$\frac{d\xi}{dt} = f(x_0 + \xi) = f(x_0) + \xi f'(x_0) + \frac{\xi^2}{2!} f''(x_0) + \cdots \qquad [19.2]$$

By virtue of the assumed equilibrium for $x = x_0$, x_0 is a singular point, and therefore $f(x_0) = 0$. Equation [19.2] thus reduces to

$$\frac{d\xi}{dt} = a_1 \xi + a_2 \xi^2 + \cdots \qquad [19.3]$$

where

$$a_1 = f'(x_0), \quad a_2 = \frac{f''(x_0)}{2!}, \quad \cdots$$

The method of Liapounoff consists of the following procedure: Upon dropping the non-linear terms in ξ in [19.3] one has

$$\frac{d\xi}{dt} = a_1 \xi \qquad [19.4]$$

Liapounoff's theorem states that under certain conditions which will be specified later and which are frequently encountered in physical problems, the information obtained from the linear equations of the first approximation is sufficient to give a correct answer to the question of stability of the non-linear system.

The solution of [19.4] is $\xi = C e^{a_1 t}$ where $a_1 = f'(x_0)$. Hence, according to Liapounoff, if $a_1 < 0$ the equilibrium is stable; if $a_1 > 0$ it is unstable; finally, if $a_1 = 0$ the equation of the first approximation is not applicable and a special investigation is needed. Liapounoff also indicates additional criteria required for the investigation of stability when $a_1 = 0$. For the present we shall limit ourselves to the more general case when $a_1 \neq 0$ which occurs frequently in physical problems.

The proof of the Liapounoff theorem in the more general case of Equations [3.4] is given in Section 20. In the case considered here, the proof is very simple and will enable us to exhibit Liapounoff's line of argument. If one multiplies both sides of [19.2] by ξ, one has

$$\frac{1}{2}\frac{d(\xi^2)}{dt} = a_1\xi^2 + a_2\xi^3 + \cdots \equiv F(\xi) \qquad [19.5]$$

One notes that $F(0) = F'(0) = 0$ and $F''(0) = 2a_1$. This gives

$$\frac{d\rho}{dt} = \frac{\xi^2}{1\cdot2}F''(\theta\xi) \qquad [19.6]$$

where $\rho = \frac{1}{2}\xi^2$ and $0 < \theta < 1$. In view of the assumed continuity of $F''(\xi)$, it is apparent that if $F''(0) < 0$, that is, if $a_1 < 0$, $F''(\theta\xi) < 0$ for small $|\xi|$, and therefore $d\rho/dt < 0$. Hence, if $\rho = \frac{1}{2}\xi^2$ decreases initially, it will continue to decrease, since the right-hand term of [19.6] is negative in the neighborhood of $x = x_0$, and therefore the equilibrium is stable. Likewise, if $F''(0) > 0$ by a similar argument, one finds that the equilibrium is unstable. It is seen from this particular example that the equation of the first approximation gives a correct answer to the question of stability of the non-linear Equation [19.5], the only limitation of the procedure being the condition that $a_1 \neq 0$.

One can also illustrate the preceding considerations graphically. Consider the diagrams shown in Figure 19.1 in which $z = f(x)$ is plotted against x. Figure 19.1a shows a monotonically decreasing $f(x)$; furthermore, $f(x_0) = 0$. In this case $f(x) > 0$ to the left of x_0 and $f(x) < 0$ to the right of x_0. Liapounoff's method consists in replacing the curve Mx_0N in the neighborhood of x_0, by the tangent at x_0, that is by the function $a_1(x - x_0)$, provided $a_1 \neq 0$. The direction of velocity $d\rho/dt$ is indicated on the lower part of Figure 19.1a. It is seen that this velocity is positive i.e., directed to the right, for $x < x_0$ and negative, i.e., to the left, for $x > x_0$ which clearly indicates a stable equilibrium at x_0.

Likewise, when $f(x)$ is increasing, Figure 19.1b, (from negative values for $x < x_0$ to positive ones for

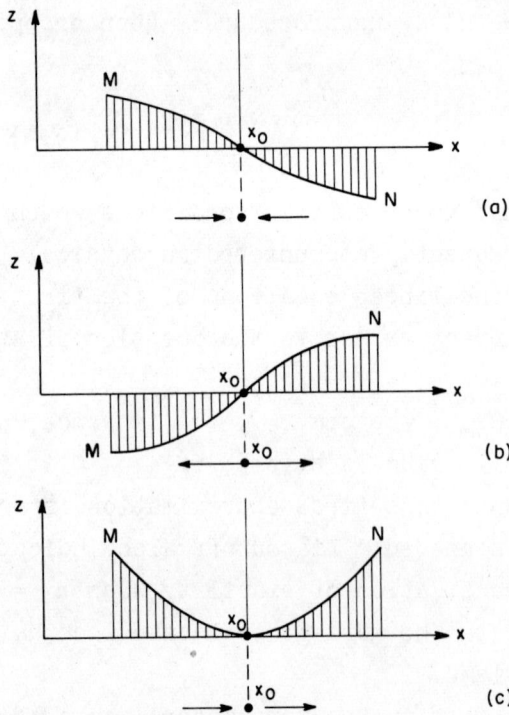

Figure 19.1

$x > x_0$), one concludes, by similar reasoning, that the equilibrium is unstable. When $f(x)$ has a minimum for $x = x_0$ with $f(x_0) = 0$, the question of equilibrium becomes more complicated. In fact, the system approaches $x = x_0$ for values $x < x_0$ as a point of stable equilibrium; for $x > x_0$ it moves away from the point $x = x_0$ as from a point of unstable equilibrium. One can designate this case, shown in Figure 19.1c, as a *half-stable equilibrium*, i.e., stable for $x < x_0$ and unstable for $x > x_0$. This half-stable case corresponds to $a_1 = 0$, in which case the equation of the first approximation ceases to be applicable, and the consideration of higher order terms becomes necessary.

20. LIAPOUNOFF'S THEOREM

In physical problems the Liapounoff theorem is generally encountered in connection with the dynamical systems

$$\frac{dx}{dt} = P(x,y); \quad \frac{dy}{dt} = Q(x,y) \qquad [20.1]$$

which are represented in the phase plane by trajectories, and the formulation of the Liapounoff theory depends then on the analytical form of Equations [20.1].

The differential equation of phase trajectories is of the form

$$\frac{dy}{dx} = \frac{Q(x,y)}{P(x,y)} \qquad [20.2]$$

The positions of equilibrium as was shown are identified with the singular points.

The preceding analysis was made under the assumption of a linear approximation in the neighborhood of $x = y = 0$ when P and Q are of the form: $P = ax + by$; $Q = cx + dy$. We have to consider now a more general case, that is, Equations [18.3] and [18.4]. A point (x_0, y_0) of equilibrium is clearly a point of intersection of the curves $P(x,y) = 0$, $Q(x,y) = 0$. In order to be able to analyze the stability of equilibrium it is necessary to give a small departure (ξ, η) from the equilibrium point; the new coordinates are now $x = x_0 + \xi$, $y = y_0 + \eta$. To simplify the procedure, the origin of coordinates can be transferred to the point (x_0, y_0); furthermore, $P(x,y)$ and $Q(x,y)$ can be expanded in a Taylor series. The differential Equations [18.3] become

$$\frac{d\xi}{dt} = a\xi + b\eta + \left[p_{11}\xi^2 + 2p_{12}\xi\eta + p_{22}\eta^2 + \cdots \right]$$

$$\frac{d\eta}{dt} = c\xi + d\eta + \left[q_{11}\xi^2 + 2q_{12}\xi\eta + q_{22}\eta^2 + \cdots \right]$$

$$[20.3]$$

where the non-written terms of Taylor's expansions are at least of third degree in ξ, η and $a = P_x(x_0, y_0)$; $b = P_y(x_0, y_0)$; $c = Q_x(x_0, y_0)$; $d = Q_y(x_0, y_0)$.

The theorem of Liapounoff states: If the real parts of the roots of the characteristic equation corresponding to the equations of the first approximation are different from zero, the equations of the first approximation always give a correct answer to the question of stability of a non-linear system.

More specifically, if the real parts of these roots are negative, the equilibrium is stable; if at least one root has a positive real part, the equilibrium is unstable.

The starting point for this proof is to reduce the non-linear system to a canonical form by making use of [18.13] and [18.14]. Thus we have

$$\frac{du}{dt} = S_1 u + (p'_{11} u^2 + p'_{12} uv + p'_{22} v^2) + \cdots$$

$$\frac{dv}{dt} = S_2 v + (q'_{11} u^2 + q'_{12} uv + q'_{22} v^2) + \cdots$$

[20.4]

where $p'_{11}, \cdots, q'_{22}$ are the new constants. Multiplying the first Equation [20.4] by u and the second by v and adding, one obtains

$$\frac{1}{2} \frac{d\rho}{dt} = S_1 u^2 + S_2 v^2 + \cdots \equiv \phi(u, v)$$

[20.5]

where $\rho = u^2 + v^2$. Let us now investigate the behavior of the curve $\phi(u, v) = 0$ in the neighborhood of the point $u = v = 0$ for different forms of the roots of Equation [18.10] and thus establish the above stated theorem.

1. Consider first the case when S_1 and S_2 are both real and negative. In this case the surface $z = \phi(u, v)$ has a maximum $z = 0$ at the origin and the curve $\phi(u, v) = 0$ reduces to one point, $u = v = 0$. Write

$$\phi(u, v) = S_1 u^2 + S_2 v^2 + \psi(u, v)$$

whence

$$\frac{1}{2} \frac{d\rho}{dt} = S_1 u^2 + S_2 v^2 + \psi(u, v)$$

[20.6]

We can find a region S, Figure 20.1, around the point $u = v = 0$, where $|\psi(u, v)| < \frac{1}{2} |S_1 u^2 + S_2 v^2|$, so that $\phi(u, v) < 0$ in S with the exception of the point $u = v = 0$, where $\phi(0, 0) = 0$. Moreover, for all points (u, v) in S

$$\frac{1}{2} \left| \frac{d\rho}{dt} \right| \geq \frac{1}{2} \left| (S_1 u^2 + S_2 v^2) \right|$$

[20.7]

Let δ be a circular region situated inside S. If the point R is initially placed inside δ it is easy to show it will never cross the boundary of δ.

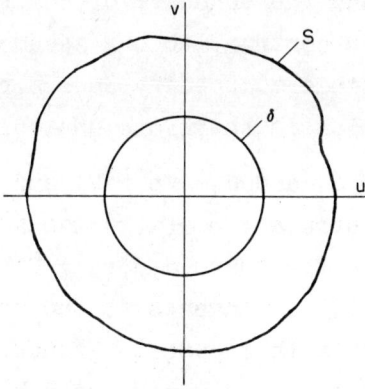

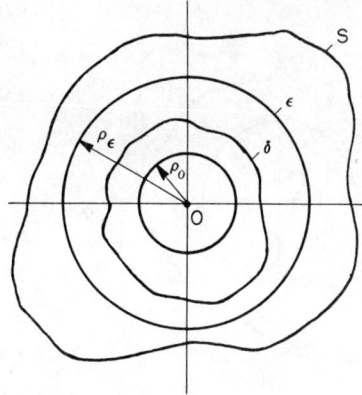

Figure 20.1   Figure 20.2

In fact, for all points of δ, with the exception of the origin, $d\rho/dt < 0$ so that $\lim\limits_{t\to\infty} \rho = \rho_0 \geq 0$ necessarily exists and is reached decreasingly. If $\rho_0 > 0$, then for $t \geq t_0$ sufficiently large, R remains inside S but outside the circle with center at 0 and radius $\rho_0/2$. It follows, if $|S_1| \leq |S_2|$, that $|S_1 u^2 + S_2 v^2| \geq |S_1|\,(u^2 + v^2) \geq |S_1|\,\rho_0^2/4$ for $t \geq t_0$. From [20.7], we have

$$\frac{1}{2}\left|\frac{d\rho}{dt}\right| \geq \frac{1}{2}\,\frac{\rho_0^{\,2}}{4}\,|S_1| > 0, \ t \geq t_0$$

$$\left|\rho(t) - \rho(t_0)\right| = \int_{t_0}^{t}\left|\frac{d\rho}{dt}\right|\,dt > \frac{1}{4}\,\frac{\rho_0^{\,2}}{4}\,|S_1|\,(t - t_0)$$

and $\lim\limits_{t\to\infty} \rho(t) = \infty$ which is impossible. We have thus shown that $\lim\limits_{t\to\infty} \rho(t) = 0$. Hence the equilibrium is stable.

2. When S_1 and S_2 are both real and positive, the surface $z = \phi(u,v)$ has a minimum $z = 0$ at 0, and the curve $\phi(u,v) = 0$ reduces to the point, $u = v = 0$. Hence, there exists a region S around 0 in which $\phi(u,v) > 0$ with the exception of point 0 for which $\phi(0,0) = 0$. As the region ϵ we can take now a circle lying inside S, Figure 20.2.

It can be shown that it is impossible to determine a region δ such that if a point R is placed initially in δ it would not reach the boundary of ϵ after a finite time. Let us assume first that such a region δ exists. Further, let R be placed in any point of δ except at the origin. Since $\phi(u,v) = d\rho/dt > 0$ inside S except at the origin, the distance OR increases monotonically as long as R remains in S. Let $\rho_0 = u_0^{\,2} + v_0^{\,2} = OR$ for $t = 0$ and $\rho_\epsilon = u_\epsilon^{\,2} + v_\epsilon^{\,2}$. It is apparent that in the region between $\rho = \rho_0$ and $\rho = \rho_\epsilon$, the function $\phi(u,v)$ and hence $d\rho/dt$ has a positive lower bound. It follows that R will move in the annular region between ρ_0 and ρ_ϵ with a non-zero velocity

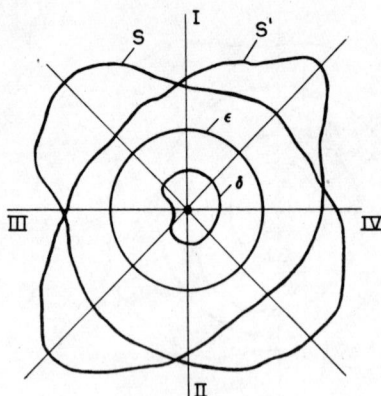

Figure 20.3

and will reach the boundary of ϵ after a finite time which is contrary to our assumption. Hence, it is impossible to specify such a region δ, and the equilibrium is therefore unstable.

3. If S_1 and S_2 are real and of different signs, the surface $z = \phi(u,v)$ has a saddle-shaped extremum, and the curve $\phi(u,v) = 0$ has a node with two distinct tangents at the origin. The region S has in this case two zones, say I and II, in which $\phi(u,v) > 0$ and two others, III and IV, in which $\phi(u,v) < 0$ as shown in Figure 20.3.

We propose to show that the equilibrium in this case is unstable. Before proceeding with the proof, it is first necessary to obtain the sign of $d^2\rho/dt^2$. Differentiating Equation [20.5] and substituting du/dt and dv/dt from [20.4], one obtains

$$\frac{1}{4}\frac{d^2\rho}{dt^2} = S_1^2 u^2 + S_2^2 v^2 + \cdots = \phi_1(u,v) \qquad [20.8]$$

The surface $z = \phi_1(u,v)$ has a minimum $z = 0$ at the origin; hence, there exists a region S' around 0 for which $\phi_1(u,v) > 0$, with the exception of the origin for which $\phi_1(0,0) = 0$. Thus in this region $d^2\rho/dt^2 > 0$. We now can give the proof of the instability of equilibrium in this case. For the region ϵ take a circle situated inside of both regions, S' and S, and drawn from the origin as center. It will be shown that it is impossible to determine a region δ containing the origin and such that if a point R is placed initially at any point of this region except the origin, it would never reach the boundary of ϵ.

Assume that such a region δ exists. Since δ surrounds the origin, there exist points inside δ for which $\phi(u,v) > 0$, and hence $d\rho/dt > 0$. If R is placed initially at such a point, it is clear that for this point $d^2\rho/dt^2 > 0$ for the region ϵ is situated inside S', by assumption. R will start moving with an accelerated velocity and will reach the boundary of ϵ in a finite time, as $d\rho/dt$ is monotonically increasing. This is contrary to our assumption concerning the existence of such a region. Hence, it is impossible to determine a region δ satisfying the above requirement, and the equilibrium is unstable.

The same conclusions reached in Cases 1, 2, and 3 hold when we transform the (u,v)-plane into the (ξ,η)-plane.

4. Finally, when the roots of the characteristic equation are conjugate complex, that is $S_1 = a_1 + ib_1$ and $S_2 = a_1 - ib_1$, then using a procedure

analogous to that given in Theorem 3 of Section 18, the non-linear system [20.4] can be reduced to

$$\frac{du_1}{dt} = a_1 u_1 - b_1 v_1 + \cdots; \quad \frac{dv_1}{dt} = a_1 v_1 + b_1 u_1 + \cdots \qquad [20.9]$$

where the non-written terms are at least of the second order in u_1 or v_1. Multiplying the first Equation [20.9] by u_1, the second by v_1, and adding, we have

$$\frac{1}{2} \frac{d\rho}{dt} = a_1(u_1^2 + v_1^2) + \cdots \equiv \psi_1(u_1, v_1) \qquad [20.10]$$

where $\rho = u_1^2 + v_1^2$, and the non-written terms are at least of the third degree. One can show as above that the existence of either maximum or minimum depends on the sign of a_1. If $a_1 < 0$, the equilibrium is stable; if $a_1 > 0$, it is unstable. This completes the proof of the theorem.

The advantage of the Liapounoff theorem lies in the fact that it enables one to apply equivalent linear criteria of stability to essentially non-linear systems and establishes the conditions under which this equivalence is valid. If these conditions are fulfilled, the theorem gives a correct answer at once, if not, one is confronted generally with a more difficult problem. This occurs, for instance, at the point E in Figure 18.1 at which the circuit ABCD intersects the q-axis ($p = 0$). At this point the roots S_1 and S_2 of the characteristic Equation [18.11] become purely imaginary, and the equations of the first approximation of Liapounoff cease to be applicable.*

Omitting this exceptional case which generally corresponds to a branch point of equilibrium (Section 27) in a great majority of practical problems, the Liapounoff theorem yields the conditions of stability in a relatively simple manner. An example is given in the following section.

21. EQUILIBRIUM OF A CIRCUIT CONTAINING A NON-LINEAR CONDUCTOR (ELECTRIC ARC)

Consider a circuit as shown in Figure 21.1 where A is an electric arc whose characteristic $V_a = \psi(i)$ is indicated in Figure 21.2. By Kirchhoff's laws, we have

$$V = L\frac{di}{dt} + \psi(i); \quad E = RI + V; \quad I = i + C\frac{dV}{dt} \qquad [21.1]$$

---

* It must be noted that, in the general theory of equilibrium, Liapounoff also considers in detail a series of particular cases which lie outside the range of validity of equations of the first approximation. We shall encounter one such case later. It is impossible, however, to give a full account of the Liapounoff theory here.

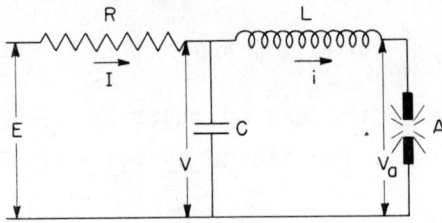

Figure 21.1

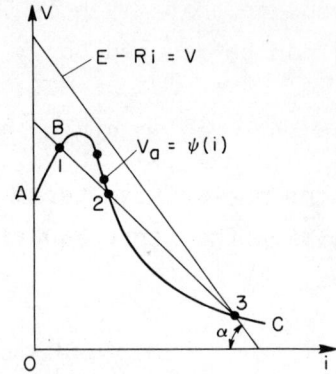

Figure 21.2

Eliminating I between Equations [21.1], one has two equations

$$\frac{dV}{dt} = \frac{E - V - Ri}{RC} \; ; \; \frac{di}{dt} = \frac{V - \psi(i)}{L}$$

[21.2]

For equilibrium ($dV/dt = di/dt = 0$) one has

$$V_0 = E - Ri_0 \; ; \; V_0 = \psi(i_0)$$

[21.3]

From Figure 21.2 it follows that for the assumed form $V_a = \psi(i)$ of the characteristic there exists either three or one position of equilibrium depending on the intersection of the line $V = E - Ri$ with the curve V_a. Let V_0 and i_0 be the coordinates of an equilibrium point and consider the small departures v and j from this point, so that the "disturbed values" of V and i are now

$$V = V_0 + v \; ; \; i = i_0 + j$$

[21.4]

Developing the function $\psi(i)$ in a Taylor series in the neighborhood of i_0 we find

$$\psi(i_0 + j) = \psi(i_0) + j\psi'(i_0) + \cdots$$

[21.5]

Following Liapounoff's method, the equations of the first approximation are obtained by substituting the values [21.4] and [21.5] into [21.2]. Upon canceling the steady-state terms, we find

$$\frac{dv}{dt} = -\frac{v}{RC} - \frac{j}{C} \; ; \; \frac{dj}{dt} = \frac{v}{L} - j\frac{\rho}{L}$$

[21.6]

where $\rho = \psi'(i_0)$ is the tangent to the characteristic of the arc at the point i_0 which has the dimension of resistance. The quantity $\psi'(i_0) = \rho$ varies with i_0 on account of non-linearity of the characteristic. On the branch BC, Figure 21.2, where the curve $\psi(i)$ is falling, $\rho < 0$; this branch is commonly designated as the range of the negative resistance of the arc.

The characteristic equation of the system [21.6] is

$$S^2 + \left(\frac{1}{RC} + \frac{\rho}{L}\right)S + \frac{1}{LC}\left(\frac{\rho}{R} + 1\right) = 0 \qquad [21.7]$$

and its roots are

$$S_{1,2} = -\frac{L + RC\rho}{2RCL} \pm \frac{1}{2RCL}\sqrt{L^2 + (RC\rho)^2 - 2RLC\rho - 4LCR^2} \quad [21.8]$$

The nature of the roots depends on four parameters R, L, C, and ρ. Since we are interested in the non-linear problem, involving the parameter ρ, three two-dimensional "cross sections" (R,ρ), (L,ρ), and (C,ρ) of the four-dimensional manifold (R, L, C, ρ) of parameters will be sufficient for this analysis. The parameters R, L, and C can have only positive values, whereas ρ may have both positive and negative values determined respectively by the branches AB and BC of the characteristic.

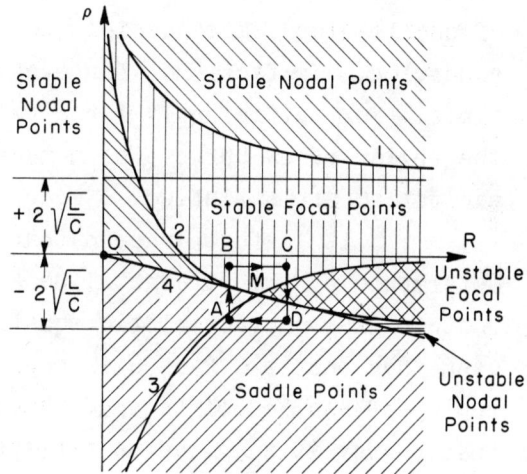

Figure 21.3

1. Diagram in the (R,ρ)-plane, Figure 21.3.

The quantity under the square root in [21.8] can be written as

$$(L - RC\rho)^2 - (2R\sqrt{LC})^2$$

The condition for complex roots is therefore

$$(L - RC\rho)^2 - (2R\sqrt{LC})^2 < 0 \qquad [21.9]$$

This leads one to consider the following two equations

$$L - RC\rho + 2R\sqrt{LC} = 0; \quad L - RC\rho - 2R\sqrt{LC} = 0 \qquad [21.10]$$

These equations represent hyperbolas in the (R,ρ)-plane, shown by Curves 1 and 2 in Figure 21.3, corresponding respectively to the first and second Equations [21.10]. The ρ-axis is an asymptote for both hyperbolas. The lines $\rho = 2\sqrt{L/C}$ and $\rho = -2\sqrt{L/C}$ are asymptotic to Curves 1 and 2 respectively. Thus, we see that the area between Hyperbolas 1 and 2 is the region of distribution of the complex roots of the characteristic equation, that is, the focal points. To distinguish between the stable and unstable focal points we equate R[S] to zero and obtain

$$L + RC\rho = 0 \qquad\qquad [21.11]$$

Since R, L, and C are positive, Equation [21.11] implies that $\rho < 0$. It is also to be noted that $CR\rho + L = 0$ is a hyperbola having the axes R and ρ as asymptotes; see Curve 3, Figure 21.3. The region between Hyperbolas 2 and 3 to the right of the Point **M**, their intersection, is thus the zone of unstable focal points. From the definition of the latter it follows that, within this range, self-excitation of oscillation is possible because the oscillations increase on the divergent spiral issuing from an unstable focal point. It is further observed that no unstable focal points, and hence no self-excitation of oscillations, are possible for $\rho > 0$. This is, however, only a necessary condition. In fact, not for every negative value of ρ is self-excitation possible. For sufficiently large values of $\rho < 0$ which correspond to points in the region below Curve 3 both necessary and sufficient conditions of self-excitation are satisfied.

It is further seen that the limit of the range of saddle points is determined by the straight line $R + \rho = 0$, Curve 4. For when $R + \rho < 0$, the roots of the characteristic equation are real and of opposite sign. It is seen thus that $\rho < 0$ as R is positive. Thus, the region below Curve 4 is the region of saddle points and, hence, of instability. Physically this means that energy is supplied to the system from an external source at a rate greater than its rate of dissipation. Thus the phenomenon "runs away," that is, either the circuit is destroyed or the fuses are blown out.

It is to be noted that Point **M** of intersection of Curves 2 and 3 has coordinates $+ \sqrt{L/C}$ and $- \sqrt{L/C}$, that is the Straight Line 4 passes through this point. This completes the picture; for as we have shown previously, the region of focal points is generally separated from that of saddle points by an intermediate region of nodal points. We infer, therefore, that the area between Curve 2 and Straight Line 4 is the zone of nodal points. The region of nodal points to the left of and above **M** corresponds to stable nodal points, that to the right of and below **M** contains the unstable nodal points. Point **M** is thus *a point of bifurcation* for the various types of equilibrium. Hence, in following a closed circuit ABCD surrounding the point M in the direction indicated, the transition of singularities in the order indicated in Figure 21.3, i.e., saddle points → stable nodal points → stable focal points → unstable focal points → unstable nodal points → saddle points, can be found.

2. Diagram in the (L, ρ)-plane, Figure 21.4.

The limits of the zone of distribution of complex roots, that is, of the focal points, is given by the equation

$$L^2 + (RC\rho)^2 - 2RCL\rho - 4LCR^2 = 0 \qquad [21.12]$$

that is

$$\rho = \frac{L}{RC} \pm 2\sqrt{\frac{L}{C}} \qquad [21.13]$$

In the (L, ρ)-plane Curve 1 represents the two branches of Equation [21.13]. It passes through the origin and has a vertical tangent at this point. The line $\rho = L/CR$ is an asymptote of this curve. Furthermore, the curve crosses the L-axis at the point $L_1 = 4R^2C$ and has a horizontal tangent passing through the point $(-R, R^2C)$.

The zone of distribution of stable focal points is separated from that of the unstable focal points by Straight Line 2, given by the equation $L + RC\rho = 0$, since this equation determines the condition for which the real part of the complex roots will vanish. Furthermore since L, R, and C are positive, this condition is fulfilled for

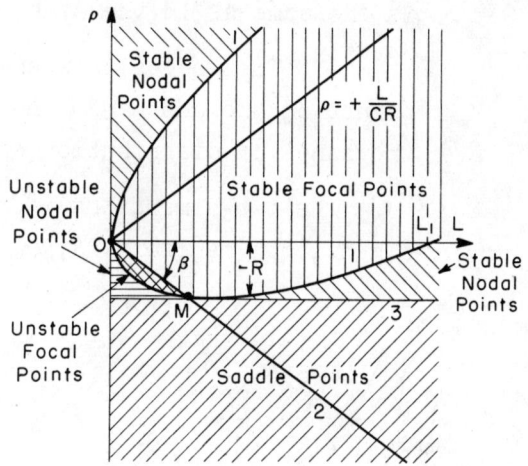

Figure 21.4

$\rho < 0$ as defined by $|\rho| = L/RC$; the slope of Line 2 is thus $\tan \beta = -1/RC$. Within the zone of the complex roots Straight Line 2 separates the region of stable focal points from that of the unstable ones; the self-excitation of oscillations is possible only in the latter region. One concludes, therefore, that self-excited oscillations are possible only:

a. for negative ρ, i.e., falling characteristic of the arc, and

b. for not too great values of the inductance L.

These facts are well known experimentally. The zone of saddle points is obtained, as in the first case (R, ρ) for $-\rho > R$. The straight line $\rho = -R$, shown as Line 3 in Figure 21.2, is thus the threshold separating the region of saddle points from the other singularities. Finally, between the ρ-axis $(L = 0)$, Straight Line 3 on the one hand and Curve 1 on the other hand, lies the region of nodal points. Following the diagram of Figure 21.4 one discriminates easily between the stable and the unstable nodal points. Points $O(\rho = L = 0)$ and $M(\rho = -R, L = R^2C)$ are the branch points of equilibrium.

3. Diagram in the (C, ρ)-plane, Figure 21.5.
    The procedure remains the same.

a. One finds the zone of the distribution of complex roots, i.e., of focal points.

b. One finds the line separating the stable focal points from the unstable ones. This line is obtained again by equating to zero the real part of the complex roots.

c. The line separating saddle points from other singularities is the same as in the other cases considered, viz: $R + \rho = 0$.

d. The wedges between the zones of distribution of saddle points on the one hand, and the focal points on the other, represent the zones of distribution of nodal points, stable or unstable.

The two-dimensional "cross sections" (R, ρ), (L, ρ), and (C, ρ) of the four-dimensional manifold (R, L, C, ρ) of parameters thus permit us to establish general criteria of stability of equilibrium in a circuit of this kind. From elementary considerations of static equilibrium of a circuit containing an arc it is known that there is, in general, either three or one equilibrium points as follows from the (V, i)-diagram of Figure 21.2 in which the series resistance R appears as the tangent of the angle α of the straight line intersecting the characteristic V_a of the arc ($\tan \alpha = R$). We shall analyze the conditions of stability of equilibrium, in the case when three equilibrium points exist, at the

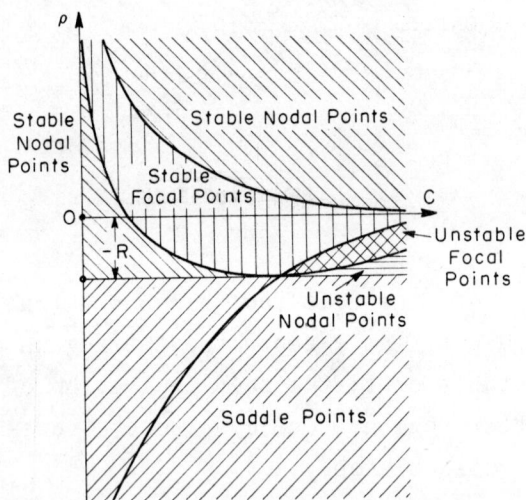

Figure 21.5

Points 1, 2, and 3, respectively, in the light of the preceding study of the "cross sections" of the phenomenon.

First, for Point 1, $\rho > 0$ as follows from all three diagrams, the singularities in this half-plane ($\rho > 0$) are stable. Point 1 is thus a position of stable equilibrium. Consider now Point 3 of equilibrium, Figure 21.2, $\rho < 0$. Since in the (V, i)-diagram the resistances are represented by the tangents to the curves, it is seen that the condition of equilibrium at this point is expressed by the fact that $|\rho| < R$; that is, the absolute value of the tangent to the falling characteristic of the arc is less than the positive inclination of the ohmic drop line. There exists a rule, known as Kaufmann's criterion of stability (17) which states that, if at the point of equilibrium $|\rho| < R$, the equilibrium is stable; if $|\rho| > R$, it is unstable. This criterion was found useful for a majority of applications. Later we shall see that certain ambiguous cases were discovered in which this criterion gave results at variance with observations.

The preceding study permits us, however, to avoid these ambiguities and gives a complete account of what happens in the various cases. In fact, from the diagram of Figure 21.3, for instance, it follows that within a certain range of $\rho < 0$, there is a zone of absolute stability (stable focal points). There is also a range of a conditional stability (unstable focal points); in this latter region the phenomenon is stable in the sense that it does not "run away," e.g., blowing fuses, but rather approaches a stationary periodic motion.* If we consider now Point 2 of equilibrium, Figure 21.2, the Kaufmann criterion states that the equilibrium is unstable. The above study indicates that absolute instability, i.e., the zone of saddle points, begins already for $|\rho| = R$ and sometimes a little earlier if there is a zone of unstable nodal points wedging in between the zone of saddle points and other singularities. Furthermore, from diagrams of Figures 21.3, 21.4, and 21.5, it is apparent that for a given value of $\rho < 0$ the question of stability or instability at a given static point (R, ρ) is also influenced by the other two parameters L and C which appear *dynamically* in the process, that is, when a transient phenomenon occurs in the circuit.

From this study it appears that the application of Liapounoff's theorem gives a rather broad approach to the investigation of problems of stability by taking into account both static and dynamic factors of equilibrium. In each particular problem one has to ascertain first which particular "cross section" of the manifold (R, ρ, L, C) is of importance and which can be neglected as not having an appreciable influence on the phenomenon.

---

* See Chapter IV.

CHAPTER IV

LIMIT CYCLES OF POINCARÉ

22. LIMIT CYCLES; DEFINITION; ANALYTICAL EXAMPLES

It was shown that in conservative systems periodic motions generally occur around the vortex points; the phase trajectories form a continuum of closed curves enclosing either one single vortex point or more generally, an odd number of vortex and saddle points, the number of the former exceeding the latter by one. In a more complicated topological picture shown in Figure 12.1 which is composed of several groups of vortex and saddle points, the continua of closed trajectories form "islands" in the phase plane limited by the separatrices connecting the adjoining saddle points. If there is one periodic trajectory, there exists also an infinity of others depending on the initial conditions; by varying these continuously one obtains the continuum of trajectories as long as they remain within the limits of the domain of periodicity determined by separatrices.

We shall now consider motions of an entirely different type observed in autonomous non-linear and non-conservative systems. Let

$$\frac{dx}{dt} = P(x,y); \quad \frac{dy}{dt} = Q(x,y)$$

be the differential equations of the system, and assume that there exists a closed trajectory C in the (x,y)-plane. Assume further that there exists also a non-closed trajectory C' represented by equations $x = x(t)$, $y = y(t)$ such that either for $t = +\infty$ or for $t = -\infty$ the representative point R' moving on C' approaches C. By this we mean that for any given number $\epsilon > 0$ one can find a value t_0 with the property that any point $[x(t), y(t)]$ on C' is at a distance $\leq \epsilon$ from some point on C either for $t > t_0$ or for $t < t_0$. Intuitively this means that C' winds around C either from the inside or from the outside like the spirals of Figure 24.1. If the closed curve C is approached in this manner by a trajectory C' we call C a *limit cycle*. A limit cycle C is called *stable* if it is approached by trajectories C' both from the inside and from the outside for $t = +\infty$; it is called *unstable* if it is approached by the trajectories C' both from the inside and outside for $t = -\infty$, and *half stable*, or *semi-stable*, if the trajectories C' approach it from the outside for $t = +\infty$ and from the inside for $t = -\infty$ or vice versa.

Limit cycles met with in practice have the property that they are approached not by merely one open trajectory C' but by every such trajectory C' originating in a certain domain of the phase plane. This means also that, whatever the initial conditions provided they are represented by points of the phase plane situated within a certain region, the ultimate motion approaches a definite periodic stationary motion represented by C either for $t = \infty$ or for $t = -\infty$, independent of the initial conditions. With this property in mind we can also say that the ultimate periodic motion on a limit cycle does not depend on the initial conditions.

It is thus seen that a periodic motion of this kind differs radically from periodic motions of conservative systems around a vortex point in that the closed trajectories occur always in continuous families in the latter case, whereas in the former they are isolated. By this we mean that if C is one such closed trajectory of a limit-cycle type there is no other limit cycle distinct from C and differing very little from it.

The question of the analytical existence of periodic motions for non-linear and non-conservative systems will be treated in Part II. In this chapter we shall give a qualitative geometrical theory of limit cycles which will provide a relatively simple illustration for the various phenomena of the limit-cycle type observed in physical problems. Andronow (18) was first to suggest that periodic phenomena in non-linear and non-conservative systems can be described mathematically in terms of limit cycles which thus made it possible to establish a connection between these phenomena and the theory of Poincaré developed for entirely different purposes.

We shall now give a few examples illustrating the preceding definitions.

1. Consider the following system of non-linear differential equations

$$\frac{dx}{dt} = y + \frac{x}{\sqrt{x^2 + y^2}}\left[1 - (x^2 + y^2)\right]$$

$$\frac{dy}{dt} = -x + \frac{y}{\sqrt{x^2 + y^2}}\left[1 - (x^2 + y^2)\right]$$

[22.1]

In polar coordinates $x = r \cos \theta$, $y = r \sin \theta$, these equations become

$$\frac{dx}{dt} = y + \frac{x}{r}(1 - r^2); \quad \frac{dy}{dt} = -x + \frac{y}{r}(1 - r^2) \qquad [22.2]$$

Multiplying the first Equation [22.2] by x, the second by y, adding and noting that $x\dot{x} + y\dot{y} = r\dot{r}$ we obtain

$$\dot{r} = 1 - r^2 \qquad [22.3]$$

Multiplying the first Equation [22.2] by y, the second by x, subtracting and noting that $y\dot{x} - x\dot{y} = r^2\dot{\theta}$ we have

$$\dot{\theta} = 1 \qquad [22.4]$$

Furthermore, $\dfrac{dr}{1 - r^2} = \dfrac{dr}{2(1 + r)} + \dfrac{dr}{2(1 - r)}$ and on integrating one gets

$$\log \frac{1 + r}{1 - r} = 2t + \log A$$

where $A = \dfrac{1 + r_0}{1 - r_0}$ is an integration constant, r_0 being the initial value of the radius vector. Thus

$$r = \frac{Ae^{2t} - 1}{Ae^{2t} + 1} \qquad [22.5]$$

For $t \to \infty$, $r \to 1$ both from the inside ($r_0 < 1$) and from the outside ($r_0 > 1$) of the circle $r = 1$. In view of the uniform rotation $\dot{\theta} = 1$, the trajectories are spirals approaching the circle $r = 1$ both from the inside and the outside as shown in Figure 24.4. Equation [22.5] cannot be used when $r_0 = 0$. From the inspection of the Equation [22.1] it is seen that the origin $x = y = 0$ is a singular point. From the preceding definitions it is apparent that the system [22.1] admits a stable limit cycle $x^2 + y^2 = 1$ as a stationary solution.

2. As another example consider the following system of differential equations

$$\frac{dx}{dt} = -y + x(x^2 + y^2 - 1)$$

$$[22.6]$$

$$\frac{dy}{dt} = x + y(x^2 + y^2 - 1)$$

In polar coordinates this system becomes

$$\dot{r} = r(r^2 - 1); \quad \dot{\theta} = -1 \qquad [22.7]$$

From the first equation we have

$$r = \frac{1}{\sqrt{1 - Ae^{2t}}} \qquad [22.8]$$

where $A = \dfrac{r_0^2 - 1}{r_0^2}$ is a constant of integration. If $r_0 < 1$, then $A < 0$ and [22.8] can be written as

$$r = \frac{1}{\sqrt{1 + |A|e^{2t}}} \qquad [22.9]$$

It is seen that for $t \to -\infty$, $r = 1$. In other words the spiral trajectories unwind from the circle $r = 1$ inwards. For $t \to +\infty$, $r = 0$, that is the spiral trajectories approach the origin which is a singular point of Equations [22.6] In this particular case the singular point is stable as can be verified from the equations of the first approximation. For $r_0 > 1$, we have $A > 0$ so that

$$r = \frac{1}{\sqrt{1 - Ae^{2t}}} \qquad [22.10]$$

For $t \to -\infty$ this equation gives $r = 1$, that is, the spiral trajectories un-wind from the circle $r = 1$ outwards. From the preceding definitions it follows that the circle $r = 1$ in this case is an *unstable limit cycle*.

3. Consider now the following system*

$$\frac{dx}{dt} = x(x^2 + y^2)^{\frac{1}{2}}(x^2 + y^2 - 1)^2 + y$$

$$\frac{dy}{dt} = y(x^2 + y^2)^{\frac{1}{2}}(x^2 + y^2 - 1)^2 - x \qquad [22.11]$$

In polar coordinates we obtain

$$\frac{dr}{dt} = r(r^2 - 1)^2; \; \frac{d\theta}{dt} = 1 \qquad [22.12]$$

Setting $r^2 = u$ we have $du/dt = 2u(u - 1)^2$. But

$$\frac{du}{u(u-1)^2} = \frac{du}{u} - \frac{du}{u-1} + \frac{du}{(u-1)^2} = 2dt$$

and therefore we obtain upon integrating

$$\log \frac{u}{u-1} - \frac{1}{u-1} = \log C + 2t$$

That is

$$\frac{u}{u-1} e^{-\frac{1}{u-1}} = Ce^{2t} \qquad [22.13]$$

Putting $u - 1 = v$ we obtain

$$\left(\frac{1}{v} + 1\right)e^{-\frac{1}{v}} = Ce^{2t} \qquad [22.14]$$

We shall investigate now the behavior of trajectories in the neighborhood $r = 1$ since for $r = 1$, $dr/dt = 0$. If $r = 1 - \epsilon$, ϵ being a small positive number, then $v < 0$, hence from [22.14] $C < 0$. Thus as $v \to 0$, i.e., $r \to 1$ from the inside of the circle $r = 1$, $t \to +\infty$, which means that the circle $r = 1$ is a stable limit cycle for the spiral trajectories inside the circle. If, however, $r \equiv 1 + \epsilon$, then $v > 0$, and hence $C > 0$. For $v \to 0$ ($r \to 1$ from

* Communicated by Professor G.D. Birkhoff.

the outside of the circle) $e^{2t} \rightarrow 0$, that is $t \rightarrow -\infty$, which means that the circle $r = 1$ is an unstable limit cycle for the outside trajectories. Hence the system [22.11] admits a half-stable limit cycle as a stationary solution.

4. As an example showing the existence of a region of accumulation of limit cycles (16) consider the following system of differential equations

$$\frac{dx}{dt} = + y + \mu(x^2 + y^2 - 1)x \sin \frac{1}{x^2 + y^2 - 1}$$

$$\frac{dy}{dt} = - x + \mu(x^2 + y^2 - 1)y \sin \frac{1}{x^2 + y^2 - 1}$$

[22.15]

In polar coordinates the equations of the phase trajectories are

$$\frac{dr}{d\theta} = \mu r(r^2 - 1) \sin \frac{1}{r^2 - 1}, \ r \neq 1$$

[22.16]

$$\frac{dr}{d\theta} = 0, \ r = 1$$

Thus there exists an infinity of circles in the neighborhood of $r = 1$ which represent the solutions of Equations [22.16] corresponding to the zeros of $\sin 1/(r^2 - 1)$. Between two consecutive zeros, and, hence between the two corresponding circles, the trajectories are spirals connecting two adjoining circles; see Section 24. The value $r = 1$ is thus a region of accumulation of the periodic solutions.

It is very easy to construct examples of limit cycles having all sorts of peculiarities by the use of polar coordinates. The above examples were obtained in this manner and the resulting equations were then transformed into rectangular coordinates; hence the apparent complications. It must be borne in mind that the unearthing of limit cycles known, or suspected, to exist in a given system is more difficult.

23. PHYSICAL EXAMPLES

Practically all self-excited oscillatory phenomena of Mechanics and Physics are governed by non-linear differential equations and illustrate limit cycles. In the past, the mathematical formulation of oscillatory phenomena has made use of some method of simplification. A typical simplification is the Method of Small Motions of Dynamics. The application of this method, as its name implies, is limited to small motions, generally studied in the vicinity of an equilibrium point. In the numerous phenomena of self-excitation of electronic circuits, circuits containing non-ohmic conductors such as arcs, gaseous discharges, and the like, the ultimate stationary oscillation is generally limited by amplitudes which cannot be considered as *small*. Likewise, in a great majority of mechanical self-excited vibrations or oscillations the phenomenon generally stabilizes itself in a range in which the non-linearity of the differential equations cannot be neglected. Such "linearized" differential equations generally leave open the question of the ultimate amplitude at which the self-excited phenomenon stabilizes itself.

Thus, for example, in the investigation of a simple linearized* problem of the Froude's pendulum, Section 8, we reach a conclusion that under certain assumed conditions the damping term is of the form $-b\dot{\phi}(b > 0)$. The conclusion, therefore, is that the general solution of Equation [8.1] is of the form $\phi = \phi_0 e^{bt} \sin(\omega t + \alpha)$, which indicates that in the early stages of the motion the amplitude is gradually increasing. Actually the amplitudes of the subsequent oscillations do not increase indefinitely however, but reach a limit when the oscillation becomes stationary. This stationary oscillation is represented by a limit cycle. Likewise, in a thermionic generator in which a similar condition exists initially, the amplitude of oscillation eventually reaches a limit cycle.

A linearization of this kind, while giving an indication as to what happens *initially*, does not give any information as to the *final* state of the stable oscillation. In other words, it does not permit the determination of the ultimate limit cycle towards which the initial process approaches asymptotically. Since limit cycles are not present in the linear systems, it is necessary to study problems which are essentially non-linear in character.

From this preliminary survey, it appears that modern electronic circuits involving electron tubes, gaseous discharges, and similar non-linear conductors, offer numerous examples of the existence of limit cycles. Although there are many examples of mechanical oscillations they have been given less attention inasmuch as they generally appear as undesirable parasitic phenomena. They occur whenever there is a so-called "closed-cycle effect," by which a certain "cause" produces an "effect" which tends to reinforce the original "cause," etc. The initial process is thus cumulative. However, in view of the non-linearity of the system for larger amplitudes of oscillations, the stable amplitude of the stationary state generally approaches that of a limit cycle. Again, the initial conditions do not play a leading role. The final amplitude depends only on the parameters of the system, but not on the initial conditions.

A commonly encountered mechanism in which limit cycles exist is an ordinary clock (19). In fact in a clock there is an oscillatory damped system, excited by shocks twice per period from a source of external energy,

---

* The expression "linearization" used here simply means dropping the non-linear terms from the differential equation. A somewhat different meaning is attached to this word by Kryloff and Bogoliuboff; see Chapter XII, Part II.

e.g., weight or main spring, released by the escapement; the impulses so released replenish the energy lost per half cycle of the oscillatory system and thus allow for the "closing" of the phase trajectories which then become limit cycles; see Part IV. In fact, if a clock is wound from rest, it is immaterial whether a small or a large impulse, e.g., shaking, is employed to start it; the ultimate operation of the clock, once it is started, is entirely independent of the initial condition which has produced the starting.

Perhaps it is not too great an exaggeration to say that the principal line of endeavor of non-linear mechanics at present is a search for limit cycles. These modern tendencies to consider the problem of self-excited oscillations as the problem of determining limit cycles seem to transcend even the domain of mathematical physics proper; in fact, attempts have been made to extend these new mathematical methods to the description of biological and statistical phenomena as well. Thus, for instance, Van der Pol and Van der Mark (20) gave a theory of the performance of the heart considered as a relaxation oscillation mechanism possessing a limit cycle. Likewise, V. Volterra (21) in his mathematical theory on the "Struggle for Life" gave examples in which limit cycles may exist.

24. TOPOLOGY OF TRAJECTORIES IN THE PRESENCE OF SINGULARITIES AND LIMIT CYCLES

Recalling the definitions of the various types of limit cycles as given in Section 22, it is seen that the trajectories in the neighborhood of stable, unstable, and half-stable limit cycles have the form shown in Figures 24.1, 24.2, and 24.3, respectively.

Trajectories winding on (unwinding from) a limit cycle may either arrive from infinity (go to infinity) or may originate (terminate) at singular points or other limit cycles. It will be shown that a necessary condition that a closed curve C in the phase plane be a trajectory is the existence of at least one point singularity of a definite type inside it. The fact that

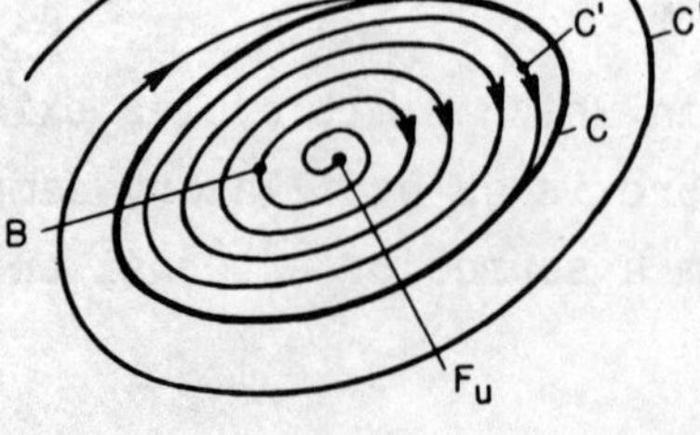

Figure 24.1

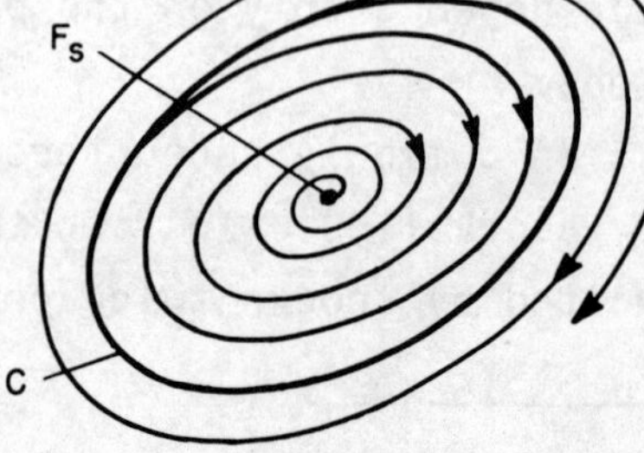

Figure 24.2

the trajectories either depart from or approach
singularities of the focal or nodal type makes
it possible to use a rather pictorial language
in describing certain topological relationships
in the phase plane by considering these singularities either as "sources" or "sinks" for
trajectories in their neighborhood.

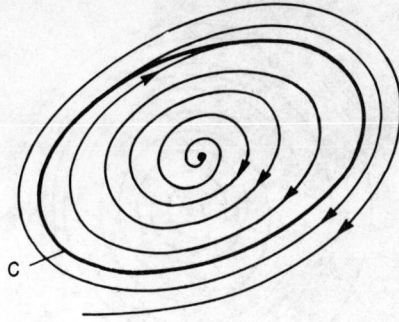

Figure 24.3

       A stable singularity or a stable lim-
it cycle considered from this viewpoint, is a
"sink" for trajectories which it approaches
asymptotically; likewise, an unstable singularity or an unstable limit cycle
appears as a "source" with respect to the trajectories from which it departs.
In this manner a number of propositions concerning these relationships become
almost self-evident.

       Very frequently a trajectory may approach a limit cycle for $t \to \infty$
and approach a singular point for $t \to -\infty$. Physically this means that the
motion develops from a state of rest and passes ultimately to a stationary
periodic state. This can be expressed in light of the above descriptive language by stating that for $t \to -\infty$ the trajectory starts from a point source
and for $t \to +\infty$ it approaches a line sink.

       In the following we shall consider focal points. There is no es-
sential difference in considering nodal points when the nature of the trajectories in the neighborhood of the singularities is taken into account.

       A point **A** on a trajectory **C** divides it into two *half-trajectories*.
If the time origin is selected when the representative point is at the point
A, these half-trajectories for $t \geq 0$ and for $t \leq 0$ describe the future and
the past history of the system. The present condition is represented by the
point **A**. If we are only interested in a physical phenomenon beginning at a
certain instant and disregard its past history, the state of the system is
then determined by the positive half-trajectory ($t \geq 0$) "originating" at the
point **A**. Very frequently this viewpoint is useful when we deal with the impulsive excitation of a dynamical system in which case the representative
point R is transferred discontinuously from one point of the phase plane to
another, say **A**. Disregarding what occurred during the period of discontinuity, or prior to it, we can consider only the half-trajectory "originating"
at **A** and study the behavior of the system from that moment.

       With this remark in mind we can say, for example, that to a set of
initial conditions represented by the point **A** in Figure 24.1 there corresponds
a half-trajectory winding onto the stable limit cycle C from the outside and
to the initial conditions represented by the point **B** there corresponds a

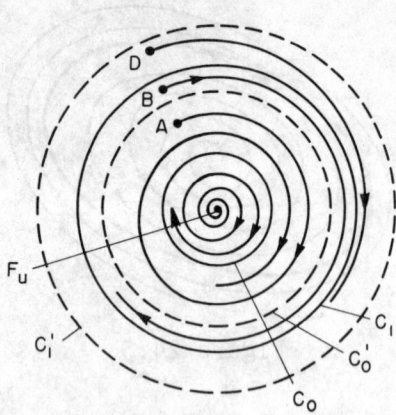

Figure 24.4

half-trajectory winding on C from the inside. There may be, of course, more complicated situations when a number of other singularities are present but for our immediate purpose it will be sufficient to consider the simple case of one singularity surrounded by one, or several, limit cycles.

Having in mind later applications let us consider the following special case. A point singularity F_u, which we shall assume to be an unstable focal point, is surrounded by several limit cycles, represented by closed curves shown as circles C_0, C_0', C_1, etc., in Figure 24.4; the circles in full lines represent the stable limit cycles and those in broken lines, the unstable ones. The fact that we assume that the limit cycles are circles is not essential since we are primarily interested in the topology of trajectories in the various domains which we are now going to specify. In order to include the half-stable limit cycles, the following terminology is convenient. A limit cycle is *inwardly* or *outwardly* stable according to the side on which stability exists; similarly, a limit cycle may be inwardly or outwardly unstable. A stable limit cycle in this terminology is one which is both inwardly and outwardly stable and an unstable limit cycle is both inwardly and outwardly unstable.

We can now formulate the following theorem* given here without proof. In a succession of concentric limit cycles considered from the center outward, an outwardly stable limit cycle is followed by one that is inwardly unstable and a cycle which is outwardly unstable is followed by one that is inwardly stable. The point singularity at the center is to be considered as a degenerate limit cycle possessing only the outward stability (or instability).

We shall consider first a few typical examples which stress the significance of this theorem. This will enable us to derive certain conclusions concerning more complicated cases which will be important later. One such case arises when a point singularity being originally unstable becomes stable or vice versa. Figure 24.4 exhibits an unstable singularity F_u surrounded by a stable limit cycle C_0 and a few other cycles (C_0', C_1' unstable, C_1 stable, etc.). It is apparent that, since the state of rest F_u is unstable, a spiral

---

* This theorem is a particular case of a more general theorem formulated by I. Bendixson (5). One can also find the proof of the proposition that two adjoining closed integral curves cannot both be stable in a recent paper by N. Levinson and O.K. Smith (22).

trajectory will originate at F_u and will approach C_0 which represents the state of the ultimate stable stationary oscillation on the limit cycle. It is readily seen, following this line of reasoning, that this state of stationary motion will be reached not only when the system starts from rest but also when it starts from any arbitrary initial conditions which are represented by a point of the phase plane inside the first unstable limit cycle C_0' such as **A**. In this sense we can state that the ultimate motion on the limit cycle C_0 is *independent of the initial conditions*.

It is apparent that the following stable cycle C_1 cannot be reached spontaneously by the system starting from rest since the oscillation cannot develop beyond C_0 on which it becomes stationary. However, in spite of this, the trajectories may approach the limit cycle C_1 if they originate from the initial conditions represented by the points situated in the annular region between C_0' and C_1' such as points B and D in Figure 24.4. It is thus seen that the unstable limit cycles C_0', $C_1' \cdots$ constitute a kind of *divide* or "barrier" for the initial conditions from which various stable limit cycles such as C_1, $C_2 \cdots$ can be reached by trajectories.

We are now in a position to formulate two definitions which will be important for the sequel.

1.   A self-excitation of a system on a limit cycle C_0 is called *soft* if it can originate spontaneously from rest.

2.   A self-excitation on a limit cycle C is called *hard* if it requires a certain finite disturbance, e.g., shock excitation, to transfer the initial conditions into the annular region between two consecutive unstable limit cycles in which C is situated.

These definitions may also be formulated in the following manner. A stable limit cycle C_0 is said to induce a soft self-excitation, whenever it contains no other limit cycle and just one singular point, an unstable singularity. In all other cases C_0 is said to induce a hard self-excitation.

This condition of "hard" self-excitation is illustrated in Figure 24.5, in which the system is in stable equilibrium when at rest. If there exists a stable limit cycle C_0, it follows from the theorem stated above that there must necessarily be an unstable limit cycle C_0' between F_s and C_0. Therefore the system cannot become self-excited and reach the stable limit cycle either from rest or from any initial conditions

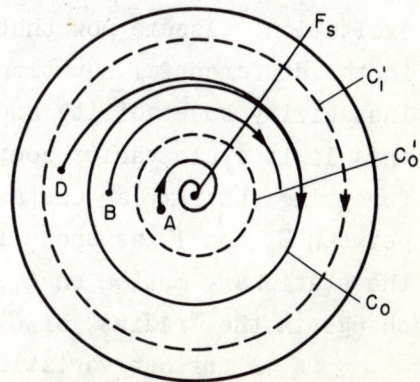

Figure 24.5

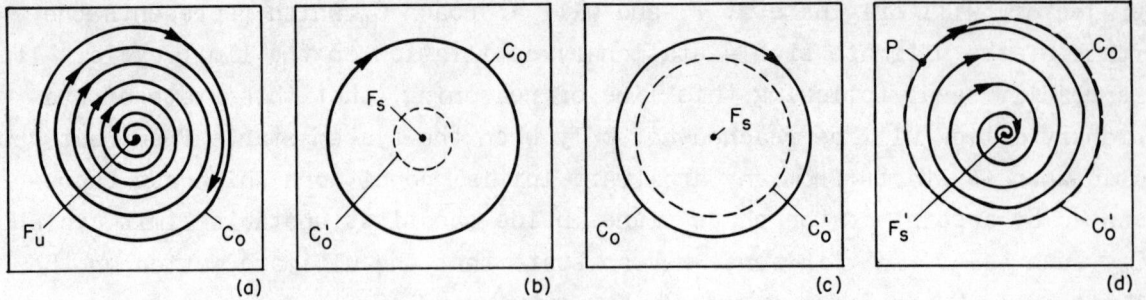

Figure 24.6

represented by a point **A** inside $C_0{}'$. In fact, in the latter case, Figure 24.5, the trajectory starting from **A** will approach the state of rest at F_s. The stable limit cycle C_0 can be approached however, if a trajectory origi- nates either at **B** or at **D**, which represent points of the annular region be- tween the divides $C_0{}'$ and $C_1{}'$, that is, the system must be given initial conditions represented by any point in this annular region.

In the following we shall be concerned with those cases in which the topology of the phase plane undergoes changes as a result of changes of a parameter in the differential equation. As we shall see these changes may be of different kinds. Thus, for example, the singularities may undergo a transition from stability to instability or vice versa, limit cycles may vary in size, a stable limit cycle may coalesce with an unstable one with the dis- appearance of both, limit cycles may shrink and coalesce with point singular- ities modifying the nature of the latter, etc. These various changes will be studied in later sections. In all cases, however complicated, we shall find that the theorem on limit cycles provides most useful information.

As an example consider the following case which we shall encounter later. Assume that there is an unstable singularity F_u surrounded by a sta- ble limit cycle C_0 as shown in Figure 24.6a. A trajectory will unwind from F_u and will approach C_0; this corresponds to the case of a soft self- excitation. Assume now that, as the result of a variation of a parameter λ in the differential equation, the singularity undergoes a transition from instability to stability and that the trajectory C_0 in the neighborhood of this limit cycle varies continuously, remaining a limit cycle. Then, by the foregoing theorem, an unstable limit cycle $C_0{}'$ must necessarily originate between C_0 and F_s as shown in Figure 24.6b. This, however, in no way affects the stationary motion on C_0, except, possibly, that there may be a slight change in the "radius" of C_0.

A further variation of the parameter λ may decrease the "radius" of C_0 and increase that of $C_0{}'$, so that the two cycles approach each other, as shown in Figure 24.6c, although the actual trajectory of the system continues to be C_0. This is often the case in considering the non-linear characteristics encountered in practice. After the coalescence of these limit cycles a number of alternatives is possible with a continuous variation of λ in the same sense.

One possibility of frequent occurrence in physical problems is the case in which there exist no limit cycles beyond this stage. Everything then takes place as if the stable and the unstable limit cycles upon coalescing destroy each other. When this situation arises, the representative point approaches the stable focal point as shown in Figure 24.6d, so that the self-excited process disappears gradually.

The coalescence of limit cycles with point singularities will be investigated in Section 29. It should be mentioned at this point that the question of coalescence of limit cycles remains relatively unexplored theoretically.

Interesting illustrations of the above definitions and theorems can be obtained experimentally by means of a cathode-ray oscillograph arranged to record the phase trajectories of a non-linear process.

It is recalled that the pattern traced by the luminous spot of a cathode-ray oscillograph is due to the alternating potentials impressed on two pairs of deflecting plates at right angles to each other. If, therefore, one pair of plates is subjected to a voltage proportional to a dynamical variable x, which may be the displacement in a mechanical oscillation or a current in a circuit, and the other pair of plates is acted on by a voltage proportional to the derivative $\dot{x}$ of that variable, it is clear that the luminous path traced by the electronic beam on the screen will give directly the phase trajectory of the process. There exist numerous, so-called differentiating circuits which give an electrical differentiation of this kind. We shall not go into a survey of these various schemes but will indicate as an example the essential points of a scheme due to Bowshewerow (23) who was

one of the first (1935) to develop the experimental technique for the investigation of phase trajectories. Consider the scheme shown in Figure 24.7 representing a thermionic generator with an adjustable inductive coupling LL'. The oscillating circuit LC of the generator contains a relatively small resistor

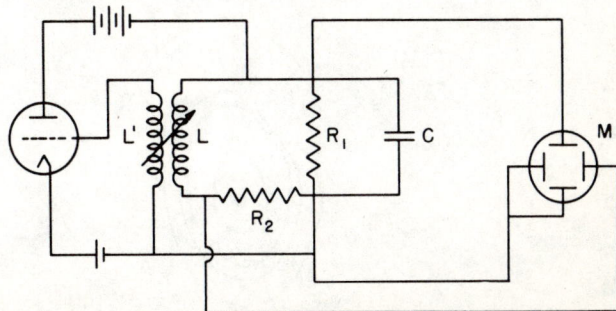

Figure 24.7

R_2 in series and a rather large resistor R_1 in parallel with L and C. It is apparent first that the potential difference across R_2 represents the oscillating current i and that across R_1 the oscillating potential V, and since these quantities are approximately in quadrature with each other, it is apparent that the oscillograph M, controlled by these potential differences, is capable of recording the phase trajectories of the process. By means of additional details not shown in Figure 24.7, it was possible to start the phenomenon from a given point (i,V) of the phase plane and also to vary the parameter λ of the process by changing the coefficient of mutual inductance between the coils L and L′. A variable bias permits fixing the equilibrium point at different points of the non-linear characteristic of the tube.

Oscillograms a, b, c, and d shown in Figure 24.8 represent the various conditions of a hard self-excitation recorded in this manner. Oscillogram a shows the disappearance of self-excitation by removing the coupling of the oscillator with the incident approach of the phase trajectory to a stable focal point. Oscillogram b shows a similar process but with a small amount of regeneration through a relatively weak coupling LL′ below the critical value at which the energy input into the oscillating circuit becomes greater than its dissipation of energy. Oscillogram c represents oscillation on the limit cycle. With the non-linear characteristic employed it is seen that there are two limit cycles C_2 and C_1, the former being stable and the

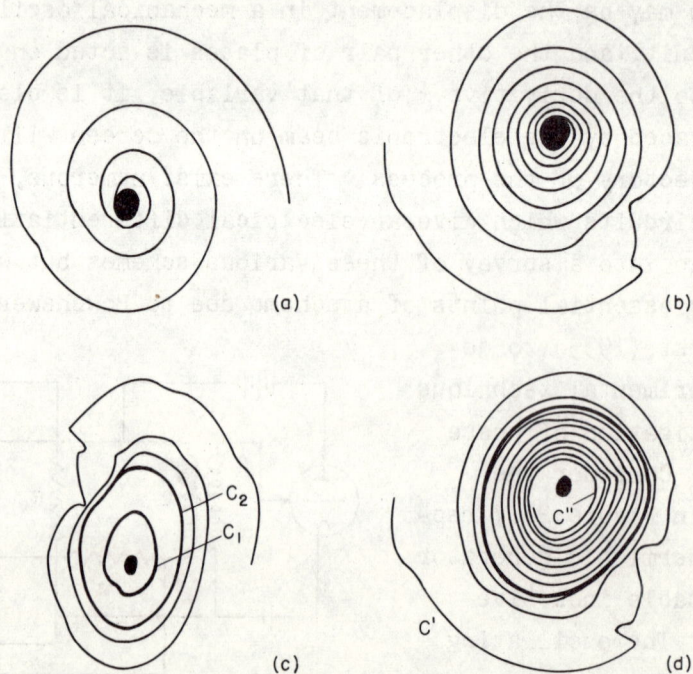

Figure 24.8

latter unstable. The black point inside C_1 is a stable focal point. By transferring the initial conditions to the different points of the phase plane the
stable limit cycles C_1 and C_2 can be reached in the manner just explained
either from the inside of these cycles or from the outside. A phase trajectory approaching C_2 from the outside has been recorded on the oscillogram.
Oscillogram d shows the approach of phase trajectories to a stable limit cycle
both from the outside (Curve C') and the inside (Curve C''); the black spot in
the middle is an unstable focal point.

25. FURTHER PROPERTIES OF LIMIT CYCLES; INDICES OF POINCARÉ; THEOREMS OF BENDIXSON

In the examples given in Section 22 the establishment of the existence of limit cycles was particularly simple. Unfortunately, given a non-
linear differential equation, the problem of establishing the existence of a
limit cycle, or cycles, is, generally, very difficult.

There exist criteria which rule out limit cycles in certain cases.
The method most frequently used for the establishment of the existence of
limit cycles within a certain domain is based on the theorem of Bendixson
formulated below. It is important to note, however, that Bendixson's theorem
cannot be applied to systems with more than one degree of freedom; furthermore, even in such systems its application is frequently handicapped by the
difficulty of determining the domain to which it can be applied. Poincaré
has given a series of *necessary* criteria for the existence of limit cycles,
based on the theory of indices associated with closed curves.

The whole situation when considered from the point of view of determining limit cycles can be best described in the words taken from the
"Theory of Oscillations" by Andronow and Chaikin:

"The present status of the theory establishing the
existence of limit cycles can be best compared to the game of
chess. There exists no theory by means of which a game can be
won. There do exist, however, alternatives which enable a
skilled partner to win a game starting from a given configuration
on the chess board."

We shall review now the three principal methods available.
A. Indices of Poincaré, B. Negative criterion of non-existence of closed
trajectories of Bendixson, C. A second theorem of Bendixson. There exists
also a fourth method of the *curve of contacts* due to Poincaré. We shall not
go into this subject here but shall mention it in a later chapter where the
use of the curve of contacts will be helpful.

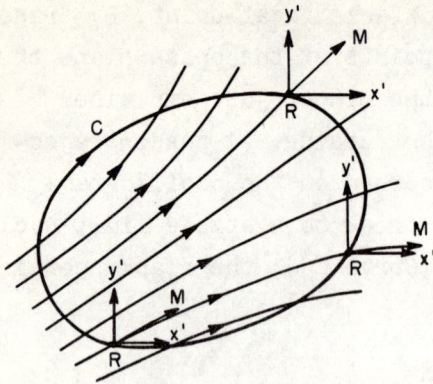

Figure 25.1

A. INDICES OF POINCARÉ

Consider a closed curve C as shown in Figure 25.1 in a vector field F.* Assume an arbitrary positive sense of rotation, say clockwise, and consider the motion of the point R on C in this positive direction. Let (x', y') be a frame of reference attached to R, the directions of which remain parallel to the axes x, y of a fixed coordinate system during the motion of R on C. If the vector $\overrightarrow{RM}$ with R as origin is drawn, so as to represent the vector of the field at R, this vector $\overrightarrow{RM}$ will turn around R in the (x', y')-system as the point R moves on C. When the circuit C is completed, the vector $\overrightarrow{RM}$ will resume its original position in the (x', y')-system.

Poincaré calls the "index j" of a closed curve with respect to a vector field the algebraic number of complete revolutions of $\overrightarrow{RM}$ when R completes one circuit C. The index may be equal to zero, which means that $\overrightarrow{RM}$ executes only an oscillation in the (x', y')-system but not a complete rotation. By the index of a singularity is meant the index of a closed curve surrounding the singularity and lying in a vector field determined by the phase trajectories.

From this definition it follows that the index of a closed trajectory enclosing a vortex, a nodal, or a focal point is + 1, Figure 25.2a, b, and c, whereas that of a trajectory surrounding a saddle point is - 1, Figure 25.2d.

Poincaré has established a series of theorems which are given here without proof (2). Some of these theorems are obvious from geometrical considerations.

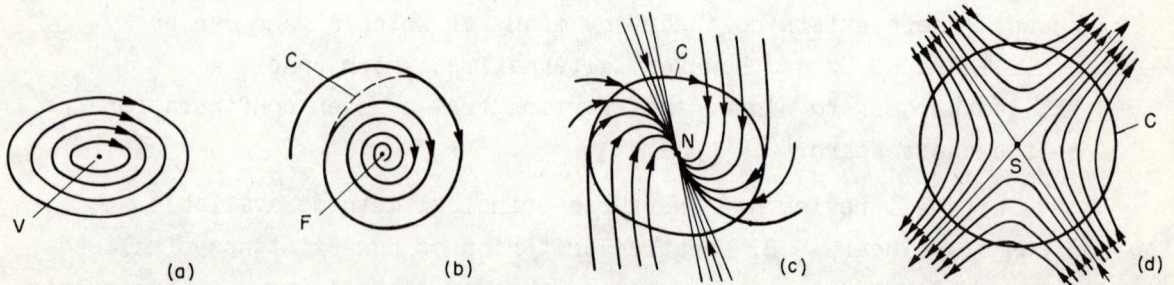

(a) (b) (c) (d)

Figure 25.2

* For such a field the line integral $\oint \vec{F} d\vec{s}$ over a closed curve is zero.

1.   The index of a closed curve not containing singularities is zero.

2.   The index of a closed curve containing several singularities is
equal to the algebraic sum of their indices.

3.   The index of a closed curve which is a phase trajectory is
always + 1.

4.   The index of a closed curve, with respect to which the field vectors are directed either inwards or outwards at all points, is always + 1.

These theorems lead to the following conclusions with regard to
closed phase trajectories.

1.   A closed trajectory contains in its interior at least one singularity the index of which is + 1.

2.   A closed trajectory may contain several singularities in which case
the algebraic sum of their indices is + 1.

By virtue of the first conclusion, limit cycles may contain in
their interior nodal or focal points, but not saddle points. By the second
conclusion the number of enclosed singularities must always be odd, the number of singularities with index + 1 must exceed the number of saddle points
by one unit. This theorem has already been established directly, see Section
12, from topological considerations.

B.   FIRST THEOREM OF BENDIXSON (THE NEGATIVE CRITERION)
The first theorem of Bendixson establishes a condition for the
non-existence of closed trajectories and, hence, for the impossibility of
periodic motions.
Let the motion in the phase plane be given by the equations

$$\dot{x} = P(x,y); \quad \dot{y} = Q(x,y) \qquad [25.1]$$

The theorem of Bendixson states: **If the expression** $\partial P/\partial x + \partial Q/\partial y$ **does not change
its sign within a domain D of the phase plane, no periodic motions can exist in that domain.**
Consider a closed circuit in D and apply Gauss's Theorem

$$\oint (P\,dy - Q\,dx) = \iint \left(\frac{\partial P}{\partial x} + \frac{\partial Q}{\partial y}\right) dx\,dy \qquad [25.2]$$

with respect to this circuit. If one assumes that the circuit is a phase
trajectory satisfying [25.1], the line integral can be written $\int (\dot{x}\dot{y}\,dt - \dot{y}\dot{x}\,dt)$
which is equal to zero. As to the double integral, it can be zero only if,
within the area limited by the closed circuit, the integrand $(\partial P/\partial x + \partial Q/\partial y)$
changes its sign. This is contrary to the assumption; hence, the closed

curve cannot be a phase trajectory which implies that no periodic motion can exist in D.

One can also state a series of additional criteria based on the negation of the theorems resulting from the theory of indices.

1.   No periodic motions and, hence, no limit cycles can exist in a system not having singularities.

2.   If a system has just one singularity and if its index is not + 1, periodic motions are impossible.

3.   In a system with several singularities the algebraic sum of whose indices is different from + 1, periodic motions on closed curves enclosing all these singularities are impossible.

4.   In a system with just one singularity having the index + 1, which is approached by trajectories going to infinity, periodic motions are impossible.

C.   SECOND THEOREM OF BENDIXSON (5)

Let $x(t)$, $y(t)$ be the parametric equations of a half-trajectory C which remains for $t \to +\infty$ inside a finite domain D without approaching any singularity. The second theorem of Bendixson asserts that only two cases are then possible.

1.   Either C is itself a closed trajectory, or

2.   C approaches asymptotically a closed trajectory C_0.

If, assuming for instance that there is only one singularity inside a closed curve C_1, one succeeds in determining a domain D limited by two closed curves C_1 and C_2, as shown in Figure 25.3, within which the half-trajectory is confined and has no singularities either in D or on its boundaries, then the theorem asserts that there exists at least one stable limit cycle in D.

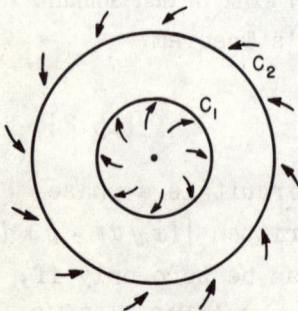

An intuitive interpretation of this theorem on the basis of singularities and limit cycles considered as "sources" and "sinks" is frequently useful. As an example consider Equations [22.3] and [22.4]. For $r < 1$, $dr/d\theta > 0$; for $r > 1$, $dr/d\theta < 0$. Choosing as the domain D an annular region limited by two concentric circles $r_1 = 1/2$ and $r_2 = 3/2$, for example, drawn from the origin as center, one readily sees that D satisfies the condition of Bendixson

Figure 25.3

since no singularities exist either in D or on its boundaries. Hence, there exists at least one limit cycle. In this particular case a direct proof of existence of a limit cycle is very simple, as appears from [22.5].

In applying the second theorem of Bendixson a difficulty often encountered consists in finding the appropriate domain D which would contain an entire half-trajectory and exclude the singularities. As an example of such a case, consider the Van der Pol equation

$$\ddot{x} - \mu(1 - x^2)\dot{x} + x = 0$$

which, as is known, has a periodic solution. More specifically, for $\mu \ll 1$, this equation admits a closed trajectory differing very little from a circle of radius $r = 2$.

If one attempts to apply the Bendixson theorem to a domain D limited by $r_1 = 1$ and $r_2 = 3$, one easily finds that the theorem fails to indicate that the trajectories cannot leave the domain D by crossing the boundary of the circle.

If, however, one succeeds in establishing a domain D for which the conditions specified by Bendixson's theorem hold, then one is certain that at least one periodic solution exists. Thus, for example, in a later chapter we shall encounter the system

$$\frac{dx}{dt} = -ay + x(1 - r^2)$$

[25.4]

$$\frac{dy}{dt} = A + ax + y(1 - r^2)$$

where A is a constant and $r^2 = x^2 + y^2$. It is apparent that, for a sufficiently large r^2, the trajectories are directed inwards. Furthermore, by transferring the origin to the singular point by a change of variables $x = x_0 + \xi$, $y = y_0 + \eta$, the system [25.4] is reduced to that of the form

$$\frac{d\xi}{dt} = \xi - a\eta + \cdots$$

[25.5]

$$\frac{d\eta}{dt} = a\xi + \eta + \cdots$$

It is thus seen that the origin is an unstable focal point and since no other singularities exist, the Bendixson theorem shows that there exists a stable periodic solution contained in a finite domain.

26. PARALLEL OPERATION OF SERIES GENERATORS

As an example of the application of the Bendixson criterion of non-existence of closed trajectories consider two series generators connected in

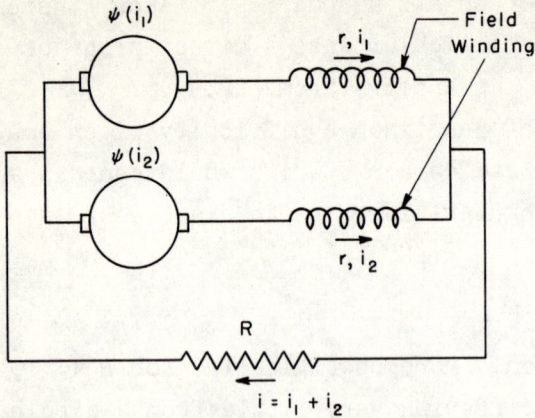

Figure 26.1

parallel with respect to the external circuit R, as shown in Figure 26.1. Selecting as the positive direction for the currents i_1 and i_2 the direction in which they contribute to the external load and designating the characteristics of series generators by $e = \psi(i)$, one obtains, by Kirchhoff's laws, the following two differential equations applied to the circuits (i_1, i) and (i_2, i).

$$\psi(i_1) - (r + R)i_1 - Ri_2 - L\frac{di_1}{dt} = 0$$

[26.1]

$$\psi(i_2) - (r + R)i_2 - Ri_1 - L\frac{di_2}{dt} = 0$$

Dividing these equations, one finds

$$\frac{di_2}{di_1} = \frac{\psi(i_2) - (r + R)i_2 - Ri_1}{\psi(i_1) - (r + R)i_1 - Ri_2}$$

[26.2]

The variables i_1 and i_2 determine the trajectories in the phase plane. The application of the first theorem of Bendixson gives

$$\frac{\partial P}{\partial i_1} = \psi_{i_1}(i_1) - (r + R); \quad \frac{\partial Q}{\partial i_2} = \psi_{i_2}(i_2) - (r + R)$$

[26.3]

If the condition of self-excitation is fulfilled, one has always $\psi_i(i) - (r + R) > 0$;* hence, no periodic motions are possible. The condition of equilibrium is obtained by setting the numerator and denominator in Equation [26.2] equal to zero and by finding the points of intersection of the resulting curves in the (i_1, i_2)-plane. One can also investigate the system of two linear equations

$$\frac{di_1}{dt} = \frac{1}{L}\left[\psi(i_1) - (r + R)i_1 - Ri_2\right]$$

[26.4]

$$\frac{di_2}{dt} = \frac{1}{L}\left[\psi(i_2) - (r + R)i_2 - Ri_1\right]$$

---

* In fact, this inequality means that the initial supply of energy must be greater than its dissipation, see Section 21.

by forming the equations of the first approximation, that is by developing $\psi(i)$ in Taylor's series and neglecting the terms of higher orders. Writing $\left(\dfrac{d\psi(i)}{di}\right)_{i=0} = (\psi_i)_{i=0} = \rho$, one has

$$(\rho - r - R)i_1 - L\frac{di_1}{dt} - Ri_2 = 0$$

$$[26.5]$$

$$- Ri_1 + (\rho - r - R)i_2 - L\frac{di_2}{dt} = 0$$

Putting $\delta = d/dt$, this can be written as

$$(\rho - r - R - L\delta)i_1 - Ri_2 = 0$$

$$[26.6]$$

$$- Ri_1 + (\rho - r - R - L\delta)i_2 = 0$$

The system [26.6] admits solutions other than the trivial ones $i_1 = i_2 = 0$, if the determinant is zero.

$$\begin{vmatrix} \rho - r - R - L\delta & - R \\ - R & \rho - r - R - L\delta \end{vmatrix} = 0 \qquad [26.7]$$

That is, $\rho - r - R - L\delta = \pm R$; whence the roots of the characteristic equation are

$$\delta_1 = \frac{1}{L}\left[\rho - (r + 2R)\right]; \quad \delta_2 = \frac{1}{L}(\rho - r) \qquad [26.8]$$

In practice generally $\rho - r > 0$; thus $\delta_2 > 0$. As regards δ_1, it may be either positive or negative. In the first case there is an unstable nodal point and in the second, a saddle point. Thus, for the assumed conditions, that is, when i_1 and i_2 *add up* with respect to the external circuit, the process is unstable and therefore cannot exist in a steady state. In fact, it is well known that a parallel connection of two series machines

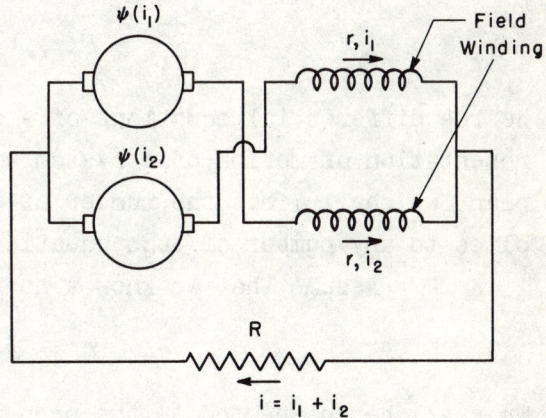

Figure 26.2

leads to an unstable parasitic performance in which one machine generates energy and the other absorbs it so that no energy flows into the external circuit. If the field connections are crossed as shown in Figure 26.2, instead of Equation [26.1] one has

$$\psi(i_1) - (r + R)i_2 - Ri_1 - L\frac{di_2}{dt} = 0$$

[26.9]

$$\psi(i_2) - (r + R)i_1 - Ri_2 - L\frac{di_1}{dt} = 0$$

The roots of the characteristic equation are

$$\delta_1 = \frac{1}{L}\left[\rho - (r + 2R)\right]; \quad \delta_2 = -\frac{1}{L}(\rho + r)$$

[26.10]

If $\rho < r + 2R$, both roots are real and negative, which corresponds to a stable nodal point and, hence, to equilibrium. The machines have a stable performance, delivering energy into the external circuit. If $\rho > r + 2R$, there is a saddle point and, hence, a loss of stability. The threshold condition $\rho = r + 2R$ is, thus, a branch point of equilibrium corresponding to the transition from a stable nodal point to a saddle point, which is in accordance with the sequence of the zones of singularities shown in Figure 18.1.

27. STABILITY OF PERIODIC MOTION

We shall now investigate the problem of stability of periodic motion, a question which was left open in Chapter III. For this purpose a few additional theorems will be useful.

Let

$$\frac{dx}{dt} = P(x,y) \quad \text{and} \quad \frac{dy}{dt} = Q(x,y)$$

[27.1]

be the differential equations of a dynamical system. Having in mind the representation of motion of a system with one degree of freedom in the phase plane we shall limit the number of these equations to two. The argument applies to any number of such equations.

Assume that we know a non-constant periodic solution of [27.1]

$$x_1 = \phi(t); \quad y_1 = \psi(t)$$

[27.2]

We shall be interested in the properties of a neighboring perturbed solution

$$x = x_1 + \xi; \quad y = y_1 + \eta$$

[27.3]

where $\xi(t)$ and $\eta(t)$ are the functions determining the perturbation. It will be assumed that the quantities $|\xi|$ and $|\eta|$ are sufficiently small so that we may neglect ξ^2, η^2, ξ^3, $\cdots$. Substituting the expressions [27.3] into the differential equations and expanding the functions in a Taylor series in the neighborhood of x_1 and y_1, one obtains the *variational* equations (3)

$$\frac{d\xi}{dt} = P_x(x_1, y_1)\xi + P_y(x_1, y_1)\eta$$

[27.4]

$$\frac{d\eta}{dt} = Q_x(x_1, y_1)\xi + Q_y(x_1, y_1)\eta$$

This is a system of linear equations of the type

$$\frac{d\xi}{dt} = a(t)\xi + b(t)\eta$$

[27.5]

$$\frac{d\eta}{dt} = c(t)\xi + d(t)\eta$$

where $a(t), \cdots, d(t)$ are periodic functions of t with a common period T.

It is known (24) that a system of the type [27.5] admits a fundamental system of solutions of the form

$$\xi_1 = e^{h_1 t}f_{11}(t); \quad \eta_1 = e^{h_2 t}f_{12}(t)$$

[27.6]

$$\xi_2 = e^{h_1 t}f_{21}(t); \quad \eta_2 = e^{h_2 t}f_{22}(t)$$

where $f_{11}, \cdots, f_{22}$ are periodic functions of time with the period T, and h_1 and h_2 are certain constants, real or complex, which are determined only to integral multiples of $2\pi i T$. These constants are called the *characteristic exponents* of the system.

The characteristic exponents satisfy the relation

$$h_1 + h_2 = \frac{1}{T}\int_0^T (a + d)\,dt$$

[27.7]

that is, the sum of the characteristic exponents is the average of the sum of the diagonal coefficients of [27.5] taken over the period T. This can be proved as follows. Substituting the expressions [27.6] into the equations [27.5] and solving for a and d we obtain

$$a = \frac{\dot{\xi}_1\eta_2 - \dot{\xi}_2\eta_1}{\xi_1\eta_2 - \xi_2\eta_1}; \quad d = \frac{\xi_1\dot{\eta}_2 - \xi_2\dot{\eta}_1}{\xi_1\eta_2 - \xi_2\eta_1}$$

[27.8]

The denominator of these expressions, upon substitution of the values for $\xi_1, \cdots, \eta_2$ obtained from [27.6], becomes

$$\xi_1\eta_2 - \xi_2\eta_1 = e^{[h_1 + h_2]t}\left[f_{11}f_{22} - f_{12}f_{21}\right] = e^{[h_1 + h_2]t}\delta$$

[27.9]

where δ is a periodic function with period T. Adding the expressions [27.8] one obtains after simple calculations

$$(a + d) = \frac{\dot{\delta}}{\delta} + (h_1 + h_2)$$

Averaging this expression over the period T one has

$$h_1 + h_2 = \frac{1}{T}\int_0^T (h_1 + h_2)\,dt = \frac{1}{T}\int_0^T (a + d)\,dt - \frac{1}{T}\int_0^T \frac{\dot{\delta}}{\delta}\,dt$$

Since the last term on the right side of this expression has period T and hence vanishes, one obtains the expression [27.7].

It should be noted further that if the system [27.5] admits a periodic solution with period T at least one of the characteristic exponents is zero (3). For suppose $\xi(t) = c_1\xi_1(t) + c_2\xi_2(t)$; $\eta(t) = c_1\eta_1(t) + c_2\eta_2(t)$ is periodic and not identically equal to zero, that is, $\xi(t + T) = \xi(t)$; $\eta(t + T) = \eta(t)$. From [27.6] one obtains easily

$$c_1(e^{h_1 t} - 1)\xi_1 + c_2(e^{h_2 t} - 1)\xi_2 = 0$$

$$c_1(e^{h_1 t} - 1)\eta_1 + c_2(e^{h_2 t} - 1)\eta_2 = 0$$

[27.10]

Since c_1 and c_2 cannot vanish simultaneously and since the solutions (ξ_1, η_1) and (ξ_2, η_2) are assumed to be linearly independent, the relations [27.10] imply that either $e^{h_2 t} = 1$ or $e^{h_1 t} = 1$. Thus, in the first case, we have $h_2 = 0$; in the second, $h_1 = 0$.

We now assert that the system [27.4] has a non-trivial periodic solution, and that one of its characteristic exponents is zero. By differentiating [27.1] we obtain

$$\frac{d^2 x}{dt^2} = P_x(x, y)\frac{dx}{dt} + P_y(x, y)\frac{dy}{dt}$$

$$\frac{d^2 y}{dt^2} = Q_x(x, y)\frac{dx}{dt} + Q_y(x, y)\frac{dy}{dt}$$

[27.11]

Comparing with [27.4] it is seen that the periodic functions dx_1/dt and dy_1/dt satisfy the latter system. Moreover, the solution dx_1/dt, dy_1/dt is a non-trivial solution of [27.4] since $x_1(t)$ and $y_1(t)$ are not constant. Knowing that one of the characteristic exponents, say h_1, is zero, we can determine the second one from [27.7]

$$h_2 = h = \frac{1}{T}\int_0^T \left[P_x(x_1, y_1) + Q_y(x_1, y_1)\right]dt \qquad [27.12]$$

Following a procedure similar to that used in the discussion of the stability of equilibrium it can be shown that the motion defined by the functions $x_1(t)$, $y_1(t)$ is stable if $h < 0$ and unstable if $h > 0$. The proof is more complicated than in the case of stability of equilibrium, owing to the fact that one of the characteristic exponents is bound to vanish. We shall omit the proof. The reader will recall that in the case of stability of equilibrium, Chapter III, the real parts of *both* roots of the characteristic equation must be negative in order to ensure the stability. Here, however, the stability depends on the sign of the real part of the non-vanishing characteristic exponent. A few examples below give an illustration of the application of Equation [27.12].

1.   The Van der Pol equation $\ddot{x} - \mu(1 - x^2)\dot{x} + x = 0$ is known to possess a periodic solution in the neighborhood of functions $x_0 = 2\cos t$, $y_0 = \dot{x}_0 = -2\sin t$, when the parameter μ is very small. Thus,

$$x_1 = 2\cos \nu t + \omega_1(\mu, t); \quad y_1 = -2\sin \nu t + \omega_2(\mu, t)$$

where $\nu = 2\pi/T \approx 1$, $T \approx 2\pi$, and $\omega_1(\mu, t)$, $\omega_2(\mu, t)$ are functions approaching zero uniformly in t when $\mu \to 0$. This gives $P_x(x_1, y_1) = 0$; $Q_y(x_1, y_1) = \mu(1 - x_1^2) = \mu[1 - 4\cos^2 \nu t + \omega_3(\mu, t)]$ and by [27.12]

$$h = \frac{\mu}{T}\int_0^T \left[1 - 4\cos^2 \nu t + \omega_3(\mu, t)\right] dt = -\mu\left[1 + \omega_4(\mu)\right]$$

Since $\omega_4(\mu) \to 0$, $h < 0$ which proves that the periodic motion in the neighborhood of (x_0, y_0) is stable, a well-known fact.

2.   As further examples we shall consider the three systems [22.1], [22.6], and [22.11] of non-linear differential equations investigated in Section 22. It was shown that these systems admit limit cycles $r = 1$, stable for the system [22.1], unstable for [22.6], and half stable for [22.11]. We shall establish here the condition of stability by means of Equation [27.12].

a.   In case of the system [22.1] we have

$$P_x = \frac{y^2}{(x^2 + y^2)^{\frac{3}{2}}}\left[1 - (x^2 + y^2)\right] - \frac{2x^2}{\sqrt{x^2 + y^2}}$$

$$Q_y = \frac{x^2}{(x^2 + y^2)^{\frac{3}{2}}}\left[1 - (x^2 + y^2)\right] - \frac{2y^2}{\sqrt{x^2 + y^2}}$$

Since this system admits a periodic solution $x_1 = \cos t$, $y_1 = -\sin t$, we have

$$P_x(x_1, y_1) = -2\cos^2 t; \quad Q_y(x_1, y_1) = -2\sin^2 t$$

and

$$h = -\frac{1}{2\pi}\int_0^{2\pi} 2(\sin^2 t + \cos^2 t)\,dt = -2$$

which shows that the limit cycle $r = 1$ is stable.

b. For the system [22.6] we obtain

$$P_x = 3x^2 + y^2 - 1; \quad Q_y = 3y^2 + x^2 - 1$$

the generating solutions being the same as above. Whence,

$$h = \frac{1}{2\pi}\int_0^{2\pi}(4 - 2)\,dt = 2 > 0$$

and the limit cycle $r = 1$ is unstable.

It is important to note that one is able to draw conclusions as to stability only when $h \neq 0$. Should h vanish the preceding argument based on the use of [27.6] is not applicable.

c. As an illustration, we shall consider two such cases: first, the system [22.11], second the harmonic case.

For the system [22.11] one finds

$$P_x(x_1, y_1) + Q_y(x_1, y_1) = 0$$

so that $h = 0$. It was noted previously that the limit cycle is half stable.

As regards the harmonic oscillator, whose non-dimensional equation is

$$\ddot{x} + x = 0$$

the corresponding first-order system is

$$\frac{dx}{dt} = y; \quad \frac{dy}{dt} = -x$$

It is observed that $P_x = Q_y \equiv 0$. The motion of a harmonic oscillator is neither stable nor unstable but rather *indifferent* in the sense that if a perturbation results in a new amplitude of motion this amplitude will be maintained without any tendency either to approach to, or to depart from, the motion with the old amplitude.

CHAPTER V

BIFURCATION THEORY (POINCARÉ)

28. INTRODUCTORY REMARKS

It has been shown in Section 13, 14, and 15 that, for certain critical or *bifurcation* values of a parameter in a differential equation, radical changes occur in the qualitative aspect of its trajectories. In this chapter we propose to go further into this subject by considering the important particular case in which a singularity undergoes a transition from stability to instability, or vice versa. There exists a number of more complicated cases in the theory of bifurcation such as bifurcation of limit cycles from separatrices, disintegration of a limit cycle into a number of cycles, and so on. We shall not go into the investigation of these complicated cases but will confine our attention to the above specified case. A preliminary qualitative investigation of the subject of this chapter has been made already at the end of Section 24 where the intuitive concepts of "sources" and "sinks" in the phase plane were applied; here we shall follow the analytical method of Poincaré.

In practice, the problems are very frequently simplified or "linearized" from the start so that some limited conclusions regarding stability may be reached. Unfortunately, such linearized equations do not give a full account of the observed phenomena. Thus under certain conditions the normal behavior of a dynamical system, e.g., an airplane, which is predictable on the basis of a "linearized" theory suddenly gives way to self-excited parasitic oscillations of large amplitudes, the "flutter" phenomenon, frequently causing destructive effects. One recognizes in these effects a typical case of the so-called "hard" self-excitation which has now been completely explained by means of the theory of bifurcation as applied to non-linear electronic circuits.

We are now entering the domain of non-linear mechanics proper, and the equations of the first approximations which we have been using in Chapter III in connection with the problem of the stability of equilibrium cease to be applicable. In other words, it is impossible to obtain the results of this chapter by linearizing the differential equations. The present topic leads to results of great practical interest in connection with the problem of self-excitation of dynamical systems in general. More specifically, all problems such as self-excitation of thermionic circuits or of electrodynamical systems, "flutter" of aircraft wings, and similar phenomena fall within the scope of this theory.

29. TRANSITION OF SINGULARITIES. BRANCH POINTS OF LIMIT CYCLES

Consider the general form of the dynamical equations and assume that the coefficients a, b, c, and d of the linear terms as well as the non-linear terms $P_2(x,y)$ and $Q_2(x,y)$ are now functions of a parameter λ. We assume further that the origin (0,0) is a focal point for all values of λ under consideration.

It was seen in Section 18 that, for a focal point, the roots of the characteristic equation are conjugate complex

$$S_1 = a_1(\lambda) + i\,b_1(\lambda)$$
$$S_2 = a_1(\lambda) - i\,b_1(\lambda)$$

[29.1]

By means of the transformations [18.16] and [18.15] the general dynamical system can be written as

$$\dot{x} = a_1(\lambda)x - b_1(\lambda)y + P_2(x,y,\lambda)$$
$$\dot{y} = b_1(\lambda)x + a_1(\lambda)y + Q_2(x,y,\lambda)$$

[29.2]

where P_2 and Q_2 are power series in x and y beginning at least with the terms of the second degree in x and y; compare with [20.9].

The focal point is stable or unstable according as $a_1 < 0$ or $a_1 > 0$, as was explained in Section 19. Multiplying the first Equation [29.2] by x, the second by y, adding the two equations, and transforming the resultant equations into polar coordinates, one obtains the equation

$$\frac{1}{2}\frac{d(r^2)}{dt} = a_1(\lambda)r^2 + P_2 r\cos\theta + Q_2 r\sin\theta$$

[29.3]

Multiplying the first Equation [29.2] by y, the second by x, and subtracting the former from the latter, one finds, similarly

$$\frac{d\theta}{dt} = \frac{1}{r^2}\left[b_1(\lambda)r^2 + Q_2 r\cos\theta - P_2 r\sin\theta\right]$$

[29.4]

Dividing Equation [29.3] by [29.4] one obtains the equation of the trajectories

$$\frac{dr}{d\theta} = r\left[\frac{a_1(\lambda)r + P_2\cos\theta + Q_2\sin\theta}{b_1(\lambda)r + Q_2\cos\theta - P_2\sin\theta}\right]$$

[29.5]

It is to be noted that for a sufficiently small r, and hence for small $|x|$ and $|y|$, the sign of $d\theta/dt$ is determined by that of $b_1(\lambda)$. Equation [29.5] reduces to the form

$$\frac{dr}{d\theta} = \left[\frac{a_1(\lambda)}{b_1(\lambda)}\,r + \frac{P_2\cos\theta + Q_2\sin\theta}{b_1(\lambda)}\right]\left[1 + \frac{P_2\sin\theta - Q_2\cos\theta}{b_1(\lambda)\,r} + \right.$$

$$\left. + \left(\frac{P_2\sin\theta - Q_2\cos\theta}{b_1(\lambda)\,r}\right)^2 + \cdots\right] \quad [29.6]$$

This expression can be written as a power series in r

$$\frac{dr}{d\theta} = R_1(\theta,\lambda)\,r + R_2(\theta,\lambda)\,r^2 + R_3(\theta,\lambda)\,r^3 + \cdots \quad [29.7]$$

where

$$R_1 = \frac{a_1(\lambda)}{b_1(\lambda)}$$

$$R_2 = \frac{a_1}{b_1^2}\left(\frac{P_2\sin\theta - Q_2\cos\theta}{r^2}\right) + \frac{P_2\cos\theta + Q_2\sin\theta}{b_1 r^2}$$

$$R_3 = \frac{a_1}{b_1^2}\left(\frac{P_2\sin\theta - Q_2\cos\theta}{r^3}\right) + \frac{a_1}{b_1^3}\left(\frac{P_2\sin\theta - Q_2\cos\theta}{r^2}\right)^2 + \quad [29.8]$$

$$+ \frac{P_2\cos\theta + Q_2\sin\theta}{b_1 r^3} + \frac{(P_2\cos\theta + Q_2\sin\theta)(P_2\sin\theta - Q_2\cos\theta)}{b_1^2 r^4}$$

$\ldots$

Since it is desirable to investigate the transition from stable focal points to the unstable ones, the branch BC of the circuit shown in Figure 18.1 must be followed; in this case $q \neq 0$. In fact, when passing from stable focal points to unstable ones the real part of the complex roots changes its sign but the imaginary part does not. In other words $b_1(\lambda)$ in Equations [29.2] does not change its sign for $\lambda_1 < \lambda < \lambda_2$ corresponding to the branch BC in Figure 18.1. The series [29.7] converges, therefore, for all values of λ in the interval (λ_1, λ_2) provided $r < \rho$, where ρ is a small fixed number not depending on either λ or θ. From [29.8] it is observed that $R_1(\theta,\lambda) = a_1(\lambda)/b_1(\lambda)$ does not depend on θ whereas all other coefficients $R_k(\theta,\lambda)$ are periodic functions of θ. The function $r = f(\theta, r_0, \lambda)$ can be developed in a power series in terms of r_0 converging for all values of θ, for $\lambda_1 < \lambda < \lambda_2$, and for $r_0 < \rho$. Thus

$$r = f(\theta, r_0, \lambda) = r_0 u_1(\theta,\lambda) + r_0^2 u_2(\theta,\lambda) + r_0^3 u_3(\theta,\lambda) + \cdots \quad [29.9]$$

Substituting this solution into [29.7] one obtains the following set of recurrent differential equations determining the functions $u_k(\theta, \lambda)$

$$\frac{du_1}{d\theta} = u_1 R_1(\theta, \lambda)$$

$$\frac{du_2}{d\theta} = u_2 R_1(\theta, \lambda) + u_1^2 R_2(\theta, \lambda)$$

[29.10]

$$\frac{du_3}{d\theta} = u_3 R_1(\theta, \lambda) + 2u_1 u_2 R_2(\theta, \lambda) + u_1^3 R_3(\theta, \lambda)$$

. . .

Since by assumption $r_0 = f(0, r_0, \lambda)$ one finds from Equation [29.9]

$$u_1(0, \lambda) = 1; \quad u_k(0, \lambda) = 0$$

[29.11]

for $k = 2, 3, \cdots$. These initial conditions, in conjunction with Equations [29.10] determine the functions $u_k(\theta, \lambda)$. The first equation gives

$$\frac{du_1}{u_1} = \frac{a_1(\lambda)}{b_1(\lambda)} d\theta$$

and, on integrating,

$$u_1(\theta, \lambda) = e^{\frac{a_1(\lambda)}{b_1(\lambda)} \theta}$$

[29.12]

Let r_0 be a small positive number. Since the sign of $d\theta/dt$ does not change for small values of r, it is apparent that the trajectory originating at the point $(r = r_0, \theta = 0)$ is a limit cycle if, and only if

$$\psi(r_0, \lambda) = 0$$

[29.13]

where

$$\psi(r_0, \lambda) \equiv f(2\pi, r_0, \lambda) - f(0, r_0, \lambda) = f(2\pi, r_0, \lambda) - r_0$$

In this expression r_0 designates the radius vector of the limit cycle in the neighborhood of the r-axis. We may use the general expression $\psi(r, \lambda)$ to designate the same function in which r is not necessarily r_0. We have

$$\psi(r_0, \lambda) = \alpha_1(\lambda) r_0 + \alpha_2(\lambda) r_0^2 + \alpha_3(\lambda) r_0^3 + \cdots$$

[29.14]

where

$$\alpha_1(\lambda) = u_1(2\pi, \lambda) - 1 = e^{\frac{a_1(\lambda)}{b_1(\lambda)} 2\pi} - 1$$

[29.15]

$$\alpha_k(\lambda) = u_k(2\pi, \lambda), \quad k = 2, 3, \cdots$$

We now consider a fixed value λ_0 of the parameter λ and distinguish two cases:

1. $a_1(\lambda_0) \neq 0$. This means that the stability conditions of the focal point do not change when λ passes through the value λ_0. By the first Equation [29.15] we have $\alpha_1(\lambda_0) \neq 0$ so that the coefficient of r_0 in the expansion [29.14] does not vanish for $\lambda = \lambda_0$. Hence, aside from the "trivial" solution $r_0 = 0$, Equation [29.14] has no real solution in r_0 and λ when r_0 and $|\lambda - \lambda_0|$ are sufficiently small. This means that a sufficiently small neighborhood of the singular point remains free of limit cycles when λ varies in a small interval around λ_0.

2. $a_1(\lambda_0) = 0$. By [29.15] this implies that $\alpha_1(\lambda_0) = 0$. Furthermore it can be shown that $\alpha_2(\lambda_0)$ is also equal to zero. The proof of this statement is omitted here. Let us now assume that

    a. $a_1'(\lambda_0) \neq 0$;

    b. $\alpha_3(\lambda_0) \neq 0$

where $a_1'(\lambda_0)$ designates the value of the derivative $da_1(\lambda)/d\lambda$ at the point $\lambda = \lambda_0$. Thus the singularity changes from a stable focal point to an unstable one or vice versa. We will show now that, at the point $\lambda = \lambda_0$ at which the stability of the singular point changes, there appears a limit cycle or cycles. Everything occurs as if the phenomenon were developing according to the following scheme:

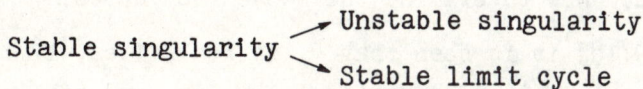

$$\text{Stable singularity} \left\langle \begin{array}{l} \nearrow \text{Unstable singularity} \\ \searrow \text{Stable limit cycle} \end{array} \right.$$

from which Poincaré's term "bifurcation" appears justified in usage.

In order to show this we can best proceed geometrically considering the (r_0, λ)-plane. It is clear that in Case 1 the variation of the parameter λ does not have any effect on r_0 since it remains identically equal to zero. In Case 2, however, the situation is different inasmuch as the curve $\psi(r_0, \lambda) = 0$ in the neighborhood of the point $r_0 = 0$; $\lambda = \lambda_0$ consists now of two branches: a straight line $r_0 = 0$ and the curve

$$\phi(r_0, \lambda) = \alpha_1(\lambda) + \alpha_2(\lambda) r_0 + \alpha_3(\lambda) r_0^2 + \cdots = 0 \qquad [29.16]$$

Expanding the functions $\alpha_1(\lambda)$ and $\alpha_2(\lambda)$ in Taylor's series in the neighborhood of $\lambda = \lambda_0$ we obtain:

$$\phi(r_0, \lambda) = (\lambda - \lambda_0)\alpha_1'(\lambda_0) + (\lambda - \lambda_0)\alpha_2'(\lambda_0) r_0 + \alpha_3(\lambda_0) r_0^2 + \cdots \qquad [29.17]$$

where $\alpha_1'(\lambda_0)$ and $\alpha_2'(\lambda_0)$ designate the values of $d\alpha_1(\lambda)/d\lambda$ and $d\alpha_2(\lambda)/d\lambda$ for $\lambda = \lambda_0$. Since $a_1(\lambda_0) \neq 0$ it follows that $\alpha_1'(\lambda_0) \neq 0$. If one now assumes that the first and the third terms on the right side of [29.17] are of the first order, the second term is of the order 3/2 and can be neglected. Equation [29.17] then becomes

$$(\lambda - \lambda_0)\alpha_1'(\lambda_0) + \alpha_3 r_0^2 = 0$$

whence

$$r_0^2 = - C\,\frac{\lambda - \lambda_0}{\alpha_3} \qquad\qquad [29.18]$$

where

$$C = \alpha_1'(\lambda_0) = \frac{a_1'(\lambda_0)}{b(\lambda_0)}\,2\pi \neq 0$$

Equation [29.18] shows that $(\lambda - \lambda_0)$ must have a sign opposite to that of C/α_3 since r_0 is to be real.

We can now distinguish four typical cases: 1. $c > 0$, $\alpha_3 > 0$; 2. $c > 0$, $\alpha_3 < 0$; 3. $c < 0$, $\alpha_3 > 0$; and 4. $c < 0$, $\alpha_3 < 0$.

It is to be noted first that $c = \alpha_1'(\lambda_0) > 0$ means that for the increasing values of the parameter λ the real parts of the characteristic roots change from negative to positive for $\lambda \gtreqless \lambda_0$. Hence, the focal point ($\lambda \lesseqgtr \lambda_0$) originally stable becomes unstable for $\lambda \gtreqless \lambda_0$. For $c < 0$ the focal point ($\lambda \lesseqgtr \lambda_0$) originally unstable becomes stable for $\lambda \gtreqless \lambda_0$.

We proceed now to examine the above four cases.

1.   From [29.18] it is seen that r_0 is real, i.e., limit cycles may exist, only for $\lambda - \lambda_0 < 0$. The region $\lambda > \lambda_0$ is free of limit cycles; see Figure 29.1a. In the region $\lambda - \lambda_0 < 0$, in which limit cycles exist, the focal points are stable. Hence, the limit cycles in that region are necessarily unstable as follows from the topological considerations of Section 24.

2.   Equation [29.18] shows that the limit cycles exist only for $\lambda \gtreqless \lambda_0$ and the region $\lambda - \lambda_0 \lesseqgtr 0$ is free of limit cycles; see Figure 29.1b. This represents the commonly encountered case of a soft self-excitation when, for a gradually increasing value of the parameter λ, the self-excitation sets in for $\lambda \gtreqless \lambda_0$. The limit cycles in this case are manifestly stable since the singularity is unstable.

3.   By a similar argument one finds that the limit cycles exist for $\lambda \gtreqless \lambda_0$; see Figure 29.1c. They are unstable since the singularity is stable in that region.

4.   In this case the limit cycles exist only for $\lambda \lesseqgtr \lambda_0$ and are stable; see Figure 29.1d.

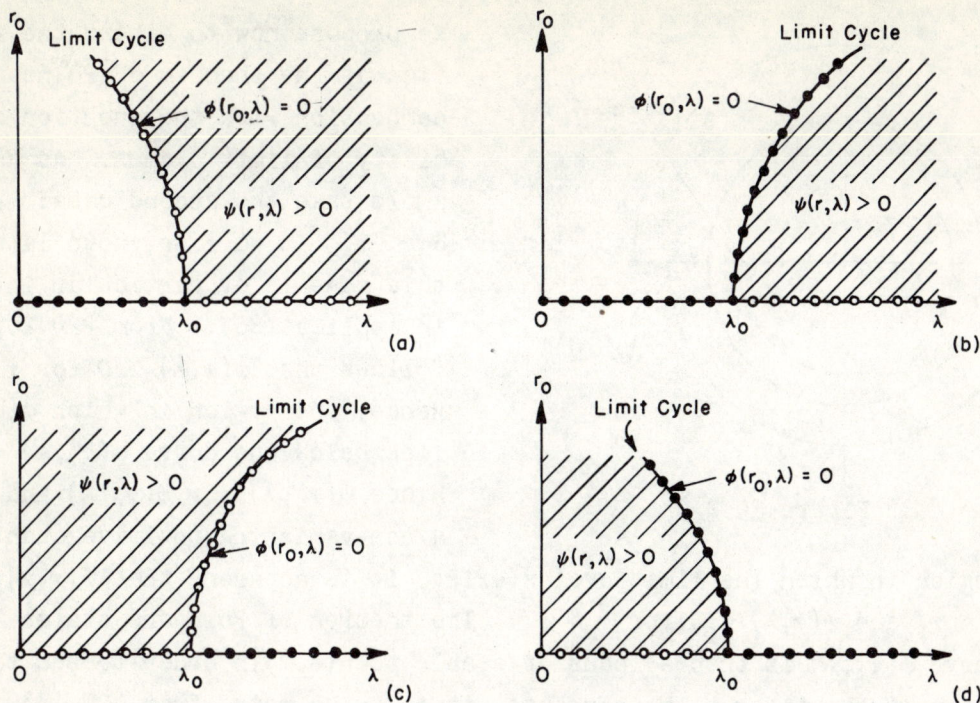

Figure 29.1

The question of stability of limit cycles can be ascertained also by means of the theorem of Poincaré given in Section 13. Although the application of that theorem was made in Section 13 in connection with the question of the stability of equilibrium it can be also applied in this case as will be shown.

It is apparent that the curves of Figure 29.1 represent Equation [29.17]. In the neighborhood of $(\lambda = \lambda_0,\ r = r_0)$ we can write

$$\phi(r,\lambda) = (\lambda - \lambda_0)\,\alpha_1'(\lambda_0) + (\lambda - \lambda_0)\,\alpha_2'(\lambda_0)\,r + \alpha_3(\lambda_0)\,r^2 + \cdots$$

Subtracting $\phi(r_0,\lambda)$ as given by [29.17] from $\phi(r,\lambda)$ we have

$$\phi(r,\lambda) - \phi(r_0,\lambda) = \phi(r,\lambda)$$

or

$$\phi(r,\lambda) = (\lambda - \lambda_0)\,\alpha_2'(\lambda_0)(r - r_0) + \alpha_3(\lambda_0)(r^2 - r_0^2) \qquad [29.19]$$

Recalling that r_0^2 and $(\lambda - \lambda_0)$ were assumed to be of the first order, it follows that, in the neighborhood of r_0, $r^2 - r_0^2$ will be of the same order as $\lambda - \lambda_0$ and, hence, the first term in the above expansion will be of the order 3/2. Neglecting this term and also terms of higher order we obtain:

$$\phi(r,\lambda_0) = \alpha_3(\lambda_0)(r^2 - r_0^2) \qquad [29.20]$$

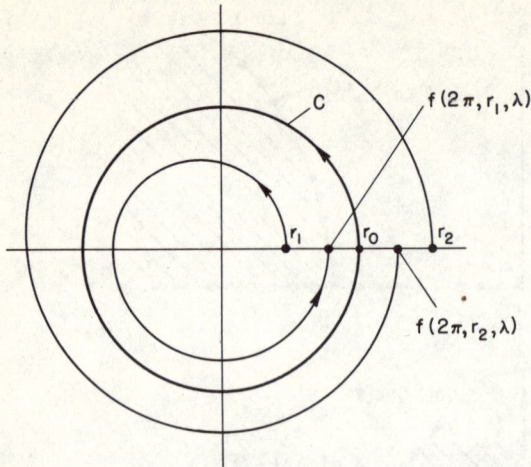

Figure 29.2

We propose now to extend the application of the theorem of Poincaré in connection with the question of stability of limit cycles. As an example take the second case: $c > 0$; $\alpha_3 < 0$. It will be shown later that this case is of particular interest in applications. From [29.20] it follows that $\phi(r,\lambda) > 0$ for $r < r_0$. Hence, the region in which $\phi(r,\lambda) > 0$ lies below the curve $\phi(r_0,\lambda) = 0$. Since $\psi(r_0,\lambda) = r_0\phi(r_0,\lambda)$ and r_0 is a non-vanishing positive quantity in the region in which the limit cycles exist, it is apparent that $\psi(r,\lambda) > 0$ for $r < r_0$ and $\psi(r,\lambda) < 0$ for $r > r_0$. The theorem of Poincaré states that the curve $\phi(r_0,\lambda)$ is then a locus of stable points. In order to see the application of the theorem in this case, it is to be noted from [29.13] that, in general, for $r \neq r_0$, $\psi(r,\lambda) = f(2\pi,r,\lambda) - r$, where r is the initial value of the radius vector and $f(2\pi,r,\lambda)$ is the value of the radius vector after one complete rotation, $\theta = 2\pi$, of the representative point on the spiral trajectory. Figure 29.2 illustrates this situation for two values of r, i.e., $r_1 < r_0$ and $r_2 > r_0$.

For $r = r_0$ the trajectory is closed, that is, a limit cycle. Since for $r_1 < r_0$, $\psi(r_1,\lambda) > 0$, it follows that $f(2\pi,r_1,\lambda) > r_1$, that is, the spiral issuing from the point r_1 after one turn approaches the limit cycle C as shown. For $r_2 > r_0$, $\psi(r_2,\lambda) < 0$, that is, $f(2\pi,r_2,\lambda) < r_2$, which means that the spiral trajectory issuing from a point r_2, external with respect to the limit cycle, approaches it after one turn. This characterizes a stable limit cycle.

It is worth mentioning once more that the existence of limit cycles ascertained by the more detailed study made in this section was possible only by considering the non-linear terms. The equations of the first approximations which were sufficient for analyzing the conditions of the equilibrium of the system are incapable of giving any information concerning the existence of limit cycles, whose determination depends on the curvature of the characteristics inasmuch as the coefficient $\alpha_3(\lambda)$ is related to the curvature as can be easily ascertained.

30. SELF-EXCITATION OF THERMIONIC GENERATORS

Although this subject has been considered to some extent at the end of the preceding section, we propose to investigate it in more detail by introducing certain analytical approximations for the characteristics of the non-linear conductor, the electron tube.

Consider the circuit shown in Figure 30.1 representing a commonly used type of thermionic generator with an inductive grid coupling. The differential equation of the circuit is

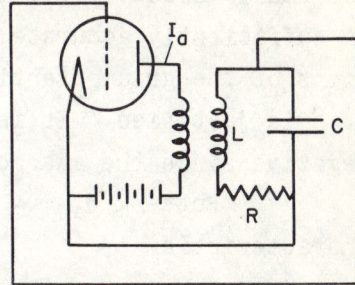

Figure 30.1

$$L \frac{di}{dt} + Ri + \frac{1}{C} \int_0^t i \, dt = \lambda \frac{dI_a}{dt} \qquad [30.1]$$

in the usual notation; the coefficient λ of mutual inductance between the anode and grid circuits will be the parameter of the preceding theory. I_a is the anode current.

Let us assume the following expression for I_a considered as a function of the grid voltage V_g

$$I_a = I_o + S_1 V_g + S_2 V_g^2 + S_3 V_g^3 + \cdots \qquad [30.2]$$

where S_1, S_2, S_3, $\cdots$ are certain numerical coefficients determined so as to fit the function $I_a = f(V_g)$ to the experimental curve. For the alternating performance of the circuit the term I_o is clearly of no interest and can be dropped since it amounts to a shift of the origin of coordinates to this point. If the characteristic were perfectly symmetrical with respect to the origin, only the odd powers would be present. In order to take into account a slight asymmetry we shall retain the term $S_2 V_g^2$ and shall limit the power series to the cubic term. The latter, as will be shown, is essential for what follows. Under these assumptions

$$I_a = S_1 V_g + S_2 V_g^2 + S_3 V_g^3 \qquad [30.3]$$

This expression for the anode current is inconvenient, however, since the coefficients S_1, S_2, $\cdots$ have different physical dimensions. In order to avoid this it is convenient to introduce a dimensionless variable $v = V_g/V_s$ where V_s is the grid voltage beyond which the anode current I_a does not change appreciably so that in an idealized case we can assume that it does not change. Putting $S_1 = \beta_1$, $S_2 V_s = \gamma_1$, and $S_3 V_s^2 = \delta_1'$ where β_1, γ_1, δ_1' have now the dimension of the "transconductance," [30.3] becomes

$$I_a = V_s(\beta_1 v + \gamma_1 v^2 + \delta_1' v^3) \qquad [30.4]$$

From the experimental curves of electron tubes it is observed that, for small values of V_g, and hence of v, the approximation $I_a = V_s(\beta_1 v + \gamma_1 v^2)$ is sufficiently accurate. During the process of self-excitation the oscillations of the grid potential V_g may be considerable so that the third term $\delta_1' v^3$ is justified. It is also noted that the coefficient δ_1' is generally negative since the characteristic exhibits an inflection point.

Putting $\delta_1 = -\delta_1'$ we obtain the following expression for the characteristic

$$I_a = V_s(\beta_1 v + \gamma_1 v^2 - \delta_1 v^3) \qquad [30.5]$$

in which β_1, γ_1, and δ_1 are positive. Introducing the "dimensionless voltage" $v = V_g/V_s$ in the other terms one gets

$$v = \frac{1}{CV_s}\int i\,dt; \quad \dot{v} = \frac{i}{CV_s}; \quad \ddot{v} = \frac{1}{CV_s}\frac{di}{dt} \qquad [30.6]$$

Differentiating Equation [30.5] one obtains

$$\frac{dI_a}{dt} = \frac{dI_a}{dv}\frac{dv}{dt} = V_s(\beta_1 + 2\gamma_1 v - 3\delta_1 v^2)\dot{v} \qquad [30.7]$$

Substituting this value into [30.1] we get

$$LC\ddot{v} + \left[RC - \lambda(\beta_1 + 2\gamma_1 v - 3\delta_1 v^2)\right]\dot{v} + v = 0 \qquad [30.8]$$

A further simplification is obtained by introducing a "dimensionless" or "cyclic" time $\tau = \omega_0 t$ where $\omega_0 = \sqrt{1/LC}$. This gives

$$\dot{v} = \frac{dv}{dt} = \frac{dv}{d\tau}\frac{d\tau}{dt} = \frac{dv}{d\tau}\omega_0$$

and similarly

$$\ddot{v} = \frac{d^2v}{dt^2} = \frac{d^2v}{d\tau^2}\omega_0^2$$

The differential Equation [30.1] reduces then to the following dimensionless form

$$\frac{d^2v}{d\tau^2} + v = \left[\beta(\lambda) + 2\gamma(\lambda)v - 3\delta(\lambda)v^2\right]\frac{dv}{d\tau} \qquad [30.9]$$

where

$$\beta(\lambda) = (\lambda\beta_1 - RC)\omega_0; \quad \gamma(\lambda) = \lambda\gamma_1\omega_0; \quad \delta(\lambda) = \lambda\delta_1\omega_0 \qquad [30.10]$$

Equation [30.9] is of the Van der Pol type. We know that the self-excited oscillations are possible.

The equivalent system of the first order is

$$\frac{dv}{d\tau} = w$$

$$\frac{dw}{d\tau} = -v + \left[\beta(\lambda) + 2\gamma(\lambda)v - 3\delta(\lambda)v^2\right]w \qquad [30.11]$$

The equations of the first approximation are

$$\frac{dv}{d\tau} = w$$

$$\frac{dw}{d\tau} = -v + \beta w \qquad [30.12]$$

The point $v = w = 0$ is a singular point. The roots of the characteristic equation are

$$S_{1,2} = \frac{\beta}{2} \pm \sqrt{\frac{\beta^2}{4} - 1}$$

Experimental evidence shows that in a great majority of cases the self-excited oscillations start in an oscillatory manner like the trajectories departing from an unstable focal point. There are cases of the so-called relaxation oscillation which will be studied in Part IV, in which the starting of oscillations occurs in the manner of trajectories departing from an unstable nodal point but we shall not treat this case here as the theory of these oscillations has not yet been established for the steady state.

For the oscillations developing from an unstable focal point (Section 8) the roots

$$S_{1,2} = \frac{\beta}{2} \pm \sqrt{\frac{\beta^2}{4} - 1}$$

of the characteristic equation corresponding to the equations of the first approximation [30.12] must be conjugate complex with a positive real part. This implies that $0 < \beta < 2$. Substituting for β its expression [30.10] we obtain the condition

$$\frac{RC}{\beta_1} < \lambda < \frac{RC}{\beta_1} + \frac{2}{\omega_0 \beta_1}$$

The critical value of the parameter is given by the equation

$$\beta = (\lambda_0 \beta_1 - RC)\omega_0 = 0$$

that is

$$\lambda_0 = \frac{RC}{\beta_1} \qquad\qquad [30.13]$$

In order to be able to ascertain the appearance of a stable limit cycle for $\lambda \geqq \lambda_0$ we have to investigate the non-linear Equations [30.11]. Making use of the transformations [18.14] and [18.16] we introduce the new variables x and y by the equations

$$v = 2a_1x + 2b_1y; \quad w = 2x$$

with $a_1(\lambda) = \beta(\lambda)/2$ and $b_1(\lambda) = \sqrt{1 - \beta^2/4}$ and obtain the system

$$\dot{x} = a_1x - b_1y + \left[4\gamma(a_1x + b_1y) - 12\delta(a_1x + b_1y)^2\right]x$$

$$[30.14]$$

$$\dot{y} = b_1x + a_1y - \frac{a_1}{b_1}\left[4\gamma(a_1x + b_1y) - 12\delta(a_1x + b_1y)^2\right]x$$

It is noted that the derivative with respect to λ of the real part of the roots $S_{1,2}$ for $\lambda = \lambda_0$ is positive; thus $a_1'(\lambda_0) > 0$. Hence if we show that $\alpha_3(\lambda_0) < 0$ we shall be dealing with Case 2 of Section 29. For $\lambda = \lambda_0$, $\beta(\lambda_0) = 0$ and hence $a_1(\lambda_0) = 0$; $b_1(\lambda_0) = 1$. Comparing [30.14] with [29.2], making use of polar coordinates and relations [29.8] we find that

$$R_1(\theta, \lambda_0) = 0$$

$$R_2(\theta, \lambda_0) = 4\gamma(\lambda_0)\sin\theta\cos^2\theta \qquad\qquad [30.15]$$

$$R_3(\theta, \lambda_0) = 16\gamma(\lambda_0)\sin^3\theta\cos^3\theta - 12\delta(\lambda_0)\sin^2\theta\cos^2\theta$$

The recurrent system [29.10] of differential equations for $\lambda = \lambda_0$ has the following form

$$\frac{du_1}{d\theta} = 0$$

$$\frac{du_2}{d\theta} = 4\gamma(\lambda_0)\sin\theta\cos^2\theta \qquad\qquad [30.16]$$

$$\frac{du_3}{d\theta} = 2u_2R_2(\theta, \lambda_0) + R_3(\theta, \lambda_0)$$

Hence, upon integrating Equations [30.16], we obtain

$$u_1(\theta, \lambda_0) = 1$$

$$u_2(\theta, \lambda_0) = \frac{4}{3}\gamma(\lambda_0)(1 - \cos^3\theta)$$

$$u_3 = -3\delta(\lambda_0)\pi$$

Making use of [30.10] we get $\alpha_3(\lambda_0) = -3\pi RC\omega_0\left(\frac{\delta_1}{\beta_1}\right) < 0$. Thus, by Case 2 of the preceding section, it follows that there is a stable limit cycle. This, in conjunction with the instability of the focal point for $\lambda \geq \lambda_0$, creates the favorable conditions for self-excitation.

Summing up the conclusions of this and of the preceding sections, it can be stated that the existence as well as the nature of limit cycles depends on the *curvature* of the non-linear characteristic of the system, whereas the condition of stability depends on its *slope at the point of equilibrium*. For this reason it was necessary to retain a cubic term in the series expansion of the plate current characteristic, Equation [30.5], in investigating limit cycles, whereas for problems of equilibrium the equations of the first approximation, containing only the first powers of the dynamical variables, were sufficient.

We have considered in this section only the case of a *soft* self-excitation of the circuit which corresponds to a non-linear characteristic capable of being approximated by a polynomial of the third degree, Equation [30.5]. An entirely different kind of self-excitation occurs when the non-linear characteristic is expressible by polynomials of a still higher degree. Self-excitation in such cases is called *hard*. We shall not enter into this subject here but will reserve it to a later chapter after we get acquainted with the analytical method of Poincaré (Part II).

31. SELF-EXCITATION OF MECHANICAL AND ELECTROMECHANICAL SYSTEMS

Mechanical systems, also, offer numerous examples of self-excited non-linear oscillations, but their study is less advanced at present than that of electrical systems. Two main reasons account for this situation. First, the self-excited mechanical oscillations in practice are always undesirable or parasitic phenomena of a "closed cycle" type (Section 23) and the main endeavor so far has been to eliminate them by breaking the closed cycle somehow, rather than to attempt to study them. Secondly, the determination of the parameters of a mechanical system is generally a more difficult problem than that of electric circuits. It is possible only in a few particularly simple cases in which the chain of "causes" and "effects" can be followed completely. The following two examples of self-excited mechanical oscillations may be mentioned.

A. SELF-EXCITED OSCILLATIONS OF A MECHANICAL CONTROL SYSTEM

Consider the following arrangement used for the study of anti-rolling stabilization of ships by the method of activated tanks (25). Two tanks are mounted on a pendulum and located symmetrically with respect to the axis of oscillation; the tanks are connected by a U-tube and filled with water. An impeller pump having a variable blade angle α is capable of displacing the water in the system so formed; the blade angle α is controlled in response to the angular motion of the pendulum as will be specified.

The system has thus two degrees of freedom, the angle θ of the pendulum and the relative angle ϕ of the water level in the tanks. In the phenomenon of non-linear oscillations analyzed below, the motion of the pendulum is exceedingly small, a fraction of one degree, and its *direct* action, that is, by direct mechanical couplings, on the motion of water in the tanks is negligible. There exists, however, an important action which is exerted through the blades actuated by the control system.

If there is no control and the pendulum is fixed, the motion of water in the system for small oscillations can be approximated by a linear equation

$$J\ddot{\phi} + b\dot{\phi} + c\phi = 0$$

where J, b, and c are constants the physical significance of which is obvious. Assume now that the pump is made to act on the liquid column in the U-tube and let the moment of the force exerted on the water by the pump be $M(\alpha)$, a function of the blade angle α. Experiment shows that this couple increases initially more or less in proportion to α and exhibits for larger angles α a "saturation" feature due to complicated hydrodynamical effects. One can approximate, therefore $M(\alpha) = M_1\alpha - M_3\alpha^3$. The arrangement of control used in this case is such that the blade angle is continuously adjusted to be proportional to the rate of flow, i.e., to $\dot{\phi}$.* The expression for the external moment is then of the form $a_1\dot{\phi} - a_3\dot{\phi}^3$.

The theory of this control is based on the linear approximation. It is found that with a control of this kind, at least within a certain range, the free oscillation of the pendulum is damped and the forced oscillation is reduced in accordance with the linear theory; these features, are, however, of no interest here. Aside from this useful effect, predictable on the basis of a linearized equation, the following parasitic effect is observed. Under certain conditions the pendulum, the water in the tanks, and the blade angle begin to oscillate or "flutter" spontaneously; the oscillation of the pendulum is, however, very small and will be neglected. The oscillation of the

---

* The blade angle in this particular case is made proportional to the angular acceleration of the pendulum. The latter, however, is in phase with the rate of flow through the tube. A complete study of the problem requires a consideration of the system with two degrees of freedom θ, ϕ comprising the pendulum and the water ballast. Insofar as this study is limited only to the motion of the latter, this complete study is omitted here. Account is taken only of its final conclusion, namely, the blade angle is proportional to the rate of flow in the U-tube.

blades, and also of the water, designated usually as "hunting" persists in-definitely and may acquire considerable amplitudes. The explanation of this phenomenon follows from the preceding theory.

The differential equation with the blades under control, as speci-fied, is

$$J\ddot{\phi} + b\dot{\phi} + c\phi = a_1\dot{\phi} - a_3\dot{\phi}^3$$

that is

$$J\ddot{\phi} + (b - a_1)\dot{\phi} + a_3\dot{\phi}^3 + c\phi = 0 \qquad [31.1]$$

We shall consider two cases according as $b - a_1 \gtrless 0$. It is to be noted that the coefficients a_1 and a_3 of the hydrodynamical couple depend on the amplification λ used in the thermionic circuit, so that we can consider them as functions $a_1(\lambda)$ and $a_3(\lambda)$ increasing monotonically with λ. Hence, for a small amplification λ, we have $b - a_1(\lambda) < 0$ and for a larger amplifi-cation $b - a_1(\lambda) > 0$.

Case 1. Weak Amplification

Dividing by J and putting $[b - a_1(\lambda)]/J = n' > 0$, $a_3/J = p'$, and $c/J = \omega^2$ we have

$$\ddot{\phi} + n'\dot{\phi} + p'\dot{\phi}^3 + \omega^2\phi = 0 \qquad [31.2]$$

By a change of the independent variable $\tau = \omega t$ we obtain the dimensionless form

$$\frac{d^2\phi}{d\tau^2} + \left[n + p\left(\frac{d\phi}{d\tau}\right)^2\right]\frac{d\phi}{d\tau} + \phi = 0 \qquad [31.3]$$

where $n = n'/\omega$ and $p = p'\omega$. Forming the equations of the first approximation, the characteristic equation is $S^2 + nS + 1 = 0$ and its roots are

$$S_{1,2} = -\frac{n}{2} \pm \sqrt{\frac{n^2}{4} - 1} \qquad [31.4]$$

Hence for $n^2/4 > 1$ the origin, $\phi = d\phi/d\tau = 0$, is a stable nodal point and for $n^2/4 < 1$ the origin, $\phi = d\phi/d\tau = 0$, is a stable focal point.

Case 2. Strong Amplification

In this case $b - a_1(\lambda) < 0$. Proceeding as previously and putting $[a_1(\mu) - b]/J = n' > 0$, $a_3/J = p'$, and $c/J = \omega^2$ we obtain

$$\frac{d^2\phi}{d\tau^2} - \left[n - p\left(\frac{d\phi}{d\tau}\right)^2\right]\frac{d\phi}{d\tau} + \phi = 0 \qquad [31.5]$$

where $n = n'/\omega$ and $p = p'\omega$. The roots of the characteristic equation in this case are

$$S_{1,2} = \frac{n}{2} \pm \sqrt{\frac{n^2}{4} - 1} \qquad [31.6]$$

Hence for $n^2/4 > 1$ the origin is an unstable nodal point, and for $n^2/4 < 1$ the origin is an unstable focal point. In the first case the control equipment functions without any parasitic oscillations. In the second case, since the singularities are unstable the trajectories approach a stable limit cycle and this characterizes a steady state of parasitic oscillations or "hunting" which is observed in such systems if the amplification is too high. Moreover, this condition generally sets in abruptly at a certain *critical* value λ_1 of the amplification factor for which $b - a_1(\lambda_1) = 0$.

The condition $n^2/4 \gtreqless 1$ is equivalent to $(b - a_1)^2/4J^2\omega^2 \gtreqless 1$. It is the same both for stable and unstable operations of the control system. The stability or instability of the system is governed by the sign of $b - a_1(\lambda)$ as previously set forth.

The condition $a_1 > b$ also has simple meaning; in fact, a_1 is the measure of the energy input on the part of the pump and b characterizes the dissipation of energy in the system. This inequality means that initially the input of energy is greater than its dissipation so that self-excitation can occur with a gradually increasing amplitude of oscillation. The critical value of the parameter is given by the equation $a_1(\lambda_1) = b$. In this particular case there are two parameters: ω_1, the speed of the pump, and ν, the amplification factor of the thermionic control system. By increasing either one, the steepness of the characteristic is increased, and hence also a_1, so that for a certain value $\lambda = \lambda_0$ the critical point is reached and the oscillation stabilizes itself on a limit cycle. Beyond this point, for $\lambda > \lambda_0$, the amplitude of the limit cycles increases monotonically with λ. We have, thus, a typical case of "soft" self-excitation; see Figure 24.6. If the characteristic has an inflection point, in addition to one for $\alpha = 0$, it can be approximated by a polynomial $M(\alpha) = M_1\alpha + M_3\alpha^3 - M_5\alpha^5$ where M_1, M_3, $M_5 > 0$. In such a case the self-excitation would appear in an entirely different manner, as will be explained in Part II.

Experiments corroborate these theoretical conclusions, at least qualitatively.

B. SELF-EXCITED OSCILLATIONS IN AN ELECTROMECHANICAL SYSTEM

Another example of the same kind is the well-known experiment (26) in which a series generator is connected to a separately excited motor.

Approximating the voltage of the series generator by a polynomial of the form $E = a_1 i - a_3 i^3$, where i is the current, and expressing the condition of dynamical equilibrium of electromotive forces in the circuit, we find

$$a_1 i - a_3 i^3 = K\omega + L\frac{di}{dt} + Ri \qquad [31.7]$$

By differentiating this equation we find

$$L\frac{d^2 i}{dt^2} - (a_1 - R - 3a_3 i^2)\frac{di}{dt} + K\frac{d\omega}{dt} = 0 \qquad [31.8]$$

The quantity $d\omega/dt$ can be eliminated from the equation by expressing that the electrical power $K\omega i$ absorbed by the motor serves to accelerate the rotor

$$K\omega i = \frac{d}{dt}\left(\frac{1}{2} J\omega^2\right) = J\omega\frac{d\omega}{dt} \qquad [31.9]$$

where J is the moment of inertia of the rotor; whence $d\omega/dt = Ki/J$. Substituting this value of $d\omega/dt$ into [31.8] one obtains the equation

$$\frac{d^2 i}{dt^2} - (m - n i^2)\frac{di}{dt} + pi = 0 \qquad [31.10]$$

where $m = (a_1 - R)/L$, $n = 3a_3/L$, $p = K^2/LJ > 0$. This equation is of Van der Pol's type. Equation [31.10] is equivalent to the system

$$\frac{di}{dt} = y; \quad \dot{y} - (m - n i^2)y + pi = 0 \qquad [31.11]$$

The equations of the first approximations are

$$\frac{di}{dt} = y; \quad \frac{dy}{dt} = -pi + my \qquad [31.12]$$

The characteristic equation is $S^2 - mS + p = 0$ and its roots are

$$S_{1,2} = \frac{m}{2} \pm \sqrt{\frac{m^2}{4} - p}$$

The singularity is a nodal point if $m^2/4 - p > 0$ and is a focal point if $m^2/4 - p < 0$. This singularity is unstable if $m = (a_1 - R)/L > 0$, that is $a_1 > R$, and stable for $a_1 < R$. For a sustained self-excited oscillation the singularity must be an unstable focal point, whence the conditions

$$a_1 > R; \quad \left(\frac{a_1 - R}{2L}\right)^2 - \frac{K^2}{LJ} < 0 \qquad [31.13]$$

The first condition is a static criterion which has been analyzed in the preceding example. The second criterion is dynamical; it is generally fulfilled for not too great a moment of inertia J of the motor. The critical value of the parameter occurs for $a_1 = R$. In practice one can select either R or a_1 as the parameter λ of the general theory. In the latter case it is convenient to introduce an auxiliary saturation winding on the series generator field which modifies the state of saturation in the machine and, hence, the coefficients a_1 and a_3 of the non-linear element of the system.

One can go a step further and determine the amplitude of the self-excited oscillation but for this purpose we shall need the analytical method of Poincaré outlined in Part II. The remaining conclusions are the same as in the preceding example.

CHAPTER VI

GEOMETRICAL ANALYSIS OF EXISTENCE OF PERIODIC SOLUTIONS

32. INTRODUCTORY REMARKS

In the preceding chapter we have investigated the principal properties of limit cycles which characterized periodic motion in non-linear and non-conservative systems. We shall now be concerned with the question of the *existence* of such motions, a rather difficult question for which the relatively simple criteria of Poincaré and Bendixson give only limited information. In Part II we shall enter into this question in more detail in connection with the analytical methods of Poincaré and Liapounoff. In this chapter we shall investigate the results obtained by Liénard (27) by studying the trajectories in a special phase plane. Further progress in this direction was made recently by N. Levinson and O.K. Smith (22).

These methods occupy an intermediate position between the topological and analytical methods and thus present particular interest as a connecting link between them. The principal aim of these geometrical methods is to formulate conditions under which trajectories become closed, i.e., when they represent periodic solutions.

The starting point is the original equation of Van der Pol

$$\ddot{x} - \mu(1 - x^2)\dot{x} + x = 0 \qquad [32.1]$$

generalized by Liénard and the Cartans (28) to

$$\ddot{x} + f(x)\dot{x} + x = 0 \qquad [32.2]$$

and by N. Levinson and O.K. Smith to

$$\ddot{x} + f(x,\dot{x})\dot{x} + g(x) = 0 \qquad [32.3]$$

The functions f and g entering into these equations are subject to certain restrictions which will be specified later.

It may be worth mentioning that the original proof of the existence of periodic solutions for [32.1] by Van der Pol rested upon the graphical method of isoclines, see Section 7. Before proceeding with the geometrical analysis of the more general Equations [32.2] and [32.3] it is useful to consider the original Van der Pol Equation [32.1] from the physical standpoint.

It is apparent that [32.1] may be considered dynamically as an autonomous oscillatory system with one degree of freedom possessing a variable damping - $\mu(1 - x^2)\dot{x}$. For small deviations x the system has a negative damping, for larger x the damping becomes positive. In the light of what has been said regarding "negative damping" one concludes that for small values of

x the system *absorbs* energy from an outside source so that in the early stages the motion develops with gradually increasing amplitudes; for large x, on the contrary, the system is *dissipative*, hence, the amplitudes decrease. Ultimately a steady state is reached when absorption and dissipation of energy balance one another throughout the cycle. This is, in fact, in entire agreement with observation.

Unfortunately these physical considerations are insufficient. Since the system is non-conservative, one cannot utilize the energy integral, as was the case for a conservative system, see Chapter II. It becomes thus necessary to establish conditions for closed trajectories and to infer from them that a periodic process is possible.

33. LIÉNARD'S METHOD

Consider the following differential equation

$$\ddot{x} + \omega f(x)\dot{x} + \omega^2 x = 0 \tag{33.1}$$

where $f(x)$ is a continuous, differentiable, even function of x; additional properties of $f(x)$ will be specified later. Taking ωt as a new independent variable this equation can be written as

$$\ddot{x} + f(x)\dot{x} + x = 0 \tag{33.2}$$

Since no further confusion is to be feared we shall use the same symbols $\ddot{x}$ and $\dot{x}$ as in [33.1] although occasionally we shall write [33.2] as

$$\ddot{x} + \omega_0 f(x)\dot{x} + \omega_0^2 x = 0$$

with $\omega_0 = 1$, in order to remind one of the dimensional homogeneity of the original Equation [33.1]. It is apparent that [33.1] is a particular case of [32.3]. If $f(x) \equiv 0$, the motion is harmonic, corresponding to the equation $\ddot{x} + x = 0$. If $f(x) = C$, C being a constant, we have the well-known damped motion, either oscillatory ($|C| < 2$) or aperiodic ($|C| > 2$); see Chapter I. Setting $\dot{x} = v$, Equation [33.2] is replaced by the system

$$\dot{x} = v; \quad v\frac{dv}{dx} + f(x)v + x = 0 \tag{33.3}$$

The second Equation [33.3] can be written

$$\frac{dv}{dx} + f(x) + \frac{x}{v} = 0 \tag{33.4}$$

Introducing a new variable $y = v + F(x)$, where $F(x) = \int_0^x f(x)dx$ is odd since $f(x)$ is even, we replace [33.4] by

$$\frac{dy}{dx} + \frac{x}{y - F(x)} = 0 \tag{33.5}$$

This equation can also be written as

$$x\,dx + \left[y - F(x)\right]dy = 0 \qquad\qquad [33.6]$$

The system [33.3] can also be written in the form

$$-\frac{dy}{x} = \frac{dx}{y - F(x)} = \frac{dx}{v} = dt = \omega_0\,dt \qquad\qquad [33.7]$$

Since the independent variable t does not appear in [33.6], the latter represents the phase trajectories in the (x,y)-plane of the dynamical system [33.2]. It must be noted, however, that the (x,y)-plane of Liénard is different from the customary $(x, y = \dot{x})$-plane considered previously so that the geometrical form of the trajectories in both cases is necessarily different, as will be shown in Section 37. The use of the Liénard plane $[x, y = v + F(x)]$ makes it possible to obtain a relatively simple geometrical construction of the trajectories.

In fact, the equation of the normal at the point (x,y) on the trajectory is $(x - X)dx + (y - Y)dy = 0$, and from [33.6] we see that it is satisfied for $X = 0$, $Y = F(x)$. Therefore, the normals to the phase trajectories of Liénard's Equation [33.6], for $x = x_1$, all pass through the same point N whose coordinates are 0, $F(x_1)$. Hence, one obtains the elements of trajectories along the line $x = x_1$ by taking on the y-axis a point N_1 whose ordinate is $y_1 = F(x_1)$ and by describing with N_1 as center a series of small arcs as shown in Figure 33.1. By taking other points $x = x_2$, x_3, ... and by repeating the procedure, additional elements of trajectories are obtained.

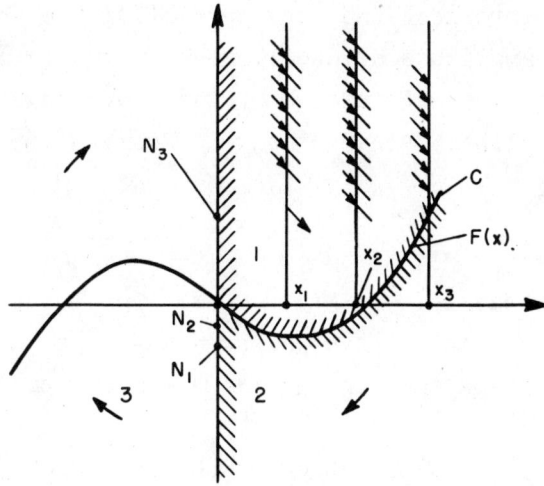

Figure 33.1

Having a field of line elements and starting from a certain initial point (x_0, y_0) a continuous curve can be traced following the line elements so traced; this curve will be clearly a trajectory of Liénard's Equation [33.5] or [33.6].

Since $F(0) = 0$, it follows that the only singular point of Equation [33.5] is the origin $x = y = 0$. Furthermore trajectories are symmetrical with respect to the origin, for the substitution of $- x$ for x and $- y$ for y does not change [33.5], since $F(x)$ is odd. Likewise, upon replacing $+ y$ by $- y$, $+ dt$ by $- dt$, $f(x)$ by $- f(x)$, Equation [33.5] is not changed; hence, this substitution transforms a trajectory into its symmetrical image relative to the x-axis. The curve $y = F(x)$ and the y-axis determine four regions 1, 2, 3, 4 shown in Figure 33.1; the limits of the first and the second regions are shown by a different shading in Figure 33.1.

From Equations [33.7] it follows that the differential elements of the trajectories in these regions for $dt > 0$ are such that dy and x are of opposite signs and that dx and $y - F(x)$ are of like signs. In terms of these regions the following table is apparent.

	x	$y - F(x)$	dx	dy
Region 1	+	+	+	-
2	+	-	-	-
3	-	-	-	+
4	-	+	+	+

From [33.6] it follows that $dy/dx = \infty$ when $y = F(x)$. Hence, the tangent to the trajectories is vertical at points C at which the trajectories intersect the curve $y = F(x)$; the abscissa of point C thus determines the amplitude of oscillation in the (x, y)-plane.

Instead of the above construction one can apply the method of isoclines, see Section 7. From [33.5] we have

$$\frac{dy}{dx} = -\frac{x}{y - F(x)} = a$$

that is, $y = F(x) - \frac{1}{a} x$. The locus of isoclines $dy/dx = a = 0$ is thus on the y-axis; that of $dy/dx = a = \infty$ is on the line $y = F(x)$; and that of $dy/dx = 1$ is on the line $y = F(x) - x$ and so on.

34. EXISTENCE OF CLOSED TRAJECTORIES IN THE LIÉNARD PLANE

We shall now consider the most important point of the Liénard theory concerning the existence of closed trajectories in the (x, y)-plane previously defined. Instead of Liénard's original proof, we shall follow the one given by N. Levinson and O.K. Smith (22). They consider an equation

$$\ddot{x} + f(x)\dot{x} + g(x) = 0 \qquad [34.1]$$

more general than that of Van der Pol (1), but possessing essentially the same characteristics which are given explicitly below.

Introduce the functions $F(x) = \int_0^x f(x)dx$ and $G(x) = \int_0^x g(x)dx$. The conditions in question are as follows.

1. All functions are continuous. $f(x)$ is an even function of x, hence, $F(x)$ is odd. $g(x)$ is an odd function of x, hence, $G(x)$ is even. The sign of $g(x)$ is that of x.

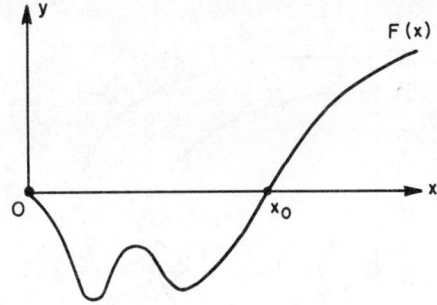

Figure 34.1

2. $F(x)$ has a single positive zero x_0. It is negative for $0 < x < x_0$. For $x > x_0$ it increases monotonically and hence is positive.

3. $F(x) \to \infty$ with x.

It is to be noted that $F(x)$ need not be monotonic for $0 < x < x_0$, as shown in Figure 34.1.

Under these assumptions, as N. Levinson and O.K. Smith show, Equation [34.1] possesses a unique periodic solution.

Following the same procedure as in Section 33, one obtains the generalized Liénard equation

$$\frac{dy}{dx} + \frac{g(x)}{y - F(x)} = 0 \qquad [34.2]$$

We shall show that there is one, and only one, closed trajectory of [34.2]. Considerations of symmetry clearly remain the same as in Section 33. This means that a closed trajectory passing through a point $(0, y_0)$ must necessarily pass through the point $(0, -y_0)$. Conversely, a trajectory passing through points $(0, y_0)$ and $(0, -y_0)$ must necessarily be closed, since on leaving $(0, y_0)$ it is symmetric with respect to the origin along the arc of the curve lying between $(0, y_0)$ and $(0, -y_0)$. The existence and uniqueness of a periodic solution will be proved if one shows that among all trajectories there is one, and only one, with equal positive and negative intercepts OA and OB. In outline this is done as follows. Introduce the function

$$\lambda(x, y) = \frac{1}{2} y^2 + G(x) \qquad [34.3]$$

Thus $\lambda(0, y) = \frac{1}{2} y^2$. In order to show that OA = OB, it is only necessary to show that $\lambda_A = \lambda_B$ sometime. Now Equation [34.2] may be written as

$$y\, dy + g(x)\, dx = F(x)\, dy = d\lambda \qquad [34.4]$$

Thus

$$\int_A^B d\lambda = \lambda_B - \lambda_A = \int_A^B F(x)\, dy \qquad [34.5]$$

where, here and throughout the rest of the section, the integrals are curvilinear integrals taken along the trajectories.

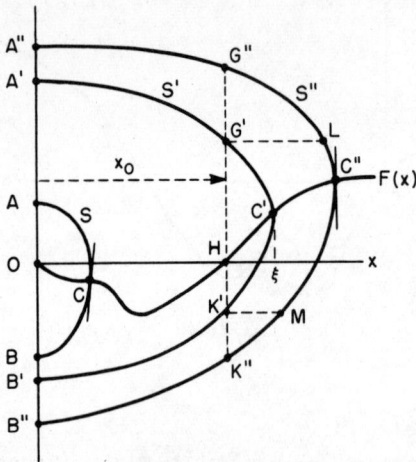

Figure 34.2

The examination of Figure 34.2 gives rapid and convincing information. In fact, if the point C at which the trajectory intersects the curve $y = F(x)$ is to the left of the point H, the curvilinear integral $\int_A^B d\lambda > 0$, since both $F(x)$ and dy are negative in that region. As the points A and B move away from the origin the contribution of the curvilinear integral in this region is decreasing monotonically while being positive. Since $F(x)$ remains negative, it follows that $|y - F(x)|$ increases indefinitely. Furthermore, since $g(x)$ is bounded and positive, we see from [34.2] that dy decreases.

Since $F(x)$ increases monotonically in the region to the right of H, the contribution to the curvilinear integral along the arc $G'C'K'$ is negative. Hence, the curvilinear integral $\int_A^B d\lambda$ decreases monotonically as A and B move away from 0 since its positive part, due to the elements to the left of H, is bounded while its negative part due to the elements situated to the right of H, is negative and increases monotonically. Hence, there exists one, and only one, position of the points A and B on the y-axis for which $\int_A^B d\lambda = 0$ and for which there corresponds a unique closed trajectory. This fact is expressed by the condition that

$$\int_A^B F(x)\, dy = 0 \qquad\qquad [34.6]$$

35. FIRST ASYMPTOTIC CASE: $\mu \ll 1$

We shall now consider Equation [32.2] in which $g(x) \equiv x$. In Liénard's form [33.6] it is

$$x\, dx + y\, dy - F(x)\, dy = 0 \qquad\qquad [35.1]$$

In the asymptotic case, when $F(x)$ is very small, we may replace $F(x)$ by $\mu F(x)$ where μ is a small number.

If $\mu = 0$, the trajectories are circles $x^2 + y^2 =$ constant. If $\mu \neq 0$, and a periodic solution exists, clearly a closed trajectory will differ but little from a neighboring circle. We propose to determine the circle in whose neighborhood there exists a closed trajectory. The criterion [34.6] which has been obtained geometrically will serve this purpose.

Making use of the polar coordinates $x = R \sin \phi$; $y = R \cos \phi$, [35.1] can be written as

$$\frac{dR}{d\phi} = - \mu \frac{F(R \sin \phi) R \sin \phi}{R - \mu F(R \sin \phi) \cos \phi}$$

or

$$\frac{dR}{d\phi} \approx - \mu F(R \sin \phi) \sin \phi \qquad [35.2]$$

Therefore, [34.6] becomes

$$\int_0^\pi F(R \sin \phi) R \sin \phi \, d\phi = 0 \qquad [35.3]$$

Thus, for Van der Pol's equation, $f(x) = x^2 - 1$; $F(x) = \frac{x^3}{3} - x$, [35.3] is

$$\frac{1}{\pi} \int_0^\pi F(R \sin \phi) \sin \phi \, d\phi = \frac{R^3}{8} - \frac{R}{2} = 0 \qquad [35.4]$$

Hence when μ is small, $R = 2$ is the radius of the circle in the vicinity of which there exists a closed trajectory. Furthermore, a simple approximation based on the smallness of μ shows that along the closed trajectory the angular velocity $\omega_0 \approx \dot{\phi}$ is constant.

It is to be observed that we have obtained a first order solution of Van der Pol's equation by a mixed method, viz., the criterion [34.6] has been established by means of a geometric method and from that point the argument has been analytic. It will be shown in Part II that the same result can be obtained by purely analytical methods.

36. SECOND ASYMPTOTIC CASE: THE PARAMETER μ IS LARGE

The case in which μ is large is of great importance in the applications, e.g., the so-called RC oscillations in modern thermionic circuits. The oscillations are now strongly distorted, showing the presence of numerous harmonics. For this reason, the application of the analytical methods of approximation given in Part II, become too laborious owing to the poor convergence of the Fourier expansion representing the oscillation. Liénard did, however, develop an approximation method yielding considerable information regarding the wave forms of the oscillations for large values of μ. We now propose to show this method.

Setting $y = \mu z$ in Equation [33.6] and replacing $F(x)$ by $\mu F(x)$, as in Section 35, we obtain

$$\left[z - F(x) \right] dz + \frac{1}{\mu^2} x \, dx = 0 \qquad [36.1]$$

For μ very large this equation can be written approximately

$$\left[z - F(x)\right] dz \approx 0 \qquad [36.2]$$

The integral curves in the (x,z)-plane consist of the principal branches $z = F(x)$ and $z =$ constant, joined by short arcs.

Referring now to Equations [33.7], we shall examine the relative order of magnitude of the terms under the assumption that μ is large; thus, terms like $\frac{1}{\mu}C$, where C is finite, are treated as small quantities of the first order. Equations [33.7] in the new variables (x,z) are

$$dt = \omega_0 dt = -\mu \frac{dz}{x}$$

$$[36.3]$$

$$dt = \omega_0 dt = \frac{dx}{\mu\left[z - F(x)\right]}$$

From the first Equation [36.3] it follows that $dz/dt \sim 1/\mu$, where the symbol $\sim$ means "of the order of," that is, of the first order, since x is finite. On the other hand, since $z \approx F(x)$ by [36.2]

$$\frac{dz}{dx} \approx \frac{dF}{dx} = f(x)$$

which is finite. But $\frac{dz}{dx} = \frac{dz}{dt}\frac{dt}{dx}$; hence, $\frac{dx}{dt} \sim \frac{1}{\mu}$. Since the velocity remains small in this finite interval, we conclude that it takes a relatively long time to traverse it. Thus, we can conclude that on the branch $z = F(x)$ the representative point R in the (x,z)-plane moves slowly; its velocity is small, of the order of $1/\mu$. Clearly, the acceleration d^2x/dt^2 is then of the second order of smallness, $1/\mu^2$, and can be neglected in the differential equation

$$\ddot{x} + \mu\omega_0 f(x)\dot{x} + \omega_0^2 x = 0 \qquad [36.4]$$

which, moreover, is Equation [32.2] since $\omega_0 = 1$. Hence, limiting the terms to the first order only, [36.4] becomes

$$\mu\omega_0 f(x)\dot{x} + \omega_0^2 x = 0 \qquad [36.5]$$

Thus, under the assumed approximation, the second order Equation [36.4] can be replaced by the *degenerate* Equation [36.5] of the first order, with an error of the order of $1/\mu^2$. This subject will be considered more fully in Part IV.

One must ascertain the order of the approximation $z - F(x) \approx 0$, arising from the use of [36.2] instead of [36.1]. First, from the comparison of [36.1] and [36.2] it follows that the approximation is of the order of

$1/\mu^2$. One can also see this from the second Equation [36.3], since $dx/dt \sim 1/\mu$. We thus infer that on the branches $z \approx F(x)$ of integral curves, the representative point R moves slowly with a velocity of the order of $1/\mu$ and an acceleration of the order of $1/\mu^2$. It takes, therefore, a relatively long time to traverse these arcs in view of the fact that x is finite.

We shall now investigate the motion on the other typical arcs for which $dz \approx 0$, that is $z \approx$ constant; $z - F(x)$ is finite and stays away from zero. From the second Equation [36.3] we observe that $dx/dt \sim \mu$, that is, $d^2x/dt^2 \sim \mu^2$, so that we can now neglect the term $\omega_0^2 x$ in [36.4] and write

$$\ddot{x} + \mu\omega_0 f(x)\dot{x} = 0 \qquad [36.6]$$

From [36.1] it follows that $dz/dx \sim 1/\mu^2$; hence, in the (x,z)-plane the slope of the curve is very small for this second characteristic branch, $dz \approx 0$. This almost horizontal branch in the (x,z)-plane is traversed very rapidly, since $dx/dt \sim \mu$ and μ is very large in this case.

37. LIMIT CYCLES IN THE VAN DER POL AND LIÉNARD PLANES

We may now summarize Liénard's principal results and compare them with the earlier results obtained by Van der Pol. The experimental results in connection with Van der Pol's equation

$$\ddot{x} - \mu(1 - x^2)\dot{x} + x = 0 \qquad [37.1]$$

in the (x,t)-plane are shown in Figure 37.1 for three values of the parameter μ (1). For the representation of the trajectories of [37.1], Van der Pol uses the $(x,\dot{x})$-plane with which we were concerned throughout the first four chapters of this report.

Van der Pol originally obtained the phase trajectories for [37.1] by the graphical method of isoclines; these results are shown in Figure 37.2.

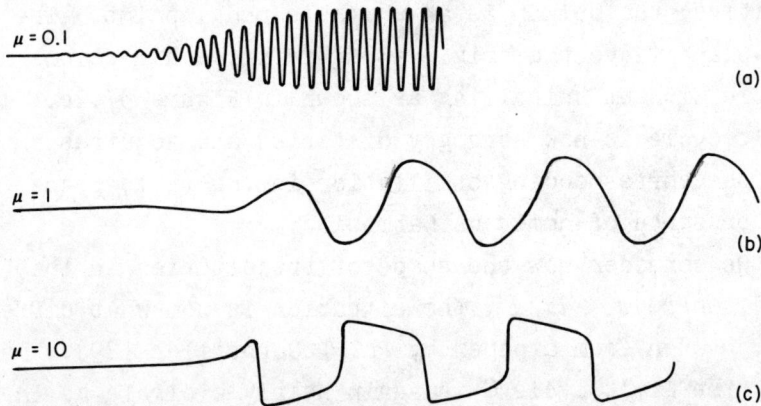

Figure 37.1

114

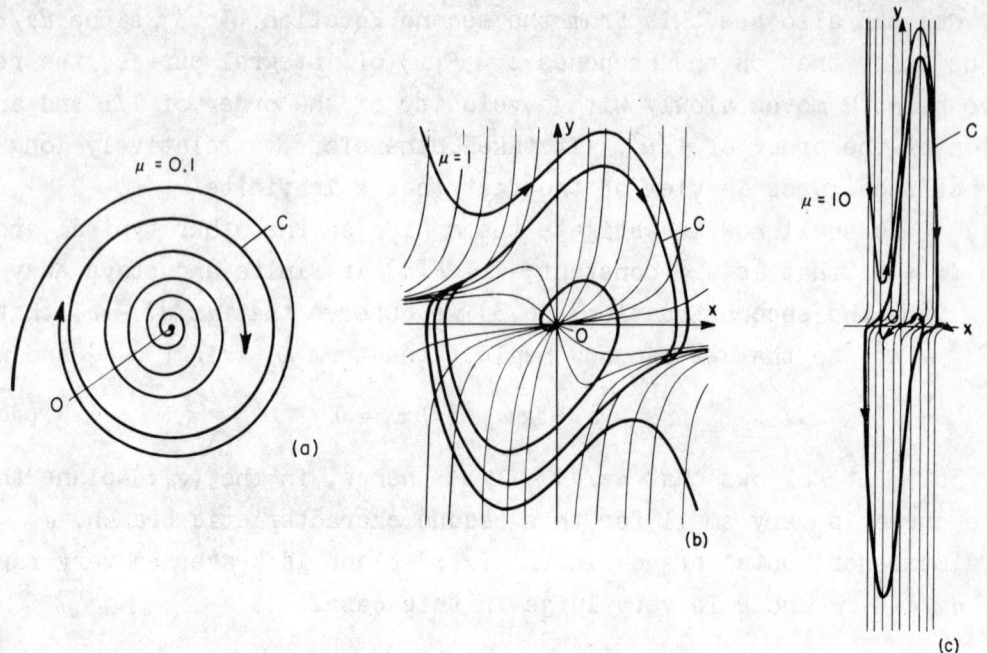

Figure 37.2

In fact, Liapounoff's equations of the first approximation are $\dot{x} = y$, $\dot{y} = -x + \mu y$; the characteristic equation is

$$S^2 - \mu S + 1 = 0 \qquad [37.2]$$

For $0 < \mu < 2$ the roots are conjugate complex with a positive real part, and the origin is, thus, an unstable focal point. For $\mu = 0.1$, the limit cycle C differs very little from a circle of radius 2 and the trajectories approach it both from the inside and the outside as shown in Figure 37.2a. For $\mu = 1.0$, the origin is still an unstable focal point but the limit cycle C differs considerably from a circle as shown in Figure 37.2b corresponding to the experimental curve in Figure 37.1b. For $\mu = 10$, the roots of [37.2] are real and positive; the origin is an unstable nodal point. The trajectories in the $(x, \dot{x})$-plane leave the origin along definite directions and approach the limit cycle without spiralling as shown in Figure 37.2c. It is observed that the limit cycle is now strongly distorted and acquires an elongated narrow form; the corresponding oscillation in the (x, t)-plane, Figure 37.1c, exhibits the presence of numerous harmonics.

If we consider now the shape of trajectories in the Liénard plane $[x, \nu + F(x)]$, where $\nu = dx/dt$, the situation is somewhat different, as shown in Figure 37.3 taken from a paper by Ph. LeCorbeiller (29). For $\mu = 0.1$, Figure 37.3a, the limit cycle C is again nearly a circle as in the $(x, \dot{x})$-plane. For larger values of μ, Figures 37.3b and 37.3c, the limit cycle undergoes a

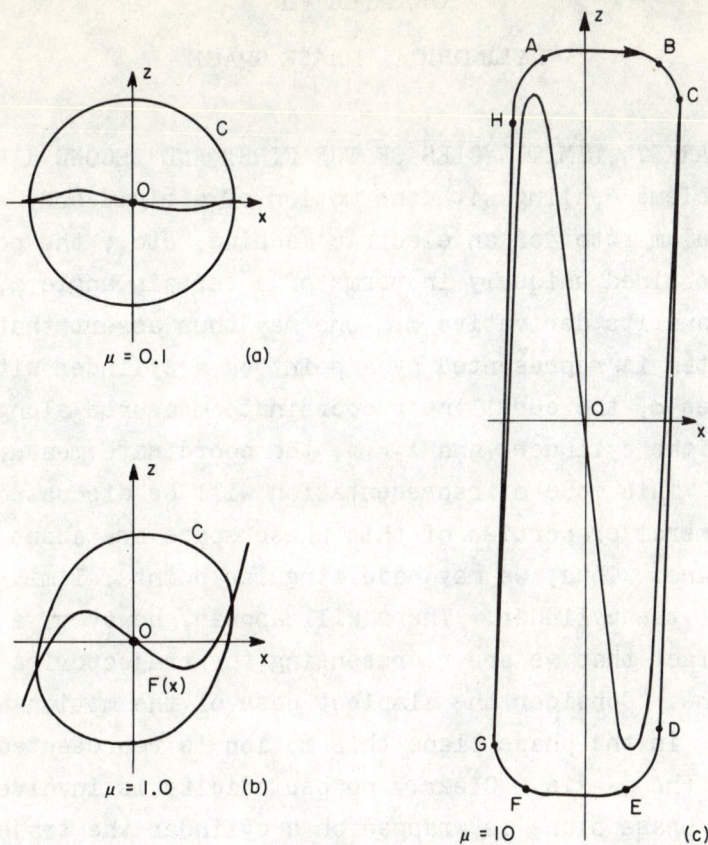

Figure 37.3

different kind of deformation as compared to that in the $(x, \dot{x})$-plane and acquires an almost rectangular form for $\mu = 10$ as shown in Figure 37.3c. One
recognizes in this figure the second asymptotic case, $\mu \gg 1$, of Liénard
discussed in the preceding section.

The peculiar motion of the representative point on a distorted
limit cycle as shown in Figure 37.3c represents a typical case of *relaxation*
oscillations for large values of the parameter μ appearing in a great number
of applications.

38.   GENERAL REMARKS.   LIMIT CYCLES OF THE FIRST AND SECOND KIND

In problems dealing with the motion of a rigid body about a fixed axis, e.g., pendulum rotor of an electric machine, etc., the position and velocity are determined uniquely in terms of a certain angle ϕ, to within a multiple of 2π, and its derivative $\dot{\phi}$. One may thus assert that the dynamical state of the system is represented by a point on a cylinder with the cylindrical coordinates ϕ, the curvilinear coordinate measured along the arc of a right section of the cylinder, and $z = \dot{\phi}$, the coordinate measured along the generating line. This mode of representation will be discussed here.

The general properties of this phase space are about the same as in the case of a plane. Thus, we may have singular points, limit cycles, etc., *on the surface* of the cylinder. There will appear, however, a special feature due to the fact that we are representing the trajectories on a cylinder and not on a plane. Consider the simplest case of the motion with constant velocity $z = \dot{\phi}_0$. In the phase plane this motion is represented by a straight line parallel to the ϕ-axis. Clearly no periodicity is involved in this case. If, however, the phase plane is wrapped on a cylinder the trajectory in this case becomes a right circular section and is thus closed. We thus conceive of a periodicity "around the cylinder" although we lose the grasp of this periodicity if we unwrap the cylinder on a plane. We shall call this particular form of periodicity, inherent in the form of this particular cylindrical phase space, as periodicity of the second kind.

It is apparent that this periodicity corresponds to a closed trajectory such as S in Figure 38.1. By a slight extension of the definition of the limit cycle we can say that such a closed trajectory is a *limit cycle of the second kind* if it is approached either for $t = +\infty$ or for $t = -\infty$ by non-closed trajectories going around the cylinder in the manner of the curve S′.

The limit cycles in the phase plane with which we have been concerned previously appear on the surface of the cylinder as closed curves C bounding a region of the cylindrical surface; we shall call them *limit cycles of the first kind*. It is apparent that these cycles represent the

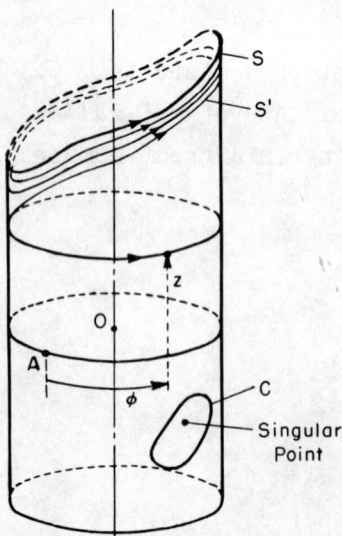

Figure 38.1

same situation which we have already studied in the phase plane; the only difference lies in the fact that the plane is wrapped on the cylinder. Furthermore, the theory of Poincaré remains applicable to these limit cycles. Thus,
for example, we can assert that inside a closed trajectory of the first kind
there must exist a number of singularities with the algebraic sum of their
indices being equal to + 1 and so on.

We cannot, however, assert this with respect to the closed trajectories of the second kind since these do not bound off any region. The important property of these closed trajectories lies in the fact that they have
a period 2π relative to ϕ which does not depend on time. This means that such
a limit cycle is fully described when the coordinate ϕ varies by 2π.

It may be observed that through a suitable transformation of coordinates the cylindrical phase space may be replaced by a plane with the ori-
gin left out. In fact, if we set $\rho = e^z$, where $z = \dot{\phi}$, then the point $M(\phi, z)$
of the cylinder goes into a point $M'(\phi, \rho)$ of the plane and the correspondence
between M and M' is one to one and continuous in both directions, that is,
topological. Since z varies between plus and minus ∞, ρ varies between 0 and
$+ \infty$, zero being excluded. Thus the cylinder is transformed into the whole
plane with the origin left out. Through this transformation the circle $z = 0$
of the cylinder goes into the circle $\rho = 1$
in the plane and the generating lines of
the cylinder are represented in the (ϕ, ρ)-
plane by the half-ray, OR, passing through
the origin. The closed trajectories of the
first kind are those which do not go around
the origin O, e.g., curve C in Figure 38.2,
whereas those of the second kind are those
which go around it, such as curve S.

Intuitively speaking, the trans-
formation $M \rightarrow M'$ is equivalent to a flat-
tening out of the cylinder into a plane.
This plane representation makes it clear
that the usual features of the planar sys-
tem should be expected here. In fact, in the planar representation, the
closed trajectory of the second kind acquires a familiar feature, that is,
the origin behaves now in all respects as a point singularity.

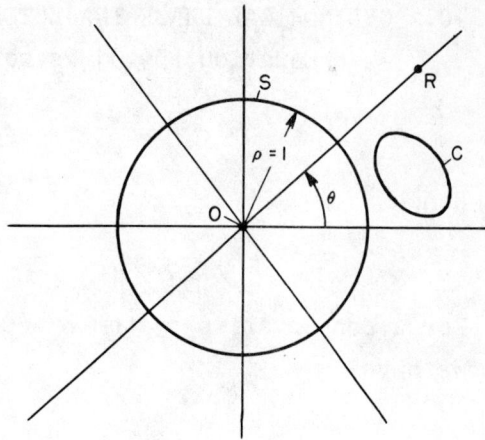

Figure 38.2

39. DIFFERENTIAL EQUATION OF AN ELECTROMECHANICAL SYSTEM

Consider the differential equation

$$A\ddot{\theta} + B\dot{\theta} + f(\theta) = M \qquad\qquad [39.1]$$

where A, B, and M are constants and $f(\theta)$ is a periodic function of θ. In the following, we take $f(\theta) = C \sin \theta$. In this case

$$A\ddot{\theta} + B\dot{\theta} + C \sin \theta = M \qquad [39.2]$$

Equations [39.1] and [39.2] are non-linear on account of the presence of the terms $f(\theta)$ and $C \sin \theta$.

As an analogue of [39.2] one may consider a physical pendulum with constants A, B, and C, acted upon by a constant moment M. The general character of the motion can be, in this case, either oscillatory or rotary according to the relative magnitude of M, "dead beat" or with dying-out oscillations, etc.

Our purpose will be to consider the solutions of this differential equation in a cylindrical phase space in which the existence of periodic trajectories of the second kind will be established. Introducing the "dimensionless time" $\tau = \omega_0 t = \sqrt{\frac{C}{A}}\, t$ and putting $\frac{B}{\sqrt{CA}} = \alpha > 0$, $\frac{M}{A\omega_0^2} = \frac{M}{C} = \beta \geqq 0$, [39.2] becomes

$$\frac{d^2\theta}{dt^2} + \alpha \frac{d\theta}{dt} + \sin \theta - \beta = 0 ^* \qquad [39.3]$$

We shall make use of this form in what follows.

40. CYLINDRICAL PHASE TRAJECTORIES OF A CONSERVATIVE SYSTEM

Equation [39.3] is equivalent to the system

$$\frac{d\theta}{dt} = z; \quad \frac{dz}{dt} = -\alpha z - \sin \theta + \beta \qquad [40.1]$$

Hence

$$\frac{dz}{d\theta} = \frac{\beta - \alpha z - \sin \theta}{z} \qquad [40.2]$$

For a conservative system $\alpha = 0$. In this case [40.2] can be integrated and we have

$$\frac{1}{2} z^2 = \beta\theta + \cos \theta + \frac{1}{2} k \qquad [40.3]$$

where $\frac{1}{2}k$ is a constant of integration. Hence

$$z = \pm \sqrt{2(\beta\theta + \cos \theta) + k} \qquad [40.4]$$

Several cases are possible, according to the value of β.

1. $\beta = 0$, hence, $M = 0$. For $k = -2$, $z = d\theta/dt = 0$, and $\theta = 0$; for $k > -2$ these are closed periodic trajectories around the singular point

---

* Since no confusion can arise, the usual notations $d^2\theta/dt^2$ and $d\theta/dt$, instead of $d^2\theta/d\tau^2$ and $d\theta/d\tau$, will be resumed.

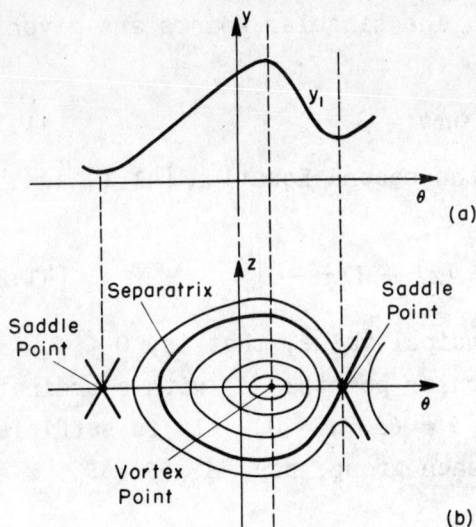

Figure 40.1

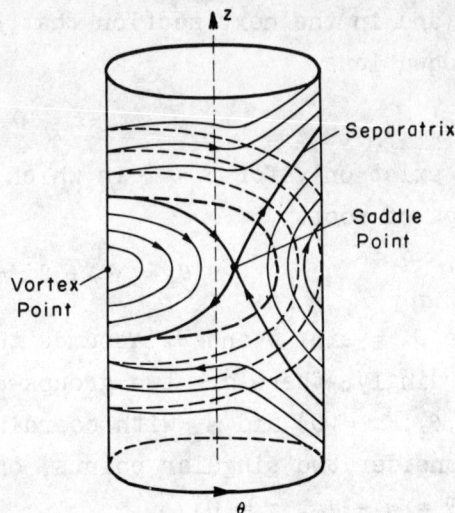

Figure 40.2

$\theta = 0$, $z = 0$. The latter is, thus, a vortex point. The periodic trajectories form a continuum of closed curves for the interval $-2 < k < +2$. For $k = +2$, we obtain separatrices limiting "the island" of closed trajectories in the phase plane. The separatrices issue from saddle points for $\theta = \pm \pi$.

Thus far the discussion has been analogous to that of Section 12. Let us wrap the plane figure on a cylinder of unit radius, see Figure 40.2; the points $\theta = -\pi$ and $\theta = +\pi$ will coincide on the cylinder. The trajectories of the second kind are those which go outside the separatrices. On the cylinder they appear as surrounding the cylinder but not the singularities.

2. $\beta \neq 0$. Let $z = \pm \sqrt{2(\beta\theta + \cos \theta) + k} = \pm \sqrt{2y_1 + k}$. The curve y_1 in Figure 40.1a has maxima and minima rising on the average due to the presence of the term $\beta\theta$. If the curve $z = z(\theta)$ in Figure 40.1b is wrapped on the cylinder, the trajectories have the appearance shown in Figure 40.2. The periodic trajectories do not go around the cylinder, hence, they are not of the second kind.

If $\beta = 1$, the curve $y_1 = z(\beta\theta + \cos \theta)$ has only an inflection point but no maxima or minima; for $\beta > 1$, the curve y_1 is monotonic without inflection points. One can construct these curves in a plane and, by wrapping them on the cylinder, form an idea of their appearance. No periodic trajectories exist, and the use of a cylindrical phase space offers no particular advantages over the phase plane.

41. CYLINDRICAL PHASE TRAJECTORIES OF A NON-CONSERVATIVE SYSTEM

For a non-conservative system, $\alpha \neq 0$ and we must, therefore, consider [40.2]. This equation cannot be integrated directly. We assume in this and in the next section that $\beta \neq 1$. The singular points are given by the equations

$$z = 0; \quad \beta - \sin \theta = 0 \qquad [41.1]$$

They exist only for $\beta < 1$ in which case the second Equation [41.1] admits two groups of roots

$$\theta_i = \theta_0 + 2k\pi; \quad \theta_j = (2k + 1)\pi - \theta_0 \qquad [41.2]$$

where $\theta_0 = \sin^{-1}\beta$ and θ_0 assumes the principal value, that is, $0 < \theta_0 < \pi/2$. Accordingly, there are two groups of singular points: A_i with coordinates $(\theta = \theta_i,\ z = 0)$ and A_j with coordinates $(\theta = \theta_j,\ z = 0)$. It is sufficient to consider two singular points, one in each group, say, $A_{i0}(\theta = \theta_0,\ z = 0)$; $A_{j0}(\theta = \pi - \theta_0,\ z = 0)$.

1. Group A_i. For this group $\theta_i = 2k\pi + \theta_0,\ z = 0$. Consider a slight departure ϵ from θ_0. We have $\theta = \theta_0 + \epsilon$, $d\theta = d\epsilon$, and, by [40.2]

$$\frac{dz}{d\theta} = \frac{dz}{d\epsilon} = \frac{\beta - \alpha z - \sin(\theta_0 + \epsilon)}{z} \qquad [41.3]$$

Developing $\sin(\theta_0 + \epsilon)$ in this equation, one has $\sin(\theta_0 + \epsilon) = \sin\theta_0 + \epsilon \cos\theta_0$. Since, for the singular point, $\beta = \sin\theta_0$, we have from the equation of the first approximation

$$\frac{dz}{d\epsilon} = \frac{-\alpha z - \epsilon \cos\theta_0}{z} \qquad [41.4]$$

corresponding to the system

$$\frac{dz}{dt} = -\alpha z - \epsilon \cos\theta_0; \quad \frac{d\epsilon}{dt} = z \qquad [41.5]$$

The characteristic equation is

$$S^2 + \alpha S + \cos\theta_0 = 0; \quad \alpha > 0 \qquad [41.6]$$

Using the criterion given in Section 18, we find that, if $\alpha^2 < 4\cos\theta_0$, the singularity is a stable focal point; if $\alpha^2 > 4\cos\theta_0$, it is a stable nodal point.

2. Group A_j. For this group of singularities, the coordinates are $\theta_j = (2k + 1)\pi - \theta_0,\ z = 0$. Proceeding as before, one finds

$$\frac{dz}{d\epsilon} = \frac{-\alpha z + \epsilon \cos\theta_0}{z} \qquad [41.7]$$

and the characteristic equation is

$$S^2 + \alpha S - \cos\theta_0 = 0 \qquad [41.8]$$

Its roots are

$$S_{1,2} = -\frac{\alpha}{2} \pm \sqrt{\frac{\alpha^2}{4} + \cos\theta_0} \qquad [41.9]$$

The singularities of this second group A_j are thus saddle points.

42. CLOSED TRAJECTORIES OF THE SECOND KIND IN NON-CONSERVATIVE SYSTEMS

We shall now investigate periodic solutions of the second kind of a non-conservative system, $\alpha > 0$. Two cases are to be distinguished.

1. $\beta > 1$. In this case there exists exactly *one* periodic solution with the period 2π. In order to establish the existence of such a periodic solution it is sufficient to prove the existence of two particular solutions $z_1(\theta)$ and $z_2(\theta)$ such that for an arbitrary θ, $z_1(\theta + 2\pi) \geqq z_1(\theta)$, $z_2(\theta + 2\pi) \leqq z_2(\theta)$. The existence of a solution satisfying $z(\theta + 2\pi) = z(\theta)$ follows then by continuity reasons since there are no singular points if $\beta > 1$. From [40.2] it is noted that the equation of the isocline $dz/d\theta = 0$ is

$$z = \frac{\beta - \sin\theta}{\alpha} \qquad [42.1]$$

Curve [42.1] in the (z,θ)-plane is, therefore, a locus of points at which $dz/d\theta = 0$. This curve crosses the axis of θ, i.e., $z = 0$, only if $\beta < 1$. If $\beta > 1$ the curve is above that axis. These two cases are shown in Figures 42.1a and 42.1b. From [40.2], it follows that for $z = 0$, $dz/d\theta = \infty$. Moreover, the shaded areas in Figures 42.1a and 42.1b correspond to regions in which $dz/d\theta > 0$; the non-shaded areas correspond to $dz/d\theta < 0$.

In order to find one of the two particular solutions, it is necessary to express the fact that this solution goes *above* the sinusoid of Figure 42.1. Since in this region $dz/d\theta < 0$, and hence, $z_1(\theta_0 + 2\pi) < z_1(\theta_0)$. One solution of this type can be found if we take $z_1(\theta_0) > (1 + \beta)/\alpha$, because this initial point lies certainly *above* the curve $z = (\beta - \sin\theta)/\alpha$, that is, in the region in which $dz/d\theta < 0$. This solution satisfies the above condition required for z_1.

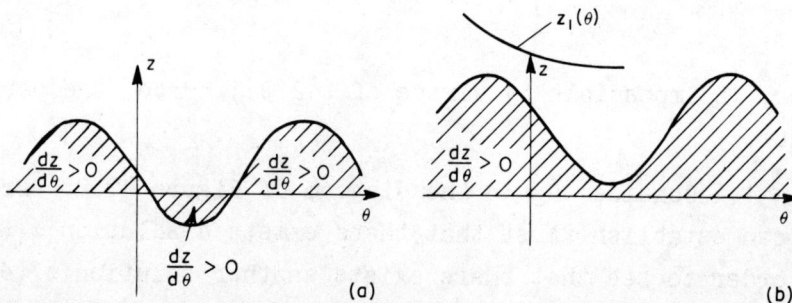

Figure 42.1

In order to find the second particular solution z_2 satisfying the condition $z_2(\theta_0 + 2\pi) > z_2(\theta_0)$, consider the minimum point A on the curve of Figure 42.2. For this point $\theta = \pi/2$ and $z = (\beta - 1)/\alpha$. A curve $z_2(\theta)$ issuing from A is in the region where $dz/d\theta > 0$; hence, the curve $z_2(\theta)$ is rising and must intersect the sinusoid at a certain point M. Since the sine curve is the locus of $dz/d\theta = 0$, clearly, M is a maximum point for $z_2(\theta)$. Beyond the point M, the curve $z_2(\theta)$ decreases. Furthermore, the next intersection M_1, cannot be lower than the point B, since at the point of intersection M , the curve $z_2(\theta)$ has a horizontal tangent. It is thus seen that the condition $z_2(\theta_0 + 2\pi) \leqq z_2(\theta_0)$ is fulfilled, and hence, by virtue of the continuity of the sequence $z(\theta)$ in the interval (z_1, z_2) there is a periodic solution z_0 in the interval (z_1, z_2).

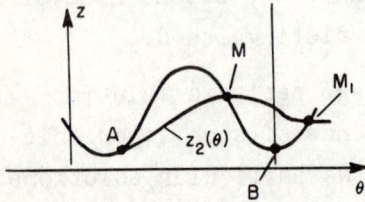

Figure 42.2

It now will be shown that this periodic solution z_0 is unique. In fact, integrating [40.2] between θ_1 and $\theta_1 + 2\pi$ one has

$$\frac{1}{2} z^2(\theta_1 + 2\pi) - \frac{1}{2} z^2(\theta_1) = - \alpha \int_{\theta_1}^{\theta_1 + 2\pi} z\, d\theta + 2\pi\beta \qquad [42.2]$$

If the solution is periodic then $z(\theta_1 + 2\pi) = z(\theta_1)$, whence

$$\int_{\theta_1}^{\theta_1 + 2\pi} z\, d\theta = \frac{2\pi\beta}{\alpha} \qquad [42.3]$$

Equation [42.3] expresses the condition of periodicity. Assume now that there are two periodic solutions $z_{01}(\theta)$ and $z_{02}(\theta)$. Since there are no singularities, these solutions cannot intersect each other, so that one of them is always greater than the other, e.g., $z_{01}(\theta) > z_{02}(\theta)$ for all θ, whence

$$\int_{\theta_1}^{\theta_1 + 2\pi} z_{01}(\theta)\, d\theta > \int_{\theta_1}^{\theta_1 + 2\pi} z_{02}(\theta)\, d\theta$$

This, however, is impossible by virtue of [42.3]; hence, the periodic solution is unique.

2. $\beta < 1$. Consider again the diagram of Figure 42.2. Proceeding as before, one can establish first that there exists a solution $z_1(\theta_0 + 2\pi) \leqq z_1(\theta_0)$. In order to see that there exists another solution $z_2(\theta_0)$, such that $z_2(\theta_0 + 2\pi) \geqq z_2(\theta_0)$, it is convenient to consider two integral curves Γ_1 and

Γ_2 on the surface of the cylinder passing through two adjoining saddle points, singular points of group A_j, separated by 2π. The curve Γ_1 has the same slope at the point A_{j1} as the asymptote of the positive slope and Γ_2 has the same slope at the next saddle point A_{j2} as the asymptote of the negative slope. One can show that, for sufficiently small values of α, the condition $z_2(\theta_0 + 2\pi) \geqq z_2(\theta_0)$ is fulfilled. Hence, for sufficiently small values of α and of the constant B, Equation [39.2], a periodic solution of the second kind exists.

Physically this condition is obvious; in fact, since the system is acted upon by a constant moment of force M, one can readily see that, if the damping is not too great, the rotary motion of the pendulum may become periodic when the energy communicated by the moment M per cycle is just equal on the average to the energy dissipated by damping. If the damping is just slightly below or above this critical value the rotary motion will become either damped, i.e., the trajectory approaches a focal point, or will continue with an increasing angular velocity. In the latter case a state of periodicity of the second kind will eventually be reached when the energy communicated to the system by the constant moment M will be just equal to the energy dissipated by damping. As a result there will appear a *periodic trajectory of the second kind* closed around the cylinder and not enclosing any point singularities on its surface.

The topological picture on the surface of the cylinder will thus have the various aspects shown in Figure 42.3. The separatrices issuing from a saddle point may either approach a limit cycle of the second kind extending around the cylinder or approach a stable focal point. In the former case the originally unstable motion will have a tendency to approach a periodic rotary motion; in the latter case the motion will approach a definite angle around which the oscillations will gradually die out. There exist also separatrices of the second kind, i.e., turning around the cylinder, which approach a saddle point; in this case the trajectory will approach the saddle point asymptotically. Since the latter is unstable, it will depart from it following one of the other two asymptotes either to a periodic trajectory of the second kind or to a stable focal point.

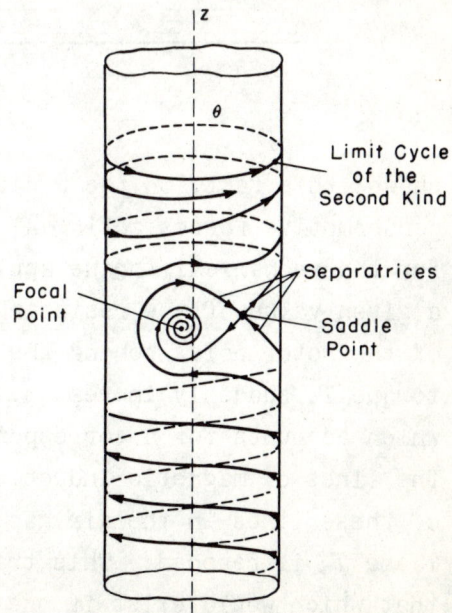

Figure 42.3

From this study it follows that the advantage of analyzing a phenomenon of this kind in a cylindrical phase space is particularly marked when
the process extends over a number of periods of the system.

43. OSCILLATIONS OF A SYNCHRONOUS MOTOR

A noteworthy situation, calling also for a cylindrical phase space,
is the investigation by Vlasov (30) of the oscillations of a synchronous
motor around its average angular velocity. As is known, a synchronous motor
is a mechanical system, a rotor, with one degree of freedom ϕ about its axis
of rotation, driven normally at a constant angular velocity ω_0 by the electromagnetic driving torque T produced by a rotating magnetic field. This
field is excited by a polyphase stator winding and "locked" in synchronism
with the corresponding field of the salient poles on the rotor excited by a
direct current. The manner in which both fields on the stator and rotor are
locked is represented graphically in Figure 43.1 by the lines of magnetic induction. It is observed that these lines cross the air gap obliquely as

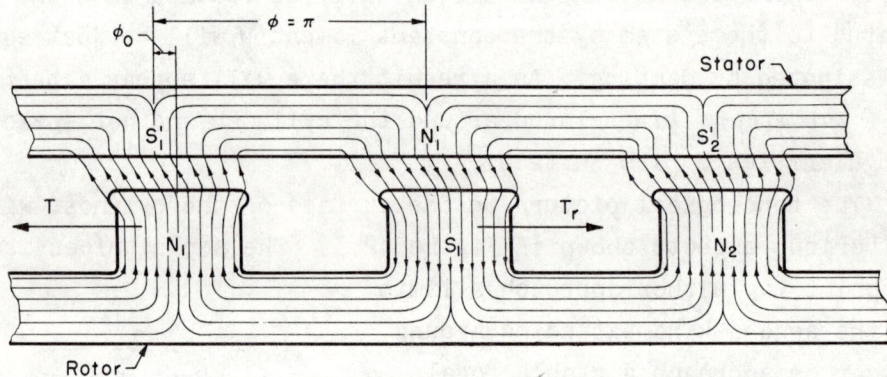

Figure 43.1

shown; this fact, on the basis of the Faraday-Maxwell theory concerning the
pondermotive forces acting along the lines of magnetic induction, accounts
for the mechanical torque applied to the rotor. It is seen, thus, that for
a given value of the resisting torque T_r, there corresponds a given lag ϕ_0
of the rotor poles behind the corresponding stator poles. If the resisting
torque T_r suddenly increases, for instance, the relative angle ϕ increases
which accounts for a corresponding increase of the tangential component of
the lines of magnetic induction in the air gap owing to a greater obliquity
of these lines in the air gap. This occurs until a new equilibrium between
T and T_r is reached. This transient state is, in all respects, similar to
that which would exist if one had two rotating mechanical systems connected
by springs. It is apparent, however, that if the resisting torque T_r becomes

so great that the relative angle ϕ
reaches the value $\phi = \pi$, this similarity with the above mentioned mechanical
picture ceases because an S-pole on the
stator comes in front of an S-pole on
the rotor and instability results in the
interval $(\pi, 2\pi)$ inasmuch as the like
poles repel each other. Furthermore,
the rotor has a tendency "to drop out
of step" and slow down still further.
It may, however, "get into step" again

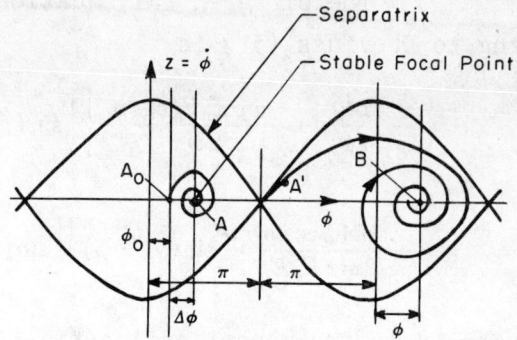

Figure 43.2

when N_1 comes in alignment with S_2 since a stable configuration reappears exactly similar to that which existed originally. It follows that, if the disturbance causing a change $\Delta\phi$ of the angle ϕ is such that the new equilibrium
point A is within the region of stability, there appears a relative trajectory approaching the point A in the manner of a spiral approaching a focal
point; see Figure 43.2. If, however, the disturbance is so great as to carry
the representative point to a point A′ on the other side of the saddle point
S_1 limiting the region of stability, the spiral trajectory originating at A′
will approach another focal point B situated at an angular distance $\phi = 2\pi$
from the former point of equilibrium A.

It may happen under special conditions, which were produced electrically by Vlasov but not commonly encountered in connection with the industrial synchronous motors, that the rotor runs at a certain speed below the
synchronous speed. In such a case, the rotor poles "slip" continuously behind the stator poles and the performance in this case is called *asynchronous*.
It is apparent that this mode of operation is possible only when a certain
asymmetry exists in the driving torque so that a continuous slipping of rotor
poles behind the stator poles is accompanied by a certain average value of
the driving torque for the angular period $\phi = 2\pi$. Thus it is clear that a
steady state of asynchronous performance corresponds to a limit cycle of the
second kind. It is to be noted also that, under certain conditions usually
eliminated in industrial motors, a steady sustained oscillation of the rotor
speed about its normal synchronous speed ω_0 may arise. It is generally impossible to eliminate an oscillation of this kind by any damping devices and,
therefore, it is particularly objectionable. These self-sustained oscillations are characterized by the existence of limit cycles of the first kind.
With this physical picture of the phenomena involved we can now proceed with
a brief outline of Vlasov's theory.

The differential equation of motion of a synchronous motor according to Dreyfuss (31) is

$$\frac{I}{p}\frac{d^2\gamma}{dt^2} + \frac{mpE_0V_0\cos\rho}{2\omega x}\left\{\left[\sin(\gamma+\rho) - \frac{E_0}{V_0}\sin\rho - \frac{E_0}{V_0}\frac{\sin 4\rho}{4\omega\cos\rho}\frac{d\gamma}{dt} + \right.\right.$$

$$\left.\left. + \frac{mV_0\cos\rho}{2\omega xR_eE_0}y^2\sin(\gamma+\rho)\right]\left[\sin(\gamma+\rho) - \frac{2E_0}{V_0}\sin\rho\right]\frac{d\gamma}{dt}\right\} = M \qquad [43.1]$$

where I is the moment of inertia of the rotor,

$\quad m$ is the number of phases,

$\quad p$ is the number of pairs of poles,

$\quad E_0$ is the electromotive force induced per phase of the stator in a steady state,

$\quad y = dE_0/di_e$ is the tangent to the saturation curve $E_0 = f(i_e)$ where i_e is the d-c excitation,

$\quad V_0$ is the voltage applied to one phase of the stator,

$\pi - \gamma$ is the angle between vectors E and V,

$\quad \rho = \tan^{-1}\frac{r}{x}$ where r is the ohmic resistance and x is the resistance per phase of the stator,

$\quad M$ is the driving moment,

$\quad R_e$ is the resistance of exciting winding, and

$\quad \omega = 2\pi f$ is the angular frequency where f is the frequency.

Introducing the constant factors

$$\frac{E_0}{V_0} = K, \quad \frac{mp^2kV_0^2}{2p\omega x}\cos\rho = a^2, \quad \frac{a}{4\omega} = b, \quad \frac{my^2a}{2\omega xR_e} = c, \quad \frac{2M\omega x}{mpV_0^2} = \beta \quad [43.2]$$

and the new variables $\phi = \gamma + \rho$ at $t = \tau$, one transforms [43.1] into the dimensionless form

$$\frac{d^2\phi}{d\tau^2} + \sin\phi + \left[\frac{c}{K}\cos\rho\sin\phi(\sin\phi - 2K\sin\rho) - \right.$$

$$\left. - Kb\frac{\sin 4\rho}{\cos\rho}\right]\frac{d\phi}{dt} = \frac{\beta}{K\cos\rho} + K\sin\rho \qquad [43.3]$$

This equation corresponds to the system

$$\frac{d\phi}{d\tau} = z$$

$$\qquad\qquad [43.4]$$

$$\frac{dz}{d\tau} = \frac{\beta}{K\cos\rho} + K\sin\rho - \sin\phi + \left[Kb\frac{\sin 4\rho}{\cos\rho} - \frac{c}{K}\cos\rho\sin\phi(\sin\phi - 2K\sin\rho)\right]z$$

Consider now a cylindrical phase space with the axis of the cylinder parallel to the z-axis. This is an appropriate representation since the form of [43.4] does not change when ϕ is replaced by $\phi + 2K\pi$; the ϕ-axis is curvilinear along the circular cross section of the cylinder. Equations [43.4] can be written as

$$\frac{d\phi}{d\tau} = z; \quad \frac{dz}{d\tau} = \nu - \sin\phi + f(\phi)z \qquad [43.5]$$

where

$$\nu = \frac{\beta}{K\cos\rho} + K\sin\rho > 0$$

and

$$f(\phi) = Kb\frac{\sin 4\rho}{\cos\rho} - \frac{c}{K}\cos\rho\sin\rho(\sin\phi - 2K\sin\rho) \qquad [43.6]$$

Equating the right-hand terms of [43.5] to zero, one obtains the singular points. If $\nu > 1$, singular points are absent. If $\nu = 1$, there is one singular point of a higher order representing the coalescence of two simple singular points. If $\nu < 1$, there are two singular points.

Consider the last case. The coordinates of the singular points are clearly $\phi_1 = \sin^{-1}\nu$, $z = 0$ and $\phi_2 = \pi - \phi_1$, $z = 0$. In forming the equations of the first approximation, Section 18, it is assumed that $f(\phi_1) \neq 0$, $f(\phi_2) \neq 0$. Setting $\phi = \phi_1 + \epsilon$, $d\phi = d\epsilon$ and observing that

$$\sin\phi = \sin(\phi_1 + \epsilon) \approx \sin\phi_1 + \epsilon\cos\phi_1$$

[43.5] then becomes

$$\frac{d\epsilon}{d\tau} = z; \quad \frac{dz}{d\tau} = -\epsilon\cos\phi_1 + f(\phi_1)z \qquad [43.7]$$

The characteristic equation is $S^2 - f(\phi_1)S + \cos\phi_1 = 0$, and its roots are

$$S_{1,2} = \frac{1}{2}\left[f(\phi_1) \pm \sqrt{f^2(\phi_1) - 4\cos\phi_1}\right] \qquad [43.8]$$

According as the sign of $f^2(\phi_1) - 4\cos\phi_1 \gtrless 0$ one has either a nodal point or a focal point. In practice one usually encounters focal points. In such cases the equilibrium is stable for $f(\phi_1) < 0$ and unstable for $f(\phi_1) > 0$.

Following a similar procedure one finds that the second singular point (ϕ_2, $z = 0$) is always a saddle point. Thus there exist two types of singularities situated on the ϕ-axis which have been already investigated in Section 41. The only additional feature is the existence of a threshold $f(\phi) = 0$, separating stability [$f(\phi) < 0$] from instability [$f(\phi) > 0$].

It is to be observed that in practical problems the quantities $K = E_0/V_0$, $y = dE_0/di_0$, and b may be considered as small quantities of the first order. Furthermore, from expressions [43.2] one ascertains that c/K is also small. Thus, generally, the value of $f(\phi)$ in practice is small and can be put in a form $f(\phi) = \mu f_0(\phi)$ where μ is a small parameter. There is a certain degree of arbitrariness in the choice of this parameter, depending on the relative order of magnitude of the small quantities K, y, b, $\cdots$, characterizing each particular case. Under these conditions, [43.5] can be put in the form

$$\frac{d\phi}{d\tau} = z; \quad \frac{dz}{d\tau} = \nu - \sin\phi + \mu f_0(\phi)z \qquad [43.9]$$

The system [43.9] is conservative for $\mu = 0$ although non-linear and can be analyzed by the method indicated in Section 40. The phase trajectories are given by the equation

$$\frac{dz}{d\phi} = \frac{\nu - \sin\phi}{z} \qquad [43.10]$$

which is readily integrated, giving

$$z = \pm \sqrt{2(\cos\phi + \nu\phi + h)}; \quad h = \text{constant} \qquad [43.11]$$

This equation has the same form as [40.4].

The conclusions thus remain the same, viz: there are no trajectories of the second kind, although there may be closed periodic trajectories surrounding a vortex point and forming a continuum, "the island," limited by separatrices issuing from saddle points. Physically this means that there will be oscillations of the rotor about its uniform speed of rotation. These oscillations, in general, are not of the "relaxation type" but are ordinary oscillations of a quasi-linear type, see Section 11, depending on the initial conditions such as may arise from accidental disturbances. Oscillations of this kind are not important, however, because they are rapidly damped out by the squirrel-cage damping arrangement, the effect of which is not considered here.

We shall now investigate the system [43.9] assuming it to approximate a conservative system, that is, taking $\mu \neq 0$ but very small. Physically this means that the performance, instead of being synchronous, becomes asynchronous, that is, the motor begins to "slip" and settles on a subsynchronous speed.

The equation of phase trajectories becomes

$$\frac{dz}{d\phi} = \frac{\nu - \sin\phi}{z} + \mu f_0(\phi) \qquad [43.12]$$

It is seen that when $|z|$ is small
the trajectories differ but little
from those of [43.10], that is,
the separatrices still exist and
the area of the "islands" of periodicity changes slightly. No trajectories of the second kind exist
in the neighborhood of the ϕ-axis.
Hence, in order to ascertain the
existence of closed trajectories
of the second kind, we have to investigate the regions of the cylin-
drical phase space when $|z|$ is
large. Equation [43.12] in such a case becomes

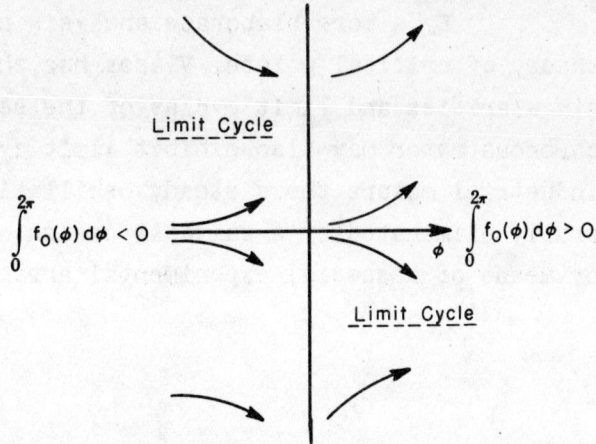

Figure 43.3

$$\frac{dz}{d\phi} \approx \mu f_0(\phi)$$

and the condition of periodicity of the second kind

$$z(2\pi) - z(0) = \mu \int_0^{2\pi} f_0(\phi)\,d\phi = \left[Kb\,\frac{\sin 4\rho}{\cos \rho} + 2c\cos \rho \sin^2\rho\right] 2\pi \quad [43.13]$$

Two cases will be considered according to the sign of the right-hand term
of [43.13].

    a. $Kb\,\dfrac{\sin 4\rho}{\cos \rho} + 2c\cos \rho \sin^2 \rho < 0$. As a consequence we
have $z(2\pi) - z(0) < 0$. Thus, when $|z|$ is large, $z > 0$, the tra-
jectories approach the ϕ-axis. On the other hand, when z is
small and greater than zero, they depart from the ϕ-axis as do
the trajectories of the conservative system [43.10] for any
$z > 0$. Since all point singularities are situated on the ϕ-axis,
there exists at least one limit cycle of the second kind and it
is stable. The same reasoning applied to $z < 0$ shows that there
is no limit cycle.

    b. $Kb\,\dfrac{\sin 4\rho}{\cos \rho} + 2c\cos \rho \sin^2 \rho > 0$. Then $z(2\pi) - z(0) > 0$.
In this case the trajectories depart from the ϕ-axis when $|z|$ is
large, $z > 0$, and also when z is small, as was shown previously.
Hence, no closed trajectories of the second kind exist for $z > 0$.
If, however, $z < 0$, the trajectories approach the ϕ-axis when $|z|$
is large and depart from it when $|z|$ is small. Hence, for $z < 0$,
there exists at least one limit cycle of the second kind.

This situation is illustrated in Figure 43.3 which is self-explanatory.

By a more elaborate analysis not discussed here, involving the theory of critical points, Vlasov has shown that, in addition to the point singularities and limit cycles of the second kind, the operation of a synchronous motor may also exhibit limit cycles of the first kind. In ordinary industrial motors these steady oscillations of a "relaxation" type are generally eliminated by a suitable design. Vlasov succeeded in producing them by means of a special experimental arrangement.

REFERENCES

(1)   "On Relaxation Oscillations," by B. Van der Pol, Philosophical Magazine, Vol. 2, November 1926.

(2)   "Sur les courbes définies par une équation différentielle" (On Curves Defined by a Differential Equation), by H. Poincaré, Ouevres, Gauthier-Villars, Paris, Vol. 1, 1928.

(3)   "Les méthodes nouvelles de la mécanique céleste" (New Methods in Celestial Mechanics), by H. Poincaré, Gauthier-Villars, Paris, Vol. 1, 1892.

(4)   "Problème général de la stabilité du mouvement" (General Problem of Stability of Motion), by M.A. Liapounoff, Annales de Toulouse, Paris, Vol. 9, 1907. This is a translation from the Russian by E. Davaux.

(5)   "Sur les courbes définies par des équations différentielles" (On Curves Defined by Differential Equations), by I. Bendixson, Acta Mathematica, Vol. 24, 1901.

(6)   "Quelques théorèmes générales sur le mouvement des systèmes dynamiques" (Some General Theorems on the Movement of Dynamical Systems), by G.D. Birkhoff, Bulletin Societé Mathématique, France, Vol. 40, 1912.

(7)   "Vibration Problems in Engineering," by S. Timoshenko, D. Van Nostrand Company, New York, N.Y., Second Edition, 1937, Chapter 2.

(8)   "Mechanical Vibrations," by J.P. Den Hartog, McGraw-Hill Book Company, New York, N.Y., Second Edition, 1940, Chapters 7 and 8.

(9)   "The Engineer Grapples with Non-Linear Problems," by Th. Von Kármán, Bulletin of the American Mathematical Society, Vol. 46, August 1940.

(10)   "Traité de la mécanique rationelle" (Treatise on Theoretical Mechanics), by P. Appell, Vol. 1, Paris.

(11)   "Problems of Anti-Rolling Stabilization of Ships," by N. Minorsky, American Society of Naval Engineers, Vol. 47, February 1935.

(12)   "Froude's Pendulum," by S. Strelkoff, Journal of Technical Physics, USSR, (Russian), Vol. 3, 1933.

(13)   "Theory of Sound," by Lord Rayleigh, London, Vol. 1, 1894, p. 212.

(14)   "Sur l'équilibre d'une masse fluide animée d'un mouvement de rotation" (On Equilibrium of a Rotating Fluid Mass), by H. Poincaré, Acta Mathematica, Vol. 7.

132

(15) "Figures d'équilibre d'une masse fluide" (Figures of Equilibrium of a Fluid Mass), by H. Poincaré, Paris, 1903.

(16) "Differentialgleichungen" (Differential Equations), by L. Bieberbach, J. Springer, Berlin, Third Edition, 1930, Part 1, Chapter 4.

(17) Article by W. Kaufmann, Annalen der Physik, Vol. 2, 1900.

(18) "Les cycles limites de Poincaré et la théorie des oscillations auto-entretenues" (Limit Cycles of Poincaré and the Theory of Self-Excited Oscillations), by A. Andronow, Comptes Rendus, Paris, Vol. 189, 1929.

(19) "Theory of Oscillations," by A. Andronow and S. Chaikin, Moscow, (Russian), 1937.

(20) "Le battement du coeur considéré comme oscillation de relaxation" (Heart Beat Considered as a Relaxation Oscillation), by B. Van der Pol and M. Van der Mark, Onde Électrique, 1928, p. 365.

(21) "Leçons sur la théorie mathématique de la lutte pour la vie" (Lectures on the Mathematical Theory of the Struggle for Life), by V. Volterra, Gauthier-Villars, Paris, 1931.

(22) "A General Equation for Relaxation Oscillations," by N. Levinson and O.K. Smith, Duke Mathematical Journal, Vol. 9, June 1942.

(23) "Experimentelle Untersuchung des Phasenraumes Autoschwingender Systeme" (Experimental Investigation on the Phase Space of Self-Excited Oscillatory Systems), by V. Bowshewerow, Technical Physics, USSR, Vol. 2, 1935.

(24) "Gewöhnliche Differentialgleichungen beliebiger Ordnung" (Ordinary Differential Equations of Arbitrary Order), by J. Horn, Leipzig, 1905.

(25) "On Mechanical Self-Excited Oscillations," by N. Minorsky, Proceedings of the National Academy of Sciences, October 1944.

(26) "Note sur une ancienne experience d'électricité" (Memoir on an Old Electrical Experiment), by M. Janet, Annales des Postes Télégraphes et Téléphones, December 1925.

(27) "Étude des oscillations entretenues" (Study of Self-Excited Oscillations), by A. Liénard, Revue Générale d'Électricité, Vol. 23, 1928.

(28) "Note sur la génération des oscillations entretenues" (Memoir on the Generation of Self-Excited Oscillations), by E. and H. Cartan, Annales des Postes Télégraphes et Téléphones, December 1925.

(29) "Les systèmes auto-entretenues" (Self-Excited Systems), by Ph. LeCorbeiller, Librairie Scientifique, Hermann et Cie., Paris, 1931.

(30) "Oscillations of a Synchronous Motor," by N. Vlasov, Journal of Technical Physics, USSR, (Russian), Vol. 9, 1939.

(31) "Electrotechnik und Maschinenbau" (Electrical and Mechanical Engineering), by L. Dreyfuss, 1911.

PART II

ANALYTICAL METHODS OF NON-LINEAR MECHANICS*

44. INTRODUCTORY REMARKS

It is apparent that for practical applications the general qualitative methods reviewed in Part I are not sufficient, and that quantitative methods capable of yielding numerical solutions of differential equations are necessary. Thus, for example, a physicist or an engineer may wish to determine the amplitude and phase of an oscillatory process with a certain prescribed accuracy once the general qualitative aspects of the phenomenon have been ascertained.

In general, there exist no methods capable of yielding exact solutions of non-linear differential equations, and the only methods available are those of approximations. A typical and very general class of non-linear differential equations encountered in applications is represented by the equation

$$\ddot{x} + \omega^2 x = \mu f(x, \dot{x}, t) \qquad [44.1]$$

The solutions of this equation are periodic with frequency ω if $\mu = 0$. Poincaré (1)** has shown that very near some of these solutions, when $\mu = 0$, periodic solutions of Equation [44.1] may exist for very small values of the parameter μ. The search for these solutions is the object of *the method of small parameters* of Poincaré. This method, with its various ramifications, constitutes the principal subject of Part II.

The scope of the quantitative methods available at present is rather limited. It is restricted, in fact, to the class of non-linear differential equations of the type [44.1], and for this class it is further restricted by the condition that the parameter μ should be very small, that is, $\mu \ll 1$. In spite of these limitations, the usefulness of the method is very great and its applications in various branches of applied science are extensive. Only in special cases when the parameter μ is large does the theory

---

* The text of Part II follows the presentation contained in the two treatises on Non-Linear Mechanics:
  "Theory of Oscillations," by A. Andronow and S. Chaikin, Moscow, (Russian), 1937, Chapters VII and VIII.
  "Introduction to Non-Linear Mechanics," by N. Kryloff and N. Bogoliuboff, Kieff, (Russian), 1937, Chapters X, XI, and XIII.

** Numbers in parentheses indicate references on page 112 of this report.

of Poincaré cease to be applicable, and for such cases analytical methods are practically unexplored.*

We shall frequently refer to Equation [44.1], with $\mu \ll 1$, as *quasilinear*, which means that the solutions of this equation do not differ appreciably from solutions of the corresponding linear equation when $\mu = 0$. The important point to be noted is that, although the solutions of [44.1] do not differ much from the solutions of the corresponding linear equation if μ is very small, these periodic solutions do not exist in the neighborhood of *any* periodic solution of the corresponding linear equation but only in the neighborhood of *certain special* solutions of that equation. The establishment of conditions for the existence of periodic solutions of [44.1] when $\mu \ll 1$ thus constitutes the crux of the theory of Poincaré.

Another important point is the effect of the so-called *secular terms* in the approximate solutions obtained by these quantitative methods. Poincaré's method consists in substituting certain power series in Equation [44.1] and in determining the coefficients of these series by a recurrence procedure. As a result of this, there may appear terms such as $t^n \sin \omega t$ and $t^n \cos \omega t$, the *secular terms*, in which the time t appears *explicitly* in the expansions. It is apparent that the existence of these terms, which grow beyond any bound as $t \to \infty$, destroys the periodicity one is seeking. This can be illustrated by the following argument.

Let $\omega = \alpha + \beta$. Then

$$\sin \omega t = \sin \alpha t \cos \beta t + \cos \alpha t \sin \beta t$$

$$= \left[\alpha t - \frac{(\alpha t)^3}{3!} + \cdots \right] \cos \beta t + \left[1 - \frac{(\alpha t)^2}{2!} + \cdots \right] \sin \beta t \qquad [44.2]$$

The terms $\alpha t \cos \beta t$, $\frac{(\alpha t)^3}{3!} \cos \beta t$, and so on, in this expression are secular terms. It is obvious that if the series expansion of $\sin \alpha t$ and $\cos \alpha t$ is limited to a finite number of terms one cannot speak of the "periodicity" of the expression on the right side of Equation [44.2] since the polynominals in the parentheses of this expression will increase indefinitely as $t \to \infty$. If, however, $n \to \infty$, the expressions in parentheses approach $\sin \alpha t$ and $\cos \alpha t$, and the whole expression [44.2] then becomes a periodic function of time with period $T = 2\pi/\omega$.

In practice it is necessary to stop the series expansions at a certain finite number of terms; hence one is generally confronted with secular terms. In the original work of Poincaré this difficulty was obviated by limiting the expansions to a certain finite time interval sufficient for

* See, for example, the paper by J.A. Shohat (2).

astronomical purposes. Gylden and Lindstedt (3) have avoided this difficulty
by eliminating the secular terms in each step of the recurrence procedure by
which the coefficients of the expansion are determined. These methods will
be mentioned briefly in Chapter XI.

For this reason the transfer of the methods of celestial mechanics
to the problems of non-linear oscillations presented certain difficulties.
In fact, if one attempts to apply Poincaré's method, for example, to a thermionic generator oscillating with a frequency of several megacycles per second, it is apparent that in a few seconds such a generator will pass through
stages corresponding to those through which an astronomical system passes in
many millions of years. The effect of secular terms in such a case should
be felt within a few seconds. Nothing of the kind, however, is observed.

In view of this it becomes necessary, in adapting these methods to
the theory of non-linear oscillations, to follow the method of Lindstedt,
which eliminates the secular terms in each step of the recurrence procedure.
This was accomplished by Kryloff and Bogoliuboff. We shall return to this
question in Section 58.

In spite of the difficulty of using the original theory of Poincaré
for studies of non-linear oscillation, this theory is still capable of yielding a considerable amount of information. Chapter VIII outlines the salient
points of Poincaré's method as outlined in "Theory of Oscillations," by A.
Andronow and S. Chaikin, (4).

Chapter IX is devoted to the Van der Pol method; its presentation
follows closely the text of Andronow and Chaikin. Chapter X concerns the
theory of the first approximation of Kryloff and Bogoliuboff (5).

These two methods of Van der Pol and of Kryloff and Bogoliuboff are
analogous in some respects and follow a method similar to the *method of variation of constants* of Lagrange.

Chapter XI deals with Lindstedt's method, as applied by Kryloff and
Bogoliuboff to approximations of orders higher than the first.

Chapter XII is devoted to the *method of equivalent linearization* of
Kryloff and Bogoliuboff, which is an attempt to simplify the problem by reducing the given non-linear differential equation to an equivalent linear one.

CHAPTER VIII

METHOD OF POINCARÉ

45. CONDITION OF PERIODICITY

Consider a system of differential equations

$$\dot{x} = ax + by + \mu f_1(x,y); \quad \dot{y} = cx + dy + \mu f_2(x,y) \qquad [45.1]$$

where f_1 and f_2 are the non-linear elements of the system and μ is a parameter. It will be assumed that f_1 and f_2 are analytic functions of their variables in certain intervals under consideration.

For $\mu = 0$ the system becomes linear. In general, we shall be interested in periodic solutions of the non-linear system. Let us consider, first the periodic solutions of the system [45.1] when $\mu = 0$. Forming the characteristic equation, we obtain

$$S^2 - (a + d)S + (ad - bc) = 0 \qquad [45.2]$$

The periodic solutions of [45.1] for $\mu = 0$ correspond clearly to purely imaginary roots of Equation [45.2]. We thus obtain the following conditions of periodicity

$$a + d = 0; \quad ad - bc > 0 \qquad [45.3]$$

Under these conditions the linear system admits an infinity of periodic solutions of the form

$$x = K \cos(\omega t + \phi); \quad y = gK \sin(\omega t + \phi + \chi) \qquad [45.4]$$

where $\omega = \sqrt{ad - bc}$ and g is a determined constant. Obviously, the phase angle ϕ is arbitrary and can be made equal to zero by a suitable choice of the origin of time. K and the relative phase angle χ appear as the integration constants determined by the initial conditions.

The general form of periodic solutions of [45.1] for $\mu = 0$ is then

$$x = x_0(t,K) = K \cos \omega t; \quad y = y_0(t,K) = gK \sin(\omega t + \chi) \qquad [45.5]$$

so that $x_0(t,K)$ and $y_0(t,K)$ are periodic functions with period $2\pi/\omega$. Let us assume now that periodic solutions exist for small values of $\mu \neq 0$ and let $x = x(t,\mu,K)$ and $y = y(t,\mu,K)$ be these solutions. For $t = 0$ the solutions are $x(0,\mu,K)$ and $y(0,\mu,K)$ and we can write

$$x(0,\mu,K) = x_0(0,K) + \beta_1 \quad \text{and} \quad y(0,\mu,K) = y_0(0,K) + \beta_2 \qquad [45.6]$$

which defines the functions $\beta_1(\mu)$ and $\beta_2(\mu)$. It is obvious that $\beta_1(0) = \beta_2(0) = 0$.

The method of Poincaré consists in developing the solutions $x(t,\mu,K)$ and $y(t,\mu,K)$ as power series in μ, β_1, and β_2. Poincaré shows (6) that the expansions converge if the values of $|\mu|$, $|\beta_1|$, and $|\beta_2|$ are sufficiently small. Moreover, this convergence is uniform for any finite time interval $0 < t < t_1$. The coefficients of the expansions so obtained are functions of time. By substituting these expansions in the differential equations [45.1] it is possible to determine these coefficients by equating like powers of μ, β_1, and β_2. One obtains in this manner a system of differential equations subject to certain initial conditions.

Let us write the solutions of [45.1] in the form

$$x = x(t,\mu,\beta_1,\beta_2,K); \quad y = y(t,\mu,\beta_1,\beta_2,K)$$

Since we are looking for periodic solutions of [45.1] in the neighborhood of a known periodic solution with period T, when $\mu = 0$, it is logical to assume that in this neighborhood the period of the solution [45.1] will be $T + \tau$, where $\tau(\mu)$ is a small correction which approaches zero as μ approaches zero. Our chief objective is to show that under certain conditions periodic solutions *may* exist provided μ is small. The condition for the periodicity of [45.1] is clearly

$$x(T + \tau, \mu,\beta_1,\beta_2,K) - x(0,\mu,\beta_1,\beta_2,K) = 0$$
$$y(T + \tau, \mu,\beta_1,\beta_2,K) - y(0,\mu,\beta_1,\beta_2,K) = 0$$

[45.7]

For given values of μ and K we must select functions $\beta_1(\mu)$, $\beta_2(\mu)$, and $\tau(\mu)$ so as to satisfy Equations [45.7]. Furthermore, the non-linear equation becomes linear when $\mu = 0$ so that

$$\tau(0) = \beta_1(0) = \beta_2(0) = 0 \qquad [45.8]$$

The phase is arbitrary, however, so that it is possible to assume that one of the β's, say β_1, equals zero. Putting $\beta_2 = \beta$, the conditions [45.7] can be written as

$$x(T + \tau,\mu,0,\beta,K) - x(0,\mu,0,\beta,K) = \phi(\tau,\mu,\beta,K)$$
$$y(T + \tau,\mu,0,\beta,K) - y(0,\mu,0,\beta,K) = \psi(\tau,\mu,\beta,K)$$

[45.9]

It is apparent that, when $\mu = 0$ and hence $\tau(0) = \beta(0) = 0$, the system [45.1], with the conditions expressed by [45.3], has an infinity of periodic solutions corresponding to the arbitrary values of the integration constants K and X in Equations [45.4]. In such a case Equations [45.9] become identically satisfied for any value of K. One can express this by writing

$$\phi(\tau,\mu,\beta,K) = \mu\phi_1(\tau,\mu,\beta,K) = 0$$
$$\psi(\tau,\mu,\beta,K) = \mu\psi_1(\tau,\mu,\beta,K) = 0$$

[45.10]

The right-hand side of these equations represents a straight line $\mu = 0$ in the (μ, K)-plane and a point represented by the intersection of the curves $\bar{\phi}_1(\mu, K) = 0$ and $\bar{\psi}_1(\mu, K) = 0$, where $\bar{\phi}_1$ and $\bar{\psi}_1$ are the functions ϕ_1 and ψ_1 in which $\tau(\mu)$ and $\beta(\mu)$ have been expressed in terms of μ. We can, for instance, represent $\tau(\mu)$ and $\beta(\mu)$ by power series

$$\tau(\mu) = d\mu + e\mu^2 + \cdots; \quad \beta(\mu) = d_1\mu + e_1\mu^2 + \cdots \qquad [45.11]$$

Expanding the functions $\phi_1(\tau, \mu, \beta, K)$ and $\psi_1(\tau, \mu, \beta, K)$ we get

$$\phi_1 = \phi_{01} + a\mu + b\tau + c\beta + \cdots = 0$$

$$\psi_1 = \psi_{01} + a_1\mu + b_1\tau + c_1\beta + \cdots = 0$$

$$[45.12]$$

Substituting in these expressions the values of $\tau(\mu)$ and $\beta(\mu)$ from [45.11] and considering μ as a small quantity of the first order, one obtains

$$\phi_1 = \phi_{01} + \mu(a + bd + cd_1) = 0$$

$$\psi_1 = \psi_{01} + \mu(a_1 + b_1 d + c_1 d_1) = 0$$

$$[45.13]$$

These equations hold only when μ is very small so that the terms containing powers of μ greater than the first are negligible.

Since these two equations must be satisfied for a sufficiently small μ, two conditions must be fulfilled:

$$\phi_{01} = \phi_{01}(K) = 0; \quad \psi_{01} = \psi_{01}(K) = 0 \qquad [45.14]$$

$$a + bd + cd_1 = 0; \quad a_1 + b_1 d + c_1 d_1 = 0 \qquad [45.15]$$

The condition [45.14] states that the terms independent of μ must be equal to zero and [45.15] that the system of the two equations must yield the values of d and d_1 which determine the quantities $\tau(\mu)$ and $\beta(\mu)$ to the first order. It is apparent that this is possible whenever the determinant $\begin{vmatrix} b & c \\ b_1 & c_1 \end{vmatrix} \neq 0$. With Expressions [45.12] taken into account, this is equivalent to the condition

$$J = \begin{vmatrix} \dfrac{\partial \phi_1}{\partial \tau} & \dfrac{\partial \phi_1}{\partial \beta} \\ \dfrac{\partial \psi_1}{\partial \tau} & \dfrac{\partial \psi_1}{\partial \beta} \end{vmatrix} = \dfrac{\partial(\phi_1, \psi_1)}{\partial(\tau, \beta)} \neq 0 \qquad [45.16]$$

Hence, whenever the Jacobian [45.16] is different from zero, periodic solutions of the non-linear problem exist since it is possible then to determine the functions $\tau(\mu)$ and $\beta(\mu)$ provided μ is sufficiently small and provided the conditions [45.14] are fulfilled. If Equations [45.14] can be solved, one obtains one or several values of K; hence the problem is solved.

We can recapitulate the problem somewhat differently using the terminology of the phase plane. For $\mu = 0$ there is a continuum of closed trajectories corresponding to different values of the integration constants, as was shown in Section 1. For $\mu \neq 0$ but very small, closed trajectories may exist in certain restricted regions of the phase plane in which the condition [45.16] is fulfilled; the value of the integration constant K_1, the amplitude, is determined by solving Equations [45.14]. The solution of [45.1], when $\mu = 0$ and $K = K_1$ as just explained, is called the *generating solution*. We shall see numerous examples of this procedure in what follows.

46. EXPANSIONS OF POINCARÉ; GENERATING SOLUTIONS; SECULAR TERMS

Instead of Equations [45.1], we shall consider now a non-linear differential equation of the form

$$\ddot{x} + x = \mu f(x,\dot{x}) \qquad [46.1]$$

Let $x = x(t,\mu,\beta_1,\beta_2,K)$ be its periodic solution in the neighborhood of $\mu = 0$. Expanding this solution into a power series of μ, β_1, and β_2, we know by the theorem of Poincaré that this expansion converges in any arbitrary but finite time interval provided these quantities are sufficiently small in absolute value. We obtain

$$x = \phi_0(t) + A\beta_1 + B\beta_2 + C\mu + D\beta_1\mu + E\beta_2\mu + F\mu^2 + \cdots \qquad [46.2]$$

where ϕ_0, A, B, $\cdots$ are functions of t. Our purpose will be to identify the expansion [46.2] with a periodic solution of [46.1] provided $|\mu|$, $|\beta_1(\mu)|$, and $|\beta_2(\mu)|$ are small. Differentiating [46.2] with respect to t, we obtain the following equations

$$\dot{x} = \dot{\phi}_0(t) + \dot{A}\beta_1 + \dot{B}\beta_2 + \cdots; \quad \ddot{x} = \ddot{\phi}_0(t) + \ddot{A}\beta_1 + \ddot{B}\beta_2 + \cdots \qquad [46.3]$$

Expanding $f(x,\dot{x})$ in a Taylor series around the values x_0, $\dot{x}_0$ we get

$$f(x,\dot{x}) = f(x_0,\dot{x}_0) + (x - x_0)\left(\frac{\partial f}{\partial x}\right)_0 + (\dot{x} - \dot{x}_0)\left(\frac{\partial f}{\partial \dot{x}}\right)_0 + \frac{1}{2}(x - x_0)^2\left(\frac{\partial^2 f}{\partial x^2}\right)_0 +$$

$$+ \frac{1}{2}(\dot{x} - \dot{x}_0)^2\left(\frac{\partial^2 f}{\partial \dot{x}^2}\right)_0 + (x - x_0)(\dot{x} - \dot{x}_0)\left(\frac{\partial^2 f}{\partial x \partial \dot{x}}\right)_0 + \cdots \qquad [46.4]$$

Substituting $x - x_0 = x - \phi_0(t)$; $\dot{x} - \dot{x}_0 = \dot{x} - \dot{\phi}_0(t)$ as given by [46.2] and [46.3] into [46.4] and replacing x, $\ddot{x}$, and $f(x,\dot{x})$ by their values [46.2], [46.3], and [46.4] in the differential equation [46.1], one obtains a series arranged in terms of μ, β_1, β_2, $\beta_1\mu$, $\beta_2\mu$, μ^2, $\cdots$ which by the theorem of Poincaré (6) converges. By equating the coefficients of μ, β_1, $\cdots$, one obtains a set of differential equations. If the expansion is limited to the second order, one obtains nine differential equations, of which three are identically satisfied and the remaining six are as follows:

$$\ddot{A} + A = 0; \quad \ddot{B} + B = 0 \qquad [46.5]$$

$$\ddot{C} + C = f(x_0, \dot{x}_0); \quad \ddot{D} + D = \left(\frac{\partial f}{\partial x}\right)_0 A + \left(\frac{\partial f}{\partial \dot{x}}\right)_0 \dot{A}$$

$$\ddot{E} + E = \left(\frac{\partial f}{\partial x}\right)_0 B + \left(\frac{\partial f}{\partial \dot{x}}\right)_0 \dot{B}; \quad \ddot{F} + F = \left(\frac{\partial f}{\partial x}\right)_0 C + \left(\frac{\partial f}{\partial \dot{x}}\right)_0 \dot{C}$$

[46.5]

Here the symbols $\left(\frac{\partial f}{\partial x}\right)_0$ and $\left(\frac{\partial f}{\partial \dot{x}}\right)_0$ designate the partial derivatives of f with respect to the variables x and $\dot{x}$ in which the generating solutions $x_0 = \phi_0(t)$ and $\dot{x}_0 = \dot{\phi}_0(t)$ have been substituted after differentiation.

Writing [46.2] and its derived equation for $t = 0$ in the form

$$x - x_0 = \beta_1 = A\beta_1 + B\beta_2 + C\mu + D\beta_1\mu + \cdots$$

$$\dot{x} - \dot{x}_0 = \beta_2 = \dot{A}\beta_1 + \dot{B}\beta_2 + \dot{C}\mu + \dot{D}\beta_1\mu + \cdots$$

[46.6]

one obtains the following initial conditions

$$A(0) = 1; \quad \dot{B}(0) = 1$$

[46.7]

$$B(0) = C(0) = D(0) = E(0) = F(0) = \dot{A}(0) = \dot{C}(0) = \dot{D}(0) = \dot{E}(0) = \dot{F}(0) = 0$$

With these initial conditions the first two equations [46.5] have the solutions

$$A = \cos t; \quad B = \sin t$$

with period 2π.

The remaining four equations [46.5] are of the form $\ddot{v} + v = V(t)$, having the initial conditions $v(0) = \dot{v}(0) = 0$. The solution of this equation is

$$v = \int_0^t V(u) \sin(t - u)\, du$$

[46.8]

Replacing $V(u)$ in Equation [46.8] by the right-hand terms of the last four equations [46.5], one obtains the following expressions:

$$A = \cos t; \quad \dot{A} = -\sin t$$

$$B = \sin t; \quad \dot{B} = \cos t$$

$$C = \int_0^t f[\phi_0(u), \dot{\phi}_0(u)] \sin(t - u)\, du; \quad \dot{C} = \int_0^t f[\phi_0(u), \dot{\phi}_0(u)] \cos(t - u)\, du$$

[46.9]

$$D = \int_0^t \left[\frac{\partial f}{\partial x_0}\cos u - \frac{\partial f}{\partial \dot{x}_0}\sin u\right]\sin(t - u)\, du; \quad \dot{D} = \int_0^t \left[\frac{\partial f}{\partial x_0}\cos u - \frac{\partial f}{\partial \dot{x}_0}\sin u\right]\cos(t - u)\, du$$

$$E = \int_0^t \left[\frac{\partial f}{\partial x_0}\sin u + \frac{\partial f}{\partial \dot{x}_0}\cos u\right]\sin(t - u)\, du; \quad \dot{E} = \int_0^t \left[\frac{\partial f}{\partial x_0}\sin u + \frac{\partial f}{\partial \dot{x}_0}\cos u\right]\cos(t - u)\, du$$

$$F = \int_0^t \left[\frac{\partial f}{\partial x_0}C + \frac{\partial f}{\partial \dot{x}_0}\dot{C}\right]\sin(t - u)\, du; \quad \dot{F} = \int_0^t \left[\frac{\partial f}{\partial x_0}C + \frac{\partial f}{\partial \dot{x}_0}\dot{C}\right]\cos(t - u)\, du$$

where $x_0 = K \cos t$ and $\dot{x}_0 = - K \sin t$ are the generating solutions in which the phase is taken equal to zero.

Inasmuch as only periodic solutions are of interest here, it is important to know the values of A, B, $\cdots F$ after one period. Replacing t by 2π in Expressions [46.9], one obtains

$$A(2\pi) = 1; \quad \dot{A}(2\pi) = 0$$

$$B(2\pi) = 0; \quad \dot{B}(2\pi) = 1$$

$$C(2\pi) = - \int_0^{2\pi} f(x_0, \dot{x}_0) \sin u \, du; \quad \dot{C}(2\pi) = \int_0^{2\pi} f(x_0, \dot{x}_0) \cos u \, du$$

$$D(2\pi) = \int_0^{2\pi} \left[-\frac{1}{2} \frac{\partial f}{\partial x_0} \sin 2u + \frac{\partial f}{\partial \dot{x}_0} \sin^2 u \right] du; \quad \dot{D}(2\pi) = \int_0^{2\pi} \left[\frac{\partial f}{\partial x_0} \cos^2 u - \frac{1}{2} \frac{\partial f}{\partial \dot{x}_0} \sin 2u \right] du$$

$$\text{[46.10]}$$

$$E(2\pi) = \int_0^{2\pi} \left[-\frac{\partial f}{\partial x_0} \sin^2 u - \frac{1}{2} \frac{\partial f}{\partial \dot{x}_0} \sin 2u \right] du; \quad \dot{E}(2\pi) = \int_0^{2\pi} \left[\frac{1}{2} \frac{\partial f}{\partial x_0} \sin 2u + \frac{\partial f}{\partial \dot{x}_0} \cos^2 u \right] du$$

$$F(2\pi) = \int_0^{2\pi} \left[-\frac{\partial f}{\partial x_0} C(u) \sin u - \frac{\partial f}{\partial \dot{x}_0} \dot{C}(u) \sin u \right] du$$

$$\dot{F}(2\pi) = \int_0^{2\pi} \left[\frac{\partial f}{\partial x_0} C(u) \cos u + \frac{\partial f}{\partial \dot{x}_0} \dot{C}(u) \cos u \right] du$$

The expressions for D and E can be further simplified by expressing the values of $\frac{1}{K} \frac{d}{du}(f \cos u)$ and $\frac{1}{K} \frac{d}{du}(f \sin u)$ differently.

We have

$$\frac{d}{du}(f \cos u) = \frac{df}{du} \cos u - f \sin u; \quad \frac{df}{du} = \frac{\partial f}{\partial x_0} \frac{\partial x_0}{\partial u} + \frac{\partial f}{\partial \dot{x}_0} \frac{\partial \dot{x}_0}{\partial u}$$

Since the generating solutions x_0 and $\dot{x}_0$ are

$$x_0 = K \cos u; \quad \dot{x}_0 = - K \sin u$$

$$\frac{\partial x_0}{\partial u} = - K \sin u; \quad \frac{\partial \dot{x}_0}{\partial u} = - K \cos u$$

hence

$$\frac{df}{du} = - K \frac{\partial f}{\partial x_0} \sin u - K \frac{\partial f}{\partial \dot{x}_0} \cos u$$

and thus

$$\frac{1}{K} \frac{d}{du}(f \cos u) = - \frac{\partial f}{\partial x_0} \sin u \cos u - \frac{\partial f}{\partial \dot{x}_0} \cos^2 u - \frac{f}{K} \sin u$$

or

$$\frac{1}{K} \frac{d}{du}(f \cos u) = - \frac{1}{2} \frac{\partial f}{\partial x_0} \sin 2u - \frac{\partial f}{\partial \dot{x}_0} \cos^2 u - \frac{f}{K} \sin u \qquad \text{[46.11]}$$

and similarly

$$\frac{1}{K} \frac{d}{du}(f \sin u) = -\frac{\partial f}{\partial x_0} \sin^2 u - \frac{1}{2} \frac{\partial f}{\partial \dot{x}_0} \sin 2u + \frac{f}{K} \cos u \qquad [46.12]$$

Expressions [46.10] for D, $\dot{D}$, E, and $\dot{E}$, taking into account the expression for C, are simplified by means of Equations [46.11] and [46.12] and assume the following symmetrical form:

$$D(2\pi) = \int_0^{2\pi} \frac{\partial f}{\partial \dot{x}_0} du - \frac{C(2\pi)}{K}; \quad \dot{D}(2\pi) = \int_0^{2\pi} \frac{\partial f}{\partial x_0} du - \frac{\dot{C}(2\pi)}{K}$$

$$[46.13]$$

$$E(2\pi) = -\frac{1}{K}\dot{C}(2\pi); \quad \dot{E}(2\pi) = \frac{1}{K}C(2\pi)$$

If $C(2\pi) = 0$ and $\dot{C}(2\pi) \neq 0$, Equations [46.13] become

$$D(2\pi) = \int_0^{2\pi} \frac{\partial f}{\partial \dot{x}_0} du; \quad \dot{D}(2\pi) = \int_0^{2\pi} \frac{\partial f}{\partial x_0} du - \frac{\dot{C}(2\pi)}{K}$$

$$[46.14]$$

$$E(2\pi) = -\frac{1}{K}\dot{C}(2\pi); \quad \dot{E}(2\pi) = 0$$

If $C(2\pi) = \dot{C}(2\pi) = 0$, one has

$$D(2\pi) = \int_0^{2\pi} \frac{\partial f}{\partial \dot{x}_0} du; \quad \dot{D}(2\pi) = \int_0^{2\pi} \frac{\partial f}{\partial x_0} du$$

$$[46.15]$$

$$E(2\pi) = 0; \quad \dot{E}(2\pi) = 0$$

From the latter form of the expressions for $D(2\pi)$ and $\dot{D}(2\pi)$, it is apparent that they represent the constant terms in the Fourier expansion of $\frac{\partial f}{\partial \dot{x}_0}$ and $\frac{\partial f}{\partial x_0}$, multiplied by 2π. On the other hand, $-C(2\pi)$ and $\dot{C}(2\pi)$, as given by Equation [46.10], are the coefficients of $\sin t$, $\cos t$ in the expansion of $f(x_0, \dot{x}_0)$, multiplied by π. Hence, if $f(x_0, \dot{x}_0)$ is given, these coefficients can be calculated directly from Equations [46.10].

We are now in a position to write Equations [45.10] in a new form, expressing the existence of periodic solutions. It is apparent that by the choice of generating solutions in the form $x_0(t) = K \cos t$ and $\dot{x}_0(t) = -K \sin t$, the amplitude K is already contained in the expressions for β_1 and β_2 so that Equations [45.10] can be written as

$$\phi(\tau, \mu, \beta_1, \beta_2) = 0 \quad \text{and} \quad \psi(\tau, \mu, \beta_1, \beta_2) = 0 \qquad [46.16]$$

These equations express sufficient conditions for the existence of periodic solutions. There are thus two equations with three unknowns, τ, β_1, and β_2. One of the β's, however, is arbitrary and can be taken equal to zero, as previously mentioned. If, therefore, Equations [46.16] can be solved giving τ and β_1 as functions of μ in such a manner that for $\mu \to 0$, $\tau(\mu) \to 0$, and $\beta_1(\mu) \to 0$, the problem is solved. If this is impossible, there is still another alternative. We may put $\beta_1 = 0$ and try to solve for τ and β_2 as unknown functions of μ.

The left-hand terms of Equations [46.16] represent the differences $x(2\pi + \tau) - x(0)$ and $\dot{x}(2\pi + \tau) - \dot{x}(0)$. Expanding $x(2\pi + \tau)$ and $\dot{x}(2\pi + \tau)$ in a Taylor series in which τ is considered small, we have

$$x(2\pi + \tau) = x(2\pi) + \tau \dot{x}(2\pi) + \cdots$$

$$\dot{x}(2\pi + \tau) = \dot{x}(2\pi) + \tau \ddot{x}(2\pi) + \cdots$$

[46.17]

Here we substitute the series expansions [46.2] and [46.3]. The coefficients $A(2\pi)$, $B(2\pi)$, $\cdots$ have already been calculated in Equations [46.10]. Considering τ and μ as small quantities of the first order and carrying out the expansions to the second order, one has

$$x(2\pi + \tau) = x_0(2\pi) + A(2\pi)\beta_1 + B(2\pi)\beta_2 + C(2\pi)\mu + D(2\pi)\beta_1\mu + E(2\pi)\beta_2\mu +$$

$$+ F(2\pi)\mu^2 + \tau \dot{x}_0(2\pi) + \tau \dot{A}(2\pi)\beta_1 + \tau \dot{B}(2\pi)\beta_2 + \tau \dot{C}(2\pi)\mu + \frac{\tau^2}{2}\ddot{x}_0(2\pi) \quad [46.18]$$

$$\dot{x}(2\pi + \tau) = \dot{x}_0(2\pi) + \dot{A}(2\pi)\beta_1 + \dot{B}(2\pi)\beta_2 + \dot{C}(2\pi)\mu + \dot{D}(2\pi)\beta_1\mu + \dot{E}(2\pi)\beta_2\mu +$$

$$+ \dot{F}(2\pi)\mu^2 + \tau \ddot{x}_0(2\pi) + \tau \ddot{A}(2\pi)\beta_1 + \tau \ddot{B}(2\pi)\beta_2 + \tau \ddot{C}(2\pi)\mu + \frac{\tau^2}{2}\dddot{x}_0(2\pi) \quad [46.19]$$

But $x_0(2\pi) = x_0(0)$ and $\dot{x}_0(2\pi) = \dot{x}_0(0)$. Furthermore, $A(2\pi) = 1$, $\dot{A}(2\pi) = 0$, $B(2\pi) = 0$, and $\dot{B}(2\pi) = 1$. With these values of the coefficients, Equations [46.18] and [46.19] become

$$x(2\pi + \tau) - x(0) = -K\frac{\tau^2}{2} + \tau\beta_2 + C(2\pi)\mu + \dot{C}(2\pi)\tau\mu +$$

$$+ D(2\pi)\beta_1\mu + E(2\pi)\beta_2\mu + F(2\pi)\mu^2 = 0 \quad [46.20]$$

and

$$\dot{x}(2\pi + \tau) - \dot{x}(0) = -K\tau - \tau\beta_1 + \dot{C}(2\pi)\mu + \ddot{C}(2\pi)\tau\mu +$$

$$+ \dot{D}(2\pi)\beta_1\mu + \dot{E}(2\pi)\beta_2\mu + \dot{F}(2\pi)\mu^2 = 0 \quad [46.21]$$

One of the parameters β can be fixed as we please. Thus for a given value of one β these equations determine the other β and the correction τ for the period. Since μ, β_1, β_2, and τ are small quantities of the first order, one can obtain different conditions according to the order of the approximation. The simplest case is that in which one considers the first-order solution, dropping terms of the second order. The only term of the first order in [46.20] is $C(2\pi)\mu$, and in [46.21] there are two terms of the first order, $- K\tau$ and $\dot{C}(2\pi)\mu$. By equating these terms to zero, we obtain the following two equations

$$C(2\pi) = - \int_0^{2\pi} f(K\cos u, - K\sin u)\sin u\, du \equiv \phi(K) = 0 \qquad [46.22]$$

$$\tau = \frac{\dot{C}(2\pi)\mu}{K} = \frac{\mu}{K} \int_0^{2\pi} f(K\cos u, - K\sin u)\cos u\, du \equiv \mu\psi(K) \qquad [46.23]$$

Equation [46.22] determines the amplitude K of the generating solution in the neighborhood of which exist periodic solutions of [46.1], and Equation [46.23] gives the correction τ for the period, provided $C(2\pi) \neq 0$. If $\dot{C}(2\pi) = 0$, from [46.15], $E(2\pi) = \dot{E}(2\pi) = 0$. Hence, Equation [46.20] reduces to

$$D(2\pi)\beta_1 + F(2\pi)\mu = 0 \qquad [46.24]$$

Since τ in this case is zero to the first order, we may proceed to the second order and put $\tau = \sigma\mu^2$. From [46.21], in which we can put $\beta_2 = 0$, and where $\dot{C}(2\pi) = 0$, $\ddot{C}(2\pi) = 0$, and $\dot{E}(2\pi) = 0$, we obtain

$$- K\sigma\mu^2 + \dot{D}(2\pi)\beta_1\mu + \dot{F}(2\pi)\mu^2 = 0$$

Dividing by μ and substituting the value of β_1 derived from [46.24] into this expression, we obtain

$$\sigma = \frac{\dot{F}(2\pi)D(2\pi) - F(2\pi)\dot{D}(2\pi)}{K \cdot D(2\pi)} \qquad [46.25]$$

The correction $\tau = \sigma\mu^2$ must be introduced each time the motion is isochronous to the first order. Thus, if $K \neq 0$ and $D(2\pi) \neq 0$, Equations [46.24] and [46.25] determine β_1 and $\tau = \sigma\mu^2$, the amplitude K having been determined from Equation [46.22]. Substituting the values of A, B, C, and β_1 in Equation [46.2], we obtain

$$x = K\cos t + \mu\left[\int_0^t f(K\cos u, - K\sin u)\sin(t - u)\, du - \frac{F(2\pi)}{D(2\pi)}\cos t\right] \qquad [46.26]$$

where K has been calculated from Equation [46.22].*

It is to be noted that the term $\frac{2}{T+\tau} \int_{0}^{T+\tau} f(x_0, \dot{x}_0) \sin(t-u)\, du$
represents the first term of the Fourier expansion of the function appearing
on the right side of Equation [46.1]. Moreover, the period has been changed
because of the presence of the term τ, the correction for the period. The
function $x(t)$ given by Equation [46.26] remains periodic.

It should be mentioned here again that the presence of secular
terms does not destroy the periodicity but merely accounts for a modification
of the period, as was explained in connection with Equation [44.2]. The
effect of the appearance of secular terms can also be ascertained from the
following example. Assume that we have a periodic function

$$x(t) = \sum_{K=0}^{\infty} \left[a_K(\mu) \cos K\omega(\mu)t + b_K(\mu) \sin K\omega(\mu)t \right] \qquad [46.27]$$

in which both the amplitudes and frequencies are functions of a parameter μ.
Expansion of this function in a power series of μ gives

$$x(t) = \sum_{K=0}^{\infty} \left[a_K(0) \cos K\omega(0)t + b_K(0) \sin K\omega(0)t \right] +$$

$$+ \mu \sum_{K=0}^{\infty} \left[a_K'(0) \cos K\omega(0)t + b_K'(0) \sin K\omega(0)t - \right.$$

$$\left. - a_K(0)\omega'(0)Kt \sin K\omega(0)t + b_K(0)\omega'(0)Kt \cos K\omega(0)t \right] + \mu^2 \sum_{K=0}^{\infty} \cdots \quad [46.28]$$

where a_K', b_K', and ω' designate the derivatives of the functions $a_K(\mu)$, $b_K(\mu)$,
and $\omega(\mu)$ with respect to μ in which the value $\mu = 0$ has been substituted after
differentiation. It is observed that, since the function $x(t)$ is periodic,
the appearance of secular terms does not destroy the periodicity in view of
the summation of these terms from 0 to ∞. This might not be the case if only
a few secular terms were considered in the expansion.

With reference to [46.26], it is to be noted that the secular terms
do not appear in the expansion for $x(t)$ if the correction τ can be calculated
first, which requires that $D(2\pi) \neq 0$. It is sufficient then to use as the
period over which the functions A, B, $\cdots$ of Poincaré are determined, the
corrected period $T + \tau$, which amounts to the choice of generating solutions
x_0 and $\dot{x}_0$ in the form $K \cos\left[1 - \frac{\sigma\mu^2}{2\pi}\right]t$ and $-K \sin\left[1 - \frac{\sigma\mu^2}{2\pi}\right]t$, instead of
$K \cos t$ and $-K \sin t$. The question of secular terms will be discussed in more
detail in Section 58.

---

* In order to re-establish the arbitrariness of the phase, t should be replaced by $t + \delta$, where δ is
an arbitrary phase.

47. SYSTEMS WITH TWO DEGREES OF FREEDOM

In the preceding sections we have been concerned with the establishment of conditions for periodicity of solutions of a single non-linear differential equation [46.1] of the second order, which generally represents in applications a dynamical system with one degree of freedom. The only stationary solutions in this case are periodic ones, and the topological representation of such motions in the phase plane does not present any particular difficulty, as was shown in Part I.

Although theoretically the extension of Poincaré's method to systems with several degrees of freedom follows the same argument, the practical difficulties rapidly increase and the benefit derived from topological considerations disappears.* Moreover, the stationary motions in systems of more than one degree of freedom are not necessarily periodic. It thus becomes necessary to restrict the analysis somewhat by endeavoring to formulate only the conditions of stability, which in applications is equivalent to the physical possibility of a particular motion. Systems with two degrees of freedom play an important role in applications, and for that reason it may be of interest to give a brief outline of the method of Poincaré in connection with such systems, omitting the details which have already been explained. The calculations of Andronow and Witt (7) (8) are given in this and the following sections.

Consider a quasi-linear system of two differential equations of the second order

$$\ddot{x} + \omega_1^2 x = \mu f(x, \dot{x}, y, \dot{y}; \mu)$$

$$\ddot{y} + \omega_2^2 y = \mu g(x, \dot{x}, y, \dot{y}; \mu)$$

[47.1]

where μ is a small positive number and the functions f and g are analytic functions of the indicated variables. Since there are two degrees of freedom, one has a greater variety of limit conditions for $\mu = 0$ than in the previously discussed case of a single equation [46.1]. Thus we can write the limit conditions either as

---

* In fact, a dynamical system with two degrees of freedom is generally reducible to a system of four differential equations of the first order, and its representation in a phase plane becomes generally impossible. Only in very special cases of the so-called "degeneration" defined in Part IV is a planar representation possible, but such "degenerate" systems possess entirely new features which are not investigated here.

$$x = R\cos\omega_1 t = \phi_0(t); \quad y = 0 \quad \text{with period} \quad T = \frac{2\pi}{\omega_1}$$

or   [47.2]

$$x = 0; \quad y = R\cos\omega_2 t = \psi_0(t) \quad \text{with period} \quad T = \frac{2\pi}{\omega_2}$$

The question as to which of these two generating solutions the dynamical system will "select" will form an important object of a later study.

The procedure initially follows the pattern outlined in connection with a single equation [46.1]. Let us assume that we select the first alternative of [47.2] and apply the perturbation method by putting

$$x = \phi_0(t) + \xi; \quad y = 0 + \eta \qquad [47.3]$$

In terms of the perturbations ξ and η, Equations [47.1] become

$$\ddot{\xi} + \omega_1^2\xi = \mu\Big[f(\phi_0,\dot{\phi}_0,0,0;0) + f_x\xi + f_{\dot{x}}\dot{\xi} + f_y\eta + f_{\dot{y}}\dot{\eta} + f_\mu\mu + O_2(\xi,\dot{\xi},\eta,\dot{\eta},\mu)\Big]$$

$$[47.4]$$

$$\ddot{\eta} + \omega_2^2\eta = \mu\Big[g(\phi_0,\dot{\phi}_0,0,0;0) + g_x\xi + g_{\dot{x}}\dot{\xi} + g_y\eta + g_{\dot{y}}\dot{\eta} + g_\mu\mu + O_2(\xi,\dot{\xi},\eta,\dot{\eta},\mu)\Big]$$

where the quantity O_2 contains terms of a degree higher than the first in $\xi, \cdots \mu$. According to Poincaré, the solutions of these equations can be taken as power series

$$\xi = \beta_1 A + \beta_2 B + \beta_3 C + \beta_4 D + \mu\Big[E + \beta_1 F + \beta_2 G + \beta_3 H + \beta_4 K + \mu L +$$

$$+ O_2(\beta_1,\beta_2,\beta_3,\beta_4,\mu)\Big] + \overline{O}_2(\beta_1,\beta_2,\beta_3,\beta_4)$$

$$[47.5]$$

$$\eta = \beta_1\overline{A} + \beta_2\overline{B} + \beta_3\overline{C} + \beta_4\overline{D} + \mu\Big[\overline{E} + \beta_1\overline{F} + \beta_2\overline{G} + \beta_3\overline{H} + \beta_4\overline{K} + \mu\overline{L} +$$

$$+ O_2(\beta_1,\beta_2,\beta_3,\beta_4,\mu)\Big] + \overline{O}_2(\beta_1,\beta_2,\beta_3,\beta_4)$$

where $A, \cdots L$ and $\overline{A}, \cdots \overline{L}$ are functions of time and

$$\beta_1 = \xi(0); \quad \beta_2 = \dot{\xi}(0); \quad \beta_3 = \eta(0); \quad \beta_4 = \dot{\eta}(0) \qquad [47.6]$$

One of the β's, as will be seen, can be assumed to be equal to zero; for example, $\beta_2 = 0$. If one substitutes the expressions [47.5] into Equations [47.4] and equates the coefficients of like powers of $\beta_1, \cdots \mu$, a system of differential equations results from which the functions $A, \cdots L$ and $\overline{A}, \cdots \overline{L}$ can be determined. One obtains the following expressions:

$$A = \cos\omega_1 t; \quad C = 0; \quad D = 0; \quad O_2(\beta_1,\beta_3,\beta_4) = 0$$

$$E = \frac{1}{\omega_1}\int_0^t f(\phi_0,\dot{\phi}_0,0,0;0)\sin\omega_1(t-u)\,du$$

$$F = \frac{1}{\omega_1}\int_0^t (\cos\omega_1 u \cdot f_x - \omega_1 \sin\omega_1 u \cdot f_{\dot{x}})\sin\omega_1(t-u)\,du$$

$$H = \frac{1}{\omega_1}\int_0^t (\cos\omega_2 u \cdot f_y - \omega_2 \sin\omega_2 u \cdot f_{\dot{y}})\sin\omega_1(t-u)\,du$$

$$K = \frac{1}{\omega_1}\int_0^t \left(\frac{1}{\omega_2}\sin\omega_2 u \cdot f_y + \cos\omega_2 u \cdot f_{\dot{y}}\right)\sin\omega_1(t-u)\,du$$

$$L = \frac{1}{\omega_1}\int_0^t \left[Ef_x + \dot{E}f_{\dot{x}} + \overline{E}f_y + \dot{\overline{E}}f_{\dot{y}} + f_\mu\right]\sin\omega_1(t-u)\,du$$

[47.7]

$$\overline{A} = 0; \quad \overline{C} = \cos\omega_2 t; \quad \overline{D} = \frac{1}{\omega_2}\sin\omega_2 t; \quad \overline{O}_2(\beta_1,\beta_3,\beta_4) = 0$$

$$\overline{E} = \frac{1}{\omega_2}\int_0^t g(\phi_0,\dot{\phi}_0,0,0;0)\sin\omega_2(t-u)\,du$$

$$\overline{F} = \frac{1}{\omega_2}\int_0^t (\cos\omega_1 u \cdot g_x - \omega_1 \sin\omega_1 u \cdot g_{\dot{x}})\sin\omega_2(t-u)\,du$$

$$\overline{H} = \frac{1}{\omega_2}\int_0^t (\cos\omega_2 u \cdot g_y - \omega_2 \sin\omega_2 u \cdot g_{\dot{y}})\sin\omega_2(t-u)\,du$$

$$\overline{K} = \frac{1}{\omega_2}\int_0^t \left(\frac{1}{\omega_2}\sin\omega_2 u \cdot g_y + \cos\omega_2 u \cdot g_{\dot{y}}\right)\sin\omega_2(t-u)\,du$$

$$\overline{L} = \frac{1}{\omega_2}\int_0^t \left[Eg_x + \dot{E}g_{\dot{x}} + \overline{E}g_y + \dot{\overline{E}}g_{\dot{y}} + g_\mu\right]\sin\omega_2(t-u)\,du$$

The conditions of periodicity for the solutions [47.3] are

$$[x] = x\left(\frac{2\pi}{\omega_1}+\tau\right) - x(0) = 0; \quad [\dot{x}] = \dot{x}\left(\frac{2\pi}{\omega_1}+\tau\right) - \dot{x}(0) = 0$$

[47.8]

$$[y] = y\left(\frac{2\pi}{\omega_1}+\tau\right) - y(0) = 0; \quad [\dot{y}] = \dot{y}\left(\frac{2\pi}{\omega_1}+\tau\right) - \dot{y}(0) = 0$$

These four conditions, with the use of the symbols [ ] defined by [47.8], become

$$R\left[\cos\omega_1 t\right] + \beta_1[A] + \mu\left([E] + \beta_1[F] + \beta_3[H] + \beta_4[K] + \mu[L] + [O_2(\beta_1,\beta_3,\beta_4,\mu)]\right) = 0$$

$$R\left[-\omega_1\sin\omega_1 t\right] + \beta_1[\dot{A}] + \mu\left([\dot{E}] + \beta_1[\dot{F}] + \beta_3[\dot{H}] + \beta_4[\dot{K}] + \mu[\dot{L}] + [O_2(\beta_1,\beta_3,\beta_4,\mu)]\right) = 0$$

$$[47.9]$$

$$\beta_3[\overline{C}] + \beta_4[\overline{D}] + \mu\left([\overline{E}] + \beta_1[\overline{F}] + \beta_3[\overline{H}] + \beta_4[\overline{K}] + \mu[\overline{L}] + [O_2(\beta_1,\beta_3,\beta_4,\mu)]\right) = 0$$

$$\beta_3[\dot{\overline{C}}] + \beta_4[\dot{\overline{D}}] + \mu\left([\dot{\overline{E}}] + \beta_1[\dot{\overline{F}}] + \beta_3[\dot{\overline{H}}] + \beta_4[\dot{\overline{K}}] + \mu[\dot{\overline{L}}] + [O_2(\beta_1,\beta_3,\beta_4,\mu)]\right) = 0$$

Developing the expressions indicated by the symbols [ ] in power series of τ, the correction for the period, one obtains

$$[A] = A\left(\frac{2\pi}{\omega_1} + \tau\right) - A(0) = a_0 + a_1\tau + a_2\tau^2 + \cdots$$

$$[47.10]$$

$$[\dot{A}] = \dot{A}\left(\frac{2\pi}{\omega_1} + \tau\right) - \dot{A}(0) = \dot{a}_0 + \dot{a}_1\tau + \dot{a}_2\tau^2 + \cdots$$

$$\cdots \cdots \cdots \cdots \cdots$$

where $a_0, \cdots$ and $\dot{a}_0, \cdots$ can be calculated by Equations [47.7]. One obtains from [47.10] the following equations

$$-\frac{R\omega_1^2\tau}{2} + \beta_1(a_0 + a_1\tau) + \mu(e_0 + e_1\tau + \beta_1 f_0 + \beta_3 h_0 + \beta_4 k_0 + \mu l_0) + O_3(\beta_1,\beta_3,\beta_4,\mu,\tau) = 0$$

$$-R\omega_1^2\tau + \beta_1(\dot{C}_0 + a_1\tau) + \mu(\dot{e}_0 + \dot{e}_1\tau + \beta_1\dot{f}_0 + \beta_3\dot{h}_0 + \beta_4\dot{k}_0 + \mu\dot{i}_0) + O_3(\beta_1,\beta_3,\beta_4,\mu,\tau) = 0$$

$$[47.11]$$

$$\beta_3(\overline{C}_0 + \overline{C}_1\tau) + \beta_4(\overline{d}_0 + \overline{d}_1\tau) + \mu(\overline{e}_0 + \overline{e}_1\tau + \beta_1\overline{f}_0 + \beta_3\overline{h}_0 + \beta_4\overline{k}_0 + \mu\overline{l}_0) + O_3(\beta_1,\beta_3,\beta_4,\mu,\tau) = 0$$

$$\beta_3(\dot{\overline{C}}_0 + \dot{\overline{C}}_1\tau) + \beta_4(\dot{\overline{d}}_0 + \dot{\overline{d}}_1\tau) + \mu(\dot{\overline{e}}_0 + \dot{\overline{e}}_1\tau + \beta_1\dot{\overline{f}}_0 + \beta_3\dot{\overline{h}}_0 + \beta_4\dot{\overline{k}}_0 + \mu\dot{\overline{l}}_0) + O_3(\beta_1,\beta_3,\beta_4,\mu,\tau) = 0$$

In these equations certain coefficients do not depend on the choice of the functions f and g. Thus, one always has

$$a_0 = 0; \quad a_1 = 0; \quad \dot{a}_0 = 0; \quad \dot{a}_1 = -\omega_1^2$$

$$[47.12]$$

$$\overline{C}_0 = \cos\gamma - 1; \quad \overline{d}_0 = \frac{1}{\omega_2}\sin\gamma; \quad \dot{\overline{C}}_0 = -\omega_2\sin\gamma; \quad \dot{\overline{d}}_0 = \cos\gamma - 1$$

where $\gamma = 2\pi\dfrac{\omega_2}{\omega_1}$.

The second equation [47.11], taking into consideration [47.12] and $O_3(\beta_1,\beta_3,\beta_4,\mu)$, gives τ, viz.,

$$\tau = \mu\left[\alpha_0 + \beta_1\alpha_1 + \beta_3\alpha_3 + \beta_4\alpha_4 + \mu\alpha_5 + O_2(\beta_1,\beta_3,\beta_4,\mu)\right] \qquad [47.13]$$

where

$$\alpha_0 = \frac{\dot{e}_0}{R\omega_1^2}; \quad \alpha_1 = \frac{R\dot{f}_0 - \dot{e}_0}{R^2\omega_1^2}; \quad \alpha_3 = \frac{\dot{h}_0}{R\omega_1^2}; \quad \alpha_4 = \frac{\dot{k}_0}{R\omega_1^2}; \quad \alpha_5 = \frac{R\omega_1^2 \dot{l}_0 + \dot{e}_0\dot{e}_1}{R^2\omega_1^4}$$

Introducing the value of τ given in Equation [47.13] into the remaining equations [47.11], one obtains the following three equations:

$$e_0 + \beta_1 f_0 + \beta_3 h_0 + \beta_4 k_0 + \mu\left(l_0 + a_0 e_1 - \frac{R}{2}\omega_1^2 a_0^2\right) + O_2(\beta_1, \beta_3, \beta_4, \mu) = 0$$

$$\beta_3(\cos\gamma - 1) + \beta_4\left(\frac{1}{\omega_2}\sin\gamma\right) + \mu\overline{e}_0 + O_2(\beta_1, \beta_3, \beta_4, \mu) = 0 \qquad [47.14]$$

$$\beta_3(-\omega_2\sin\gamma) + \beta_4(\cos\gamma - 1) + \mu\dot{\overline{e}}_0 + O_2(\beta_1, \beta_3, \beta_4, \mu) = 0$$

Since we are looking for a periodic solution of the system [47.1], which reduces for $\mu = 0$ to the first generating solution [47.2], it is necessary that the functions $\beta_1(\mu)$, $\beta_3(\mu)$, and $\beta_4(\mu)$ approach zero as μ approaches 0. Hence, in view of [47.12], the necessary condition for the existence of a periodic solution is

$$e_0 = \int_0^{\frac{2\pi}{\omega_1}} f(R\cos\omega_1 u, -\omega_1 R\sin\omega_1 u, 0, 0; 0)\sin\omega_1 u \, du = 0 \qquad [47.15]$$

From this equation one obtains the amplitude of the periodic solution in the neighborhood of $\mu = 0$. The sufficient condition for the existence of a periodic solution is

$$\begin{vmatrix} f_0 & h_0 & k_0 \\ 0 & \cos\gamma - 1 & \frac{1}{\omega_2}\sin\gamma \\ 0 & -\omega_2\sin\gamma & \cos\gamma - 1 \end{vmatrix} = 2f_0(1 - \cos\gamma) \neq 0 \qquad [47.16]$$

In this condition the value of R, and hence of f_0, is the one which satisfies the amplitude equation [47.15].

If $\omega_2 \neq n\omega_1$, that is, if $\gamma \neq 2\pi n$, where n is an integer, the condition for the existence of a periodic solution can be written as

$$f_0 = \int_0^{\frac{2\pi}{\omega_1}} (\cos\omega_1 u \cdot f_x - \omega_1\sin\omega_1 u \cdot f_{\dot{x}})\sin\omega_1 u \, du \neq 0 \qquad [47.17]$$

If the determinant [47.16] is zero, it is sufficient for the existence of a periodic solution that one of the determinants, obtained by equating to zero a β other than β_2 as assumed here, be different from zero. If all determinants are zero, a special study is required.

The periodic solution thus obtained is of the form

$$x = \phi(t) = R\cos\omega_1 t + \beta_1 A + \mu\big[E + \beta_1 F + \beta_3 H + \beta_4 K + \mu L + O_2(\beta_1,\beta_3,\beta_4,\mu)\big]$$

[47.18]

$$y = \overline{\phi}(t) = \beta_3\overline{C} + \beta_4\overline{D} + \mu\big[\overline{E} + \beta_1\overline{F} + \beta_3\overline{H} + \beta_4\overline{K} + \mu\overline{L} + O_2(\beta_1,\beta_3,\beta_4,\mu)\big]$$

where R is determined by [47.15]; A, E, F, $\cdots$ by [47.7]; and β_1, β_3, and β_4 by [47.14]. Replacing β_1, β_3, and β_4 by their values in [47.18] and arranging the terms of the series according to the powers of μ, one obtains

$$x = \phi(t) = \phi_0 + \mu\phi_1 + \mu^2\phi_2 + \mu^3\phi_3 + \cdots$$

[47.19]

$$y = \overline{\phi}(t) = \mu\overline{\phi}_1 + \mu^2\overline{\phi}_2 + \mu^3\overline{\phi}_3 + \cdots$$

It is apparent that similar results can be obtained if one starts with the second generating solution [47.2].

48. STABILITY OF A PERIODIC SOLUTION

The stability of the periodic solutions [47.18] can be investigated by the perturbation method. Consider the perturbed solution

$$x = \phi(t) + u; \quad y = \overline{\phi}(t) + v$$ [48.1]

The variational equations obtained from [47.1] are

$$\ddot{u} + \omega_1^2 u = \mu(f_x u + f_{\dot{x}}\dot{u} + f_y v + f_{\dot{y}}\dot{v})$$

[48.2]

$$\ddot{v} + \omega_2^2 u = \mu(g_x u + g_{\dot{x}}\dot{u} + g_y v + g_{\dot{y}}\dot{v})$$

In these equations the non-linear terms in u and v are left out and the functions f_x, $\cdots$ $g_{\dot{y}}$ are the derivatives of f and g with respect to the indicated variables in which x, $\dot{x}$, y, and $\dot{y}$ are replaced by $\phi(t)$, $\dot{\phi}(t)$, $\overline{\phi}(t)$ and $\dot{\overline{\phi}}(t)$ respectively. These equations have periodic coefficients, and we can expect solutions of the form

$$u = A\overline{\beta}_1 + B\overline{\beta}_2 + C\overline{\beta}_3 + D\overline{\beta}_4$$

[48.3]

$$v = \overline{A}\overline{\beta}_1 + \overline{B}\overline{\beta}_2 + \overline{C}\overline{\beta}_3 + \overline{D}\overline{\beta}_4$$

where A, $\cdots$ $\overline{D}$ are unknown functions of time and the $\overline{\beta}$'s are initial values

$$u(0) = \overline{\beta}_1; \quad \dot{u}(0) = \overline{\beta}_2; \quad v(0) = \overline{\beta}_3; \quad \dot{v}(0) = \overline{\beta}_4$$ [48.4]

Since the functions $f_x, \cdots g_{\dot{y}}$ appearing in [48.2] can be developed in power series in terms of μ, the functions $A, \cdots \overline{D}$ can be assumed to be also of the form

$$A = A_0 + \mu A_1 + \mu^2 A_2 + \cdots$$

$$\overline{A} = \overline{A}_0 + \mu \overline{A}_1 + \mu^2 \overline{A}_2 + \cdots$$

[48.5]

Substituting the expressions [48.3] into [48.2], taking into account their form [48.5], and comparing the terms with the same powers of μ, one obtains a number of differential equations from which the coefficients $A_0, A_1, \cdots \overline{A}_0, \overline{A}_1$ can be determined. One obtains in this manner the following expressions:

$$A_0 = \cos\omega_1 t; \quad A_1 = F; \text{ etc.}$$

$$B_0 = \frac{1}{\omega_1} \sin\omega_1 t; \quad B_1 = \frac{1}{\omega_1} \int_0^t \left(\frac{1}{\omega_1} \sin\omega_1 u \cdot f_x + \cos\omega_1 u \cdot f_{\dot{x}}\right) \sin\omega_1(t - u)\, du; \text{ etc.}$$

$$C_0 = 0; \quad C_1 = H; \text{ etc.}$$

[48.6]

$$D_0 = 0; \quad D_1 = K; \text{ etc.}$$

$$\overline{A}_0 = 0; \quad \overline{A}_1 = \overline{F}; \text{ etc.}$$

$$\cdots \cdots \cdots \cdots \cdots$$

Introducing the notations of Poincaré, viz.,

$$u(T) - u(0) = [u] = \psi_1; \quad \dot{u}(T) - \dot{u}(0) = [\dot{u}] = \psi_2$$

$$v(T) - v(0) = [v] = \psi_3; \quad \dot{v}(T) - \dot{v}(0) = [\dot{v}] = \psi_4$$

[48.7]

where $T = \frac{2\pi}{\omega_1} + \tau$, τ being the correction for the period given by [47.13], one obtains the equation for the determination of the characteristic exponents in the form

$$\Delta = \begin{vmatrix} \dfrac{\partial\psi_1}{\partial\beta_1} + 1 - e^{\alpha T} & \dfrac{\partial\psi_1}{\partial\beta_2} & \dfrac{\partial\psi_1}{\partial\beta_3} & \dfrac{\partial\psi_1}{\partial\beta_4} \\[2ex] \dfrac{\partial\psi_2}{\partial\beta_1} & \dfrac{\partial\psi_2}{\partial\beta_2} + 1 - e^{\alpha T} & \dfrac{\partial\psi_2}{\partial\beta_3} & \dfrac{\partial\psi_2}{\partial\beta_4} \\[2ex] \dfrac{\partial\psi_3}{\partial\beta_1} & \dfrac{\partial\psi_3}{\partial\beta_2} & \dfrac{\partial\psi_3}{\partial\beta_3} + 1 - e^{\alpha T} & \dfrac{\partial\psi_3}{\partial\beta_4} \\[2ex] \dfrac{\partial\psi_4}{\partial\beta_1} & \dfrac{\partial\psi_4}{\partial\beta_2} & \dfrac{\partial\psi_4}{\partial\beta_3} & \dfrac{\partial\psi_4}{\partial\beta_4} + 1 - e^{\alpha T} \end{vmatrix} = 0 \quad [48.8]$$

This reduces to the form

$$\Delta = \begin{vmatrix} [A] + 1 - e^{\alpha T} & [B] & [C] & [D] \\ [\dot{A}] & [\dot{B}] + 1 - e^{\alpha T} & [\dot{C}] & [\dot{D}] \\ [\overline{A}] & [\overline{B}] & [\overline{C}] + 1 - e^{\alpha T} & [\overline{D}] \\ [\dot{\overline{A}}] & [\dot{\overline{B}}] & [\dot{\overline{C}}] & [\dot{\overline{D}}] + 1 - e^{\alpha T} \end{vmatrix} = 0 \qquad [48.9]$$

with $[A] = A\left(\dfrac{2\pi}{\omega_1} + \tau\right) - A(0)$, etc. Putting $1 - e^{\alpha T} = \rho$, this equation can be written in the form

$$\Delta(\rho) = \begin{vmatrix} a_{11} + \rho & a_{12} & a_{13} & a_{14} \\ a_{21} & a_{22} + \rho & a_{23} & a_{24} \\ a_{31} & a_{32} & a_{33} + \rho & a_{34} \\ a_{41} & a_{42} & a_{43} & a_{44} + \rho \end{vmatrix} = 0 \qquad [48.10]$$

which reduces to the quartic equation

$$\rho^4 + a\rho^3 + b\rho^2 + c\rho + d = 0 \qquad [48.11]$$

with

$$a = a_{11} + a_{22} + a_{33} + a_{44}; \quad b = A_{22}^{11} + A_{33}^{11} + A_{44}^{11} + A_{33}^{22} + A_{44}^{22} + A_{44}^{33}$$

$$[48.12]$$

$$c = A_{11} + A_{22} + A_{33} + A_{44}; \quad d = \Delta(0)$$

where $A_{11}, \cdots A_{44}$ and $A_{22}^{11}, \cdots A_{44}^{33}$ are the diagonal minors of Δ.

Since one of the characteristic exponents is always zero (9) because the equations are autonomous, $d = 0$, and the quartic equation thus reduces to a cubic one

$$\rho^3 + a\rho^2 + b\rho + c = 0 \qquad [48.13]$$

If the motion is stable in the sense of Liapounoff, the remaining three characteristic exponents must have negative real parts, which means that the moduli of the quantities $e^{\alpha T}$ must be less than one. This means that the complex number $\rho = 1 - e^{\alpha T}$ must be represented in the complex plane ρ by points situated inside a circle of radius 1 whose center is on the real axis at a unit distance from the origin, see Figure 48.1.

By means of the function $\rho = \dfrac{2}{1 - z}$, the interior of the circle in the (ρ_1, ρ_2)-plane is mapped into a half plane (z_1, z_2) so that the circles, see broken line in Figure 48.1, transform into straight lines, see broken line in Figure 48.2, parallel to the z_2-axis on the axis of the negative z_1.

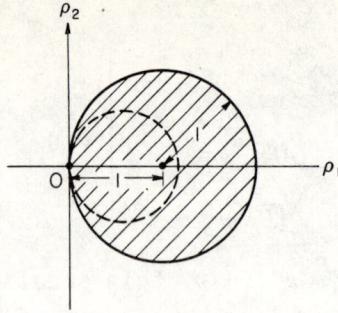

Figure 48.1

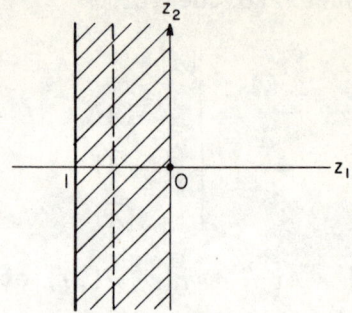

Figure 48.2

By this transformation the problem of finding the roots of [48.13] with moduli situated inside the circle of the (ρ_1, ρ_2)-plane is reduced to that of determining the roots of the transformed equation having negative real parts. This brings the problem within the scope of the Routh-Hurwitz criteria. If this transformation is carried out, Equation [48.13] becomes

$$z^3(-c) + z^2(2b + 3c) + z(-4a - 4b - 3c) + (8 + 4a + 2b + c) = 0 \quad [48.14]$$

The Routh-Hurwitz criteria of stability (10) (11) are

$$\frac{2b + 3c}{-c} > 0; \quad b^2 + c^2 + 2bc + ab + ac - c < 0; \quad \frac{8 + 4a + 2b + c}{-c} > 0 \quad [48.15]$$

These are the necessary and sufficient conditions for the roots of Equation [48.14] to have negative real parts, or, which is the same, for the roots of [48.13] to have moduli less than two, which assures the stability of the periodic motion. The conditions [48.15] can be written also in the form

$$2b + 3c > 0; \quad c < 0; \quad (b + c)^2 + a(b + c) - c < 0; \quad 8 + 4a + 2b + c > 0 \quad [48.16]$$

In order to apply these conditions of stability, it is necessary to calculate the determinant [48.9]. The quantities $[A]$, $[B]$, $\cdots$ can be developed in power series in terms of μ, for example

$$a_{11} = [A] = [A_0] + \mu[A_1] + \mu^2[A_2] + \cdots = b_{11}\mu + O_2(\mu)$$

$$a_{12} = [B] = [B_0] + \mu[B_1] + \mu^2[B_2] + \cdots = b_{12}\mu + O_2(\mu)$$

. . . .

The value of the determinant $\Delta(0)$, in which are written only terms containing linear terms in μ and terms independent of μ, is

$$\Delta(0) = \begin{vmatrix} b_{11}\mu + \cdots & b_{12}\mu + \cdots & b_{13}\mu + \cdots & b_{14}\mu + \cdots \\ b_{21}\mu + \cdots & b_{22}\mu + \cdots & b_{23}\mu + \cdots & b_{24}\mu + \cdots \\ b_{31}\mu + \cdots & b_{32}\mu + \cdots & (\cos\gamma - 1) + b_{33}\mu + \cdots & \dfrac{\sin\gamma}{\omega_2} + b_{34}\mu + \cdots \\ b_{41}\mu + \cdots & b_{42}\mu + \cdots & -\omega_2\sin\gamma + b_{43}\mu + \cdots & (\cos\gamma - 1) + b_{44}\mu + \cdots \end{vmatrix}$$

[48.17]

The values of b_{11}, b_{12}, $\cdots$ are determined from Equations [48.6]. Taking into account [48.12], one obtains the following relations

$$c = \mu 2(1 - \cos\gamma)(b_{11} + b_{22}) + O_2(\mu)$$

$$(b + c)^2 + a(b + c) - c = \mu 2(1 - \cos\gamma)\left[\cos\gamma(b_{33} + b_{44}) + \sin\gamma\left(\omega_2 b_{34} - \frac{b_{43}}{\omega_2}\right)\right] + O_2(\mu)$$

[48.18]

$$8 + 4a + 2b + c = 4(1 + \cos\gamma) + O_1(\mu)$$

$$2b + 3c = 4(1 - \cos\gamma) + O_1(\mu)$$

If we consider $\mu \ll 1$, $\gamma \neq 2\pi n$, and $\gamma \neq 2(n + 1)\pi$, n being an integer, the stability conditions reduce to the following

$$b_{11} + b_{22} < 0$$

[48.19]

$$\cos\gamma(b_{33} + b_{44}) + \sin\gamma\left(\omega_2 b_{34} - \frac{b_{43}}{\omega_2}\right) < 0$$

The values of b_{11}, b_{22}, $\cdots$ are given by the expressions

$$b_{11} = \frac{1}{\omega_1}\int_0^{\frac{2\pi}{\omega_1}}(\cos\omega_1 u \cdot f_x - \omega_1\sin\omega_1 u \cdot f_{\dot{x}})\sin\omega_1\left(\frac{2\pi}{\omega_1} - u\right)du$$

$$b_{22} = \int_0^{\frac{2\pi}{\omega_1}}\left(\frac{1}{\omega_1}\sin\omega_1 u \cdot f_x + \cos\omega_1 u \cdot f_{\dot{x}}\right)\cos\omega_1\left(\frac{2\pi}{\omega_1} - u\right)du$$

$$b_{33} = \int_0^{\frac{2\pi}{\omega_1}}\left(\cos\omega_2 u \cdot g_y - \omega_2\sin\omega_2 u \cdot g_{\dot{y}}\right)\sin\omega_2\left(\frac{2\pi}{\omega_1} - u\right)du - a_0\omega_2\sin\gamma$$

[48.20]

$$b_{44} = \int_0^{\frac{2\pi}{\omega_1}}\left(\frac{1}{\omega_2}\sin\omega_2 u \cdot g_y + \cos\omega_2 u \cdot g_{\dot{y}}\right)\cos\left(\frac{2\pi}{\omega_1} - u\right)du - a_0\omega_2\sin\gamma$$

$$b_{34} = \frac{1}{\omega_2}\int_0^{\frac{2\pi}{\omega_1}}\left(\frac{1}{\omega_2}\sin\omega_2 u \cdot g_y + \cos\omega_2 u \cdot g_{\dot{y}}\right)\sin\omega_2\left(\frac{2\pi}{\omega_1} - u\right)du + a_0\cos\gamma$$

$$b_{43} = \int_0^{\frac{2\pi}{\omega_1}}\left(\cos\omega_2 u \cdot g_y - \omega_2\sin\omega_2 u \cdot g_{\dot{y}}\right)\cos\omega_2\left(\frac{2\pi}{\omega_1} - u\right)du - a_0\omega_2^2\cos\gamma$$

Introducing these values into the inequalities [48.19], one obtains the following conditions of stability

$$\int_0^{\frac{2\pi}{\omega_1}} f_x \, du < 0; \qquad \int_0^{\frac{2\pi}{\omega_1}} g_{\dot{y}} \, du < 0 \qquad\qquad [48.21]$$

In applying these criteria one has to take $x = R \cos \omega_1 u$; $\dot{x} = - R \omega_1 \sin \omega_1 u$; $y = 0$; $\dot{y} = 0$; and $\mu = 0$. R is determined by [47.15].

We shall return to this matter in Part III in connection with the question of stability of coupled electronic oscillators. This problem is expressible in terms of two non-linear differential equations of the second order.

49. LIMIT CYCLE AND FREQUENCY OF A THERMIONIC GENERATOR

We propose to apply the preceding theory to Equation [30.9] of a thermionic generator. The quadratic term $\gamma_1 v^2$ in Expression [30.5] of the characteristic will be dropped, inasmuch as this term accounts for only a slight asymmetry of the characteristic and has no effect on the calculation of the stationary motion.*

The simplified equation [30.9] can be written as

$$\ddot{v} + v = \mu(\beta - 3\delta v^2)\dot{v} \qquad\qquad [49.1]$$

This equation is dimensionless; $\beta > 0$ and $\delta > 0$. The small parameter μ is introduced so that we may consider the oscillation in the quasi-linear range and therefore be able to apply the preceding theory.

For $\mu = 0$ the generating solutions are of the form

$$v_0 = \phi_0(t) = K \cos t; \quad \dot{v}_0 = \dot{\phi}_0(t) = - K \sin t \qquad\qquad [49.2]$$

In this case $f(v, \dot{v}) = \beta\dot{v} - 3\delta v^2 \dot{v}$ and hence

$$f(v_0, \dot{v}_0) = - \beta K \sin t + 3\delta K^3 \cos^2 t \sin t \qquad\qquad [49.3]$$

Making use of the condition of Poincaré, Equation [46.22], upon integrating Equation [49.3] we obtain $\beta K - \frac{3}{4}\delta K^3 = 0$ and hence

$$K^2 = \frac{4\beta}{3\delta} \qquad\qquad [49.4]$$

Thus the amplitude of the generating solution to the first approximation depends on the ratio $\sqrt{\frac{\beta}{\delta}}$. In other words, the amplitude of oscillation reached

---

* The reader will note that by retaining the quadratic term $\gamma_1 v^2$ in Equation [30.5] one would have Equation [30.9] instead of Equation [49.1]. The integral from 0 to 2π of the term $2\gamma v \dot{v}$ in Equation [46.22] vanishes, which proves that the term $\gamma_1 v^2$ has no effect on the calculation of the stationary motion. This remark applies also to all *even* terms in the polynomial [30.4]. See also Section 54.

by the self-excited process will be greater as the value of δ is smaller. This is physically obvious, for as $\delta \to 0$ the self-excitation would build up indefinitely since the factor that eventually limits it is precisely the non-linearity of the characteristic expressed by the term $- \delta_1 v^3$ in Equation [30.5]. Returning to the non-linear term $f(v, \dot{v})$, we find that $\frac{\partial f}{\partial v} = - 6 \delta v \dot{v}$ and $\frac{\partial f}{\partial \dot{v}} = \beta - 3 \delta v^2$, so that

$$\frac{\partial f}{\partial v_0} = 6 \delta K^2 \cos t \sin t = 3 \delta K^2 \sin 2t$$

and

$$\frac{\partial f}{\partial \dot{v}_0} = \beta - 3 \delta K^2 \cos^2 t$$

From [46.14] we have, upon taking account of [49.4],

$$D(2\pi) = \int_0^{2\pi} (\beta - 3 \delta K^2 \cos^2 t) \, dt = 2\pi \left(\beta - \frac{3 \delta K^2}{2} \right) = - 2\pi \beta \qquad [49.5]$$

One finds also that $\dot{D}(2\pi) = 0$. From Equation [46.26] the correction for the period $\tau = \sigma \mu^2$ is

$$\tau = \frac{\dot{F}(2\pi)}{K} \mu^2 \qquad [49.6]$$

Calculating $\dot{F}(2\pi)$ from the last equation [46.10], one obtains

$$\tau = \pi \mu^2 \beta^2 \qquad [49.7]$$

The coefficient $C(t)$ given by Equation [46.9] after a calculation is

$$C(t) = - \frac{3 \delta K^3}{32} \sin 3t + \frac{15 \delta K^3}{32} \sin t = - \frac{\beta}{4} \sqrt{\frac{\beta}{3\delta}} \sin 3t + \frac{5\beta}{4} \sqrt{\frac{\beta}{3\delta}} \sin t$$

so that the periodic solution without secular terms is then

$$v = 2 \sqrt{\frac{\beta}{3\delta}} \cos \left[\left(1 - \frac{\mu^2 \beta^2}{2} \right) t + \psi \right] + \mu \left(- \frac{\beta}{4} \right) \sqrt{\frac{\beta}{3\delta}} \sin 3 \left[\left(1 - \frac{\mu^2 \beta^2}{2} \right) t + \psi \right] +$$

$$+ \mu \frac{5\beta}{4} \sqrt{\frac{\beta}{3\delta}} \sin \left[\left(1 - \frac{\mu^2 \beta^2}{2} \right) t + \psi \right] + \mu^2 \Big[\qquad \Big] + \cdots \qquad [49.8]$$

where ψ is an arbitrary phase angle. It is clear that the periodic solution occurs in the neighborhood of the amplitude $2 \sqrt{\frac{\beta}{3\delta}}$. The correction for the period is of the second order and hence can be neglected for small values of μ. The secular terms do not appear here in view of the fact that the correction τ for the period has been calculated first.

50. BIFURCATION THEORY FOR QUASI-LINEAR SYSTEMS

The results obtained in Section 29 can be somewhat extended by means of the quantitative method of Poincaré, see Section 46. In order to obtain this extension, we shall consider instead of Equation [46.1] the equation

$$\ddot{x} + x = \mu f(x, \dot{x}, \lambda) \qquad [50.1]$$

in which there appears an additional parameter λ which we have encountered in the bifurcation theory. The procedure remains substantially the same as before; that is, there appear certain generating solutions in the neighborhood of which periodic solutions exist when μ is small.

We propose to investigate now what happens to these generating solutions when the parameter λ determining the state of the system varies and reaches a critical value.

It was shown in Section 46 that the amplitude K of the generating solutions is given by Equation [46.22], which can be written here in the form

$$\frac{C(2\pi)}{2\pi} = -\frac{1}{2\pi} \int_0^{2\pi} f(K\cos u, -K\sin u, \lambda) \sin u \, du = 0 \qquad [50.2]$$

Putting $K^2 = \rho$ and multiplying Equation [50.2] by $2\sqrt{\rho}$, we have

$$\frac{C(2\pi)}{\pi} \sqrt{\rho} \equiv \phi(\rho, \lambda) = -\frac{1}{\pi} \int_0^{2\pi} f(\sqrt{\rho}\cos u, -\sqrt{\rho}\sin u, \lambda) \sqrt{\rho} \sin u \, du \qquad [50.3]$$

Differentiating this equation with respect to ρ, we have

$$\phi_\rho(\rho, \lambda) = -\frac{1}{2\pi\rho} \int_0^{2\pi} \left[f_x \sqrt{\rho} \sin u \cos u + f_{\dot{x}} \sqrt{\rho} \cos^2 u \right] du +$$

$$+ \frac{1}{2\pi} \int_0^{2\pi} f_{\dot{x}} \, du - \frac{1}{2\pi\sqrt{\rho}} \int_0^{2\pi} f \sin u \, du \qquad [50.4]$$

The first term on the right side of Equation [50.4] is equal to

$$\frac{1}{2\pi\sqrt{\rho}} \left[f \cos u \right]_0^{2\pi} + \frac{1}{2\pi\sqrt{\rho}} \int_0^{2\pi} f \sin u \, du$$

as is easily verified by integrating the term $\frac{1}{2\pi\sqrt{\rho}} \int_0^{2\pi} f \sin u \, du$ by parts. Equation [50.4] reduces then to a simple form

$$\phi_\rho(\rho, \lambda) = \frac{1}{2\pi} \int_0^{2\pi} f_{\dot{x}} \, du \qquad [50.5]$$

In Section 13 it was shown that, in a conservative system containing a parameter λ, the conditions for stable equilibrium are

$$f(x,\lambda) = 0; \quad f_x(x,\lambda) < 0 \qquad [50.6]$$

Suppose we now impose the condition that $\int_0^{2\pi} f_{\dot{x}} \, du < 0$ so that $\phi_\rho(\rho,\lambda) < 0$. Associating the function $\phi(\rho,\lambda)$ with $f(x,\lambda)$, we may infer that the limit cycles are stable if

$$\phi(\rho,\lambda) = 0; \quad \phi_\rho(\rho,\lambda) < 0 \qquad [50.7]$$

This is by no means a proof, but merely a plausible deduction. A proof for the conditions under which stationary motion is stable may be found in Chapter III of Liapounoff's treatise (12).

The remainder of the bifurcation theory applies directly to limit cycles, the coordinate x of equilibrium being replaced by $\rho = K^2$, the square of the amplitude of the limit cycle.

In a number of problems of non-linear mechanics, the function $f(x,\dot{x},\lambda)$ is of the form

$$f(x,\dot{x},\lambda) = f_1(x,\lambda)\dot{x} \qquad [50.8]$$

where $f_1(x,\lambda)$ is a polynomial of the form

$$f_1(x,\lambda) = a_0(\lambda) + a_1(\lambda)x + a_2(\lambda)x^2 + \cdots \qquad [50.9]$$

To this class belong equations of the generalized Van der Pol type. Substituting $f = f_1\dot{x}$ in Equation [50.3], with the generating solutions $x = \sqrt{\rho}\cos u$ and $\dot{x} = -\sqrt{\rho}\sin u$, and carrying out the integrations, one has

$$\phi(\rho,\lambda) = \frac{1}{2}\left[a_0\rho + \frac{a_2\rho^2}{4} + \frac{a_4\rho^3}{8} + \cdots\right]$$

$$[50.10]$$

$$\phi_\rho(\rho,\lambda) = \frac{1}{2}\left[a_0 + \frac{a_2\rho}{2} + \frac{3a_4\rho^2}{8} + \cdots\right]$$

In these equations the coefficients $a_0, a_2, a_4, \cdots$ are functions of λ.

51. "SOFT" AND "HARD" SELF-EXCITATION OF THERMIONIC GENERATORS; OSCILLATION HYSTERESIS

It is well known that there are two kinds of self-excitation of thermionic circuits designated as "soft" and "hard." It is observed that by increasing the coefficient of mutual induction λ between the anode and the grid circuits, self-excitation starts smoothly as soon as a critical value $\lambda = \lambda_0$ of this parameter is reached; for $\lambda > \lambda_0$ the amplitude of oscillations steadily increases with increasing λ, as shown in Figure 51.1 representing this "soft" case of excitation; upon decreasing λ the phenomenon takes place in the opposite direction, as shown by the arrows. The theory of soft self-excitation has been studied in Section 29.

In some cases, however, a different type of self-excitation occurs, as shown in Figure 51.2. With increasing λ it is observed that the self-excitation starts *abruptly* with a finite amplitude for λ = λ₁ and increases

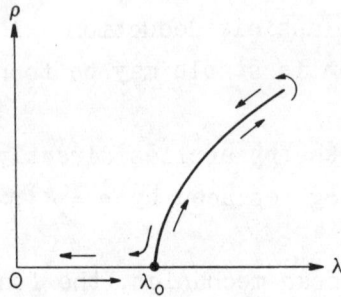

Figure 51.1

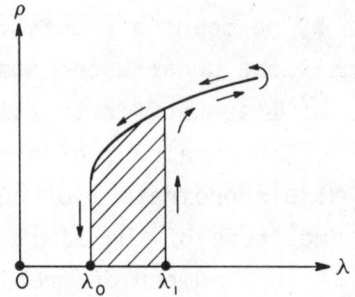

Figure 51.2

smoothly for λ ≧ λ₁. For decreasing λ it is observed, however, that the phenomenon is different; namely, for λ = λ₁ the self-excitation does not disappear; it disappears at λ = λ₀ < λ₁. There exists a kind of "hysteresis cycle" shown by the shading in Figure 51.2. This type of self-excitation is called "hard." These phenomena are due to the non-linearity of the system, and the hysteresis cycle referred to above is sometimes called "oscillation hysteresis" (13). We have already analyzed this situation qualitatively in Section 24. In this section we propose to investigate this effect utilizing the theory of Poincaré.

Consider the circuit shown in Figure 51.3 with positive directions indicated. The differential equation of the oscillating circuit is

$$L\frac{di}{dt} + Ri + \frac{1}{C}\int_0^t (i - I_a)\, dt = 0 \qquad [51.1]$$

where $I_a = f(V)$ is the non-linear function expressing the anode current I_a as a function of grid voltage V. Let us approximate this function by a power series in V limited to terms through V^5 for reasons which will appear later. We have

$$I_a = f(V) = \alpha_0 V + \beta_0 V^2 + \gamma_0 V^3 + \delta_0 V^4 + \epsilon_0 V^5 \qquad [51.2]$$

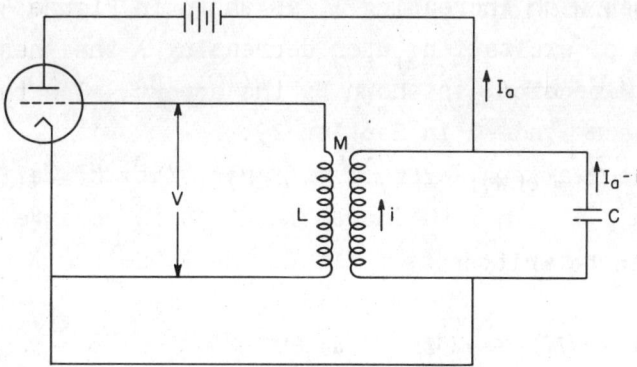

Figure 51.3

It is convenient to introduce a dimensionless variable $x = V/V_s$ where V_s is the "saturation voltage," that is, a sufficiently high grid voltage beyond which the current I_a does not change appreciably. Since $V = M\dfrac{di}{dt}$ we can write

$$x = \frac{M}{V_s}\frac{di}{dt} \qquad [51.3]$$

From this equation we obtain

$$\frac{di}{dt} = \frac{V_s}{M}x; \quad \frac{d^2i}{dt^2} = \frac{V_s}{M}\dot{x}; \quad i = \frac{V_s}{M}\int x\,dt$$

Substituting these values in [51.1] and differentiating we get, after a few simplifications,

$$LC\ddot{x} + RC\dot{x} + x = M\left[\alpha_0 + 2\beta_0 V_s x + 3\gamma_0 V_s^2 x^2 + 4\delta_0 V_s^3 x^3 + 5\epsilon_0 V_s^4 x^4\right]\frac{dx}{dt} \quad [51.4]$$

Introducing the new independent variable $\tau = \omega_0 t$, where $\omega_0 = 1/\sqrt{LC}$, the preceding equation becomes

$$\frac{d^2x}{d\tau^2} + x = \omega_0 M\left[\left(\alpha_0 - \frac{RC}{M}\right) + 2\beta_0 V_s x + 3\gamma_0 V_s^2 x^2 + 4\delta_0 V_s^3 x^3 + 5\epsilon_0 V_s^4 x^4\right]\frac{dx}{d\tau}$$

The condition of quasi-linearity is fulfilled if we assume that the coefficients $\alpha_0, \cdots \epsilon_0$ of [51.2] are small. One can take one of these coefficients, for example β_0, as a factor and write

$$\frac{d^2x}{d\tau^2} + x = \beta_0 V_s \omega_0 M\left[\frac{\alpha_0 M - RC}{M\beta_0 V_s} + 2x + \frac{3\gamma_0 V_s}{\beta_0}x^2 + \frac{4\delta_0 V_s^2}{\beta_0}x^3 + \frac{5\epsilon_0 V_s^3}{\beta_0}x^4\right]\frac{dx}{d\tau} \quad [51.5]$$

By introducing the notations

$$\beta_0 V_s \omega_0 = \mu; \quad \frac{\alpha_0 M - RC}{\beta_0 V_s} = a(M); \quad 2M = b(M);$$

$$\frac{3\gamma_0 V_s M}{\beta_0} = c(M); \quad \frac{4\delta_0 V_s^2 M}{\beta_0} = d(M); \quad \frac{5\epsilon_0 V_s^3 M}{\beta_0} = e(M)$$

Equation [51.5] can be written as

$$\frac{d^2 x}{d\tau^2} + x = \mu \left[a(M) + b(M)x + c(M)x^2 + d(M)x^3 + e(M)x^4 \right] \frac{dx}{d\tau} = \mu f_1(x; M) \frac{dx}{d\tau} \quad [51.6]$$

that is, the function $f(x, \dot{x}, M) = f_1(x; M)\frac{dx}{d\tau}$ has the form [50.8].

The function $\phi(\rho, M)$ given by [50.10] can be written, after certain transformations, as

$$\phi(\rho, M) = a_1 \rho + a_2' \gamma_0 M \rho^2 + a_3 \epsilon_0 M \rho^3 \qquad [51.7]$$

where

$$a_1 = \frac{\alpha_0 M - RC}{\beta_0 V_s}; \quad a_2' = \frac{3V_s}{4\beta_0}; \quad a_3 = \frac{5V_s^3}{8\beta_0}$$

Differentiating Equation [51.7] with respect to ρ, one has

$$\phi_\rho(\rho, M) = a_1 + 2a_2' \gamma_0 M \rho + 3a_3 \epsilon_0 M \rho^2 \qquad [51.8]$$

The discussion of Equations [51.7] and [51.8] yields the qualitative features of the phenomena.

A. CONDITION FOR A SOFT SELF-EXCITATION

If $a_1 > 0$, $\gamma_0 < 0$, and $\epsilon_0 = 0$, Equation [51.7] becomes

$$\phi(\rho, M) = (a_1 - a_2'|\gamma_0|M\rho)\rho = (\alpha_0 M - RC - a_2|\gamma_0|M\rho)\rho = 0 \qquad [51.9]$$

where a_2 absorbs the constant factor V_s which is of no further interest. In the (ρ, M)-plane this equation represents a straight line $\rho = 0$ and a hyperbola

$$M\alpha_0 - RC - a_2|\gamma_0|M\rho = 0 \qquad [51.10]$$

The point of intersection of $\rho = 0$ and the curve [51.10] is given by the equation $M_1 \alpha_0 - RC = 0$. The value

$$M_1 = \frac{RC}{\alpha_0} \qquad [51.11]$$

is a critical value of the parameter M. Following the method of Poincaré, Section 13, one obtains the diagram of Figure 29.1b. By increasing the parameter M from small values, one has a locus ($\rho = 0$) of stable focal points. The point $M = M_0$ is a branch point of equilibrium; here the focal point undergoes a transition from stability ($M < M_0$) to instability ($M > M_0$), and a stable limit cycle appears; the square of the amplitude of the latter increases with M, following the hyperbolic branch. The asymptotic value of ρ for $M \to \infty$ is clearly $\alpha_0/\alpha_2 \overline{\gamma}_0$, which represents the square of the amplitude for infinitely strong coupling M.

The curves representing this case are shown in Figure 29.1a and b. The former represents the condition for $M > M_0$, the latter, the condition for $M < M_0$. The phenomenon is reversible, as shown in Figure 51.1.

B. CONDITION FOR A HARD SELF-EXCITATION

If $\alpha_0 > 0$, $\gamma_0 > 0$ and $\epsilon_0 < 0$, and if we designate by $\overline{\epsilon}_0$ the absolute value of ϵ_0, and put for abbreviation $a_2' \gamma_0 = m$ and $a_3 \overline{\epsilon}_0 = n$, Equation [51.6] becomes

$$\phi(\rho, M) = (a_1 + mM\rho - nM\rho^2)\rho = 0 \qquad [51.12]$$

In the (ρ, M)-plane, this equation represents a straight line $\rho = 0$ and a curve

$$(M\alpha_0 - RC) + mM\rho - nM\rho^2 = 0 \qquad [51.13]$$

The intersection of this curve with the line $\rho = 0$ is clearly $a_1 = 0$, which gives the value M_1 previously found, see Equation [51.11].

The tangent to the curve [51.13] is given by the equation

$$\frac{d\rho}{dM} = -\frac{\dfrac{\partial \phi}{\partial M}}{\dfrac{\partial \phi}{\partial \rho}} = -\frac{\alpha_0 + m\rho - n\rho^2}{M(m - 2n\rho)} \qquad [51.14]$$

The curve has a vertical tangent for $\rho_0 = m/2n$; for this value

$$M_0 = \frac{RC}{\alpha_0 + \dfrac{m^2}{4n}} \qquad [51.15]$$

When M_0 is compared with M_1 from Equation [51.11], it is seen that $M_0 < M_1$. Furthermore, it can be shown that the curve does not go to the left of the value $M = M_0$ and has a horizontal asymptote for $\rho = m/n$. This defines the curve shown in Figure 51.4. It is easily seen that $\phi(\rho, M) > 0$ in the shaded area; whence, applying the criteria of Poincaré, Section 13,

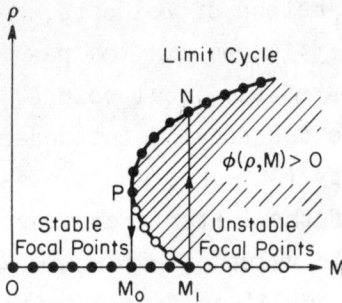

Figure 51.4

one finds that the branch of the curve above point P is stable and below this point unstable. The axis $\rho = 0$ is stable for $M < M_1$ and unstable for $M > M_1$. If M is increased gradually below the value $M = M_1$, the focal points are stable. For $M = M_1$ there is a finite stable limit cycle and a discontinuous jump M_1N, shown in Figure 51.4. If $M > M_1$ and M increases, there is a continuous variation of the amplitude of the limit cycle. If, however, $M > M_1$ and M decreases, when $M = M_1$ is reached, the limit cycle is still stable although there is a transition of the point singularity from instability to stability. This corresponds to Figures 24.6b and c. It follows, therefore, that when M decreases from M_1 to M_0, the stable limit cycle is still being followed. When the point $M = M_0$ is reached, the stable and the unstable limit cycles coalesce, and no limit cycle exists for $M < M_0$, which accounts for the jump PM_0, shown in Figure 51.4.

By comparing the results of this section with those of Section 29 it is seen that if the non-linear characteristic can be approximated by an expression of the form $F_1(x) = a_1 x - a_3 x^3$, where a_1 and a_3 are positive, one has a soft type of self-excitation. If, however, it can be approximated by an expression $F_2(x) = a_1 x + a_3 x^3 - a_5 x^5$, where a_1, a_3, and a_5 are positive, the self-excitation is of a hard type.

In the first case the characteristic has no inflection point (except the point $x = 0$, which is of no interest); in the second case, there is an additional inflection point for $x_1 = \sqrt{\dfrac{3a_3}{a_5}}$. Since an electon tube exhibits characteristics of both types of self-excitation, depending on the point at which it is biased, each of these cases can be obtained in practice by a suitable adjustment of the circuit.

CHAPTER IX

METHOD OF VAN DER POL

52. ROTATING SYSTEM OF AXES; EQUATIONS OF THE FIRST APPROXIMATION
Consider again the quasi-linear equation

$$\ddot{x} + x = \mu f(x, \dot{x})$$

Its equivalent system is

$$\dot{x} = y; \quad \dot{y} = -x + \mu f(x, y) \qquad [52.1]$$

the notations being the same as in the preceding chapter. For $\mu = 0$, one has
the linear equation $\ddot{x} + x = 0$, having a harmonic solution

$$x = a\cos t + b\sin t, \quad \text{with} \quad \dot{x} = -a\sin t + b\cos t \qquad [52.2]$$

where a and b are constants of integration.

The phase trajectories in this case are circles of radii $K = \sqrt{a^2 + b^2}$. If, instead of considering a coordinate system $(x, \dot{x})$ in a fixed
phase plane, one introduces a system rotating with angular velocity $\omega = 1$
about the common origin of both systems, in this rotating phase plane Equation [52.2] will represent a fixed point A at a distance $OA = K = \sqrt{a^2 + b^2}$
from origin O. The inclination of OA to a reference line in the rotating
plane is given by the angle $\theta = \tan^{-1}\frac{b}{a}$. It is to be noted that this transformation is nothing but the usual method of representing sinusoidal quantities by vectors, used in the theory of alternating currents. We shall call
the rotating plane of the variables (a, b) the Van der Pol plane.

Consider now Equations [52.2] as a transformation defining x and $\dot{x}$
in terms of the new variables a and b. This implies that

$$\frac{da}{dt}\cos t + \frac{db}{dt}\sin t = 0$$

$$[52.3]$$

$$-\frac{da}{dt}\sin t + \frac{db}{dt}\cos t = \mu f(a\cos t + b\sin t, -a\sin t + b\cos t)$$

whence

$$\frac{da}{dt} = -\mu f(a\cos t + b\sin t, -a\sin t + b\cos t)\sin t$$

$$[52.4]$$

$$\frac{db}{dt} = \mu f(a\cos t + b\sin t, -a\sin t + b\cos t)\cos t$$

Since μ is small, by assumption, da/dt and db/dt are also small because $f(x, y)$ is bounded. In other words, a and b are slowly varying quantities in comparison with the rapidly varying trigonometric terms of frequency
$\omega = 1$.

For the first approximation it is sufficient therefore to consider a and b as constants on the right side of Equations [52.4]. However, if x and y are replaced by their expressions [52.2], the right sides of [52.4] are periodic and can be expanded in a Fourier series so that [52.4] becomes

$$\frac{da}{dt} = \mu \left[\frac{\phi_0(a,b)}{2} + \phi_1(a,b) \cos t + \overline{\phi}_1(a,b) \sin t + \phi_2(a,b) \cos 2t + \cdots \right]$$

$$\frac{db}{dt} = \mu \left[\frac{\psi_0(a,b)}{2} + \psi_1(a,b) \cos t + \overline{\psi}_1(a,b) \sin t + \psi_2(a,b) \cos 2t + \cdots \right]$$

[52.5]

It must be noted that the system [52.5] now contains t explicitly, whereas the original system [52.1] does not. Van der Pol considers the following "abbreviated" equations as equations of the first approximation

$$\frac{da}{dt} = \mu \frac{\phi_0(a,b)}{2} ; \quad \frac{db}{dt} = \mu \frac{\psi_0(a,b)}{2}$$

[52.6]

They are obtained from [52.5] by dropping the terms containing the trigonometric functions. On the other hand,

$$\frac{\phi_0(a,b)}{2} = -\frac{1}{2\pi} \int_0^{2\pi} f(a \cos \xi + b \sin \xi, -a \sin \xi + b \cos \xi) \sin \xi \, d\xi$$

[52.7]

$$\frac{\psi_0(a,b)}{2} = +\frac{1}{2\pi} \int_0^{2\pi} f(a \cos \xi + b \sin \xi, -a \sin \xi + b \cos \xi) \cos \xi \, d\xi$$

Multiplying the first equation [52.6] by a, the second by b, adding and putting $K^2 = a^2 + b^2$, one obtains

$$\frac{1}{2} \frac{dK^2}{dt} = K \frac{dK}{dt} = \frac{\mu}{2\pi} \int_0^{2\pi} f(a \cos \xi + b \sin \xi, -a \sin \xi + b \cos \xi)(-a \sin \xi + b \cos \xi) \, d\xi$$

Putting

$$a \cos \xi + b \sin \xi = K \cos(\xi - \theta)$$

and

$$-a \sin \xi + b \cos \xi = -K \sin(\xi - \theta)$$

where $\theta = \tan^{-1} \frac{b}{a}$, and introducing the variable $u = \xi - \theta$, one has

$$\frac{dK}{dt} = \mu \, \phi(K) \text{ and, by a similar transformation, } \frac{d\theta}{dt} = \mu \, \psi(K) \qquad [52.8]$$

where

$$\phi(K) = -\frac{1}{2\pi} \int_0^{2\pi} f(K\cos u, -K\sin u)\sin u \, du$$

[52.9]

$$\psi(K) = +\frac{1}{2\pi K} \int_0^{2\pi} f(K\cos u, -K\sin u)\cos u \, du$$

One notes that the definite integrals in these equations coincide with the functions $C(2\pi)$ and $\dot{C}(2\pi)$ of Poincaré, Equations [46.10].

53. TOPOLOGY OF THE PLANE OF THE VARIABLES OF VAN DER POL

In the (x,y) phase plane the limit cycle is reached when the phase trajectory is a circle; in the Van der Pol plane (a,b) the condition for the existence of a stable limit cycle is satisfied when the end of the vector K is a point of stable equilibrium, that is, at this point $\frac{dK}{dt} = \mu \, \phi(K) = 0$. Hence, limit cycles exist for radii K corresponding to the roots of

$$\phi(K) = \frac{1}{2\pi} \int_0^{2\pi} f(K\cos u, -K\sin u)\sin u \, du = 0$$

It is to be noted again that this equation coincides with Equation [46.22] of Poincaré's theory.

A root K_i of $\phi(K) = 0$ will correspond to a stable limit cycle if $\phi'(K_i) < 0$. By a method similar to that applied in connection with Equation [50.5], one finds that the condition $\phi'(K_i) < 0$, written explicitly, gives

$$\frac{1}{2\pi} \int_0^{2\pi} f_y(K_i\cos u, -K_i\sin u)\, du < 0$$

[53.1]

The limit cycle is unstable if $\phi'(K_i) > 0$.

Consider now the second equation [52.8]. Here two cases are of interest.

Case 1.

$$\psi(K) = \frac{1}{2\pi K} \int_0^{2\pi} f(K\cos u, -K\sin u)\cos u \, du = 0$$

[53.2]

In this case $\theta = \theta_0$ = constant. The topological picture of trajectories in the plane of variables (a,b) of Van der Pol, in this case, is shown in Figure 53.1. The equilibrium on a limit cycle at a point K_i for $\theta = \theta_0$ is stable if

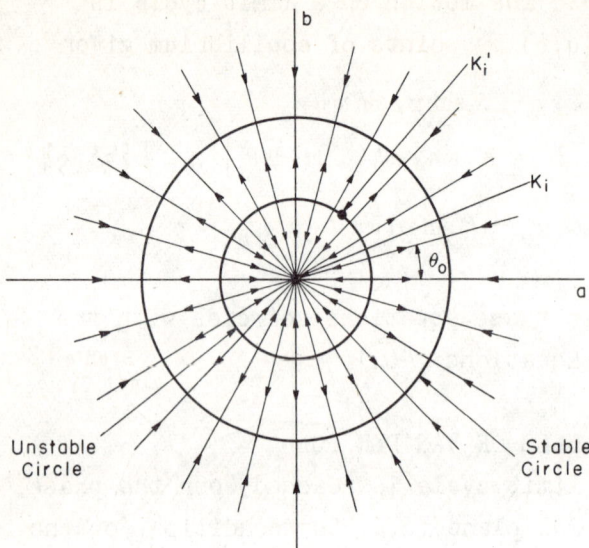

Figure 53.1

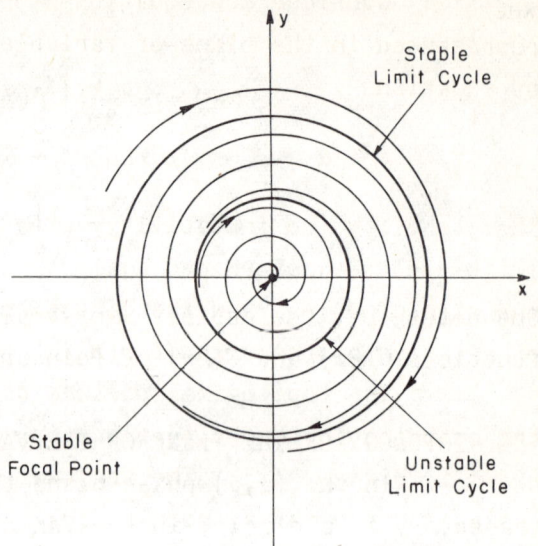

Figure 53.2

the representative point being displaced along the radius returns to K_i. If this point does not return to K_i, as for example Point K_i', such a limit cycle is unstable. The loci of limit cycles in this case are concentric circles corresponding to all possible values of the constant θ_0.

If one returns to the original variables (x,y) of the phase plane, one must apply the equations of transformation [52.2], where the variables a and b are respectively $K_i \cos \theta_0$ and $K_i \sin \theta_0$. This gives

$$x = a \cos t + b \sin t = K_i \cos \theta_0 \cos t + K_i \sin \theta_0 \sin t = K_i \cos(t - \theta_0)$$

[53.3]

$$y = -a \sin t + b \cos t = -K_i \cos \theta_0 \sin t + K_i \sin \theta_0 \cos t = -K_i \sin(t - \theta_0)$$

where θ_0 is arbitrary. This arbitrariness of θ_0 for the (x,y) phase plane is due to the fact that a point of equilibrium in the plane of variables (a,b) of Van der Pol corresponds to a circle in the phase plane of the variables (x,y). The general form of trajectories in the (x,y)-plane is shown in Figure 53.2.

Case 2.

$$\psi(K) = \frac{1}{2\pi K} \int_0^{2\pi} f(K \cos u, -K \sin u) \cos u \, du \neq 0$$

Let $\bar{K}_1$, $\bar{K}_2$, $\cdots$ be the roots of $\psi(K) = 0$, and assume that these roots are different from the roots K_1, K_2, $\cdots$ of $\phi(K) = 0$.

Consider now Equations [52.8]. **The motion on a limit cycle is** represented in the plane of variables (a,b) by points of equilibrium given by equations

$$a = K_i \cos\left[\mu\psi(K_i)\, t + \theta_0\right]; \quad b = K_i \sin\left[\mu\psi(K_i)t + \theta_0\right] \qquad [53.4]$$

The stability (or instability) of a limit cycle is determined again by the sign of $\phi'(K_i)$ and the direction of rotation by the sign of $\psi(K_i)$.

The topological picture of trajectories in the (a,b)-plane is shown in Figure 53.3. The trajectories "turn back" at points corresponding to the roots $\overline{K}_1$, $\overline{K}_2$, $\cdots$ of $\psi(K_i)$, approaching the stable limit cycles which are again the points of equilibrium in the Van der Pol plane. The topological picture of trajectories in the fixed (x,y)-plane has the same appearance as that shown in Figure 53.2. The only difference between the two cases is that, in the second case, Equations [53.3] become

Figure 53.3

$$x = a\cos t + b\sin t = K_i \cos\left(\left[1 - \mu\psi(K_i)\right] t - \theta_0\right)$$

$$[53.5]$$

$$y = -a\sin t + b\cos t = -K_i \sin\left(\left[1 - \mu\psi(K_i)\right]t - \theta_0\right)$$

It is clear that in this case a correction for frequency exists expressed by $\mu\psi(K_i)$. In other words, the velocity along the spiral trajectories is not uniform.

By a further analysis it can be shown that when $\psi(K_i) = 0$ the correction for frequency (and hence for the period) is of the order of μ^2 and consequently can be neglected in the theory of the first approximation. If, however, $\psi(K_i) \neq 0$, this frequency correction appears to the first order of μ.

To sum up the results of this section, it can be said that the use of the variables (a,b) of Van der Pol enables us, if the system is isochronous, to represent a limit cycle by a point in the plane (a,b), that is, by a constant vector. Such representation of a limit cycle is similar to the

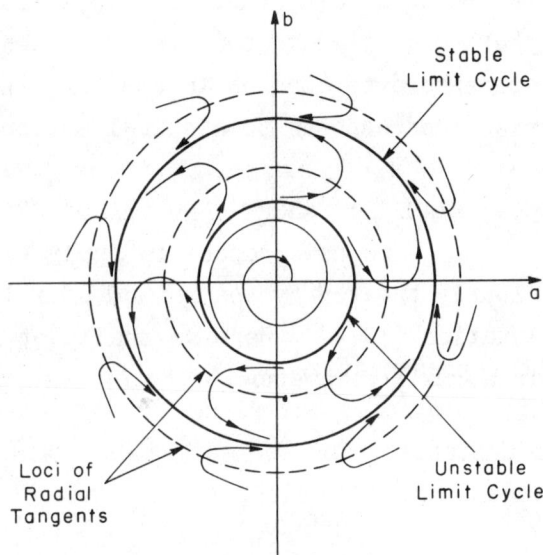

mode of representing alternating currents by vectors. For transient conditions the representative point moves toward, or away from, the limit cycle point along the length of the radius vector, since the phase angle θ_0 remains constant. The phase angle in this case has no particular physical significance if one single oscillatory phenomenon is considered. If, however, $\psi(K) \neq 0$, that is, if the motion is not isochronous, in the plane of variables (a,b) of Van der Pol the vector K_i undergoes oscillations depending on the roots of $\psi(K) = 0$. This peculiarity resembles the representation of phase-modulated vectors in radio technique. Fixed points in the (a,b)-plane correspond to circles in the (x,y)-plane, and a radial motion in the (a,b)-plane corresponds to a spiral motion in the (x,y)-plane.

54. EXAMPLE: "SOFT" AND "HARD" SELF-EXCITATION OF THERMIONIC CIRCUITS

We now propose to apply the Van der Pol method to the problem previously treated by the method of Poincaré in Section 49. Consider again Equation [30.9]. Here we shall let $\beta = \mu\beta_1$, $\gamma = \mu\gamma_1$, and $\delta = \mu\delta_1$, where μ is a small parameter.

$$\ddot{v} + v = \mu(\beta_1 + 2\gamma_1 v - 3\delta_1 v^2)\dot{v} \qquad [54.1]$$

where β_1, γ_1, and δ_1 are positive.

In this case $f(v,\dot{v}) = (\beta + 2\gamma v - 3\delta v^2)\dot{v}$. Using the first equation [52.9], we have

$$\phi(K) = + \frac{1}{2\pi} \int_0^{2\pi} (\beta + 2\gamma K \cos u - 3\delta K^2 \cos^2 u) K \sin u \sin u \, du \qquad [54.2]$$

in which the generating solutions $v = K \cos u$, $\dot{v} = -K \sin u$ are substituted. We obtain

$$\phi(K) = \frac{1}{2\pi}\left[\beta K \int_0^{2\pi} \sin^2 u \, du + 2\gamma K^2 \int_0^{2\pi} \cos u \sin^2 u \, du - 3\delta K^3 \int_0^{2\pi} \cos^2 u \sin^2 u \, du\right] \qquad [54.3]$$

Since

$$\int_0^{2\pi} \sin^2 u \, du = \pi, \quad \int_0^{2\pi} \sin^2 u \cos u \, du = \left[\frac{\sin^3 u}{3}\right]_0^{2\pi} = 0$$

and

$$\int_0^{2\pi} \cos^2 u \sin^2 u \, du = \int_0^{2\pi} \sin^2 u \, du - \int_0^{2\pi} \sin^4 u \, du = \pi - \frac{3}{4}\pi = \frac{\pi}{4}$$

we have

$$\phi(K) = \frac{1}{2}\left(\beta K - \frac{3\delta K^3}{4}\right) = \frac{K}{2}\left(\beta - \frac{3\delta K^2}{4}\right) \qquad [54.4]$$

By the first equation [52.8], the condition for the existence of a limit cycle is $\phi(K) = 0$. From Equation [54.4] this takes place for $K_1 = 0$ and $K_2 = \sqrt{\frac{4\beta}{3\delta}}$.

For $K_1 = 0$, the limit cycle reduces to one point, the singular point. The radius of a finite limit cycle is thus

$$K_2 = \sqrt{\frac{4\beta}{3\delta}} \qquad [54.5]$$

In order to ascertain that there is actually a condition of self-excitation, one has to prove that the singularity is unstable and the limit cycle is stable, see Section 29. For the proof of the first point, equations of the first approximation in the sense of Liapounoff must be formed.

The system equivalent to Equation [54.1], upon dropping the non-linear terms, is $\dot{v} = y$ and $\dot{y} + v = \mu\beta y$, that is

$$\dot{v} = y; \quad \dot{y} = -v + \mu\beta y \qquad [54.6]$$

The characteristic equation is $S^2 - \mu\beta S + 1 = 0$ whose roots are

$$S_{1,2} = \frac{\mu\beta \pm \mu\beta\sqrt{1 - \frac{4}{\mu^2\beta^2}}}{2}$$

Since μ is small, it is seen that the roots are complex, with a positive real part. Therefore the singularity is an unstable focal point from which the spiral trajectories unwind themselves approaching the limit cycle $K_2 = \sqrt{\frac{4\beta}{3\delta}}$, provided it is stable.

In order to establish the stability of the limit cycle $K_2 = \sqrt{\frac{4\beta}{3\delta}}$, it is necessary to ascertain the sign of $\phi_K(K_2)$. One finds

$$\phi_K(K_2) = \frac{1}{2}(\beta - 3\beta) < 0$$

The limit cycle is thus stable.

In this discussion it has been assumed that the coefficients β, γ, and δ entering into Equation [54.2] are positive. By waiving this assumption one could analyze additional cases following the same procedure.

It is of interest also to investigate the second equation [52.8], which concerns the frequency of oscillation, $\frac{d\theta}{dt}$.

The function $\psi(K)$ in this case is

$$\psi(K) = \frac{1}{2\pi K} \int_0^{2\pi} (\beta + 2\gamma K \cos u - 3\delta K^2 \cos^2 u)\, K \sin u \cos u \, du \qquad [54.7]$$

Developing it, we find

$$\psi(K) = \frac{1}{2\pi K}\left[\beta K \int_0^{2\pi} \sin u \cos u\, du + 2\gamma K^2 \int_0^{2\pi} \sin u \cos^2 u\, du - 3\delta K^3 \int_0^{2\pi} \cos^3 u \sin u\, du\right] \quad [54.8]$$

Each of the integrals appearing in the above expression is zero so that by the second equation [52.8] $\frac{d\theta}{dt} = 0$. This means that in the phase plane the radius vector of the representative point rotates around the origin with a constant angular velocity, and the frequency correction is zero to the first order.

In order to investigate the variation of K as a function of time, the first equation [52.8] must be integrated upon substituting for $\phi(K)$ its value given by [54.4]:

$$\phi(K) = mK - nK^3$$

where $m = \frac{\beta}{2}$ and $n = \frac{3\delta}{8}$. This gives

$$\frac{dK}{mK - nK^3} = \frac{1}{m}\frac{dK}{K(1 - pK^2)} = \mu dt$$

where $p = \frac{n}{m} = \frac{3\delta}{4\beta}$.

$$\frac{dK}{K(1 - pK^2)} = \frac{dK}{K} + \frac{pKdK}{1 - pK^2} = m\mu dt$$

That is, $d \log K - d\left[\frac{1}{2}\log(1 - pK^2)\right] = m\mu dt$, or

$$d\left(\log \frac{K}{\sqrt{1 - pK^2}}\right) = m\mu dt$$

which, upon integration, gives

$$\log \frac{K}{\sqrt{1 - pK^2}} - \log \frac{K_0}{\sqrt{1 - pK_0^2}} = m\mu t$$

or

$$\frac{K}{\sqrt{1 - pK^2}} e^{-m\mu t} = \frac{K_0}{\sqrt{1 - pK_0^2}} \qquad [54.9]$$

Finally,

$$K = \frac{K_0}{\sqrt{(1 - pK_0^2)e^{-2m\mu t} + pK_0^2}} \qquad [54.10]$$

For $t = 0$, $K = K_0 = \sqrt{\frac{4\beta}{3\delta}}$ and for $t \rightarrow -\infty$, $K \rightarrow 0$, which means that, for increasing t, the radius vector K increases from zero and approaches the value $K_0 = \sqrt{\frac{4\beta}{3\delta}}$ on the limit cycle. Furthermore, for $t \rightarrow +\infty$, $K = K_0$, which shows that the limit cycle is stable.

In order to eliminate the operation with infinities inherent in the asymptotic nature of the process, one can select instead of K and K_0 in Equation [54.10] certain initial and final values K' and K_0' slightly removed from the unstable focal point and the stable limit cycle respectively. In such a case Equation [54.10] can be used for numerical calculations with a view to ascertaining how rapidly the self-excited oscillatory process builds up as a function of time.

It is interesting to note that the terms with γ, ϵ, $\cdots$, corresponding to the even powers in the approximation of the characteristic by a series expansion, disappear from Expression [54.10] for the radius of the limit cycle in the first approximation, as was noted in connection with the vanishing of the term $2\gamma K^2 \int_0^{2\pi} \sin^2 u \cos u\, du$ in Equation [54.8].

The inverse passage from the phase plane (a,b) of Van der Pol to the ordinary phase plane (x,y) yields the expressions $x = K \cos t$ and $y = \dot{x} = -K \sin t$, where K is given by Equation [54.10].

The conditions of self-excitation considered above represent the so-called "soft" type of self-excitation. Topologically, it corresponds to the existence either of an unstable singularity surrounded by a stable limit cycle or of a stable singularity within an unstable limit cycle, see Section 29. The first case represents the building up of oscillations asymptotically approaching a stable limit cycle; the second, an asymptotic disappearance of the oscillatory process. If, however, between an unstable singularity and a stable limit cycle an unstable limit cycle exists, one is then concerned with the so-called "hard" self-excitation of oscillations. This subject has already been studied in Section 51 in connection with the theory of Poincaré.

It was shown that the characteristic in this case has an inflection point; in its approximation by expansion in a power series, one has to retain a term ϵv^5 with a negative sign. Since even terms do not have any effect on the determination of limit cycles, one can drop them from the equation. Under these conditions, Van der Pol's equation becomes

$$\ddot{v} + v = \mu(\beta + 3\delta v^2 - 5\eta v^4)\dot{v} \qquad [54.11]$$

In this case $f(v,\dot{v}) = (\beta + 3\delta v^2 - 5\eta v^4)\dot{v}$ and

$$f(K \cos u, -K \sin u) = -(\beta + 3\delta K^2 \cos^2 u - 5\eta K^4 \cos^4 u)\, K \sin u$$

From this, by the first equation [52.9], we get

$$\phi(K) = \frac{1}{2\pi}\left[\int_0^{2\pi}\beta K \sin^2 u\,du + \int_0^{2\pi}3\delta K^3\cos^2 u \sin^2 u\,du - \int_0^{2\pi}5\eta K^5\cos^4 u \sin^2 u\,du\right]$$

$$= \frac{K}{2\pi}\left[\beta\int_0^{2\pi}\sin^2 u\,du + 3\delta K^2\int_0^{2\pi}\cos^2 u \sin^2 u\,du - 5\eta K^4\int_0^{2\pi}\cos^4 u \sin^2 u\,du\right]$$

The values of these definite integrals are

$$\int_0^{2\pi}\sin^2 u\,du = \pi; \quad \int_0^{2\pi}\cos^2 u \sin^2 u\,du = \int_0^{2\pi}\sin^2 u\,du - \int\sin^4 u\,du = \pi - \frac{3}{4}\pi = \frac{\pi}{4}$$

$$\int_0^{2\pi}\cos^4 u \sin^2 u\,du = \int_0^{2\pi}\cos^4 u\,du - \int_0^{2\pi}\cos^6 u\,du = \frac{3}{4}\pi - \frac{3\cdot 5}{4\cdot 6}\pi = \frac{\pi}{8}$$

This gives

$$\phi(K) = \frac{K}{2}\left(\beta + \frac{3}{4}\delta K^2 - \frac{5}{8}\eta K^4\right) = 0 \qquad [54.12]$$

as the condition for limit cycles. It is assumed that β, γ, and η are positive. One root is clearly $K = 0$. Following the same procedure as before and making use of Liapounoff's equations of the first approximation, one finds that the singularity is an unstable focal point.

The limit cycles proper are given by the quadratic equation

$$\frac{5}{8}\eta S^2 - \frac{3}{4}\delta S - \beta = 0 \qquad [54.13]$$

where $S = K^2$. Only positive roots are to be considered because $S = K^2$ is essentially positive. Equation [54.13] can be written as

$$\beta = \frac{5}{8}\eta S^2 - \frac{3}{4}\delta S = p^2 S^2 - qS = p^2 S^2 - qS + \frac{q^2}{4p^2} - \frac{q^2}{4p^2} = \left(pS - \frac{q}{2p}\right)^2 - \frac{q^2}{4p^2}$$

where $p^2 = \frac{5}{8}\eta$ and $q = \frac{3}{4}\delta$.

If this equation is rearranged,

$$\left(\beta + \frac{q^2}{4p^2}\right) = \left[p\left(S - \frac{q}{2p^2}\right)\right]^2 \qquad [54.14]$$

Equation [54.14] represents the parabola $(\beta - \beta_0) = p^2(S - S_0)^2$, as shown in Figure 54.1. If we change the (S,β)-axes to a new system of axes (S_1,β_1) with a new origin at $(\beta_0 = -\frac{q^2}{4p^2}, S_0 = \frac{q}{2p})$, Equation [54.14] becomes

$$\beta_1 = p^2 S_1^2$$

The second root corresponds to the limit cycle $K_2 = \sqrt{\dfrac{3\delta}{5\eta}}$ and the first one to an unstable focal point which can be ascertained as explained in the beginning of this section.

For $\beta < 0$, that is, to the left of the origin O, the roots of the quadratic equation $p^2 S^2 - qS - \beta = 0$ are

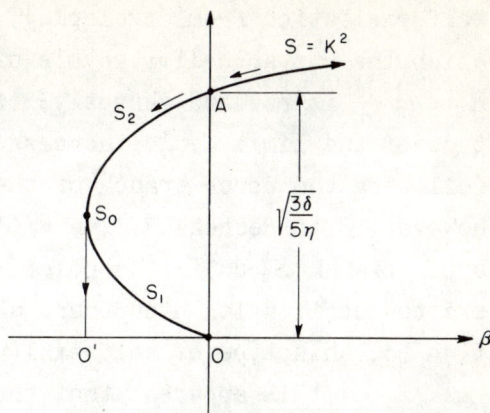

Figure 54.1

$$S_{1,2} = \frac{q \pm \sqrt{q^2 - 4\,|\beta|\,p^2}}{2\,p^2}$$

They are real and positive only as long as $q^2 - 4\,|\beta|\,p^2 \geqq 0$. They correspond to the points S_1 and S_2 of intersection of the parabola with the straight line β = constant. The condition for a double root is $|\beta_0| = \dfrac{q^2}{4p^2}$; at this value of the negative β, the value of the root is $S_0 = \dfrac{q}{2p^2}$. The tangent to the parabola at this point is vertical.

In the region $O'O$, where two roots exist, there are two limit cycles, $K_1 = \sqrt{S_1}$ and $K_2 = \sqrt{S_2}$. The first is unstable and the second stable.

To illustrate this point, differentiate Equation [54.12] with respect to K.

$$\phi'(K) = \frac{\beta}{2} + \frac{3q}{2} K^2 - \frac{5p^2}{2} K^4 = \frac{\beta}{2} + \frac{3q}{2} S - \frac{5p^2}{2} S^2 \qquad [54.15]$$

It is sufficient to substitute into this equation the values of the roots S_1 and S_2 for β in the interval $(0, -q^2/4p^2)$, since the curve does not extend to the left of $\beta = -\dfrac{q^2}{4p^2}$ and has only one root to the right of $\beta = 0$. Consider, for example, the middle value in this interval, $\beta_1 = -\dfrac{q^2}{8p^2}$. The corresponding roots are

$$S_{1,2} = \frac{q}{2p^2}\Big(1 \pm \sqrt{1 - \frac{1}{2}}\,\Big)$$

that is, $S_1 = 0.293q/2p^2$ and $S_2 = 1.707q/2p^2$.

Substituting these values in Equation [54.15], in which $\beta = -\dfrac{q}{8p^2}$, one finds, after a reduction, that $\phi'(K_1) > 0$ and $\phi'(K_2) < 0$. Hence the limit cycles on the lower branch S_1 of the parabola are unstable and on the upper branch S_2 they are stable. If β varies now from negative values and reaches the point O', there is no self-excitation throughout the range $O'O$ since the unstable limit cycles S_1, interposed between the stable focal points situated on the β-axis and the stable limit cycles S_2, act as a *barrier* preventing the

self-excitation from developing, see Chapter IV. As soon as Point O at
which the unstable limit cycle disappears is reached, the stable limit cycle
$K_2 = \sqrt{\frac{3\delta}{5\eta}}$ is reached abruptly; if β is still further increased, the amplitude of the limit cycle increases continuously, the representative point S
following the upper branch of the parabola to the right of Point A. If,
however, β is decreased, the amplitude of the stable limit cycle follows the
upper branch S_2 until the point $S_0\left(K_0 = \frac{1}{4}\sqrt{\frac{6\delta}{5\eta}}\right)$ is reached. Here the self-
excited oscillation disappears abruptly. As previously mentioned, see Sec-
tion 51, this type of self-excitation is called hard.

It is apparent that the theory of Van der Pol gives exactly the
same results as the theory of Poincaré.

55. EXAMPLE: EQUATION OF LORD RAYLEIGH; FROUDE'S PENDULUM

In his researches on the maintenance of vibrations, Lord Rayleigh
(14) came across the following equation

$$m\ddot{x} - (\alpha - \beta\dot{x}^2)\dot{x} + Kx = 0 \qquad [55.1]$$

in which there is a predominance of negative damping for small values of the
velocity $\dot{x}$; for larger velocities the damping becomes positive. By introducing "dimensionless time," as was explained in Section 30, Rayleigh's equation
can be put in the form

$$\ddot{x} + x + \mu f(x,\dot{x}) = 0 \qquad [55.2]$$

Assume that the damping terms are small enough to justify the intro-
duction of the small parameter μ. In Rayleigh's equation $f(x,\dot{x}) = f(\dot{x}) = m\dot{x}^3 - n\dot{x}$, where m and n are constants appearing instead of α and β as the result of the transformation of the independent variable. One has finally

$$\ddot{x} + x + \mu(m\dot{x}^3 - n\dot{x}) = 0 \qquad [55.3]$$

where $m > 0$ and $n > 0$.

By Equations [52.9], the functions $\phi(K)$ and $\psi(K)$ are

$$\phi(K) = \frac{1}{2\pi}\int_0^{2\pi} mK\sin^2 u\,du - \frac{1}{2\pi}\int_0^{2\pi} nK^3\sin^4 u\,du = \frac{1}{2}K\left(m - \frac{3}{4}nK^2\right) \quad [55.4]$$

and

$$\psi(K) = \frac{1}{2\pi K}\int_0^{2\pi} nK^3\sin^3 u\cos u\,du - \frac{1}{2\pi K}\int_0^{2\pi} mK\sin u\cos u\,du \qquad [55.5]$$

From Equation [55.4] we see that the conditions for limit cycles are

$$K = 0; \quad K = \sqrt{\frac{4m}{3n}} \qquad\qquad [55.6]$$

The first value $K = 0$ is clearly a point singularity. If the non-linear term $m\dot{x}^3$ is omitted, Liapounoff's equations are $\dot{x} = y$ and $\dot{y} - ny + x = 0$. From this we obtain the characteristic equation $S^2 - nS + 1 = 0$, whose roots are

$$S_{1,2} = \frac{n \pm \sqrt{n^2 - 4}}{2}$$

For $n < 2$, one has an unstable focal point, and for $n > 2$, an unstable nodal point. In both cases the point singularity $K = 0$ is unstable.

In order to ascertain the stability of the limit cycle $K = \sqrt{\frac{4m}{3n}}$, one must differentiate Equation [55.4] with respect to K

$$\phi'(K) = \frac{m}{2} - \frac{9}{8}nK^2 \qquad\qquad [55.7]$$

Substituting $K^2 = \frac{4m}{3n}$ in this expression, one finds

$$\phi'\left(\sqrt{\frac{4m}{3n}}\right) = \frac{m}{2} - \frac{9}{8}n\frac{4m}{3n} = \frac{m}{2} - \frac{3}{2}m < 0$$

The limit cycle is therefore stable. The oscillating system governed by Rayleigh's equations, [55.1] or [55.3], thus exhibits the property of being self-excited in a steady state. If the dissipative terms were of the same sign, that is, of the form $\pm(m\dot{x} + n\dot{x}^3)$, there would be no limit cycle in this case, as is easily ascertained, although the oscillation would still be governed by a non-linear differential equation of a dissipative type. The example of Section 31 belongs to the case considered in this section.

It can be shown that the oscillation of Froude's pendulum, see Section 8, is also governed by Rayleigh's equation. In the elementary theory of this phenomenon it was established that the damping is *initially* negative under certain specified conditions. A linear equation does not represent the actual phenomenon because when the coefficient of $\dot{\phi}$ is negative it indicates that the amplitudes of oscillation increase indefinitely, which is clearly impossible from physical considerations. The reason for this inconsistency is the fact that the equation was overlinearized by dropping the non-linear terms.

By conserving at least the first two non-linear terms, we shall be able to establish the existence of a finite limit cycle, characterizing the steady state of oscillation of Froude's pendulum which is actually observed. Expanding the function $M(\omega - \dot{\phi})$ of Section 8 in a Taylor series, we have

$$M(\omega - \dot{\phi}) = M(\omega) - \dot{\phi}M'(\omega) + \frac{\dot{\phi}^2}{2!}M''(\omega) - \frac{\dot{\phi}^3}{3!}M'''(\omega) + \cdots \qquad [55.8]$$

Here we assume that the function M is analytic, that is, that it admits derivatives at least as an idealized feature of the observed phenomenon.

Dividing Equation [8.1] by I, introducing dimensionless time, and keeping only the first two non-linear terms in the expansion, one obtains an equation of the form

$$\ddot{\phi} + \phi = -c\dot{\phi} + k\dot{\phi}^2 - n\dot{\phi}^3 \qquad [55.9]$$

where $c = b + M'(\omega)$, and k and n are suitable constant coefficients obtained by substituting the expansion [55.8] into Equation [8.1]. It must be noted that c is negative according to what has been stated in Section 8. Putting $c = -m$, where $m > 0$, one has

$$\ddot{\phi} + \phi = m\dot{\phi} + k\dot{\phi}^2 - n\dot{\phi}^3 \equiv \mu(m_1\dot{\phi} + k_1\dot{\phi}^2 - n_1\dot{\phi}^3)$$

whence

$$f(\dot{\phi}) = \gamma_1\dot{\phi} + k_1\dot{\phi}^2 - n_1\dot{\phi}^3$$

and

$$f(K\sin u) = m_1 K\sin u + k_1 K^2\sin^2 u - n_1 K^3\sin^3 u$$

Hence

$$\phi(K) = -\frac{1}{2\pi}\left[m_1 K\int_0^{2\pi}\sin^2 u\, du + k_1 K^2\int_0^{2\pi}\sin^3 u\, du - n_1 K^3\int_0^{2\pi}\sin^4 u\, du\right]$$

that is,

$$\phi(K) = -\frac{1}{2}\left[m_1 K - \frac{3}{4}n_1 K^3\right]$$

The equation for limit cycles is

$$K\left(m_1 - \frac{3}{4}n_1 K^2\right) = 0 \qquad [55.10]$$

The solution $K = 0$ corresponds clearly to a point singularity, and the amplitude of the limit cycle is $K = \sqrt{\dfrac{4m_1}{3n_1}}$. One can calculate m_1 and n_1 explicitly from the equations of transformation of the original equation to its form involving dimensionless time. It is to be noted that the quadratic term disappears from Expression [55.10] for the limit cycle because $\int_0^{2\pi} \sin^3 u \, du = 0$, a fact which has already been noted in Section 54.

56. MORE GENERAL FORMS OF NON-LINEAR EQUATIONS

The Van der Pol method is applicable also to non-linear equations involving, in addition to variable damping, a *variable "spring constant."* It must be noted, however, that the existence of self-excited oscillations, that is, of limit cycles, depends only on the conditions of the variable damping, as was shown by Van der Pol (15) and generalized later by E. and H. Cartan (16) and Liénard (17). In fact, the initial damping, for small x in the Van der Pol equation or for small $\dot{x}$ in the Rayleigh equation, is first negative then positive for larger values of the corresponding variable (x or $\dot{x}$). Physically this means that there exists, initially, an energy input into the system which, in later stages of motion, becomes an energy drain from the system, which then becomes dissipative. The existence of a steady oscillation, that is, of a limit cycle, depends thus on the average equality between the input and the drain per cycle. We shall come back to this important point later in connection with the Principle of Equivalent Balance of Energy formulated by Kryloff and Bogoliuboff. Consider, for example, a more general type of equation

$$m\ddot{x} + (nx^2 - \alpha)\dot{x} + \beta x + \gamma x^2 = 0 \qquad [56.1]$$

which has variable damping, the term $nx^2\dot{x}$, as well as a variable spring constant, the term $(\beta + \gamma x)x$. As long as the terms $(nx^2 - \alpha)\dot{x}$ and γx^2 are small, we can write this equation in the form

$$m\ddot{x} + \beta x = \mu\left[(\alpha_1 - n_1 x^2)\dot{x} - \gamma_1 x^2\right] \equiv \mu\phi(x,\dot{x}) \qquad [56.2]$$

We can easily reduce this equation to a form previously considered. It is sufficient to divide it by m, putting $\beta/m = \omega_0^2$, and pass to a dimensionless independent variable* in order to obtain the equation in the usual form

$$\ddot{x} + x = \mu\left[(\alpha_0 - n_0 x^2)\dot{x} - \gamma_0 x^2\right] \equiv \mu f(x,\dot{x}) \qquad [56.3]$$

---

* The last operation, although convenient for practical calculations, is not altogether necessary. In case one does not use it, the generating solutions should be taken in the form $K \cos \omega t$, $- K\omega \sin \omega t$ instead of $K \cos t$, $- K \sin t$.

and to substitute the generating solutions $K \cos u$ and $- K \sin u$ into the first equation [52.9] giving the limit cycles. The same procedure applies to the generalized Rayleigh equation with the variable spring constant.

In all cases the existence of limit cycles requires that the coefficient of $\dot{x}$ satisfy the conditions of Cartan-Liénard. If this condition is not fulfilled, no self-excited oscillations can exist in a steady state, and the system behaves as purely dissipative, while still non-linear.

CHAPTER X

THEORY OF THE FIRST APPROXIMATION OF KRYLOFF AND BOGOLIUBOFF*

57. INTRODUCTORY REMARKS

The method of Kryloff and Bogoliuboff is very similar to that of Van der Pol and is related to it in the following way. While Van der Pol applies the method of variation of constants to the basic solution $x = a \cos \omega t + b \sin \omega t$ of $\ddot{x} + \omega^2 x = 0$, Kryloff and Bogoliuboff apply the same method to the basic solution $x = a \cos (\omega t + \phi)$ of the same equation. Thus in Kryloff and Bogoliuboff's method, the "varied" constants are a and ϕ (polar coordinates), while in Van der Pol's method they are a and b (rectangular coordinates). The method of Kryloff and Bogoliuboff seems more interesting from the point of view of applications, since it deals directly with the amplitude and phase of the quasi-harmonic oscillation.

Before proceeding with a review of the method of Kryloff and Bogoliuboff, a few additional remarks concerning the effect of secular terms may be helpful.

58. EFFECT OF SECULAR TERMS IN SOLUTIONS BY EXPANSIONS IN SERIES

The difficulty arising from the appearance of secular terms has already been mentioned in Sections 44 and 46. In the example given in Section 46 that difficulty was avoided by a rather delicate change from the "old" periods to the "new," or corrected, ones. This change requires a knowledge of the correction for the period, which is not always obtainable as has been demonstrated. Unfortunately, in a great majority of cases in which the approximation consists in abbreviating an infinite series by a few terms, the situation is still more difficult.

In order to see this point, consider again a quasi-linear differential equation of the form

$$\ddot{x} + \omega^2 x + \mu f(x, \dot{x}) = 0 \qquad [58.1]$$

where μ is a small parameter, i.e., $\mu \ll 1$. Since the non-linear term appears with a small coefficient μ, Poisson suggested as a solution an expression of the form

$$x = x_0 + \mu x_1 + \mu^2 x_2 + \cdots \qquad [58.2]$$

---

* The subject matter of this and of the following two chapters is taken from the treatise of Kryloff and Bogoliuboff, Reference (5). This subject is also treated in the free translation by S. Lefschetz of the Kryloff-Bogoliuboff text, Princeton University Press, 1943.

For $\mu = 0$, $x = x_0 = a \cos \omega t$ is the known generating solution. For $0 < \mu \ll 1$, it seems logical to consider the effect of the non-linear term $\mu f(x,\dot{x})$ as a small *perturbation* and to assume that this perturbation will also be felt in the modification of the initial generating solution represented as a power series of μ, given by Equation [58.2]. The method of Poincaré, Chapter VIII, is, in fact, a further generalization of Poisson's method.

If one substitutes the solution [58.2] into the differential equation [58.1], limiting the expansion up to the power μ^K of the small parameter, one obtains the following series of differential equations by equating terms containing the same powers of μ:

$$\ddot{x}_0 + \omega^2 x_0 = 0$$

$$\ddot{x}_1 + \omega^2 x_1 = - f_1(x_0, \dot{x}_0)$$

$$\ddot{x}_2 + \omega^2 x_2 = \left[-f_x(x_0, \dot{x}_0) x_1 + f_{\dot{x}}(x_0, \dot{x}_0) \dot{x}_1 \right]$$

$$\cdots \cdots \cdots \cdots \cdots \cdots$$

[58.3]

This procedure has already been outlined in connection with Equations [46.5] of the theory of Poincaré. It is easy to show, however, that a direct application of this method is handicapped by the following difficulty.

Consider, for example, the simplest case, that in which $f(x,\dot{x}) \equiv + \dot{x}\omega$. In this case Equation [58.1] is

$$\ddot{x} + \omega^2 x + \mu \omega \dot{x} = 0$$

The exact solution of this equation is

$$x = A e^{-\frac{\mu \omega t}{2}} \cos\left[\left(\omega \sqrt{1 - \frac{\mu^2}{4}}\right) t + \phi\right]$$

[58.4]

where A and ϕ are the constants of integration determined by the initial conditions. If, however, one proceeds by substituting the expansion [58.2] into Equations [58.3], the first equation gives

$$x_0 = A \cos(\omega t + \phi)$$

Substituting this solution into the second equation [58.3], one has

$$\ddot{x}_1 + \omega^2 x_1 = - \dot{x}_0 \omega = A\omega^2 \sin(\omega t + \phi)$$

[58.5]

This equation is satisfied by

$$x_1 = - \frac{A\omega t}{2} \cos(\omega t + \phi)$$

[58.6]

Substituting these values for x_0 and x_1 into Equation [58.2], one has

$$x = A\left(1 - \frac{\mu \omega t}{2}\right)\cos(\omega t + \phi) \qquad [58.7]$$

It is clear that the amplitude of the approximate solution [58.7] increases with time t indefinitely, whereas, according to the exact solution [58.4], it approaches zero, owing to the presence of the exponential term $e^{-\frac{\mu \omega t}{2}}$

As a second example, consider the differential equation

$$\ddot{x} + \omega^2 x(1 + \mu x^2) = 0 \qquad [58.8]$$

which may be considered as the equation of motion of a mechanical mass attracted to the position of equilibrium by a force proportional to the distance, with a perturbation term proportional to the cube of the distance.

Proceeding as before and seeking a solution of the form $x = x_0 + \mu x$, one has

$$\ddot{x}_0 + \omega^2 x_0 = 0$$

$$\ddot{x}_1 + \omega^2 x_1 = -\omega^2 x_0^3 \qquad [58.9]$$

From the first equation [58.9], $x_0 = A \sin(\omega t + \phi)$. Substituting this value for x_0 into the second equation, one has

$$\ddot{x}_1 + \omega^2 x_1 = -\omega^2 A^3 \sin^3(\omega t + \phi) = -\frac{3}{4}\omega^2 A^3 \sin(\omega t + \phi) + \frac{1}{4}\omega^2 A^3 \sin 3(\omega t + \phi)$$

This equation is satisfied by

$$x_1 = \frac{3}{8}\omega t A^3 \cos(\omega t + \phi) - \frac{A^3}{32}\sin 3(\omega t + \phi)$$

whence

$$x = A\sin(\omega t + \phi) + \frac{3\mu}{8}\omega t A^3 \cos(\omega t + \phi) - \frac{A^3 \mu}{32}\sin 3(\omega t + \phi) \qquad [58.10]$$

The second term of this expression is a secular term. Thus, this expression for the displacement has no physical meaning. Unfortunately, in this case the exact solution is not known, as Equation [58.8] is not linear. One can, however, affirm the correctness of the above statement by invoking the law of conservation of energy, which holds in this case since the system is conservative. In fact, multiplying Equation [58.8] by $\dot{x}$, one can write

$$\dot{x}\left[\ddot{x} + (1 + \mu x^2)\omega^2 x\right] = \frac{d}{dt}\left(\frac{1}{2}\dot{x}^2 + \frac{1}{2}\omega^2 x^2 + \frac{\mu \omega^2}{4}x^4\right) = 0$$

From this we can obtain the law of conservation of energy

$$\frac{1}{2}\dot{x}^2 + \frac{1}{2}\omega^2 x^2 + \frac{\mu\omega^2}{4}x^4 = \text{constant} = E \qquad [58.11]$$

From this equation it follows that, for $\mu > 0$, the square of the amplitude x^2 has an upper bound $2E/\omega^2$. This result is to be expected, as the system has no sources of energy and is conservative. Hence there is a definite contradiction of Equation [58.10].

From these two examples, we see that the direct application of Poisson's method to problems of dynamics encounters a serious difficulty because of the presence of secular terms.

59. EQUATIONS OF THE FIRST APPROXIMATION

In this section we propose to establish the fundamental points of the theory of the first approximation of Kryloff and Bogoliuboff, which will play an important role in subsequent chapters.

For $\mu = 0$, Equation [58.1] reduces to a simple linear equation whose solution is

$$x = a\sin(\omega t + \phi); \qquad \dot{x} = a\omega\cos(\omega t + \phi) \qquad [59.1]$$

where a and ϕ are constants, the amplitude and the phase respectively. For a quasi-linear equation when $\mu \neq 0$ but is small, it appears logical to retain the form of solutions [59.1], provided that we consider the quantities a and ϕ not as constants but as certain functions of time to be determined.

Differentiating the first equation [59.1], one obtains

$$\dot{x} = \dot{a}\sin(\omega t + \phi) + a\omega\cos(\omega t + \phi) + a\dot{\phi}\cos(\omega t + \phi) \qquad [59.2]$$

Making use of the second equation [59.1], one has

$$\dot{a}\sin(\omega t + \phi) + a\dot{\phi}\cos(\omega t + \phi) = 0 \qquad [59.3]$$

Differentiating the second equation [59.1], one gets

$$\ddot{x} = \dot{a}\omega\cos(\omega t + \phi) - a\omega^2\sin(\omega t + \phi) - a\omega\dot{\phi}\sin(\omega t + \phi) \qquad [59.4]$$

Substituting these values for x, $\dot{x}$, and $\ddot{x}$ into the original quasi-linear equation [58.1], one has

$$\dot{a}\omega\cos(\omega t + \phi) - a\omega\dot{\phi}\sin(\omega t + \phi) + \mu f\left[a\sin(\omega t + \phi), a\omega\cos(\omega t + \phi)\right] = 0 \qquad [59.5]$$

Solving Equations [59.3] and [59.5] for $\dot{a}$ and ϕ, one gets

$$\dot{a} = -\frac{\mu}{\omega}f\left[a\sin(\omega t + \phi), a\omega\cos(\omega t + \phi)\right]\cos(\omega t + \phi) \qquad [59.6]$$

$$\dot{\phi} = \frac{\mu}{a\omega} f\left[a\sin(\omega t + \phi), a\omega\cos(\omega t + \phi)\right]\sin(\omega t + \phi) \qquad [59.7]$$

It can be seen that the original equation [58.1] of the second order has been reduced to a system of two equations, [59.6] and [59.7], of the first order. The interesting feature of this transformation lies in the fact that these first-order equations are now written in terms of the amplitude and phase as dependent variables. One notes a formal analogy with Equations [52.8] of Van der Pol and also with Equations [46.22] and [46.23] of Poincaré.

From the form of the right side of Equations [59.6] and [59.7], it is seen that both $\dot{a}$ and $\dot{\phi}$ are periodic functions of time. From the fact that the right-hand terms of these equations contain a small parameter μ, one can conclude that both a and ϕ, while being periodic, are functions which vary slowly during one period $T = 2\pi/\omega$ of the trigonometric functions involved.

It is reasonable, therefore, to consider a and ϕ as constant during one period T. It is possible to transform Equations [59.6] and [59.7] into a more convenient form. For this purpose, consider the Fourier expansions of the functions

$$f(a\sin\phi, a\omega\cos\phi)\cos\phi = K_0(a) + \sum_{n=1}^{\infty}\left[K_n(a)\cos n\phi + L_n(a)\sin n\phi\right]$$

$$[59.8]$$

$$f(a\sin\phi, a\omega\cos\phi)\sin\phi = P_0(a) + \sum_{n=1}^{\infty}\left[P_n(a)\cos n\phi + Q_n(a)\sin n\phi\right]$$

where

$$K_0(a) = \frac{1}{2\pi}\int_0^{2\pi} f(a\sin\phi, a\omega\cos\phi)\cos\phi\, d\phi$$

$$P_0(a) = \frac{1}{2\pi}\int_0^{2\pi} f(a\sin\phi, a\omega\cos\phi)\sin\phi\, d\phi$$

$$K_n(a) = \frac{1}{\pi}\int_0^{2\pi} f(a\sin\phi, a\omega\cos\phi)\cos\phi\cos n\phi\, d\phi$$

$$[59.9]$$

$$L_n(a) = \frac{1}{\pi}\int_0^{2\pi} f(a\sin\phi, a\omega\cos\phi)\cos\phi\sin n\phi\, d\phi$$

$$P_n(a) = \frac{1}{\pi}\int_0^{2\pi} f(a\sin\phi, a\omega\cos\phi)\sin\phi\cos n\phi\, d\phi$$

$$Q_n(a) = \frac{1}{\pi}\int_0^{2\pi} f(a\sin\phi, a\omega\cos\phi)\sin\phi\sin n\phi\, d\phi$$

Equations [59.6] and [59.7] can then be written in the form

$$\frac{da}{dt} = -\frac{\mu}{\omega} K_0(a) - \frac{\mu}{\omega} \sum_{n=1}^{\infty} \left[K_n(a) \cos n(\omega t + \phi) + L_n(a) \sin n(\omega t + \phi) \right]$$

[59.10]

$$\frac{d\phi}{dt} = \frac{\mu}{a\omega} P_0(a) + \frac{\mu}{a\omega} \sum_{n=1}^{\infty} \left[P_n(a) \cos n(\omega t + \phi) + Q_n(a) \sin n(\omega t + \phi) \right]$$

Integrating these equations between the limits t and $t + T$, and considering $a(t)$ and $\phi(t)$ as remaining approximately constant in this interval, one has as the first approximation

$$\frac{a(t + T) - a(t)}{T} = -\frac{\mu}{\omega} K_0 \Big[a(t) \Big]; \qquad \frac{\phi(t + T) - \phi(t)}{T} = \frac{\mu}{a\omega} P_0 \Big[a(t) \Big] \quad [59.11]$$

since

$$\int_t^{t+T} \cos n(\omega t + \phi)\, dt = \int_t^{t+T} \sin n(\omega t + \phi)\, dt = 0$$

Furthermore, since, by assumption, the variations Δa and $\Delta \phi$ of amplitude and phase are small during the interval $(t, t + T)$, one can write Equations [59.11] to the first approximation

$$\frac{da}{dt} = -\frac{\mu}{\omega} K_0(a); \qquad \frac{d\phi}{dt} = \frac{\mu}{a\omega} P_0(a) \qquad [59.12]$$

If these equations are compared with the exact equations [59.10], it is seen that the equations of the first approximation are obtained from the exact equations by *averaging the latter equations over the period*, thus eliminating the rest of the Fourier series under the summation sign. The analogy between Equations [59.12] and the "abbreviated" equations [52.6] of Van der Pol should be noted.

Letting $\psi = \omega t + \phi$, the *total phase* of the motion, we have $d\psi/dt = \omega + d\phi/dt$. Making use of these relations and the relation for $K_0(a)$ and $P_0(a)$ in [59.9], we obtain for the equations of the first approximation

$$\frac{da}{dt} = -\frac{\mu}{\omega} \frac{1}{2\pi} \int_0^{2\pi} f(a \sin \phi, a\omega \cos \phi) \cos \phi \, d\phi \equiv \Phi(a) \qquad [59.13]$$

$$\frac{d\psi}{dt} = \omega + \frac{\mu}{a\omega} \frac{1}{2\pi} \int_0^{2\pi} f(a \sin \phi, a\omega \cos \phi) \sin \phi \, d\phi \equiv \Omega(a) \qquad [59.14]$$

The first approximation will then be $x = a \sin \psi$, where the amplitude a and the phase ψ are obtained from Equations [59.13] and [59.14].

60. NON-LINEAR CONSERVATIVE SYSTEMS

Consider again a quasi-linear differential equation

$$\ddot{x} + \omega^2 x + \mu f(x) = 0$$

in which $f(x)$ does not contain the velocity $\dot{x}$. Equation [59.13] gives

$$\frac{da}{dt} = -\frac{\mu}{2\pi\omega} \int_0^{2\pi} f(a\sin\phi)\cos\phi \, d\phi \qquad [60.1]$$

and Equation [59.14] gives

$$\frac{d\psi}{dt} = \omega + \frac{\mu}{2\pi a\omega} \int_0^{2\pi} f(a\sin\phi)\sin\phi \, d\phi \qquad [60.2]$$

Noting that

$$\int_0^{2\pi} f(a\sin\phi)\cos\phi \, d\phi = \frac{1}{a} \, \psi(a\sin\phi)\Big|_0^{2\pi} = 0$$

where $\psi(x) = \int_0^x f(\xi)d\xi$, Equation [60.1] gives a = constant. Hence, from the first approximation, it follows that the amplitude does not change in the course of time; the system is thus conservative. This can be seen from *a priori* considerations, because the function f does not depend on the velocity $\dot{x}$, whereas dissipative forces generally do depend on $\dot{x}$.

From Equation [59.14] it follows that

$$\psi = \Omega(a)t + \psi_0 \qquad [60.3]$$

since $\Omega(a)$ does not depend on t in this case; ψ_0 is a constant of integration.

Thus, the oscillations will be of the form

$$x = a\sin\left[\Omega(a)t + \psi_0\right] \qquad [60.4]$$

Therefore, to the first approximation, the effect of a non-linearity of this type will be felt only in that the frequency of oscillation will depend on the amplitude a, that is, the oscillations are not isochronous, but the decrement of oscillation is zero since the system is conservative.

Squaring Equation [59.14] and neglecting the term of the second order in μ, one has

$$\Omega^2(a) = \omega^2 + \frac{\mu}{\pi a} \int_0^{2\pi} f(a\sin\phi)\sin\phi \, d\phi = \frac{1}{\pi a}\left[\omega^2 a \int_0^{2\pi}\sin^2\phi \, d\phi + \mu\int_0^{2\pi} f(a\sin\phi)\sin\phi \, d\phi\right]$$

$$= \frac{1}{\pi a}\int_0^{2\pi}\left[\omega^2 a\sin\phi + \mu f(a\sin\phi)\right]\sin\phi \, d\phi = \frac{1}{\pi a}\int_0^{2\pi} F(a\sin\phi)\sin\phi \, d\phi \qquad [60.5]$$

where

$$F(a \sin \phi) = \omega^2 a \sin \phi + \mu f(a \sin \phi) \qquad [60.6]$$

On the other hand, the general form of a non-linear equation, in which the non-linearity is only in the spring constant, is of the form $\ddot{x} + F(x) = 0$. If the term $F(x)$ is not far from linearity, it can be written as $F(x) = \omega^2 x + \mu f(x)$, where $f(x)$ is the non-linear component of $F(x)$. Comparing this expression with Equation [60.6], one finds exactly the same result provided one substitutes the generating solution $a \sin \phi$ for x. From this we obtain the following theorem:

When a system is conservative but not linear, the amplitude a remains constant and the frequency $\Omega(a)$ is given by Equation [60.5], in which $F(x)$ is the term entering into the equation $\ddot{x} + F(x) = 0$, without the necessity of splitting it into a linear component $\omega^2 x$ and a non-linear one, $\mu f(x)$.

In the following section examples are given illustrating the application of the theory of the first approximation.

61. EXAMPLES OF NON-LINEAR CONSERVATIVE SYSTEMS

A. PENDULUM

The differential equation for a pendulum is $\ddot{\theta} + \frac{g}{L} \sin \theta = 0$. In elementary theory, which we may designate as an *approximation of zero order*, it is assumed that for small angles $\sin \theta \approx \theta$. The well-known solution for the period, $T = 2\pi \sqrt{L/g}$, is obtained. It is to be noted that oscillations are isochronous under this assumption.

For the first approximation we can take $\sin \theta \approx \theta - \frac{\theta^3}{6}$; the differential equation then becomes $\ddot{\theta} + \omega^2(\theta - \frac{\theta^3}{6}) = 0$, where $\omega^2 = g/L$. Using Equation [60.5], one obtains

$$\Omega^2(a) = \frac{\omega^2}{\pi a} \int_0^{2\pi} \left(a \sin \phi - \frac{a^3 \sin^3 \phi}{6} \right) \sin \phi \, d\phi$$

$$= \frac{\omega^2}{\pi a} \left[a \int_0^{2\pi} \sin^2 \phi \, d\phi - \frac{a^3}{6} \int_0^{2\pi} \sin^4 \phi \, d\phi \right] = \omega^2 \left(1 - \frac{a^2}{8} \right)$$

that is,

$$\Omega(a) = \omega \sqrt{1 - \frac{a^2}{8}} \approx \omega \left(1 - \frac{a^2}{16} \right) \qquad [61.1]$$

or, in terms of the period

$$T(a) = T \left(1 + \frac{a^2}{16} \right) \qquad [61.2]$$

It is thus seen that the oscillation is not isochronous; the period increases slightly with increasing amplitudes of oscillation.

Thus, for example,

for amplitudes of the order of 10 degrees, $T(a) = T \times 1.001$;

for amplitudes of the order of 20 degrees, $T(a) = T \times 1.006$;

for amplitudes of the order of 30 degrees, $T(a) = T \times 1.014$.

It should be observed that, although the expression for the period can be established in this case by means of elliptic functions, the theory of the first approximation leads to this result by a more general procedure. Furthermore, the latter method easily leads to correct results in more complicated cases for which exact methods are not available.

B. TORSIONAL OSCILLATIONS OF A SHAFT

Let J_1 and J_2 be the moments of inertia of rotating masses placed at the ends of a shaft S, see Figure 61.1. If θ_1 and θ_2 are the two angles determining the angular position of the masses J_1 and J_2 with respect to a fixed reference angle, the torsional moment M is a certain function of the difference $(\theta_1 - \theta_2)$, say $C(\theta_1 - \theta_2) = M(\theta)$.*

The differential equations of the coupled system are

$$J_1\ddot{\theta}_1 + C(\theta_1 - \theta_2) = 0 \quad \text{and} \quad J_2\ddot{\theta}_2 - C(\theta_1 - \theta_2) = 0$$

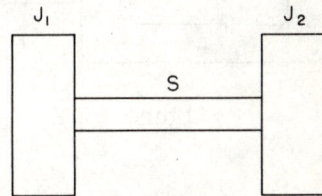

Figure 61.1

Subtracting the second equation from the first and letting $\theta = \theta_1 - \theta_2$, we obtain

$$J_1 J_2 \ddot{\theta} + (J_1 + J_2) C(\theta) = 0 \qquad [61.3]$$

which is the non-linear differential equation of the torsional oscillation of the system.

Equation [61.3] can be written as $\ddot{\theta} + K^2 C(\theta) = 0$, where $K^2 = (J_1 + J_2)/J_1 J_2$. Assume that $C(\theta)$ is of the form $C(\theta) = C_0\theta \pm C_1\theta^3$, where $C_1\theta^3$ is a small non-linear term. From this,

$$F(\theta) = K^2 C_0 \theta \pm K^2 C_1 \theta^3 = m\theta \pm n\theta^3$$

and the frequency is given by

$$\Omega^2(a) = \frac{1}{\pi a} \int_0^{2\pi} (ma\sin\phi \pm na^3\sin^3\phi)\sin\phi \, d\phi = \omega_0^2 \pm \frac{3}{4}K^2 C_1 a^2$$

---

* $C(\theta_1 - \theta_2)$ in these notations should be read: C is a function of $(\theta_1 - \theta_2)$, and not C times $(\theta_1 - \theta_2)$.

or

$$\Omega(a) \approx \omega_0\left(1 \pm \frac{3}{8}\,\frac{K^2 C_1 a^2}{\omega_0^{\,2}}\right)$$

The non-linear frequency (and therefore the period) will thus depend on the amplitude. The amplitude of the vibration is constant, but the vibration is not isochronous.

C. ELECTRICAL OSCILLATIONS OF A CIRCUIT CONTAINING AN IRON CORE

Let a circuit be composed of an inductance L and a capacity C with negligible resistance. The inductance coil is wound on an iron circuit A, see Figure 61.2, subject to magnetic saturation. The condition of equilibrium of electromotive forces in the circuit gives

$$\frac{d\Phi}{dt} + \frac{1}{C}\int_0^t i\,dt = 0$$

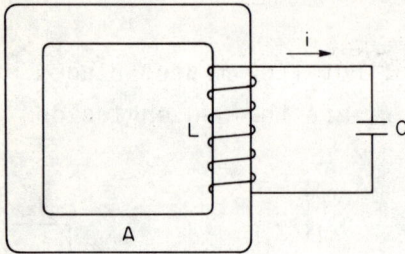

Figure 61.2

where Φ is the totalized flux through the coil. The condition of saturation can be approximated by the equation $i = A\Phi + B\Phi^3$, whence from the preceding equation one has

$$\ddot{\Phi} + \frac{A\Phi + B\Phi^3}{C} = 0 \qquad\qquad [61.4]$$

Equation [61.4] is the non-linear equation of oscillation. Reducing it to the standard form of a quasi-linear equation, where $A/C = \omega^2 =$ constant, and assuming that the ratio $\frac{B}{A}\Phi^2 \ll 1$, one can apply Formula [60.5] and obtain

$$\Omega^2(a) = \frac{1}{\pi a C}\int_0^{2\pi}(Aa\sin\phi + Ba^3\sin^3\phi)\sin\phi\,d\phi = \frac{A}{C}\left(1 + \frac{3Ba^2}{4A}\right)$$

that is,

$$\Omega(a) = \omega\sqrt{1 + \frac{3Ba^2}{4A}} \approx \omega\left(1 + \frac{3}{8}\,\frac{Ba^2}{A}\right) \qquad\qquad [61.5]$$

The actual frequency $\Omega(a)$ is thus increased in comparison with the frequency ω for small amplitudes, owing to a decrease of L with the amplitude a of the oscillation. Thus the oscillation is non-isochronous.

62. SYSTEMS WITH NON-LINEAR DAMPING OF A DISSIPATIVE TYPE

Consider the differential equation

$$m\ddot{x} + Kx + f(\dot{x}) = 0$$

Dividing it by m and putting $K/m = \omega^2$, we get

$$\ddot{x} + \omega^2 x + \frac{1}{m} f(\dot{x}) = 0$$

We shall keep within the limits of the quasi-harmonic theory. In this case $\frac{1}{m} f(\dot{x})$ plays the role taken by $\mu f(x,\dot{x})$ in the general theory. The expressions

$$\int_0^{2\pi} f(a \sin\phi, \, a\omega \cos\phi) \cos\phi \, d\phi \quad \text{and} \quad \int_0^{2\pi} f(a \sin\phi, \, a\omega \cos\phi) \sin\phi \, d\phi$$

entering into Equations [59.13] and [59.14] of the first approximation, in this case are

$$\int_0^{2\pi} f(a\omega \cos\phi) \cos\phi \, d\phi \quad \text{and} \quad \int_0^{2\pi} f(a\omega \cos\phi) \sin\phi \, d\phi$$

respectively, since $f(x,\dot{x})$ reduces to $f(\dot{x})$.

We note that

$$\int_0^{2\pi} f(a\omega \cos\phi) \sin\phi \, d\phi = -\frac{1}{a\omega} \int_0^{2\pi} f(a\omega \cos\phi) \, d(a\omega \cos\phi) = -\frac{1}{a\omega} \Phi(a\omega \cos\phi) \Big|_0^{2\pi} = 0$$

so that, by Equation [59.14],

$$\frac{d\psi}{dt} = \omega \qquad\qquad [62.1]$$

Furthermore, Equation [59.13] can be written as

$$\frac{da}{dt} = \dot{a} = -\frac{1}{2\pi m \omega} \int_0^{2\pi} f(a\omega \cos\phi) \cos\phi \, d\phi \qquad\qquad [62.2]$$

It is clear that the instantaneous frequency $d\psi/dt$ is equal to the constant "linear" frequency ω, and the amplitude a varies according to Equation [62.2]. Thus, the oscillation is generally of the form $x = a \sin(\omega t + \psi_0)$, where ψ_0 is a constant. The frequency is not changed since the frequency correction is of the second order and therefore does not appear in equations of the first approximation. A few examples given below illustrate the application of Equation [62.2] to various types of non-linear damping $f(\dot{x})$.

A. LINEAR DAMPING: $f(\dot{x}) = \lambda \dot{x}$

In this case

$$\int_0^{2\pi} f(a\omega \cos\phi) \cos\phi \, d\phi = a\omega\lambda \int_0^{2\pi} \cos^2\phi \, d\phi = a\omega\lambda\pi$$

and Equation [62.2] gives

$$\dot{a} = -\frac{1}{2\pi m \omega} \cdot a\omega\lambda\pi = -\frac{\lambda a}{2m}$$

whence

$$a = a_0 e^{-\frac{\lambda t}{2m}} \qquad\qquad [62.3]$$

Comparing this with the exact solution

$$x = a_0 e^{-\frac{\lambda t}{2m}} \sin(\omega_1 t + \psi_0)$$

where

$$\omega_1 = \omega\sqrt{1 - \frac{1}{4}\left(\frac{\lambda}{\sqrt{Km}}\right)^2}$$

one notes that the first approximation gives the same expression for the amplitude as the exact solution; the difference between the expressions for frequency ω and ω_1 is of the order of $\frac{1}{8}(\lambda/\sqrt{Km})^2$, that is, of the second order, if λ is of the first order, as previously set forth.

B. QUADRATIC DAMPING: $f(\dot{x}) = b\dot{x}^2$

Since $f(\dot{x})$ is an even function of $\dot{x}$, and from physical considerations it should be an odd function of $\dot{x}$, we should write the above expression as $f(\dot{x}) = b|\dot{x}|\dot{x}$. In this case

$$\int_0^{2\pi} f(a\omega\cos\phi)\cos\phi\,d\phi = ba^2\omega^2\int_0^{2\pi}|\cos\phi|\cos^2\phi\,d\phi = ba^2\omega^2\left[\int_0^{\frac{\pi}{2}}\cos^3\phi\,d\phi + \int_{\frac{3\pi}{2}}^{2\pi}\cos^3\phi\,d\phi -\right.$$

$$\left.-\int_{\frac{\pi}{2}}^{\frac{3\pi}{2}}\cos^3\phi\,d\phi\right] = ba^2\omega^2\left[\frac{2}{3} + \frac{2}{3} + \frac{4}{3}\right] = \frac{8}{3}ba^2\omega^2$$

From Equation [62.2] we get

$$\frac{da}{dt} = -\frac{1}{2\pi m \omega}\int_0^{2\pi} f(a\omega\cos\phi)\cos\phi\,d\phi = -\frac{4b\omega a^2}{3\pi m}$$

that is,

$$-\frac{1}{a^2}\frac{da}{dt} = \frac{d\left(\frac{1}{a}\right)}{dt} = \frac{4b\omega}{3\pi m}$$

From this, on integrating, we obtain

$$\frac{1}{a} - \frac{1}{a_0} = \frac{4b\omega t}{3\pi m} \quad \text{or} \quad a = \frac{a_0}{1 + \dfrac{4b\omega a_0}{3\pi m}t} \qquad [62.4]$$

It is seen that the law of variation of the amplitude with time in this case is entirely different from that given for Case A.

C. COULOMB DAMPING: $f(\dot{x}) = A\,\text{sgn}(\dot{x})$*
    From this equation

$$\int_0^{2\pi} f(a\omega\cos\phi)\cos\phi\,d\phi = A\left[\int_0^{\frac{\pi}{2}}\cos\phi\,d\phi + \int_{\frac{3\pi}{2}}^{2\pi}\cos\phi\,d\phi - \int_{\frac{\pi}{2}}^{\frac{3\pi}{2}}\cos\phi\,d\phi\right] = 4A$$

for $a \neq 0$. Furthermore, $\int_0^{2\pi} f(a\omega\cos\phi)\cos\phi\,d\phi = 0$ for $a = 0$. By Equation [62.2]

$$\frac{da}{dt} = -\frac{2A}{\pi m\omega} \quad \text{if} \quad a \neq 0$$

$$\frac{da}{dt} = 0 \quad \text{if} \quad a = 0$$

$$[62.5]$$

Integrating the first equation [62.5], for $a \neq 0$, we get

$$a = a_0 - \frac{2A}{\pi m\omega}t \qquad [62.6]$$

The motion will continue as long as $a_0 - \frac{2A}{\pi m\omega}t > 0$, and will cease for t_1 defined by the equation $a_0 = \frac{2A}{\pi m\omega}t_1$. The motion thus lasts a finite time.

D. MIXED CASES: $f(\dot{x}) = \alpha\dot{x} + \beta\dot{x}^2$

In applications one frequently encounters differential equations in which both linear and quadratic damping are present. Thus, for example, Froude's differential equation for the rolling of a ship in still water is $I\ddot{\theta} + K_1\dot{\theta} + K_2\dot{\theta}^2 + Wh\theta = 0$, where I, K_1, K_2, W, and h are well-known constants. Likewise, the so-called "surge chamber" equation** in hydraulic engineering is of the form $\ddot{x} + p\dot{x}^2 + q\dot{x} + \gamma x = 0$. Writing equations of this kind in the form $\ddot{x} + \omega^2 x + \mu f(\dot{x}) = 0$, one has

---

* The symbol sgn($\dot{x}$) designates a discontinuous function defined as follows: sgn($\dot{x}$) = 1 for $\dot{x} > 0$; sgn($\dot{x}$) = -1 for $\dot{x} < 0$; and sgn($\dot{x}$) = 0 for $\dot{x} = 0$.

** The writer is indebted to Dr. W.F. Durand for bringing this equation to his attention.

$$\int_0^{2\pi} f(a\omega\cos\phi)\cos\phi\, d\phi = \alpha a\omega\int_0^{2\pi}\cos^2\phi\, d\phi + \beta a^2\omega^2\left[\int_0^{\frac{\pi}{2}}\cos^3\phi\, d\phi + \int_{\frac{3\pi}{2}}^{2\pi}\cos^3\phi\, d\phi - \right.$$

$$\left. - \int_{\frac{\pi}{2}}^{\frac{3\pi}{2}}\cos^3\phi\, d\phi\right] = \alpha a\omega\pi + \frac{8}{3}\beta a^2\omega^2$$

From this

$$\dot a = -\frac{1}{2\pi\omega}\left[\alpha a\omega\pi + \frac{8}{3}\beta a^2\omega^2\right] = -\left[\frac{\alpha}{2}a + Sa^2\right]$$

where $S = 4\beta\omega/3\pi$. Separating the variables

$$\frac{da}{\frac{\alpha}{2}a + Sa^2} = \frac{2}{\alpha}\frac{da}{a} - \frac{2}{\alpha}\frac{d\left(aS + \frac{\alpha}{2}\right)}{aS + \frac{\alpha}{2}}$$

we get

$$d\,\log\left[\frac{a}{aS + \frac{\alpha}{2}}\right] = -\frac{\alpha}{2}\,dt$$

Upon integrating and putting the constant of integration in the form $C = a_0/\left(a_0S + \frac{\alpha}{2}\right)$, we obtain

$$\frac{a}{aS + \frac{\alpha}{2}} = \frac{a_0}{a_0S + \frac{\alpha}{2}}\,e^{-\frac{\alpha}{2}t}$$

or

$$a = \frac{\frac{\alpha}{2}\frac{a_0}{a_0S + \frac{\alpha}{2}}e^{-\frac{\alpha}{2}t}}{1 - S\frac{a_0}{a_0S + \frac{\alpha}{2}}e^{-\frac{\alpha}{2}t}} \qquad [62.7]$$

For $t = 0$, one finds $a = a_0$; for $S = 0$, one finds $a = a_0 e^{-\frac{\alpha}{2}t}$, as in the case of linear damping, Case A. It is seen that the presence of quadratic damping causes a somewhat more rapid decay of amplitudes owing to the presence of the term $S\frac{a_0}{a_0S + \frac{\alpha}{2}}e^{-\frac{\alpha}{2}t}$ in the denominator than is found with a pure linear damping. This fact is to be expected on physical grounds.

63. SYSTEMS WITH NON-LINEAR VARIABLE DAMPING

By the expression "variable" damping occurring in this section, we shall understand a damping which, for small values of the determining variable (either x or $\dot{x}$ as the case may be), is negative and becomes positive above a certain critical value of the variable. Since negative damping means supply to the system, and positive damping means withdrawal of energy from it, the system considered here is non-conservative. Furthermore, stationary states, or limit cycles, are possible when the average supply of energy per cycle becomes equal to its average dissipation.

According to the mode of production of the non-linear variable damping, there exist two principal types of non-linear self-excited oscillations governed by the following equations, which are solved here by the method of the first approximation.

A. VAN DER POL'S EQUATION

The Van der Pol equation is

$$\ddot{x} + x - \mu(1 - x^2)\dot{x} = 0 \qquad [63.1]$$

We have $f(x,\dot{x}) = \mu(x^2\dot{x} - \dot{x})$; furthermore, $\omega = 1$, hence $f(a\sin\phi, a\omega\cos\phi)$ is $f(a\sin\phi, a\cos\phi)$. Since $x = a\sin\phi$ and $\dot{x} = a\cos\phi$, it follows that

$$f(x,\dot{x}) = \mu(a^3\sin^2\phi\cos\phi - a\cos\phi)$$

and

$$f(a\sin\phi, a\cos\phi)\cos\phi = \mu(a^3\sin^2\phi\cos^2\phi - a\cos^2\phi)$$

Whence, by Equation [59.13], we have

$$\frac{da}{dt} = -\frac{\mu}{2\pi}\int_0^{2\pi} f(a\sin\phi, a\cos\phi)\cos\phi\, d\phi = -\frac{\mu}{2\pi}\left[a^3\int_0^{2\pi}\sin^2\phi\cos^2\phi\, d\phi - a\int_0^{2\pi}\cos^2\phi\, d\phi\right]$$

which reduces to

$$\frac{da}{dt} = \frac{\mu a}{2}\left(1 - \frac{a^2}{4}\right) \qquad [63.2]$$

Forming the expression $\int_0^{2\pi} f(a\sin\phi, a\cos\phi)\sin\phi\, d\phi$, one finds that it is zero. From this, by Equation [59.14], $d\psi/dt = \omega = 1$, that is, $\psi = t + \psi_0$, where ψ_0 is arbitrary.

The solution of Van der Pol's equation to the first order is then of the form

$$x = a\sin(t + \psi_0) \qquad [63.3]$$

where a is given by Equation [63.2].

As we shall mention shortly, the interesting feature of this solution is the variation of the amplitude a as a function of time. From the preceding study of Van der Pol's equation we know that a limit cycle exists in this case. We propose now to establish its existence by use of Equation [63.2].

Multiplying both sides of Equation [63.2] by $2a$, we have

$$\frac{da^2}{dt} = \mu a^2 \left(1 - \frac{a^2}{4}\right)$$

that is,

$$\frac{da^2}{a^2\left(1 - \frac{a^2}{4}\right)} = d\left(\log \frac{a^2}{4 - a^2}\right) = \mu \, dt$$

Upon integration, we obtain

$$\log \frac{a^2}{4 - a^2} = \log \frac{a_0^2}{4 - a_0^2} + \mu t \qquad [63.4]$$

Expressing this relation in the equivalent form $\dfrac{a^2}{4 - a^2} = \dfrac{a_0^2}{4 - a_0^2} e^{\mu t}$ and solving for a^2, we get

$$a^2 = \frac{a_0^2 e^{\mu t}}{1 + \frac{1}{4} a_0^2 (e^{\mu t} - 1)}; \qquad a = \frac{a_0 e^{\frac{\mu t}{2}}}{\sqrt{1 + \frac{1}{4} a_0^2 (e^{\mu t} - 1)}} \qquad [63.5]$$

The fundamental equation $x = a \sin \psi$ of the theory of the first approximation is then

$$x = \frac{a_0 e^{\frac{\mu t}{2}}}{\sqrt{1 + \frac{1}{4} a_0^2 (e^{\mu t} - 1)}} \sin(t + \psi_0) = a \sin(t + \psi_0) \qquad [63.6]$$

It is apparent that Equation [63.6] describes the general nature of motion previously investigated in connection with limit cycles. In fact, if for $t = 0$, $a_0 = 0$, $x \equiv 0$. This trivial solution of the Van der Pol equation is, however, unstable. For any finite a_0, however small, the amplitudes increase, approaching the value $a(t) = 2$ as a limit. In the phase plane as $t \to +\infty$, the trajectory spirals toward the circle of radius $a = 2$ from the inside.

B. RAYLEIGH'S EQUATION

Rayleigh's equation* is

$$\ddot{x} + x + \mu(-\alpha + \beta\dot{x}^2)\dot{x} = 0 \qquad [63.7]$$

In this case $\omega = 1$ and $f(x,\dot{x}) = -\alpha\dot{x} + \beta\dot{x}^3$. Since $f(x,\dot{x}) \equiv f(\dot{x})$ and $\omega = 1$, the generating solution $a\cos\phi$ must be substituted into $f(\dot{x})$ resulting in

$$\int_0^{2\pi} f(a\cos\phi)\cos\phi\,d\phi = -\alpha a\int_0^{2\pi}\cos^2\phi\,d\phi + \beta a^3\int_0^{2\pi}\cos^4\phi\,d\phi = -\alpha a\pi + \frac{3}{4}\pi\beta a^3$$

Hence, by Equation [59.13], with $\omega = 1$, one has

$$\dot{a} = \frac{\mu a}{2}\left(\alpha - \frac{3}{4}\beta a^2\right) \qquad [63.8]$$

The system will reach the limit cycle when $\alpha = \frac{3}{4}\beta a^2$, from which the amplitude of the limit cycle is $a = \sqrt{4\alpha/3\beta}$. The radius of the limit cycle increases as the ratio β/α decreases, which is physically obvious since for $\beta = 0$ the system becomes linear and the amplitude, at least theoretically, increases indefinitely, the damping then being negative.

To find the mode of approach to the limit cycle, one must integrate Equation [63.8]. Following the procedure explained in Section 63A, one obtains**

$$a(t) = \frac{a_0 e^{\frac{\mu\alpha}{2}t}}{\sqrt{1 + \frac{3}{4}\frac{\beta}{\alpha}a_0^2(e^{\mu\alpha t}-1)}} \qquad [63.9]$$

This gives $a(t)_{t\to\infty} = \sqrt{4\alpha/3\beta}$, which is independent of the initial amplitude a_0, as required by the condition for a limit cycle.

---

* It is supposed that the original Rayleigh equation, $m\ddot{x} + Kx + (-A + B\dot{x}^2)\dot{x} = 0$, has first been divided by m and written as

$$\ddot{x} + \omega^2 x + \left(-\frac{A}{m} + \frac{B}{m}\dot{x}^2\right)\dot{x} = 0$$

where $\omega^2 = K/m$, after which a change of the independent variable brings it to the above form, with $\omega = 1$.

** In case Equation [63.7] is not reduced to a unit frequency and has the form

$$x^2 + \omega^2 x + (-\alpha + \beta\dot{x}^2)\dot{x} = 0$$

the generating solution should be taken in the form $a\omega\cos\phi$ (instead of $a\cos\phi$), which finally results in the following equation for $a(t)$

$$a(t) = \frac{a_0 e^{\frac{\mu\alpha}{2}t}}{\sqrt{1 + \frac{3}{4}\frac{\beta}{\alpha}\omega^2 a_0^2(e^{\mu\alpha t}-1)}} \qquad [63.9a]$$

64. EXISTENCE OF LIMIT CYCLES; SYSTEMS WITH SEVERAL LIMIT CYCLES

Although the scope of the method of the first approximation has been sufficiently ascertained from the previous sections of this chapter, we now propose to introduce certain additional transformations of the form of the fundamental equations [59.13] and [59.14] of this theory. The object of these transformations is to introduce functions similar to those appearing in Equations [52.8] of the Van der Pol theory. By this procedure we will prepare the groundwork for the investigation of an important subject, namely, the existence and stability of limit cycles.

It is useful for this purpose to recapitulate briefly the principal results of the theory of the first approximation.

The solution of a quasi-linear equation is considered in the form $x = a \sin \psi$, where a and ψ are given by the equations

$$\dot{a} = - \frac{\mu}{2\pi\omega} \int_0^{2\pi} f(a \sin\phi, \, a\omega \cos\phi) \cos\phi \, d\phi \equiv \Phi(a) \qquad [64.1]$$

$$\dot{\psi} = \omega + \frac{\mu}{2\pi\omega a} \int_0^{2\pi} f(a \sin\phi, \, a\omega \cos\phi) \sin\phi \, d\phi \equiv \Omega(a) \qquad [64.2]$$

The condition for a stationary oscillation on a limit cycle is

$$\Phi(a) = 0 \qquad [64.3]$$

This is exactly the condition obtained from Equation [46.22] of Poincaré's theory and the first equation [52.9] of Van der Pol's theory.

Equation [64.2] can be transformed by taking account of Equation [60.5]

$$\Omega^2(a) = \omega^2 + \frac{\mu}{\pi a} \int_0^{2\pi} f(a \sin\phi, \, a\omega \cos\phi) \sin\phi \, d\phi$$

and the identity

$$\omega^2 \equiv \frac{1}{\pi a} \int_0^{2\pi} \omega^2 a \, \sin^2\phi \, d\phi$$

Thus

$$\Omega^2(a) = \frac{1}{\pi a} \int_0^{2\pi} F(a \sin\phi, \, a\omega \cos\phi) \sin\phi \, d\phi \qquad [64.4]$$

where $F(x,\dot{x}) = \omega^2 x + \mu f(x,\dot{x})$ is the non-linear force appearing in the equation $\ddot{x} + F(x,\dot{x}) = 0$. Likewise, Equation [64.1] can be transformed by means of the identity $\int_0^{2\pi} a\omega^2 \sin\phi \cos\phi \, d\phi \equiv 0$, which gives

$$\dot{a} = \Phi(a) = -\frac{\mu}{2\pi\omega}\int_0^{2\pi} F(a\sin\phi, a\omega\cos\phi)\cos\phi\, d\phi \qquad [64.5]$$

Equations [59.13] and [59.14] appear now in the form

$$\dot{a} = \Phi(a) \qquad [64.6]$$

$$\dot{\psi} = \Omega(a) \qquad [64.7]$$

where $\Phi(a)$ and $\Omega(a)$ are given by Equations [64.5] and [64.4] in terms of the total non-linear force $F(x,\dot{x})$.

Considering the question of limit cycles generated by a harmonic $x = K \cos t$ when $\mu = 0$, we examine Equation [64.6].

If $\Phi(a) > 0$, the amplitude a increases indefinitely, and hence no such limit cycle exists.

If $\Phi(a) < 0$, the amplitude decreases, and again no such limit cycle exists. This condition characterizes dissipative systems.

If $\Phi(a_1) = 0$, we obtain the condition for a limit cycle with amplitude a_1.

The question of the existence of limit cycles which are not generated by a harmonic $x = K \cos t$ when $\mu = 0$, is not considered.

We now propose to investigate a practical case in which a limit cycle exists, as shown by experiment, and to show how this existence can be ascertained analytically on the basis of this theory. For this purpose consider the differential equation of an oscillating circuit containing a non-linear conductor characterized by a non-linear equation of the form $v = G(i)$. Putting $i = x$, the differential equation is

$$L\dot{x} + G(x) + \frac{1}{C}\int x\, dt = 0 \qquad [64.8]$$

where the constant parameters L and C designate the inductance and capacity of the circuit respectively.

Differentiating this equation with respect to t, dividing it by L, and putting for abbreviation $1/LC = \omega^2$, we obtain

$$\ddot{x} + \omega^2 x + \frac{1}{L}G'(x)\dot{x} = 0 \qquad [64.9]$$

Identifying the term $\frac{1}{L}G'(x)\dot{x}$ with $\mu f(x,\dot{x})$ of the general theory, which incidentally imposes a requirement that it be small in comparison with the first two terms, we obtain on the basis of this theory

$$\dot{a} = -\frac{1}{2\pi\omega L}\int_0^{2\pi} G'(a\sin\phi)\,a\omega\cos\phi\cdot\cos\phi\,d\phi \equiv \Phi(a) \qquad [64.10]$$

$$\dot{\psi} = \omega + \frac{1}{2\pi L}\int_0^{2\pi} G'(a\sin\phi)\cos\phi\cdot\sin\phi\,d\phi \equiv \Omega(a) \qquad [64.11]$$

Integrating by parts, we see that the second term on the right side of Equation [64.11] is zero, hence,

$$\dot{\psi} = \Omega(a) = \omega \qquad [64.12]$$

and $\psi = \omega t + \psi_0$ where ψ_0 is arbitrary. The oscillation is thus isochronous at least to the first order.

If we let $\frac{1}{\pi}\int_0^{2\pi} G'(a\sin\phi)\cos^2\phi\,d\phi = R(a)$, Equation [64.10] can be written as

$$\dot{a} = -\frac{R(a)a}{2L} = \Phi(a) \qquad [64.13]$$

From the definition of $R(a)$ it follows that $R(a) > 0$, if $G'(x) > 0$, that is, if the voltage across the non-linear conductor increases with the current. Thus, $\dot{a} < 0$, and the final state of the system is $x = 0$, as is obvious from physical considerations since a "positive resistance" characterizes a dissipation of energy. Therefore, the final state of equilibrium is stable, and the point $x = 0$ is either a stable focal, or a stable nodal, point.

If $G'(x) < 0$ (negative resistance), that is, the voltage across the non-linear conductor decreases when the current through it increases, $\Phi(a)$ is positive, and from Equation [64.13] it follows that the amplitude increases. From physical considerations it is apparent that the amplitude cannot increase indefinitely. Analytically this is expressed by the condition $\Phi(a_1) = 0$ for a certain amplitude a_1 which is the amplitude of the limit cycle.

Figures 64.1a, b, c, and d illustrate the various possible cases. Figure 64.1a represents the case of an ohmic conductor (Curve a represents an ideal, and Curve b a real, ohmic conductor). Since $G'(x) \geqq 0$ in this case, $R(a) \geqq 0$; hence $\dot{a} < 0$. The amplitudes always decrease since the system is dissipative.

Figure 64.1b corresponds to the case when $G'(x)$, and hence $R(a)$, are negative for small amplitudes and become positive for larger ones. The root a_1 of the equation $R(a_1) = 0$ corresponds to a stable amplitude $a = a_1$. If the oscillations are started from values $a < a_1$, they will increase until the amplitude $a = a_1$ is reached; if, however, they are started from a value $a > a_1$, they will decrease down to the value $a = a_1$. This condition is indicated by

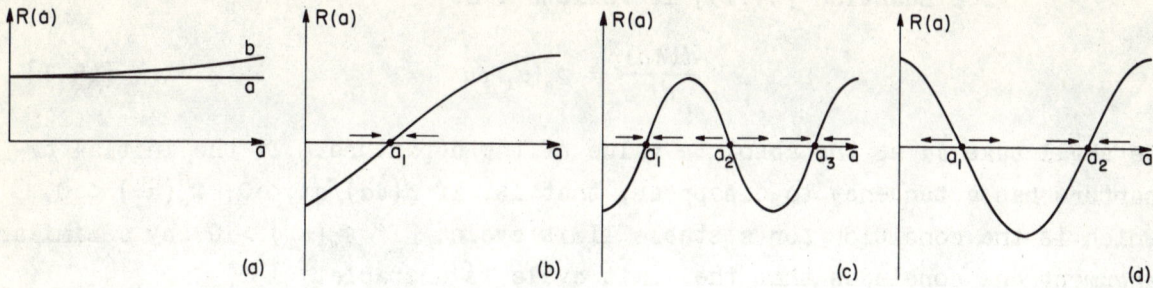

Figure 64.1

arrows in Figure 64.1b. The amplitude $a = a_1$ thus corresponds to a *stable* limit cycle.

Figure 64.1c shows a more complicated form of non-linear characteristic. By a similar argument, one finds that the amplitudes $a = a_1$ and $a = a_3$ correspond to stable limit cycles and $a = a_2$ to an unstable one.

Finally, Figure 64.1d shows a condition sometimes encountered in applications. For small amplitudes the "resistance" of a non-linear conductor is positive, that is, the energy is dissipated. Beginning with a certain critical value $a = a_1$, the resistance becomes "negative," that is, energy is conveyed into the system, and this state exists until an amplitude $a = a_2$ is reached. In such a case if the initial amplitude $a_0 < a_1$, the only stable amplitude is $a = 0$; the system cannot acquire self-excitation. If, however, $a_0 > a_1$, the amplitudes begin to grow and eventually become stabilized at a stable limit cycle a_2. A condition of this kind is designated as a "hard" type of self-excitation, which we have previously investigated.

It is thus seen that the unstable limit cycle $a = a_1$ acts as a kind of "barrier" preventing the amplitudes from building up if the initial amplitude is below the value corresponding to this barrier.

We thus find by the theory of the first approximation a situation exactly the same as that found previously by the topological methods of Poincaré.

65. STABILITY OF LIMIT CYCLES; CRITICAL VALUES OF A PARAMETER;
    SYSTEMS WITH SEVERAL LIMIT CYCLES

Let us first consider the question of the stability of limit cycles. Let a_1 be a root of the equation $\Phi(a_1) = 0$. For a slightly varied amplitude, $a_1 + \delta a$,

$$\Phi(a_1 + \delta a) = \Phi_a(a_1)\, \delta a$$

to the first order.

From Equation [59.13] it follows that

$$\frac{d(\delta a)}{dt} = \Phi_a(a_1)\,\delta a \qquad\qquad [65.1]$$

We shall take δa as the absolute value of the departure. If the initial departure has a tendency to disappear, that is, if $d(\delta a)/dt < 0$, $\Phi_a(a_1) < 0$, which is the condition for a stable limit cycle. If $\Phi_a(a_1) > 0$, by a similar argument one concludes that the limit cycle is unstable.

If self-excitation starts from rest ($a = 0$), the condition for its occurrence is

$$\Phi(0) > 0 \qquad\qquad [65.2]$$

which is equivalent to the existence of an unstable singularity in the presence of a stable limit cycle, see Part I, Chapter IV. Similarly, the condition for a critical value of some parameter can easily be established by this method. In fact, assume that $\Phi(a)$, in addition to a, also depends on a parameter λ, that is, it is a function $\Phi(a,\lambda)$. Consider the value of $\Phi(a,\lambda)$ for $a = 0$ and varying λ. When a value $\lambda = \lambda_0$ is reached for which $\Phi_a(0,\lambda) > 0$, the amplitudes begin to grow from zero and the subsequent increase of amplitudes from that moment will be determined by Equation [64.13], which now has the form

$$\dot{a} = \Phi(a,\lambda) \qquad\qquad [65.3]$$

The limit cycle is reached for a value a_1 of the amplitude for which

$$\Phi(a_1,\lambda) = 0 \qquad\qquad [65.4]$$

For a given value $\lambda = \lambda_1$, the limit cycle will be determined from the equation $\Phi(a_1,\lambda_1) = 0$, and for some other value $\lambda = \lambda_2$, from the equation $\Phi(a_2,\lambda_2) = 0$. Hence, the amplitude of the limit cycle in general is a certain function of the parameter λ.

In some cases the function $\Phi(a,\lambda)$ can be put in the form

$$\Phi(a,\lambda) = \left[\Phi(a) - \frac{a}{\lambda}\right]\Phi_1(a,\lambda) \qquad\qquad [65.5]$$

where $\Phi_1(a,\lambda) > 0$ for all values of a and λ, and $\Phi(0) = 0$. Differentiating Equation [65.5] with respect to a, one has

$$\Phi_a(a,\lambda) = \left[\Phi_a(a) - \frac{1}{\lambda}\right]\Phi_1(a,\lambda) + \left[\Phi(a) - \frac{a}{\lambda}\right]\frac{d[\Phi_1(a,\lambda)]}{da} \qquad\qquad [65.6]$$

Putting $a = 0$, one has

$$\Phi_a(0,\lambda) = \left[\Phi_a(0) - \frac{1}{\lambda}\right]\Phi_1(0,\lambda) \qquad [65.7]$$

Self-excitation will start from rest if

$$\Phi_a(0) > \frac{1}{\lambda} \qquad [65.8]$$

since $\Phi_1(0,\lambda) > 0$.

Consider a curve $y_1 = \Phi(a)$ and a straight line $y_2 = \frac{1}{\lambda}a$ shown in Figure 65.1. $\Phi_a(0)$ is the slope of the tangent to the curve $\Phi(a)$ at the origin, and $\frac{1}{\lambda}$ the slope of the straight line y_2. Condition [65.8] states that self-excitation occurs starting from rest ($a = 0$) only if the initial slope of the tangent to the curve $\Phi(a)$ is greater than the slope of the line a/λ.

As an example, one may mention the self-excitation of a shunt generator. In this case the frequency is zero but the amplitude, Equation [59.13], is still applicable. The function $\Phi(a)$ is the voltage induced in the armature, a is the exciting current, and a/λ is the ohmic drop across the field winding; whence $1/\lambda$ is the resistance of the field winding plus the field resistor. In Figure 65.1, $1/\lambda = \tan\alpha$ is the slope of the straight line $\frac{1}{\lambda}a$. If $\Phi_a(0) - 1/\lambda < 0$, there is no self-excitation. For $\frac{1}{\lambda} < \Phi_a(0)$, self-excitation is possible since $\Phi_a(0,\lambda) > 0$. The equilibrium condition is $\Phi(a_1) = a_1/\lambda$, which corresponds to the intersection of curves $y_1 = \Phi(a)$ and $y_2 = \frac{1}{\lambda}a$. It is interesting to note that the amplitude, Equation [64.10], holds in this case in spite of the fact that the frequency, Equation [64.11], is absent.

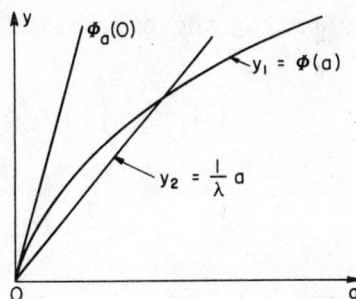

Figure 65.1

From the general considerations explained in connection with Figure 64.1, the following theorems result:*

THEOREM 1. If a system possesses several stable limit cycles forming a sequence a_1, a_3, a_5, $\cdots$, between each pair of consecutive stable limit cycles there is always one unstable limit cycle; these unstable cycles form another sequence a_2, a_4, a_6, $\cdots$.

THEOREM 2. The limit cycle reached spontaneously by a system starting from rest is always the one which corresponds to the smallest root a_1 of the sequence.

---

* It should be borne in mind that we are considering only limit cycles that are generated by circles.

THEOREM 3. The stable limit cycles corresponding to larger roots a_3, a_5, $\cdots$ of the stable sequence can be reached only if the system is given a shock excitation carrying it beyond the corresponding unstable limit cycles a_2, a_4, $\cdots$.

66. LIMIT CYCLES IN THE CASE OF POLYNOMIAL CHARACTERISTICS

Let the characteristic of a non-linear conductor be approximated by a polynomial

$$f(i) = A + Bi + Ci^2 + Di^3 + Ei^4 + Fi^5 \qquad [66.1]$$

Differentiating and setting $i = a\sin\phi$, we have

$$f'(a\sin\phi)\cos^2\phi = B\cos^2\phi + 2Ca\sin\phi\cos^2\phi + 3Da^2\sin^2\phi\cos^2\phi +$$
$$+ 4Ea^3\sin^3\phi\cos^2\phi + 5Fa^4\sin^4\phi\cos^2\phi$$

Forming the expression for $R(a) = \frac{1}{\pi}\int_0^{2\pi} f'(a\sin\phi)\cos^2\phi\,d\phi$, we have

$$R(a) = \frac{1}{\pi}\int_0^{2\pi} B\cos^2\phi\,d\phi + \frac{1}{\pi}\int_0^{2\pi} 2Ca\sin\phi\cos^2\phi\,d\phi + \frac{1}{\pi}\int_0^{2\pi} 3Da^2\sin^2\phi\cos^2\phi\,d\phi +$$

$$+ \frac{1}{\pi}\int_0^{2\pi} 4Ea^3\sin^3\phi\cos^2\phi\,d\phi + \frac{1}{\pi}\int_0^{2\pi} 5Fa^4\sin^4\phi\cos^2\phi\,d\phi \qquad [66.2]$$

The second and the fourth terms on the right side of this equation are zero. The remaining terms are

$$\frac{B}{\pi}\int_0^{2\pi}\cos^2\phi\,d\phi = B$$
$$[66.3]$$

$$\frac{1}{\pi}\int_0^{2\pi} 3Da^2\sin^2\phi\cos^2\phi\,d\phi = \frac{3Da^2}{\pi}\left[\int_0^{2\pi}\sin^2\phi\,d\phi - \int_0^{2\pi}\sin^4\phi\,d\phi\right] = \frac{3Da^2}{\pi}\,\pi\left(1 - \frac{3}{4}\right) = \frac{3}{4}Da^2$$

$$\frac{1}{\pi}\int_0^{2\pi} 5Fa^4\sin^4\phi\cos^2\phi\,d\phi = \frac{5Fa^4}{\pi}\left[\int_0^{2\pi}\sin^4\phi\,d\phi - \int_0^{2\pi}\sin^6\phi\,d\phi\right] = \frac{5Fa^4}{\pi}\left(\frac{3}{4} - \frac{3\cdot5}{4\cdot6}\right) = \frac{5}{8}Fa^4$$

From this

$$R(a) = B + \frac{3}{4}Da^2 + \frac{5}{8}Fa^4 \qquad [66.4]$$

It must be noted that the coefficient F in this equation must be positive; otherwise, beginning with a certain value $a = a_1$, $R(a)$ would become negative and remain negative for increasing a. In such a case, by Equation [62.2], da/dt would be positive. This is impossible in a physical problem.

Setting $\frac{5}{8}F = m > 0$ and $\frac{3}{4}D = n$, the condition for the existence of a limit cycle is

$$R(a) = ma^4 + na^2 + B = 0 \qquad [66.5]$$

The roots of this biquadratic equation are

$$a_{1,2}^2 = \frac{-n \pm \sqrt{n^2 - 4mB}}{2m} \qquad [66.6]$$

For the existence of limit cycles at least one of the roots a_1^2 or a_2^2 must be positive. Since $m > 0$, the necessary and sufficient condition is that $B < 0$, which expresses the fact that the slope of the characteristic $f(i)$ is negative, that is, "negative" resistance.

When B is positive, two cases are possible:

1. $B > 0$, $n > 0$, that is, $D > 0$. In this case both roots a_1^2 and a_2^2 are negative; hence, the amplitudes a_1 and a_2 of the limit cycles are imaginary. In other words, no limit cycles exist, the system being dissipative. The amplitudes decrease indefinitely, and the only stable solution is $a = 0$.

2. $B > 0$, $n < 0$, that is, $D < 0$. In this case limit cycles are possible as long as $n^2 - 4Bm > 0$, which expresses the condition of the reality of the roots. If we substitute for n and m their values, this gives

$$B < \frac{n^2}{4m} = \frac{9}{40}\frac{D^2}{F} \qquad [66.7]$$

Summing up this discussion, one can state that with a non-linear voltage, approximated by the polynomial [66.1], of the fifth degree, the following conditions exist:

1. On physical grounds the coefficient F must always be positive.

2. If $B < 0$, there is always one stable limit cycle.

3. If $B > 0$ and $D > 0$, no limit cycles exist and the system is dissipative.

4. If $B > 0$, $D < 0$, and $B < \frac{9}{40}\frac{D^2}{F}$, limit cycles are possible with the amplitude a_1 (positive root).

5. If $B > 0$ and $D < 0$, but $B > \frac{9}{40}\frac{D^2}{F}$, the system behaves again as a dissipative one, and no limit cycles exist.

Since any experimental characteristic can be approximated by a polynomial, the coefficients $A, \cdots F$ in Equation [66.1] are known quantities, and the above procedure permits ascertaining from the form of the characteristic the behavior of the system into which the non-linear element with this particular characteristic is introduced.

CHAPTER XI

APPROXIMATIONS OF HIGHER ORDERS

67. INTRODUCTORY REMARKS

In this chapter we review the extension of the method of Kryloff and Bogoliuboff as applied to approximations of orders higher than the first. Although for practical applications the theory of the first approximation gives a satisfactory degree of accuracy, it is also interesting to consider the possibility of a further refinement of approximate solutions in case greater accuracy is required. The procedure of Kryloff and Bogoliuboff is derived from the classical methods of Gylden and Lindstedt used in celestial mechanics. As explained in Section 44, the object of these methods is to eliminate the secular terms resulting from the resonance effect of subsequent harmonics in the recurrence procedure by which the higher-order terms are determined. The method can be summarized as follows.

Assume that we wish to find a periodic solution of the differential equation

$$\ddot{x} + \omega^2 x + \mu f(x) = 0 \qquad [67.1]$$

with a certain unknown period T. Introducing a new independent variable $\tau = 2\pi t/T = \Omega t$, where $\Omega = 2\pi/T$, we shall look for a solution $x(t) = z(\tau)$, where $z(\tau)$ is a periodic function with period 2π. We shall try to represent the periodic solution in the form

$$z(\tau) = \sum_{n=0}^{\infty} \mu^n z_n(\tau) \qquad [67.2]$$

where $z_n(\tau)$ with $n = 1, 2, \cdots$, are periodic functions with period 2π. We further assume that

$$\Omega^2 = \sum_{n=0}^{\infty} \alpha_n \mu^n \qquad [67.3]$$

where α_n is constant. The transformed equation [67.1] then becomes

$$\Omega^2 \frac{d^2 z}{d\tau^2} + \omega^2 z + \mu f(z) = 0 \qquad [67.4]$$

If one substitutes into this equation the series expansions [67.2] and [67.3], one obtains a series of recurrent differential equations resulting from equating to zero the coefficients of equal powers of μ. For the subsequent approximations one thus obtains a series of differential equations

$$\alpha_0 \frac{d^2 z_0}{d\tau^2} + \omega^2 z_0 = 0$$

$$\alpha_0 \frac{d^2 z_1}{d\tau^2} + \omega^2 z_1 = -f(z_0) - \alpha_1 \frac{d^2 z_0}{d\tau^2}$$

$$\alpha_0 \frac{d^2 z_2}{d\tau^2} + \omega^2 z_2 = -f'(z_0)z_1 - \alpha_2 \frac{d^2 z_0}{d\tau^2} - \alpha_1 \frac{d^2 z_1}{d\tau^2}$$

[67.5]

$$\cdots \cdots \cdots \cdots \cdots \cdots$$

$$\alpha_0 \frac{d^2 z_{n+1}}{d\tau^2} + \omega^2 z_{n+1} = F(z_0, z_1, \cdots, z_n) - \alpha_{n+1} \frac{d^2 z_0}{d\tau^2} - \alpha_n \frac{d^2 z_1}{d\tau^2} - \cdots - \alpha_1 \frac{d^2 z_n}{d\tau^2}$$

where $F(z_0, z_1, \cdots, z_n)$ is a certain polynomial in $z_0, z_1, \cdots, z_n$. It is apparent that if $z_0, z_1, \cdots, z_N$ and $\alpha_0, \alpha_1, \cdots, \alpha_N$ satisfy the first $(N+1)$ equations of the system [67.5], then the expressions

$$x = \sum_{n=0}^{N} \mu^n z_n(\tau) \quad \text{and} \quad \Omega^2 = \sum_{n=0}^{N} \mu^n \alpha_n$$

[67.6]

also satisfy [67.1] up to the order μ^{N+1} and, hence, may be considered as the $(N+1)^{\text{th}}$ approximation.

The method of Lindstedt, which Kryloff and Bogoliuboff follow, consists in determining the coefficients α_i in the subsequent stages of the recurrence procedure so as to eliminate terms with the fundamental period 2π. In fact, if these terms were left on the right side of Equations [67.5], they would account for the "resonance terms," which are of secular form, as previously defined. The determination of α_i by this procedure at the same time leads to the expression for frequency given by Equation [67.3]. By this method the difficulties encountered in the theory of Poincaré (see Chapter VIII) in connection with the appearance of secular terms in the expansions are eliminated, and solutions without secular terms can be obtained.

Poincaré has shown by an example that the approximations generally do not converge. However, nothing better is available, and, in practice, the second or third approximation (and usually, in fact, the first) gives entirely satisfactory results.

The subject matter of this chapter is considerably abbreviated, compared with Kryloff and Bogoliuboff's text (5), and for that reason the reader should refer to the original text for additional details.

68. IMPROVED FIRST APPROXIMATION

Equations [59.13] and [59.14] of the first approximation were obtained by dropping the higher harmonics in the Fourier series on the right side of Equations [59.10]. In reality, owing to the presence of these terms, the slowly varying quantities a and ϕ undergo oscillations of a relatively high frequency.

In order to take this into account, it is convenient to consider the quantities a and ϕ in Equations [59.10] as practically constant in comparison with the rapidly varying trigonometric terms $\cos n(\omega t + \phi)$ and $\sin n(\omega t + \phi)$.

Designating the left sides of Equations [59.10] by $d\bar{a}/dt$ and $d\bar{\phi}/dt$, and noting that $-\frac{\mu}{\omega} K_0(a) = \frac{da}{dt}$ and $\frac{\mu}{a\omega} P_0(a) = \frac{d\phi}{dt}$, upon integration of Equations [59.10], one has

$$\bar{a} = a - \frac{\mu}{\omega} \sum_{n=1}^{\infty} \frac{K_n(a)\sin n(\omega t + \phi) - L_n(a)\cos n(\omega t + \phi)}{n\omega}$$

$$\bar{\phi} = \phi + \frac{\mu}{a\omega} \sum_{n=1}^{\infty} \frac{P_n(a)\sin n(\omega t + \phi) - Q_n(a)\cos n(\omega t + \phi)}{n\omega}$$

[68.1]

where a designates the first approximation for the amplitude given by Equation [59.13].

Substituting these values into the equation $x = \bar{a}\sin(\omega t + \bar{\phi})$, one has

$$x = \left[a - \frac{\mu}{\omega^2} \sum_{n=1}^{\infty} \frac{K_n\sin n(\omega t + \phi) - L_n\cos n(\omega t + \phi)}{n}\right] \sin\left[\omega t + \phi + \right.$$

$$\left. + \frac{\mu}{a\omega^2} \sum_{n=1}^{\infty} \frac{P_n\sin n(\omega t + \phi) - Q_n\cos n(\omega t + \phi)}{n}\right]$$

[68.2]

If we let

$$S = \frac{1}{a\omega^2} \sum_{n=1}^{\infty} \frac{P_n\sin n(\omega t + \phi) - Q_n\cos n(\omega t + \phi)}{n}$$

the sine term of this expression can be written as

$$\sin(\omega t + \phi + \mu S) = \sin(\omega t + \phi)\cos\mu S + \cos(\omega t + \phi)\sin\mu S$$

$$\approx \sin(\omega t + \phi) + \mu S\cos(\omega t + \phi)$$

since μ is small. Substituting this into Equation [68.2], one has

$$x = \left[a - \frac{\mu}{\omega^2} \sum_{n=1}^{\infty} \frac{K_n\sin n(\omega t + \phi) - L_n\cos n(\omega t + \phi)}{n}\right]\left[\sin(\omega t + \phi) + \mu S\cos(\omega t + \phi)\right]$$

[68.3]

whence, neglecting the terms with μ^2, μ^3, $\cdots$, one has

$$x = a\sin(\omega t + \phi) - \frac{\mu}{\omega^2} \sum_{n=1}^{\infty} \frac{K_n \sin n(\omega t + \phi) - L_n \cos n(\omega t + \phi)}{n} \sin(\omega t + \phi) +$$

$$+ \frac{a\mu}{a\omega^2} \sum_{n=1}^{\infty} \frac{P_n \sin n(\omega t + \phi) - Q_n \cos n(\omega t + \phi)}{n} \cos(\omega t + \phi) \qquad [68.4]$$

If we put $\omega t + \phi = \tau$,

$$\sum_{n=1}^{\infty} \frac{K_n \sin n\tau - L_n \cos n\tau}{n} = u(\tau)$$

$$\qquad [68.5]$$

$$\sum_{n=1}^{\infty} \frac{P_n \sin n\tau - Q_n \cos n\tau}{n} = v(\tau)$$

and

$$u(\tau)\sin\tau - v(\tau)\cos\tau = w(\tau) \qquad [68.6]$$

We now rewrite [68.4] as

$$x = a\sin\tau - \frac{\mu}{\omega^2} w(\tau) \qquad [68.7]$$

From Equations [68.5], in view of [59.8], one has further

$$u'(\tau) = f(a\sin\tau, a\omega\cos\tau)\cos\tau - K_0(a)$$

$$\qquad [68.8]$$

$$v'(\tau) = f(a\sin\tau, a\omega\cos\tau)\sin\tau - P_0(a)$$

On the other hand, differentiating Equation [68.6], one has

$$u'(\tau)\sin\tau - v'(\tau)\cos\tau + u(\tau)\cos\tau + v(\tau)\sin\tau = w'(\tau) \qquad [68.9]$$

If the values [68.8] are substituted into Equation [68.9], one finds

$$w'(\tau) = P_0(a)\cos\tau - K_0(a)\sin\tau + u\cos\tau + v\sin\tau \qquad [68.10]$$

$$w''(\tau) = -P_0(a)\sin\tau - K_0(a)\cos\tau - u\sin\tau + v\cos\tau + u'\cos\tau + v'\sin\tau \qquad [68.11]$$

Thus

$$w''(\tau) + w(\tau) = -P_0(a)\sin\tau - K_0(a)\cos\tau - u\sin\tau + v\cos\tau + u'\cos\tau + v'\sin\tau$$

$$+ u\sin\tau - v\cos\tau = -P_0(a)\sin\tau - K_0(a)\cos\tau + u'\cos\tau + v'\sin\tau \qquad [68.12]$$

Noting that

$$u'(\tau)\cos\tau + v'(\tau)\sin\tau = f(a\sin\tau, a\omega\cos\tau) - K_0(a)\cos\tau - P_0(a)\sin\tau$$

one obtains from Equations [68.8]

$$w''(\tau) + w(\tau) = f(a\sin\tau, a\omega\cos\tau) - 2K_0(a)\cos\tau - 2P_0(a)\sin\tau \quad [68.13]$$

In order to determine the corrective term $w(\tau)$ of the improved first approximation, it is necessary to transform the right-hand term of [68.13] into the known Fourier series.

For this purpose consider the Fourier expansion

$$f(a\sin\tau, a\omega\cos\tau) = f_0(a) + \sum_{n=1}^{\infty}\left[f_n(a)\cos n\tau + g_n(a)\sin n\tau\right] \quad [68.14]$$

in which the coefficients f and g are given by the equations

$$f_0(a) = \frac{1}{2\pi}\int_0^{2\pi} f(a\sin\tau, a\omega\cos\tau)\,d\tau$$

$$f_n(a) = \frac{1}{\pi}\int_0^{2\pi} f(a\sin\tau, a\omega\cos\tau)\cos n\tau\,d\tau \quad [68.15]$$

$$g_n(a) = \frac{1}{\pi}\int_0^{2\pi} f(a\sin\tau, a\omega\cos\tau)\sin n\tau\,d\tau$$

On the other hand, by [59.9], $K_0(a) = \frac{1}{2}f_1$ and $P_0(a) = \frac{1}{2}g_1$. From this

$$f(a\sin\tau, a\omega\cos\tau) - 2K_0(a)\cos\tau - 2P_0(a)\sin\tau$$

$$= f_0 + \sum_{n=2}^{\infty}(f_n\cos n\tau + g_n\sin n\tau) \quad [68.16]$$

Substituting the right-hand term of Equation [68.16] into Equation [68.13], one gets

$$w''(\tau) + w(\tau) = f_0 + \sum_{n=2}^{\infty}(f_n\cos n\tau + g_n\sin n\tau) \quad [68.17]$$

Looking for a solution of Equation [68.17] of the form

$$w(\tau) = a_0 + \sum_{n=2}^{\infty}(a_n\cos n\tau + b_n\sin n\tau)$$

one obtains by identification of the coefficients after the substitution of this expression into the differential equation [68.17]

$$w(\tau) = f_0 - \sum_{n=2}^{\infty} \frac{f_n \cos n\tau + g_n \sin n\tau}{n^2 - 1} \qquad [68.18]$$

Substituting this expression into Equation [68.7], one finally obtains the following expression for the improved first approximation

$$x = a \sin(\omega t + \phi) - \frac{\mu}{\omega^2} f_0(a) + \frac{\mu}{\omega^2} \sum_{n=2}^{\infty} \frac{f_n \cos n(\omega t + \phi) + g_n \sin n(\omega t + \phi)}{n^2 - 1} \qquad [68.19]$$

where a and ϕ satisfy the equations of the first approximation, Equations [59.12], that is, $\dot{a} = -\frac{\mu}{2\omega} f_1(a)$ and $\dot{\phi} = \frac{\mu}{2\omega a} g_1(a)$.

In order to see whether the solution [68.19] satisfies the original quasi-linear equation $\ddot{x} + \omega^2 x + \mu f(x, \dot{x}) = 0$, substitute the solution [68.19] in that equation. This gives, on the other hand,

$$\ddot{x} + \omega^2 x = -\left[\sum_{n=1}^{\infty} f_n \cos n(\omega t + \phi) + g_n \sin n(\omega t + \phi) + f_0 \right] + O_1(\mu^2) \quad [68.20]$$

where O_1 is of the order of μ^2.

On the other hand, in view of Equation [68.19], one has

$$\mu f(x, \dot{x}) = \mu f\left[a \sin(\omega t + \phi),\ a\omega \cos(\omega t + \phi) \right] + O_2(\mu^2)$$

whence, by [68.14],

$$\ddot{x} + \omega^2 x + \mu f(x, \dot{x}) = O_1(\mu^2) - O_2(\mu^2)$$

Thus the expression [68.19] satisfies the original differential equation with accuracy of the order of μ^2.

Furthermore, it can be shown, upon developing the expressions for $O_1(\mu^2)$ and $O_2(\mu^2)$, that the error in the approximate solution [68.19] is uniform in the interval $0 \leq t < \infty$.

69. APPLICATIONS OF THE THEORY OF THE IMPROVED FIRST APPROXIMATION

We shall consider first oscillations of a conservative system acted on by a non-linear force represented by an odd function of the dependent variable. In this case, $f(x) + f(-x) \equiv 0$. Since the function is odd, no cosine terms are present in the Fourier expansion. Hence

$$f(a \sin \tau) = \sum_{n=1}^{\infty} g_n(a) \sin n\tau$$

and

$$g_n(a) = \frac{2}{\pi} \int_0^\pi f(a \sin\tau) \sin n\tau \, d\tau$$

By Equation [68.19], the improved first approximation is

$$x = a \sin(\omega t + \phi) + \frac{\mu}{\omega^2} \sum_{n=2}^{\infty} \frac{g_n(a) \sin n(\omega t + \phi)}{n^2 - 1} \qquad [69.1]$$

The frequency is given by the equation

$$\Omega(a) = \omega + \frac{\mu}{2\omega a} g_1(a)$$

that is,

$$\Omega^2(a) = \omega^2 + \frac{\mu}{a} g_1(a)$$

to the first order.

We shall now discuss three applications of the theory of the improved first approximation.

A. VARIABLE "SPRING CONSTANT"

Consider the differential equation

$$\ddot{x} + \omega^2 x = 0$$

where $\omega^2 = \omega_0^2 + \mu x^2$, which gives

$$\ddot{x} + \omega_0^2 x + \mu x^3 = 0 \qquad [69.2]$$

so that

$$f(x) = x^3; \quad f(a \sin\tau) = a^3 \sin^3\tau = \frac{3}{4} a^3 \sin\tau - \frac{1}{4} a^3 \sin 3\tau$$

whence

$$g_1(a) = \frac{2}{\pi} \int_0^\pi \left(\frac{3}{4} a^3 \sin\tau - \frac{1}{4} a^3 \sin 3\tau \right) \sin\tau \, d\tau = \frac{3}{4} a^3$$

and

$$\Omega(a) = \omega_0 + \frac{\mu}{2\omega_0 a} g_1(a) = \omega_0 + \frac{3}{8} \omega_0 \mu a^2$$

For the next harmonic

$$g_3(a) = \frac{2}{\pi} \int_0^\pi \left(\frac{3}{4} a^3 \sin \tau - \frac{1}{4} a^3 \sin 3\tau \right) \sin 3\tau \, d\tau = -\frac{a^3}{2\pi} \int_0^\pi \sin^2 3\tau \, d\tau$$

$$= -\frac{a^3}{6\pi} \int_0^{3\pi} \sin^2 x \, dx = -\frac{3\pi a^3}{12\pi} = -\frac{a^3}{4}$$

From this, by Equation [69.1]

$$x = a \sin(\omega_0 t + \phi) - \frac{\mu a^3}{4 \omega_0^2} \left(\frac{1}{3^2 - 1} \right) \sin 3(\omega_0 t + \phi)$$

$$= a \sin(\omega_0 t + \phi) - \frac{\mu a^3}{32 \omega_0^2} \sin 3(\omega_0 t + \phi) \qquad [69.3]$$

Thus the improved first approximation introduces a small corrective term $\frac{\mu a^3}{32} \sin 3(\omega_0 t + \phi)$ in the form of a third harmonic.

B.   VARIABLE DAMPING

Consider a differential equation of the form

$$\ddot{x} + \omega^2 x + \mu f(x) \dot{x} = 0$$

The non-linear term in this case is

$$f(x) \dot{x} = f(a \sin \tau) a \omega \cos \tau$$

Consider the function $F(\lambda) = \int_0^\lambda f(\xi) \, d\xi$. For $\lambda = a \cos \phi$, the development of $F(a \cos \phi)$ in a Fourier series gives

$$F(a \cos \phi) = \sum_{n=0}^{\infty} F_n(a) \cos n\phi \qquad [69.4]$$

Differentiating this equation, we have

$$a f(a \cos \phi) \sin \phi = \sum_{n=1}^{\infty} n F_n(a) \sin n\phi$$

Putting $\phi = \tau + \frac{3\pi}{2}$, one obtains

$$f(a \sin \tau) a \omega \cos \tau = -\omega \sum_{n=0}^{\infty} n F_n(a) \sin n \left(\omega t + \frac{3\pi}{2} + \phi_0 \right)$$

where ϕ_0 is an arbitrary phase angle. Hence, by Equation [69.1], the solution is

$$x = a \sin(\Omega t + \phi_0) - \frac{\mu}{\omega} \sum_{n=2}^{\infty} \frac{n}{n^2 - 1} F_n(a) \sin n \left(\Omega t + \frac{3\pi}{2} + \phi_0 \right) \qquad [69.5]$$

assuming that $\omega = \Omega$, since in this case the correction for frequency is of a higher order.

If one introduces $\theta_0 = \phi_0 - \pi/2$, Equation [69.5] has the form

$$x = a \cos(\Omega t + \theta_0) - \frac{\mu}{\omega} \sum_{n=2}^{\infty} \frac{n}{n^2 - 1} F_n(a) \sin n(\Omega t + \theta_0) \qquad [69.6]$$

For example, consider the Van der Pol equation

$$\ddot{x} + x - \mu(1 - x^2)\dot{x} = 0$$

In this case $f(x) = x^2 - 1$, $F(x) = \frac{x^3}{3} - x$, and $\omega = 1$, whence

$$F(a \cos \phi) = \frac{a^3 \cos^3 \phi}{3} - a \cos \phi = a\left(\frac{a^2}{4} - 1\right)\cos \phi + \frac{a^3}{12} \cos 3\phi$$

It follows that $F_1(a) = a\left(\frac{a^2}{4} - 1\right)$ and $F_3(a) = \frac{a^3}{12}$, the other $F_n(a)$ being zero. By Equation [69.6], the oscillation is

$$x = a \cos(t + \theta_0) - \frac{\mu a^3}{32} \sin 3(t + \theta_0) \qquad [69.7]$$

The differential equation for the amplitude is obtained from the equations of the first approximation

$$\frac{da}{dt} = \frac{\mu a}{2}\left(1 - \frac{a^2}{4}\right)$$

For a steady-state condition, $a = 2$; Equation [69.7] in this case becomes

$$x = 2 \cos(t + \theta_0) - \frac{\mu}{4} \sin 3(t + \theta_0) \qquad [69.8]$$

C. CORRECTION FOR FREQUENCY

In the preceding notations ω is the linear frequency when $\mu = 0$, and Ω is the frequency of the quasi-linear oscillation when $\mu \neq 0$. For quasi-isochronous motions to the first order, $\omega \approx \Omega$.

It is to be noted first that the exact solution for stationary oscillations can always be developed in a Fourier series

$$x = a \cos(\Omega t + \theta_0) + \sum_{n=2}^{\infty} \left[A_n \cos n(\Omega t + \theta_0) + B_n \sin n(\Omega t + \theta_0)\right] \qquad [69.9]$$

One has identically

$$\int_0^T [\ddot{x}x + \omega^2 x^2 + \mu f(x)x\dot{x}]\,dt = 0 \qquad [69.10]$$

218

since

$$\ddot{x} + \omega^2 x + \mu f(x)\dot{x} = 0$$

On the other hand,

$$\ddot{x}x + \dot{x}^2 = \frac{d}{dt}(x\dot{x})$$

and

$$\int_0^T \ddot{x}x\, dt + \int_0^T \dot{x}^2\, dt = x\dot{x}\Big|_0^T = 0$$

in view of the periodicity. Hence

$$\int_0^T \ddot{x}x\, dt = -\int_0^T \dot{x}^2\, dt$$

Likewise

$$\int_0^T f(x)\, x\dot{x}\, dt = 0$$

for the same reason. Hence,

$$\int_0^T \dot{x}^2\, dt = \omega^2 \int_0^T x^2\, dt \qquad\qquad [69.11]$$

If one replaces x by its expression [69.9] and $\dot{x}$ by its expression obtained by differentiating Equation [69.9], one obtains finally

$$\Omega^2\Big[a^2 + \sum_{n=2}^{\infty} n^2(A_n^2 + B_n^2)\Big] = \omega^2\Big[a^2 + \sum_{n=2}^{\infty}(A_n^2 + B_n^2)\Big] \qquad [69.12]$$

since the terms of the form $A_p B_q \cos p(\Omega t + \theta_0) \sin q(\Omega t + \theta_0)$ disappear when integrated over the period   It follows that

$$\frac{\Omega^2}{\omega^2} = \frac{a^2 + \sum_{n=2}^{\infty}(A_n^2 + B_n^2)}{a^2 + \sum_{n=2}^{\infty} n^2(A_n^2 + B_n^2)} \qquad\qquad [69.13]$$

On the other hand, under the assumption that $f(x,\dot{x}) = f(x)\dot{x}$, by Equation [69.6], $A_n = 0$ and $B_n = -\dfrac{\mu}{\omega}\dfrac{n}{n^2 - 1} F_n(a)$.

Substituting these values for A_n and B_n into Equation [69.13], one has

$$\frac{\Omega^2}{\omega^2} = \frac{1 + \dfrac{\mu^2}{\omega^2 a^2} \displaystyle\sum_{n=2}^{\infty} \left[\dfrac{n}{n^2 - 1} F_n(a) \right]^2}{1 + \dfrac{\mu^2}{\omega^2 a^2} \displaystyle\sum_{n=2}^{\infty} n^2 \left[\dfrac{n}{n^2 - 1} F_n(a) \right]^2} \qquad [69.14]$$

If we let $\dfrac{\mu^2}{\omega^2} = K^2$ and $\left[\dfrac{F_n(a)}{a} \right] = b_n$, the preceding equation can be written

$$\frac{\Omega^2}{\omega^2} = \frac{1 + K^2 \displaystyle\sum_{n=2}^{\infty} \left(\dfrac{n}{n^2 - 1} b_n \right)^2}{1 + K^2 \displaystyle\sum_{n=2}^{\infty} n^2 \left(\dfrac{n}{n^2 - 1} b_n \right)^2}$$

$$= \left[1 + K^2 \sum_{n=2}^{\infty} \left(\frac{n}{n^2 - 1} b_n \right)^2 \right] \left[1 - K^2 \sum_{n=2}^{\infty} n^2 \left(\frac{n}{n^2 - 1} b_n \right)^2 \right] \qquad [69.15]$$

Hence, to the second order of the small quantity K, one has

$$\Omega = \omega \left[1 - \frac{\mu^2}{2\omega^2} \sum_{n=2}^{\infty} \left(\frac{n^2}{n^2 - 1} \right) \frac{F_n^2(a)}{a^2} \right] \qquad [69.16]$$

Applying this formula to the Van der Pol equation with $a = 2$, $F_3(a) = \dfrac{a^3}{12} = \dfrac{2}{3}$, and $F_n(a) = 0$ for $n \neq 3$, one has

$$\Omega = 1 - \frac{\mu^2}{16}$$

70. APPROXIMATIONS OF HIGHER ORDERS

Consider, first, the quasi-linear equation

$$\ddot{x} + \omega^2 x + \mu f(x) = 0$$

and assume that it has one or several periodic solutions. Let $x = x(t)$ be such a solution, with an unknown period T and frequency $\Omega = 2\pi/T$. Let $x = z(\Omega t + \phi) \equiv z(\tau)$, with $\tau = \Omega t + \phi$. Then $z(\tau)$ has the period 2π.

Changing the independent variable in the original equation $\ddot{x} + \omega^2 x + \mu f(x) = 0$, one obtains

$$\Omega^2 \ddot{z} + \omega^2 z + \mu f(z) = 0 \qquad [70.1]$$

From now on the differential notation $\ddot{z}$ will designate differentiation with respect to τ. By hypothesis, Equation [70.1] has a periodic solution with period 2π. We shall look for solutions $z(\tau)$ and Ω^2 in the form of a power series in μ:

$$z(\tau) = \sum_{n=0}^{\infty} \mu^n z_n(\tau) \quad \text{and} \quad \Omega^2 = \sum_{n=0}^{\infty} \mu^n \alpha_n \qquad [70.2]$$

with $\alpha_0 = \omega^2$, since the existence of a periodic solution of period 2π for [70.1] with $\mu = 0$ requires that $\Omega^2 = \omega^2$.

Furthermore,

$$f(z) = f(z_0 + \mu z_1 + \mu^2 z_2 + \cdots)$$

$$= f(z_0) + \mu z_1 f'(z_0) + \mu^2 \left[z_2 f'(z_0) + \frac{z_1^2 f''(z_0)}{2} \right] + \cdots$$

The substitution of these values into Equation [70.1] gives rise to the following recurrent differential equations obtained by equating to zero the coefficients of μ^0, μ^1, μ^2, $\cdots$.

$$\omega^2 \ddot{z}_0 + \omega^2 z_0 = 0$$

$$\omega^2 \ddot{z}_1 + \omega^2 z_1 = -f(z_0) - \alpha_1 \ddot{z}_0$$

$$\omega^2 \ddot{z}_2 + \omega^2 z_2 = -f'(z_0) z_1 - \alpha_2 \ddot{z}_0 - \alpha_1 \ddot{z}_1 \qquad [70.3]$$

$$\cdots \cdots \cdots \cdots \cdots$$

$$\omega^2 \ddot{z}_{n+1} + \omega^2 z_{n+1} = F(z_0, z_1, \cdots, z_n) - \alpha_{n+1} \ddot{z}_0 - \alpha_n \ddot{z}_1 - \cdots - \alpha_1 \ddot{z}_n$$

$$\cdots \cdots \cdots \cdots \cdots$$

where $F(z_0, z_1, \cdots, z_n)$ is a polynomial in $z_1, z_2, \cdots, z_n$.

The solution $z(\tau)$ under consideration is determined up to a translation on τ. We can choose the origin, that is, ϕ, in the substitution $\tau = \Omega t + \phi$ so that

$$\dot{z}(0) = 0 \qquad\qquad [70.4]$$

The condition [70.4] then yields the following conditions for $z_n(\tau)$, which are periodic functions of period 2π and which we take as being represented by their Fourier series,

$$\dot{z}_n(0) = 0 \quad \text{for} \quad n = 1, 2, 3 \cdots \qquad\qquad [70.5]$$

Let $z_0, z_1, \cdots, z_n$ and $\alpha_1, \cdots, \alpha_n$ be the solutions of the first $(N+1)$ equations of the system [70.3]; it is then clear that

$$x = \sum_{n=0}^{N} \mu^n z_n(\tau) \quad \text{and} \quad \Omega^2 = \sum_{n=0}^{N} \mu^n \alpha_n$$

will satisfy the equation $\ddot{x} + \omega^2 x + \mu f(x) = 0$ to the order of μ^{N+1}, and hence can be considered as the $(N+1)^{\text{th}}$ approximation of x.

The first equation [70.3] gives, in view of [70.5], $z_0 = a \cos \tau$, where a is an arbitrary constant. There exists, however, a certain arbitrariness in the following steps, that is, in the successive determination of z_1, z_2, $\cdots$. We can remove this arbitrariness by requiring that no fundamental harmonic shall appear on the right side of Equations [70.3], for otherwise some z_n would contain secular terms. We wish, however, to obtain a function $z(\tau) = x(t)$ representing the periodic solution of our quasi-linear equation in the whole interval $0 \leqq t < \infty$.

Consider now the second equation of System [70.3]

$$\omega^2(\ddot{z}_1 + z_1) = - f(a \cos \tau) + \alpha_1 a \cos \tau$$

The function $f(a \cos \tau)$ can be developed in a Fourier series which contains only cosine terms, that is,

$$f(a \cos \tau) = \sum_{n=0}^{\infty} f_n(a) \cos n\tau = f_0(a) + f_1(a) \cos \tau + \sum_{n=2}^{\infty} f_n(a) \cos n\tau$$

$$[70.6]$$

$$\omega^2(\ddot{z}_1 + z_1) = - \sum_{n=2}^{\infty} f_n(a) \cos n\tau + \Big[\alpha_1 a - f_1(a)\Big] \cos \tau - f_0(a)$$

It is noted that the secular term is bound to appear in this case unless the coefficient of $\cos \tau$ on the right side of Equation [70.6] is zero. Hence, the condition for the elimination of the secular term is

$$\alpha_1 = \frac{f_1(a)}{a} \qquad [70.7]$$

which determines the approximation (z_1, α_1). One has

$$\ddot{z}_1 + z_1 = - \frac{1}{\omega^2}\Big[f_0(a) + \sum_{n=2}^{\infty} f_n(a) \cos n\tau\Big] \qquad [70.8]$$

In view of [70.5], the solution of [70.8] is

$$z_1 = A \cos \tau - \frac{1}{\omega^2} f_0(a) + \frac{1}{\omega^2}\sum_{n=2}^{\infty} \frac{f_n \cos n\tau}{n^2 - 1} \qquad [70.9]$$

with $f_n = f_n(a)$ where A is a constant. Substituting z_0 and z_1 into the right side of Equation [70.3] for z_2 and annulling the fundamental harmonic, we obtain an equation involving α_2 and A, so that A remains arbitrary. In order to simplify our solution, we take $A = 0$ so that

$$z_1 = - \frac{1}{\omega^2} f_0 + \frac{1}{\omega^2}\sum_{n=2}^{\infty} \frac{f_n \cos n\tau}{n^2 - 1} \qquad [70.10]$$

and the equation linking α_0 and A, where we set $A = 0$, now yields the value of α_2. By proceeding in this manner the following terms z_2, z_3, $\cdots$ and α_2, α_8, $\cdots$ can be determined. We require that none of $z_n (n \geqq 3)$ should contain the fundamental harmonic, by analogy with z_2. The condition [70.5] is then automatically satisfied. We proceed to show by induction that any z_n can be determined in this manner from Equation [70.3].

Assume that z_1, z_2, $\cdots$, z_n and α_1, α_2, $\cdots$, α_n, satisfying the first n equations of the system [70.3], have been determined.

The $(n + 1)^{\text{th}}$ equation is

$$\omega^2(\ddot{z}_{n+1} + z_{n+1}) = F(z_0, z_1, \cdots, z_n) - \alpha_n\ddot{z}_1 - \cdots - \alpha_1\ddot{z}_n + \alpha_{n+1}a\cos\tau \quad [70.11]$$

where $z_0 = a \cos \tau$, as before.

Since z_1, $\cdots$, z_n and $\ddot{z}_1$, $\cdots$, $\ddot{z}_n$ contain only cosine terms, $F(z_0, z_1, \cdots, z_n)$ also contains terms of this kind only.

Putting $F(z_0, z_1, \cdots, z_n) - \alpha_n\ddot{z}_1 - \alpha_{n-1}\ddot{z}_2 - \cdots - \alpha_1\ddot{z}_n = \sum_{m=0}^{\infty} b_m \cos m\tau$, one can write Equation [70.11] as

$$\ddot{z}_{n+1} + z_{n+1} = \frac{1}{\omega^2}\left[b_0 + \sum_{m=2}^{\infty} b_m \cos m\tau\right] + \frac{1}{\omega^2}(\alpha_{n+1}a + b_1)\cos\tau \quad [70.12]$$

The condition for the absence of secular terms is again

$$\alpha_{n+1} = -\frac{b_1}{a} \quad [70.13]$$

Equation [70.12] now becomes

$$\ddot{z}_{n+1} + z_{n+1} = \frac{1}{\omega^2}\left[b_0 + \sum_{m=2}^{\infty} b_m \cos m\tau\right] \quad [70.14]$$

The solution of this differential equation is

$$z_{n+1} = \frac{1}{\omega^2}\left[b_0 - \sum_{m=2}^{\infty} b_m \frac{\cos m\tau}{m^2 - 1}\right] \quad [70.15]$$

the secular term having been removed again from the solution.

71. MOTION OF A CONSERVATIVE NON-LINEAR SYSTEM WITH A CUBIC TERM

As an example of an application of this method, consider the differential equation

$$\ddot{x} + x + \mu x^3 = 0 \quad [71.1]$$

The integration of this equation by the method of the first approximation was given in Chapter X.

We propose now to determine the approximations of higher orders, following the method explained in the preceding section.

Taking as generating solutions $z_0(\tau) = a \cos \tau$, $\omega^2 = 1$, and $\alpha_0 = 1$, we have

$$\ddot{z}_1 + z_1 = - z_0^3 - \alpha_1 \ddot{z}_0 = - a^3 \cos^3 \tau + \alpha_1 a \cos \tau = \left(\alpha_1 a - \frac{3}{4} a^3 \right) \cos \tau - \frac{a^3}{4} \cos 3 \tau$$

The elimination of the secular term gives

$$\alpha_1 = \frac{3}{4} a^2 \qquad\qquad [71.2]$$

and the solution of this equation gives

$$z_1 = \frac{3}{32} a^3 \cos 3 \tau \qquad\qquad [71.3]$$

If we substitute for α_1 and z_1 their values, the third equation [70.3] becomes

$$\ddot{z}_2 + z_2 = - \frac{3}{32} a^5 \cos^2 \tau \cos 3 \tau + \alpha_2 a \cos \tau + \frac{27}{128} \cos 3 \tau$$

$$= \left(\alpha_2 a - \frac{3}{128} a^5 \right) \cos \tau + \frac{21}{128} a^5 \cos 3 \tau - \frac{3}{128} a^5 \cos 5 \tau \qquad [71.4]$$

The condition for the absence of the secular term gives $\alpha_2 = \frac{3}{128} a^4$. Thus the solution of Equation [71.4] is

$$z_2 = - \frac{21}{1024} a^5 \cos 3 \tau + \frac{a^5}{1024} \cos 5 \tau$$

Consequently the approximate solution satisfying Equation [71.1] to the order of μ^2 is

$$x = a \cos (\omega t + \phi) + \mu \frac{a^3}{32} \left(1 - \mu \frac{21}{32} \right) \cos (3 \omega t + \phi) + \mu^2 \frac{a^5}{1024} \cos (5 \omega t + \phi) \quad [71.5]$$

where a and ϕ are constants of integration.

The frequency Ω is given by the second expression of [70.2], in which α_1, α_2, $\cdots$ have already been determined

$$\Omega^2 = 1 + \frac{3}{4} \mu a^2 + \frac{3}{128} \mu^2 a^4 \qquad\qquad [71.6]$$

72. HIGHER APPROXIMATIONS FOR NON-LINEAR, NON-CONSERVATIVE SYSTEMS

We now consider the general form of a quasi-linear equation

$$\ddot{x} + \omega^2 x + \mu f(x, \dot{x}) = 0 \qquad\qquad [72.1]$$

We shall attempt to write the general solution for higher approximations in the form of an improved first approximation by replacing $\omega t + \phi$ by $\omega t + \phi - \frac{\pi}{2} = \psi$. One then obtains from Equation [68.19]

$$x = a\cos\psi - \frac{\mu}{\omega^2}F_0(a) + \frac{\mu}{\omega^2}\sum_{n=2}^{\infty}\frac{F_n(a)\cos n\psi + G_n(a)\sin n\psi}{n^2 - 1} \qquad [72.2]$$

with equations of the first approximation

$$\frac{da}{dt} = \frac{\mu}{2\omega}G_1(a); \quad \frac{d\psi}{dt} = \Omega(a) \qquad [72.3]$$

$$\Omega(a) = \omega + \frac{\mu}{2\omega a}F_1(a) \qquad [72.4]$$

The F_n and G_n in Equation [72.2] are the Fourier coefficients in the development of

$$f(a\cos\tau, -a\omega\sin\tau) = \sum_{n=0}^{\infty}\Big[F_n(a)\cos n\tau + G_n(a)\sin n\tau\Big] \qquad [72.4a]$$

The condition for a steady state is

$$G_1(a) = 0; \quad \psi = \Omega(a)t + \psi_0 \qquad [72.5]$$

where ψ_0 is an arbitrary constant.

Equation [72.2] for a steady state becomes

$$x = a\cos\Big[\Omega(a)t + \psi_0\Big] - \frac{\mu}{\omega^2}F_0(a) +$$

$$+ \frac{\mu}{\omega^2}\sum_{n=2}^{\infty}\frac{F_n(a)\cos n\,[\Omega(a)t + \psi_0] + G_n(a)\sin n\,[\Omega(a)t + \psi_0]}{n^2 - 1} \qquad [72.6]$$

It was seen that for conservative systems $G_1(a) \equiv 0$. In such a case, Equation [72.6] has two integration constants a and ψ_0, as is to be expected for an equation of the second order. If, however, $G_1(a) = 0$ has only simple roots without being equal to zero identically, the solution [72.6] has only one integration constant ψ_0 since a is determined from the equation $G_1(a) = 0$. This case corresponds, therefore, to the existence of limit cycles corresponding to the roots of $G_1(a) = 0$. In fact, as was shown previously, the stationary oscillation in this case does not depend on the initial amplitude.

We now propose to establish the existence of periodic solutions, that is, of limit cycles in non-conservative systems.

If $x = z(\Omega t + \phi)$ is such a solution, it must clearly satisfy the differential equation

$$\Omega^2 \ddot{z} + \omega^2 z + \mu f(z, \Omega \dot{z}) = 0 \qquad [72.7]$$

We can follow the same procedure as before, assuming solutions of the form

$$z = z_0 + \mu z_1 + \mu^2 z_2 + \cdots$$

$$\Omega = \Omega_0 + \mu \Omega_1 + \mu^2 \Omega_2 + \cdots \qquad [72.8]$$

where z_n are periodic with period 2π. Here we take z_n as represented by their Fourier series.

Forming $\dot{z}$ and $\ddot{z}$ and substituting the values of z, $\dot{z}$, $\ddot{z}$, and Ω into Equation [72.7], one obtains again a series of recurrent differential equations by equating to zero the coefficients of various powers of μ. One has

$$\Omega_0^2 \ddot{z}_0 + \omega^2 z_0 = 0$$

$$\Omega_0^2 \ddot{z}_1 + \omega^2 z_1 = -f(z_0, \Omega_0 \dot{z}_0) - 2\Omega_0 \Omega_1 \ddot{z}_0$$

$$\Omega_0^2 \ddot{z}_2 + \omega^2 z_2 = -f_z(z_0, \Omega_0 \dot{z}_0) z_1 - f_{\dot{z}}(z_0, \Omega_0 \dot{z}_0) \Omega_0 \dot{z}_1 - 2\Omega_0 \Omega_2 \ddot{z}_0 -$$

$$- 2\Omega_0 \Omega_1 \ddot{z}_1 - \Omega_1^2 \ddot{z}_0 - f_{\dot{z}}(z_0, \Omega_0 \dot{z}_0) \Omega_1 \dot{z}_0 \qquad [72.9]$$

$$\cdots \cdots \cdots \cdots \cdots \cdots$$

$$\Omega_0^2 \ddot{z}_{n+1} + \omega^2 z_{n+1} = -f_z(z_0, \Omega_0 \dot{z}_0) z_n - f_{\dot{z}}(z_0, \Omega_0 \dot{z}_0) \Omega_0 \dot{z}_n - 2\Omega_0 \Omega_{n+1} \ddot{z}_0 -$$

$$- 2\Omega_0 \Omega_1 \ddot{z}_n - F_n(z_0 \cdots z_{n-1}; \dot{z}_0 \cdots \dot{z}_{n-1}; \ddot{z}_0 \cdots \ddot{z}_{n-1}; \Omega_0 \cdots \Omega_{n-1})$$

where F_n is a known function of the indicated arguments. As before, $\Omega_0^2 = \omega^2$; we require that $\dot{z}(0) = 0$. Hence $\dot{z}_n(0) = 0$, where $n = 0, 1, 2, \cdots$, so that $z_0 = a \cos \tau$, where a is a constant to be determined, and z_1, z_2, $\cdots$ do not contain sine terms.

Substituting these values for z_0 and Ω_0 into the second equation [72.9], one gets

$$\omega^2(\ddot{z}_1 + z_1) = -f(a \cos \tau, -a\omega \sin \tau) + 2\omega \Omega_1 a \cos \tau$$

$$= -\sum_{n=0}^{\infty} \left[F_n(a) \cos n\tau + G_n(a) \sin n\tau \right] + 2\omega \Omega_1 a \cos \tau \qquad [72.10]$$

The condition for absence of a secular term gives

$$G_1(a) = 0 ; \qquad \Omega_1 = \frac{F_1(a)}{2\omega a} \qquad [72.11]$$

From Equations [72.11], a and Ω_1 can be determined. Equation [72.10] then becomes

$$\omega^2(\ddot{z}_1 + z_1) = -F_0(a) - \sum_{n=2}^{\infty} \Big[F_n(a)\cos n\tau + G_n(a)\sin n\tau \Big] \qquad [72.12]$$

The solution of Equations [72.12] is

$$z_1 = a_1\cos\tau - \frac{F_0(a)}{\omega^2} + \frac{1}{\omega^2}\sum_{n=2}^{\infty} \frac{[F_n(a)\cos n\tau + G_n(a)\sin n\tau]}{n^2 - 1} \qquad [72.13]$$

in which the amplitude a_1 is to be determined by the condition for the elimination of secular terms on the right side of Equation [72.9] for z_2.

Writing Equation [72.13] as $z_1 = a_1 \cos\tau + u$ where

$$u = -\frac{F_0(a)}{\omega^2} + \frac{1}{\omega^2}\sum_{n=2}^{\infty} \frac{F_n(a)\cos n\tau + G_n(a)\sin n\tau}{n^2 - 1} \qquad [72.14]$$

and substituting it into the third equation [72.9], one has

$$\omega^2(\ddot{z}_2 + z_2) = -f_z(a\cos\tau, -a\omega\sin\tau)a_1\cos\tau +$$

$$+ f_{\dot{z}}(a\cos\tau, -a\omega\sin\tau)a_1\omega\sin\tau + 2\omega\Omega_1 a_1\cos\tau + 2\omega\Omega_2 a\cos\tau + v(\tau)$$

where $v(\tau)$ is a periodic function containing the remaining terms of the third equation [72.9]. Since $v(\tau)$ is periodic, one can represent it by a Fourier series

$$v(\tau) = \sum_{n=0}^{\infty} \Big[p_n \cos n\tau + q_n \sin n\tau \Big]$$

Furthermore, one has the identity

$$-f_z a_1\cos\tau + f_{\dot{z}}a_1\omega\sin\tau = -\frac{\partial}{\partial\mu} f\Big[(a+\mu a_1)\cos\tau, -(a+\mu a_1)\omega\sin\tau\Big]_{\mu=0}$$

whence, by Equation [72.4a],

$$-f_z a_1\cos\tau + f_{\dot{z}}a_1\omega\sin\tau = -a_1\sum_{n=0}^{\infty} \Big[F_n'(a)\cos n\tau + G_n'(a)\sin n\tau \Big] \qquad [72.15]$$

where $F_n'(a)$ and $G_n'(a)$ designate the derivatives of $F_n(a)$ and $G_n(a)$. Substituting f_z and $f_{\dot{z}}$ into the third equation [72.9], one gets

$$\omega^2(\ddot{z}_2 + z_2) = -a_1 \sum_{n=0}^{\infty} \left[F_n'(a) \cos n\tau + G_n'(a) \sin n\tau \right] +$$

$$+ 2\omega(\Omega_1 a_1 + \Omega_2 a) \cos \tau + \sum_{n=0}^{\infty} \left[p_n \cos n\tau + q_n \sin n\tau \right] \quad [72.16]$$

In view of the periodicity of z_2, the secular terms must be eliminated again. Their elimination gives the conditions

$$a_1 G_1'(a) = q_1 \quad \text{and} \quad \Omega_1 a_1 + \Omega_2 a = -\frac{p_1}{2\omega} + \frac{a_1 F_1'}{2\omega} \quad [72.17]$$

It follows that

$$a_1 = \frac{q_1}{G_1'(a)} \quad [72.18]$$

Since we are in search of the condition for the existence of limit cycles, $G_1(a) = 0$ by the first equation [72.3], we have to add now a second condition $G_1'(a) \neq 0$, since only in this case does Equation [72.18] give the determination of a_1. The equation $G_1'(a) \neq 0$ shows that the root of the equation $G(a) = 0$, which gives the limit cycle, is a simple root.

From the second equation [72.17]

$$\Omega_2 = -\frac{1}{a}\left(\frac{p_1}{2\omega} + \Omega_1 a_1 - \frac{a_1 F_1'}{2\omega} \right) \quad [72.19]$$

Hence, Equation [72.16] can now be written as

$$\omega^2(\ddot{z}_2 + z_2) = (p_0 - a_1 F_0') +$$

$$+ \sum_{n=2}^{\infty} \left\{ \left[p_n - a_1 F_n'(a) \right] \cos n\tau + \left[q_n - a_1 G_n'(a) \right] \sin n\tau \right\} \quad [72.20]$$

The solution of this equation is

$$z_2 = a_2 \cos \tau + \frac{1}{\omega^2}\left(p_0 - a_1 F_0' \right) +$$

$$+ \frac{1}{\omega^2} \sum_{n=2}^{\infty} \left[(p_n - a_1 F_n') \cos n\tau + (q_n - a_1 G_n') \sin n\tau \right] \frac{1}{1 - n^2} \quad [72.21]$$

where a_2 is again an undetermined coefficient, which, together with Ω_3, is determined by the condition for the absence of secular terms on the right sides of Equations [72.9] for z_3, and so on.

Following this recurrence procedure, it is apparent that subsequent equations [72.9] permit the determination of a_n and Ω_{n+1} from the equations for the elimination of secular terms.

$$a_n G_n^{'}(a) = \xi_n \quad \text{and} \quad 2\omega\,(\Omega_{n+1}\,a + \Omega_1 a_n) = \eta_n \qquad [72.22]$$

in which ξ_n and η_n are known from the preceding recurrent operations.

As long as the equation $G_1(a) = 0$ has only simple roots, that is, $G_1^{'}(a) \neq 0$, the process can be continued indefinitely up to any value of the index n.

The expressions for the non-linear oscillation x and its frequency Ω, up to the order of μ^N inclusive, are of the following form

$$x = z_0(\Omega t + \phi) + \mu z_1(\Omega t + \phi) + \cdots + \mu^N z_N(\Omega t + \phi)$$

$$\qquad [72.23]$$

$$\Omega = \omega + \mu \Omega_1 + \cdots + \mu^N \Omega_N$$

Following this procedure, one finds, as an example, for the second approximation

$$x = (a + \mu a_1) \cos(\Omega t + \phi) - \frac{\mu}{\omega^2}\,F_0(a) +$$

$$+ \frac{\mu}{\omega^2} \sum_{n=2}^{\infty} \frac{F_n(a)\cos n\,(\Omega t + \phi) + G_n(a)\sin n(\Omega t + \phi)}{n^2 - 1} \qquad [72.24]$$

where

$$\Omega = \omega + \mu\,\frac{F_1(a)}{2\omega a}$$

If we compare this expression with the earlier formula [72.6], it is observed that the only difference between these expressions is in the amplitude of the first harmonic, which is now $a + \mu a_1$ instead of a, where a is the root of $G_1(a) = 0$.

This difference is due to the fact that for higher approximations, as can be shown, the amplitude equation is

$$\frac{da}{dt} = \frac{\mu}{2\omega}\,G_1(a) + \mu^2 S_1(a) + \mu^3 S_2(a) + \cdots \qquad [72.25]$$

If the limit cycle is reached,

$$\frac{\mu}{2\omega}\,G_1(a) + \mu^2 S_1(a) + \cdots = 0$$

Hence, in view of the factor μ before $G_1(a)$, it is seen that by stopping the approximation for a certain value $n = N$ of the index, the error in the determination of the first harmonic of the limit cycle is only of the order $(N - 1)$, and not of the Nth order.

Hence, the Nth approximation determines the amplitude to the order $(N + 1)$ and the frequency to the order $(N + 2)$.

For $N = 0$, one has

$$x = a \cos(\Omega t + \phi); \quad \Omega = \omega + \frac{\mu F_1(a)}{2\omega a} \qquad [72.26]$$

which represents the first approximation obtained by a different method in Chapter VIII.

For $N = 1$, x is given by Equation [72.23] and

$$\Omega = \omega + \mu \frac{F_1(a)}{2\omega} + \mu^2 \Omega_2 \qquad [72.27]$$

In order to establish the explicit expression for this approximation, one has to determine a_1 and Ω_2 entering into these formulas.

73. GENERAL FORM OF EQUATIONS OF HIGHER APPROXIMATIONS

We shall now review a generalization of the preceding theory applicable to steady oscillations as well as to the transient conditions of a quasi-linear system

$$\ddot{x} + \omega^2 x + \mu f(x, \dot{x}) = 0 \qquad [73.1]$$

One may attempt to find a periodic solution of the form

$$x = z(\psi, a) \qquad [73.2]$$

Furthermore, by analogy with equations of the first approximation, one can postulate that

$$\frac{da}{dt} = A(a)$$

$$\frac{d\psi}{dt} = \Omega(a) \qquad [73.3]$$

For the time being, the functions $A(a)$ and $\Omega(a)$ remain unknown. In fact, their determination constitutes the object of this procedure.

Proceeding formally, we obtain

$$\dot{x} = \frac{\partial z}{\partial \psi} \Omega + \frac{\partial z}{\partial a} A \qquad [73.4]$$

Differentiating the second time, we find

$$\ddot{x} = \frac{\partial^2 z}{\partial \psi^2} \, \Omega^2 + 2 \, \frac{\partial^2 z}{\partial \psi \partial a} \, \Omega A + \frac{\partial^2 z}{\partial a^2} \, A^2 + \frac{\partial z}{\partial \psi} \, \frac{\partial \Omega}{\partial a} \, A + \frac{\partial z}{\partial a} \, \frac{\partial A}{\partial a} \, A \quad [73.5]$$

Replacing x, $\dot{x}$, and $\ddot{x}$ in the quasi-linear equation [73.1] by their expressions [73.2], [73.4], and [73.5], one gets

$$\frac{\partial^2 z}{\partial \psi^2} \, \Omega^2 + 2 \, \frac{\partial^2 z}{\partial \psi \partial a} \, \Omega A + \frac{\partial^2 z}{\partial a^2} \, A^2 + \frac{\partial z}{\partial \psi} \, \frac{\partial \Omega}{\partial a} \, A +$$

$$+ \frac{\partial z}{\partial a} \, \frac{\partial A}{\partial a} \, A + \omega^2 z + \mu f \left(z, \frac{\partial z}{\partial \psi} \, \Omega + \frac{\partial z}{\partial a} \, A \right) = 0 \quad [73.6]$$

It is apparent that if one finds expressions for z, A, and Ω satisfying this equation to a certain degree μ^N of accuracy, these solutions will satisfy the original quasi-linear equation [73.1] to the same degree of approximation, conditions [73.3] being satisfied.

In order to apply the method of successive approximations, let us represent the solutions in the form

$$z(\psi, a) = z_0(\psi, a) + \mu z_1(\psi, a) + \mu^2 z_2(\psi, a) + \cdots$$

$$A(a) = \mu A_1(a) + \mu^2 A_2(a) + \cdots \qquad [73.7]$$

$$\Omega(a) = \omega + \mu \Omega_1(a) + \mu^2 \Omega_2(a) + \cdots$$

The method then consists in substituting the series expressions [73.7] for $z(\psi, a)$, $A(a)$, and $\Omega(a)$ into Equations [73.3] and [73.2] and equating to zero the coefficients of μ, μ^2, $\cdots$.

One obtains in this manner the following series of recurrent differential equations (compare with the analogous method of Poincaré, Chapter VIII).

$$\frac{\partial^2 z_0}{\partial \psi^2} + z_0 = 0$$

$$\left(\frac{\partial^2 z_1}{\partial \psi^2} + z_1 \right) \omega^2 = - f \left(z_0, \omega \, \frac{\partial z_0}{\partial \psi} \right) - 2 \omega \Omega_1 \frac{\partial^2 z_0}{\partial \psi^2} - 2 \omega A_1 \frac{\partial^2 z_0}{\partial \psi \partial a}$$

$$\left(\frac{\partial^2 z_2}{\partial \psi^2} + z_2 \right) \omega^2 = - f_z \left(z_0, \omega \, \frac{\partial z_0}{\partial \psi} \right) z_1 - f_{\dot{z}} \left(z_0, \omega \, \frac{\partial z_0}{\partial \psi} \right) \left(\omega \, \frac{\partial z_1}{\partial \psi} + \Omega_1 \frac{\partial z_0}{\partial \psi} + A_1 \frac{\partial z_0}{\partial a} \right) -$$

$$- 2 \omega \Omega_1 \frac{\partial^2 z_1}{\partial \psi^2} - 2 \omega A_1 \frac{\partial^2 z_1}{\partial \psi \partial a} - \Omega_1^2 \frac{\partial^2 z_0}{\partial \psi^2} - 2 \Omega_1 A_1 \frac{\partial^2 z_0}{\partial \psi \partial a} - A_1^2 \frac{\partial^2 z_0}{\partial a^2} -$$

$$- \frac{\partial z_0}{\partial \psi} \, \frac{\partial \Omega_1}{\partial a} \, A_1 - \frac{\partial z_0}{\partial a} \, A_1 \frac{\partial A_1}{\partial a} - 2 \omega \Omega_2 \frac{\partial^2 z_0}{\partial \psi^2} - 2 \omega A_2 \frac{\partial^2 z_0}{\partial \psi \partial a}$$

$$= - E_1 - 2 \omega \Omega_2 \frac{\partial^2 z_0}{\partial \psi^2} - 2 \omega A_2 \frac{\partial^2 z_0}{\partial \psi \partial a} \qquad [73.8]$$

. . . .

$$\left(\frac{\partial^2 z_{n+1}}{\partial \psi^2} + z_{n+1}\right) \omega^2 = - E_n - 2\omega\Omega_{n+1} \frac{\partial^2 z_0}{\partial \psi^2} - 2\omega A_{n+1} \frac{\partial^2 z_0}{\partial \psi \partial a} \qquad [73.8]$$

where E_n is a function of $z_1, \cdots, z_n; A_1, \cdots, A_n; \Omega_1, \cdots, \Omega_n;$ and their partial derivatives, which can be considered as known from the solution of the first n equations [73.8] by a recurrence procedure.

As before, the first equation of System [73.8] is solved by putting $z_0 = a \cos\psi$. Substituting this solution into the second equation [73.8], one obtains

$$\left(\frac{\partial^2 z_1}{\partial \psi^2} + z_1\right) \omega^2 = - f(a\cos\psi, - a\omega\sin\psi) + 2\omega\Omega_1 a\cos\psi + 2\omega A_1 \sin\psi$$

$$= - \sum_{n=0}^{\infty} \left[F_n(a)\cos n\psi + G_n(a)\sin n\psi\right] + 2\omega\Omega_1 a\cos\psi + 2\omega A_1 \sin\psi \quad [73.9]$$

Since we wish to have z_1 periodic, the secular terms on the right side of Equation [73.9] must be eliminated. The conditions for this are

$$2\omega\Omega_1 a - F_1(a) = 0 ; \quad 2\omega A_1 - G_1(a) = 0 \qquad [73.10]$$

From these conditions A_1 and Ω_1 are determined. Substituting their values into Equation [73.9], one has

$$\left(\frac{\partial^2 z_1}{\partial \psi^2} + z_1\right) \omega^2 = - F_0(a) - \sum_{n=2}^{\infty} \left[F_n(a)\cos n\psi + G_n(a)\sin n\psi\right] \qquad [73.11]$$

The solution of this equation is

$$z_1 = - \frac{1}{\omega^2} F_0(a) + \frac{1}{\omega^2} \sum_{n=2}^{\infty} \frac{F_n(a)\cos n\psi + G_n(a)\sin n\psi}{n^2 - 1} \qquad [73.12]$$

Substituting the values of A_1 and Ω_1 from Equations [73.10] and that of z_1 from Equation [73.12] into the third equation [73.8], one has

$$\left(\frac{\partial^2 z_2}{\partial \psi^2} + z_2\right) \omega^2 = - \sum_{n=0}^{\infty}\left[F_n^{(')}(a)\cos n\psi + G_n^{(')}(a)\sin n\psi\right] +$$

$$+ 2\omega\Omega_2 a\cos\psi + 2\omega A_2 \sin\psi \qquad [73.13]$$

where $F^{(')}$ and $G^{(')}$ are certain functions of a.

The elimination of secular terms again permits determining A_2 and Ω_2 from the equations.

$$2\omega\Omega_2 a - F_1^{(')}(a) = 0 ; \quad 2\omega A_2 - G_1^{(')}(a) = 0 \qquad [73.14]$$

and the substitution of these values into Equation [73.13] reduces it to

$$\left(\frac{\partial^2 z_2}{\partial \psi^2} + z_2\right)\omega^2 = -F_0^{(')}(a) - \sum_{n=2}^{\infty} \frac{F_n^{(')}(a)\cos n\psi + G_n^{(')}(a)\sin n\psi}{n^2 - 1} \qquad [73.15]$$

The recurrence procedure is now apparent. It is thus seen that the solution so obtained is of the form

$$x = a\cos\psi + \mu z_1(\psi, a) + \mu^2 z_2(\psi, a) + \cdots \qquad [73.16]$$

where a and ψ are given by the equations

$$\frac{da}{dt} = \mu A_1(a) + \mu^2 A_2(a) + \cdots + \mu^N A_N(a) \qquad [73.17]$$

$$\frac{d\psi}{dt} = \omega + \mu \Omega_1(a) + \mu^2 \Omega_2(a) + \cdots + \mu^N \Omega_N(a) \qquad [73.18]$$

On the other hand, by Equations [73.10], $A_1 = \frac{G_1(a)}{2\omega}$ and $\Omega_1 = \frac{F_1(a)}{2\omega a}$, whence

$$\frac{da}{dt} = \mu\,\frac{G_1(a)}{2\omega} - \mu^2 A_2(a) + \mu^3 A_3(a) + \cdots + \mu^N A_N(a)$$

$$\frac{d\psi}{dt} = \omega + \mu\,\frac{F_1(a)}{2\omega a} + \mu^2 \Omega_2(a) + \mu^3 \Omega_3(a) + \cdots + \mu^N \Omega_N(a)$$

$$[73.19]$$

For $N = 1$, Equations [73.19] give the improved first approximation, Equation [68.19].

Furthermore, since by the method of elimination of secular terms the quantities $A_1, A_2, \cdots, A_n$ are expressed in terms of the subsequent first harmonics which are eliminated from expressions $z_1(\psi, a), \cdots, z_n(\psi, a)$, it is apparent that the first equation [73.19] relates to the amplitude of the fundamental harmonic.

The second equation [73.19], viz.,

$$\Omega(a) = \frac{d\psi}{dt} = \omega + \mu\,\frac{F_1(a)}{2\omega a} + \mu^2 \Omega_2(a) + \cdots \qquad [73.20]$$

may be designated as the equation of the instantaneous frequency $\Omega(a)$ of the non-linear oscillation.

CHAPTER XII

METHOD OF EQUIVALENT LINEARIZATION OF KRYLOFF AND BOGOLIUBOFF

74. INTRODUCTORY REMARKS

The method of Kryloff and Bogoliuboff outlined in Chapter X was established by assuming a sinusoidal solution $x = a \sin \psi$ for a quasi-linear equation [58.1] and by determining the functions $a(t)$, the amplitude, and $\psi(t)$, the total phase, so as to satisfy the differential equation [58.1] with accuracy of the order of μ^2. As was mentioned, from the standpoint of formal procedure the method resembles that of the variation of constants of Lagrange.

The method of the first approximation stated in Chapter X gives approximate expressions for the frequency and the amplitude of a non-linear oscillation for small values of μ. It is plausible to think that these same approximate relations may be obtained from a linear equation in which the coefficients have been suitably chosen. This is essentially what Kryloff and Bogoliuboff have done and which is designated by them as the *method of equivalent linearization*. The essence of the method is the determination of the *equivalent parameters*, as is indicated in Section 75.

On the basis of formal procedure it is not clear why this particular determination of parameters leads to the possibility of approximating the solutions of a quasi-linear equation by those of a corresponding linear one in which equivalent parameters appear. In order to justify the procedure, Kryloff and Bogoliuboff observe that a non-linear oscillatory process is generally characterized by a certain Fourier spectrum of the component frequencies resulting from the non-linearity of the system. If, however, one limits oneself to the theory of the first approximation, it is logical to assume that the fundamental harmonic of the spectrum should be considered. Hence it is sufficient to determine the equivalent parameters so as to obtain in the linearized problem the same oscillation which appears as the fundamental harmonic of the quasi-linear system. In fact, if one assumes this to be an *a priori* proposition, the Principle of Harmonic Balance, it can be shown that the formulas giving the equivalent parameters follow directly from this principle, see Section 77. One can also justify the introduction of equivalent parameters by postulating that the work per cycle done by a non-linear force F_g and by a corresponding linear one is the same. In fact, if one assumes a Principle of Equivalent Balance of Energy of this kind, one likewise obtains the same formulas for the equivalent parameters, see Section 76.

Viewed from this standpoint, the Principle of Harmonic Balance enables us to determine the equivalent parameters without actually writing the non-linear differential equation. Kryloff and Bogoliuboff show that the solutions so obtained do not differ much from those of the corresponding linear equation. It is to be noted, however, that this argument should not be considered as a proof. In spite of this, the method of equivalent linearization, as we shall see particularly in Part III, plays an important role in the quasi-linear theory and leads to results consistent with experimental data. Thus, for instance, the generalization of the concept of equivalent parameters for several variables makes it possible to absorb the effect of an external periodic excitation by the equivalent parameter and thus to explain a number of phenomena such as asynchronous quenching and excitation, and similar phenomena. Moreover, when an equivalent parameter is a function of the amplitude, the approach of the phenomenon to a limit cycle in this representation amounts to the approach of the equivalent parameter to a critical value at which the linearized decrement vanishes and the oscillation becomes stationary.

We shall encounter numerous applications of the method of equivalent linearization in Part III. In this chapter we shall establish the principal definitions of equivalent parameters and give a few applications of this method.

75. METHOD OF EQUIVALENT LINEARIZATION

It was shown in Chapter X that the solution of a quasi-linear equation

$$m\ddot{x} + Kx + \mu f(x,\dot{x}) = 0 \qquad [75.1]$$

can be written $x = a \cos \psi$,* where the amplitude a and the total phase ψ are given by two differential equations of the first order.

Applying Equations [59.13] and [59.14] to Equation [75.1] with this form of solution, one obtains

$$\frac{da}{dt} = \frac{\mu}{2\pi\omega m} \int_0^{2\pi} f(a\cos\phi, -a\omega\sin\phi)\sin\phi\, d\phi \equiv \Phi(a) \qquad [75.2]$$

$$\frac{d\psi}{dt} = \Omega(a) \qquad [75.3]$$

where

$$\Omega^2(a) = \omega^2 + \frac{\mu}{\pi m a} \int_0^{2\pi} f(a\cos\phi, -a\omega\sin\phi)\cos\phi\, d\phi \qquad [75.4]$$

---

* As a matter of fact, this solution in Chapter X was taken as $x = a \sin \psi$, which merely reverses the sin ϕ and cos ϕ under the integral sign in the amplitude and phase equations. The notation in the present chapter complies with that used in the text of Kryloff and Bogoliuboff.

The second term on the right side of Equation [75.4] is the frequency correction between the linear, $\omega^2 = \dfrac{K}{m}$, and the non-linear, $\Omega^2(a)$, frequencies.

If one defines two constants $\overline{\lambda}$ and $\overline{K}$, the equivalent parameters, by the equations

$$\overline{\lambda} = -\frac{\mu}{\pi a \omega} \int_0^{2\pi} f(a\cos\phi, -a\omega\sin\phi)\sin\phi\, d\phi \qquad [75.5]$$

$$\overline{K} = K + \frac{\mu}{\pi a} \int_0^{2\pi} f(a\cos\phi, -a\omega\sin\phi)\cos\phi\, d\phi \qquad [75.6]$$

it can be shown that an "equivalent" linear equation, with coefficients $\overline{\lambda}$ and $\overline{K}$, approximates the solution of the quasi-linear equation [75.1] to an accuracy of the order of μ^2.

In fact, with values [75.5] and [75.6], the amplitude equation [75.2] becomes

$$\dot{a} = -\frac{\overline{\lambda}}{2m}\, a \qquad [75.7]$$

and the phase equation

$$\dot{\psi} = \Omega(a) = \sqrt{\frac{\overline{K}}{m}} \qquad [75.8]$$

One recognizes these expressions as the usual ones for the decrement and frequency of an ordinary linear equation of the second order.

In order to make sure that the solution $x = a\cos\psi$, with a and ψ given by Equations [75.7] and [75.8], actually satisfies the equivalent linear equation, with accuracy of the order of μ^2, substitute the values x and $\ddot{x}$ into the equivalent linear equation

$$m\ddot{x} + \overline{\lambda}\dot{x} + \overline{K}x = 0 \qquad [75.9]$$

We have

$$\dot{x} = \dot{a}\cos\psi - a\sin\psi\cdot\dot{\psi} = -\frac{\overline{\lambda}}{2m}a\cos\psi - a\Omega\sin\psi$$

$$\ddot{x} = -a\frac{\overline{K}}{m}\cos\psi + \frac{\overline{\lambda}}{m}a\Omega\sin\psi + \frac{\overline{\lambda}}{2m}a^2\frac{\partial\Omega}{\partial a}\sin\psi + \frac{1}{2m}\frac{\partial\overline{\lambda}}{\partial a}\frac{\overline{\lambda}}{2m}a^2\cos\psi \quad [75.10]$$

$$= -\frac{\overline{K}}{m}x - \frac{\overline{\lambda}}{m}\dot{x} + \frac{\overline{\lambda}}{2m}a^2\frac{\partial\Omega}{\partial a}\sin\psi + \frac{1}{2m}\frac{\partial\overline{\lambda}}{\partial a}\frac{\overline{\lambda}}{2m}ax - \left(\frac{\overline{\lambda}}{m}\right)^2\frac{a}{2}\cos\psi$$

Substituting x, $\dot{x}$, and $\ddot{x}$ from these equations into the equivalent linear equation [75.9], one sees that the quasi-linear differential equation [75.1] reduces to a residue of the form $R(\mu^2)$, which proves that the equivalent linear equation is satisfied with accuracy of the order of μ^2.

The transformation of the original quasi-linear equation

$$m\ddot{x} + Kx + \mu f(x,\dot{x}) = 0$$

into an equivalent linear one is accomplished by replacing the term $\mu f(x,\dot{x})$ of the quasi-linear equation by $K_1 x + \bar{\lambda}\dot{x}$, where $K_1 = \bar{K} - K$.

It is apparent that the quantity $\bar{\delta} = \bar{\lambda}/2m = -\dot{a}/a$, as determined by Equation [75.7], is the decrement, and $\Omega = \sqrt{K/m}$ is the frequency of the equivalent linear equation. If one substitutes for $\bar{\lambda}$ and $\bar{K}$ their expressions [75.5] and [75.6], one finds equations of the first approximation.

In this manner one obtains a purely formal connection between the equations of the first approximation and the equivalent linear equation with parameters $\bar{\lambda}$ and $\bar{K}$, as defined by Equations [75.5] and [75.6].

76. PRINCIPLE OF EQUIVALENT BALANCE OF ENERGY

From the preceding section it appears that the method of equivalent linearization consists in replacing a quasi-linear force, $F_g = \mu f(x,\dot{x})$, by a linear one, $F_L = K_1 x + \bar{\lambda}\dot{x}$. Furthermore, it has been shown that if the equivalent parameters K_1 and $\bar{\lambda}$ are defined by Equations [75.5] and [75.6], with $K_1 = \bar{K} - K$, the solution of the equivalent linear equation [75.9] differs by a small quantity of the second order from the solution of the original quasi-linear equation [75.1]. We propose now to show why this particular definition of equivalent parameters K_1 and $\bar{\lambda}$ has been adopted. The physical justification for this definition lies in the Principle of Equivalent Balance of Energy, which requires that *the work per cycle of F_g and F_L be the same*, that is

$$\mu \int_0^T f(x,\dot{x})\dot{x}\,dt = \bar{\lambda}\int_0^T \dot{x}^2\,dt \qquad [76.1]$$

The term with K_1 does not enter into this expression because the work of a conservative force per cycle is always zero.

It is to be noted, in view of the fact that the integral in Equation [75.5] is finite, that $\bar{\lambda}$ is of the same order as μ, that is, it is small. On the other hand, to the first approximation, $x = a\cos\psi$ and $\dot{x} = -a\omega\sin\psi$, where $\psi = \omega t + \psi_0$, and a and ψ_0 can be considered as approximately constant during the time interval $2\pi/\omega$. The left side of Equation [76.1], upon changing the limit of integration and substituting the generating solutions $x = a\cos\psi$ and $\dot{x} = -a\omega\sin\psi$, becomes

$$-\mu \int_0^{2\pi} f(a_1\cos\psi, - a\omega\sin\psi)\, a\sin\psi\, d\psi \qquad\qquad [76.2]$$

and the right side is clearly

$$\overline{\lambda} \int_0^{\frac{2\pi}{\omega}} a^2\omega^2\sin^2\psi\, dt = \overline{\lambda} a^2\omega \int_0^{2\pi} \sin^2\psi\, d\psi = \overline{\lambda} a^2\omega\pi \qquad\qquad [76.3]$$

Hence, by Equation [76.1],

$$\overline{\lambda} = - \frac{\mu}{\pi a \omega} \int_0^{2\pi} f(a\cos\phi, - a\omega\sin\phi)\sin\phi\, d\phi \qquad\qquad [76.4]$$

This is precisely the first equation [75.5], by which the parameter $\overline{\lambda}$ was originally defined.

It is thus seen that the introduction of the equivalent parameter $\overline{\lambda}$ is dictated by the equivalence of work per cycle in both the quasi-linear and the equivalent linear systems.

We next give a suitable physical interpretation to the other equivalent factor, K_1, which does not appear in the energy equation [76.1]. For this purpose it is helpful to utilize the definition of "wattless" or reactive power commonly used in the theory of alternating currents. In this theory the energy (or active) component of power W_a and its wattless (or reactive) counterpart W_r are defined as

$$W_a = \frac{1}{T} \int_0^T ei\cos\phi\, dt \qquad \text{and} \qquad W_r = \frac{1}{T} \int_0^T ei\sin\phi\, dt$$

where e, i, and ϕ are voltage, current, and phase angle respectively.

Defining the active W_a and the reactive W_r components of power for a mechanical system in a similar manner, we have

$$W_a = \frac{1}{T} \int_0^T F(t)\,\dot{x}(t)\, dt ; \qquad W_r = \frac{1}{T} \int_0^T F(t)\,\dot{x}\left(t - \frac{T}{4}\right) dt$$

Hence, by equating the expressions for the "reactive powers" for a quasi-linear and for an equivalent linear system, we obtain

$$\mu\, \frac{1}{T} \int_0^T f\left[x(t), \dot{x}(t)\right] \dot{x}\left(t - \frac{T}{4}\right) dt = \frac{1}{T} \int_0^T \left[K_1 x(t) + \overline{\lambda}\, \dot{x}(t)\right] \dot{x}\left(t - \frac{T}{4}\right) dt \qquad [76.5]$$

Since in this equation both μ and $\overline{\lambda}$ are of the first order, K_1 is of the same order.

Substituting the generating solutions $x = a \cos(\omega t + \theta)$, $\dot{x} = -a\omega \sin(\omega t + \theta)$, and $T = 2\pi/\omega$, the left side of Equation [76.5] becomes

$$\frac{a\omega\mu}{2\pi} \int_0^{2\pi} f(a\cos\phi, \; -\, a\omega\sin\phi)\cos\phi \, d\phi$$

and its right side is $a^2 \omega K_1/2$. It follows that

$$K_1 = \frac{\mu}{\pi a} \int_0^{2\pi} f(a\cos\phi, \; -\, a\omega\sin\phi)\cos\phi \, d\phi \qquad [76.6]$$

which is Equation [75.6].

77. PRINCIPLE OF HARMONIC BALANCE

An alternative auxiliary principle serving the same purpose can be described as follows. Consider again the non-linear force $F = \mu f(x, \dot{x})$ and the equivalent linear one, $F_L = K_1 x + \overline{\lambda}\dot{x}$. The harmonic oscillation $x = a \cos(\omega t + \theta)$, where ω is the frequency of the "zero" approximation, is taken again as a generating solution. With this solution, F_L can be written as $F_L = F_{L0} \cos(\omega t + \theta_L)$, where F_{L0} and θ_L are the amplitudes and the phase respectively of F_L. The non-linear force F is represented by a Fourier series of which the fundamental harmonic is $F = F_0 \cos(\omega t + \theta)$. If one makes $F = F_L$, which constitutes the *Principle of Harmonic Balance*, it entails two equations, $F_0 = F_{L0}$ and $\theta = \theta_L$, from which again the two parameters $\overline{\lambda}$ and K_1 can be obtained. In fact,

$$F_L = K_1 a \cos(\omega t + \theta_L) - \omega\overline{\lambda} a \sin(\omega t + \theta_L) \qquad [77.1]$$

and the fundamental harmonic of the non-linear force is

$$F = \frac{1}{\pi}\left[\int_0^{2\pi} f(a\cos\tau, \; -\, a\sin\tau)\cos\tau \, d\tau\right]\cos(\omega t + \theta) +$$

$$+ \frac{1}{\pi}\left[\int_0^{2\pi} f(a\cos\tau, \; -\, a\sin\tau)\sin\tau \, d\tau\right]\sin(\omega t + \theta) \qquad [77.2]$$

Equating the coefficients of $\cos(\omega t + \theta)$ and $\sin(\omega t + \theta)$ in Equations [77.1] and [77.2], since $\theta = \theta_L$, one obtains the same expressions for K_1 and $\overline{\lambda}$ as before.

It is seen that both principles, that of the Equivalent Balance of Energy and that of Harmonic Balance, are equivalent, because the work of higher harmonics per cycle of the fundamental frequency is zero.

Summing up the results of this and of the preceding sections, one can state:

1. The Principle of Equivalent Linearization consists in defining an equivalent linear system as a system with parameters $\overline{\lambda}$ and K_1 expressing the equality of work per cycle for the non-linear and the equivalent linear systems.

2. The parameter $\overline{\lambda}$ is obtained by equating the active components of power in both cases; K_1, by equating the reactive components.

3. When the equivalent parameters $\overline{\lambda}$ and K_1 are so determined, the equivalent linear differential equation admits a solution differing from that of the quasi-linear equation by a small quantity of the order of μ^2.

4. For practical purposes the formation of the equivalent parameters $\overline{\lambda}$ and K_1 is the only requirement for the solution of the quasi-linear equation, in view of Statement 3.

78. EXAMPLES OF APPLICATION OF THE METHOD OF EQUIVALENT LINEARIZATION

A few examples given below illustrate the application of this method.

A. NON-LINEAR RESTORING FORCE

Consider the differential equation

$$m\ddot{x} + F(x) = 0 \qquad [78.1]$$

where $F(x)$ is of a quasi-linear type. For example, $F(x) = cx + \mu x^3$, where c and μ are constant. The condition for quasi-linearity is that $\frac{\mu x^3}{cx} \ll 1$. Since the system is conservative, the amplitude a remains constant, but the oscillations are not isochronous. Substituting the value of $F(x)$ into Equation [78.1], one has

$$m\ddot{x} + cx + \mu x^3 = 0 \qquad [78.2]$$

Hence $f(x,\dot{x}) = f(x) = \mu x^3$ and, by Equation [76.6],

$$K_1(a) = \frac{\mu}{\pi a}\int_0^{2\pi} f(a\cos\phi)\cos\phi\, d\phi = \frac{\mu a^2}{2}$$

The equivalent spring constant in this case will be $c + \frac{\mu a^2}{2}$, whence

$$\Omega_a = \sqrt{\frac{c + K_1(a)}{m}} = \sqrt{\omega^2 + \frac{\mu a^2}{2m}} = \omega\sqrt{1 + \frac{\mu a^2}{2m\omega^2}} \approx \omega\left(1 + \frac{\mu a^2}{4m\omega^2}\right) = \omega(1 + \alpha a^2)$$

where $\alpha = \frac{\mu}{4m\omega^2}$. \qquad [78.3]

The frequency of non-linear oscillation is here a function of the amplitude a. The oscillation is thus non-isochronous, although the amplitude a is constant. One can easily discover this fact formally by calculating the expression for $\overline{\lambda}$ from Equation [75.5], which in this case gives $\overline{\lambda} = 0$.

B. NON-LINEAR DISSIPATIVE DAMPING

Consider a differential equation of the form

$$m\ddot{x} + Kx + \mu f(\dot{x}) = 0$$

In order to be more specific, assume quadratic damping, that is,

$$\mu f(\dot{x}) = b|\dot{x}|\dot{x}$$

Equation [75.5] for $\overline{\lambda}$ in this case is

$$\overline{\lambda} = -\frac{b}{\pi a \omega} \int_0^{2\pi} f(-a\omega \sin\phi)\sin\phi\, d\phi = \frac{b}{\pi a \omega} \int_0^{2\pi} f(a\omega\cos\phi)\cos\phi\, d\phi$$

where

$$\int_0^{2\pi} f(a\omega\cos\phi)\cos\phi\, d\phi = a^2\omega^2 \int_0^{2\pi}|\cos\phi|\cos^2\phi\, d\phi = a^2\omega^2\left[\int_0^{\frac{\pi}{2}}\cos^3\phi\, d\phi - \right.$$

$$\left. - \int_{\frac{\pi}{2}}^{\frac{3\pi}{2}}\cos^3\phi\, d\phi + \int_{\frac{3\pi}{2}}^{2\pi}\cos^3\phi\, d\phi\right] = \frac{8}{3}a^2\omega^2$$

Hence, $\overline{\lambda} = \frac{8}{3}\frac{ba\omega}{\pi}$. The equivalent decrement $\overline{\delta} = \frac{\overline{\lambda}}{2m} = \frac{4}{3}\frac{ba\omega}{m\pi}$; it is seen that the decrement in this case varies with the amplitude.

Applying Equation [76.6], one finds

$$K_1 = \frac{\mu b a \omega^2}{\pi}\int_0^{2\pi}|\sin\phi|\sin\phi\cos\phi\, d\phi = 0$$

Hence the non-linear correction for the frequency in this case is zero to the first order.

From the fact that for quadratic damping the decrement varies with the amplitude, one concludes that for large amplitudes quadratic damping is more efficient, and for small amplitudes less efficient, than is linear damping, the decrement of which does not depend on the amplitude.

Since the decrement $\overline{\delta} = \frac{4}{3}\frac{b\omega}{m\pi}a \equiv Sa$, where $S = \frac{4}{3}\frac{b\omega}{m\pi}$, the motion under the effect of quadratic damping can be determined. We have

$$\overline{\delta} = Sa = -\frac{\dot{a}}{a} = -\frac{1}{a}\frac{da}{dt}$$

whence

$$S = -\frac{1}{a^2}\frac{da}{dt} = \frac{d}{dt}\left(\frac{1}{a}\right) .$$

Hence, on integrating, $\frac{1}{a} - \frac{1}{a_0} = St$, so that finally

$$a = \frac{a_0}{1 + \frac{4}{3}\frac{b\omega}{m\pi}a_0 t} \qquad [78.4]$$

which coincides with Equation [62.4], obtained by the theory of the first approximation.

C. NON-LINEAR RESTORING FORCE AND NON-LINEAR DISSIPATIVE DAMPING

The differential equation is of the form

$$m\ddot{x} + f(\dot{x}) + c(x) = 0$$

It will again be assumed that both $f(\dot{x})$ and $c(x)$ are quasi-linear, that is, they are of the form $f(\dot{x}) = \lambda_0 \dot{x} + \mu\phi(\dot{x})$ and $c(x) = c_0 x + \nu\psi(x)$, where λ_0 and c_0 are constant, μ and ν are small parameters, and $\phi(\dot{x})$ and $\psi(x)$ are non-linear terms.

The application of the method of equivalent linearization gives

$$\Omega = \sqrt{\omega^2 + \frac{\overline{K}_1}{m}} \quad \text{and} \quad \overline{\delta} = \frac{\overline{\lambda}}{2m}$$

where $\overline{K}_1$ and $\overline{\lambda}$ are again the equivalent parameters determined by Equations [75.5] and [76.6], applied to the function $f(x,\dot{x}) = \mu\phi(\dot{x}) + \nu\psi(x)$, as explained in connection with the two previous examples.

Equations of this type are of frequent occurrence in practice. For example, Froude's well-known differential equation for the rolling of a ship in still water is of the form

$$I\ddot{\theta} + K_1\dot{\theta} + K_2\dot{\theta}^2 + Wh\sin\theta = 0$$

where I, W, and h are respectively the moment of inertia, the displacement, and the metacentric height of the ship, and K_1 and K_2 are Froude's coefficients of resistance to rolling. If one approximates $\sin\theta$ by $\theta - \frac{\theta^3}{6}$, one has, upon dividing the equation by I, the following equation

$$\ddot{\theta} + b_1\dot{\theta} + b_2\dot{\theta}^2 + \omega^2\theta - \frac{\omega^2\theta^3}{6} = 0$$

which is of the type considered here.

D. ELECTRICAL OSCILLATIONS IN A CIRCUIT CONTAINING A SATURATED CORE REACTOR

Consider an oscillating circuit containing a constant air-core inductance L_0, a variable saturation iron-core inductance L_1, and a fixed capacity C. The non-linearity in this case is due to L_1. In fact, the flux ϕ through the coil L_1 is $\phi = f(i)$, where i is the current. For a sinusoidal current $i = i_0 \cos(\omega t + \theta)$, the fundamental harmonic of magnetic flux is

$$\frac{1}{\pi} \int_0^{2\pi} f(i_0 \cos \phi) \cos \phi \, d\phi \cdot \cos(\omega t + \phi)$$

According to the method of equivalent linearization, the non-linear equation $\phi = f(i)$ can be replaced by the linear one $\phi = L_e i$, where L_e is the equivalent linear coefficient of self-inductance,

$$L_e = \frac{1}{\pi i_0} \int_0^{2\pi} f(i_0 \cos \phi) \cos \phi \, d\phi \qquad [78.5]$$

If the constant air-core inductance L_0 is relatively large compared with the non-linear inductance containing iron, the current will be quasi-harmonic and the expression for frequency will be

$$\omega = \frac{1}{\sqrt{(L_0 + L_e)C}} = \frac{1}{\sqrt{L_0 C}} \left(1 - \frac{L_e}{2 L_0}\right) \qquad [78.6]$$

E. NON-LINEAR CONDUCTORS

Consider a conductor and let the voltage drop e across its terminal be $e = -f(i)$.

If the current is of the form $i = i_0 \cos(\omega t + \theta)$, the fundamental harmonic of the voltage drop is

$$-\frac{1}{\pi} \int_0^{2\pi} f(i_0 \cos \phi) \cos \phi \, d\phi \cdot \cos(\omega t + \theta) = e_1$$

By putting

$$R_e = \frac{1}{\pi i_0} \int_0^{2\pi} f(i_0 \cos \phi) \cos \phi \, d\phi$$

the non-linear conductor can be replaced by an equivalent linear one having a voltage drop $e_1 = R_e i$. If $R_e > 0$, the non-linear conductor dissipates energy; if $R_e < 0$, energy is brought into the system owing to the non-linearity of the process. Likewise, if the non-linearity appears in the form $i = f(e)$ and the voltage executes a harmonic oscillation $e = e_0 \cos(\omega t + \theta)$, the fundamental harmonic of current will be $\frac{1}{\pi} \int_0^{2\pi} f(e_0 \cos \phi) \cos \phi \, d\phi$. Here again one can replace the non-linear parameter $i = f(e)$ by a linear one, $i = \sigma e$, provided that we define the equivalent conductance as

$$\sigma = \frac{1}{\pi e_0} \int_0^{2\pi} f(e_0 \cos \phi) \cos \phi \, d\phi \qquad [78.7]$$

Depending upon whether σ is greater than or less than zero, one has either absorption or generation of energy.

These considerations are useful in analyzing circuits containing electron tubes. The anode current in this case is of the form $i_a = f(E_0 + e)$, where E_0 is the constant voltage of the "B source," and e is the alternating grid voltage.

If e is sinusoidal, the fundamental harmonic of i_a will be

$$\frac{1}{\pi} \int_0^{2\pi} f(E_0 + e_0 \cos \phi) \cos \phi \, d\phi \cdot \cos(\omega t + \theta)$$

If one defines

$$S_e = \frac{1}{\pi e_0} \int_0^{2\pi} f(E_0 + e_0 \cos \phi) \cos \phi \, d\phi \qquad [78.8]$$

as the average transconductance of the tube, instead of a non-linear relation $i_a = f(E_0 + e)$, one will have an *equivalent* linear relation, $i_a = S_e e$.

F. THERMIONIC GENERATORS

Consider a thermionic circuit arranged according to the diagram shown in Figure 78.1, which is self-explanatory. The resistance R, shown to be in parallel, is supposed to be large so as to obtain only rather small damping in the oscillating circuit LC.

The control voltage is $e = (M - DL)\dfrac{di}{dt}$, where the term $DL\dfrac{di}{dt}$ takes care of the anode reaction ($D \ll 1$). The alternating component of the anode current is

$$i_a = S_e\left(M - DL\right)\frac{di}{dt}$$

where S_e is the equivalent transconductance of the linearized problem.

By Kirchhoff's law, $i_a = i_L + i_R + i_C$, where $Ri_R = Li_L'$ in the LR-mesh; hence $i_R = \dfrac{L}{R} i_L'$. In the CL-mesh,

$$\frac{1}{C}\int i_C \, dt = L\frac{di_L}{dt}$$

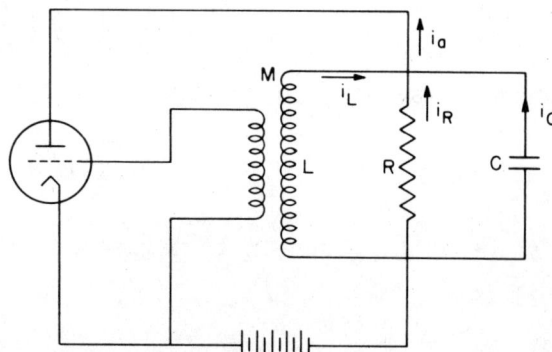

Figure 78.1

whence $i_C = LCi_L''$. Substituting these values into Kirchhoff's equation and dropping the subscript L, one obtains

$$LC \frac{d^2i}{dt^2} + \frac{L}{R} \frac{di}{dt} + i = i_a = S_e\left(M - DL\right)\frac{di}{dt}$$

Hence finally

$$LC \frac{d^2i}{dt^2} + \left[\frac{L}{R} - S_e\left(M - DL\right)\right]\frac{di}{dt} + i = 0 \qquad [78.9]$$

This equation is an equivalent linearized equation of the process, since it contains the linearized parameter S_e. From this we get the decrement

$$\delta = \frac{1}{2LC}\left[\frac{L}{R} - S_e\left(M - DL\right)\right] \qquad [78.10]$$

Equation [59.13] of the first approximation is here

$$\frac{di_0}{dt} = \frac{S_e(M - DL) - \dfrac{L}{R}}{2LC} \cdot i_0 \qquad [78.11]$$

The stable amplitude is reached when

$$S_e(M - DL) = \frac{L}{R} \qquad [78.12]$$

Since, by Equation [78.8], S_e contains e_0, the substitution for S_e of its value from [78.12] determines the equilibrium amplitude e_0 of the grid voltage at which the oscillation reaches a steady state.

As a second example, consider a somewhat modified scheme shown in Figure 78.2, in which the resistance R is supposed to be small so as to be within the range of the quasi-linear theory. If the current in the oscillating circuit is designated by i and the anode current by i_a, the differential equation is

$$L \frac{di}{dt} + Ri + \frac{1}{C}\int i\,dt = M \frac{di_a}{dt} = MS_e \frac{de}{dt} \qquad [78.13]$$

where e is the grid voltage given by the equation

$$e = \frac{1}{C}\int i\,dt + D\left(M \frac{di}{dt} - L_a \frac{di_a}{dt}\right)$$

If the anode reaction is neglected, $D \approx 0$, so that

$$e \approx \frac{1}{C}\int i\,dt \qquad [78.14]$$

Introducing the variable e instead of i in Equation [78.13], we obtain

$$LC\frac{d^2e}{dt^2} + \left(RC - MS_e\right)\frac{de}{dt} + e = 0 \qquad [78.15]$$

The stationary condition is reached when

$$S_e = \frac{RC}{M} \qquad [78.16]$$

In the transient state the decrement is

$$\delta = \frac{RC - MS_e}{2LC} \qquad [78.17]$$

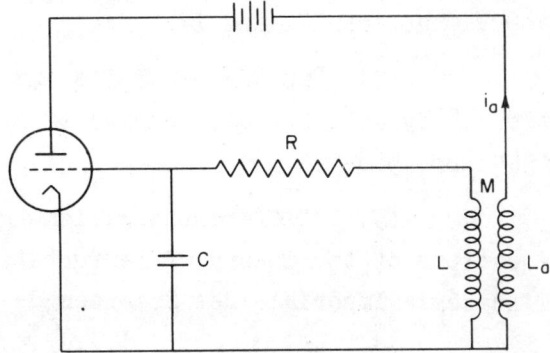

Figure 78.2

Since by [78.8] the equivalent transconductance S_e is a function of the amplitude e_0, the decrement δ varies during the transient state. If the static curve $i_a = f(e)$ is approximated by a polynomial, Equation [78.8] permits calculating the amplitude e_0' at which the decrement δ vanishes and the stationary condition is reached. Assume, for example, that the constant biasing voltage E_0 is such that the characteristic $i_a = f(e)$ of the electron tube can be approximated by the polynomial

$$f(e) = i_a = i_{a0} + \alpha_1 e + \beta_1 e^2 - \gamma_1 e^3 \qquad [78.18]$$

where α_1, β_1, and γ_1 are positive constants. Carrying out the calculation [78.8], one finds

$$S_e = \alpha_1 - \frac{3}{4}\gamma_1 e_0^2$$

and, by Equation [78.16],

$$e_0' = \sqrt{\frac{4}{3\gamma_1}\left(\alpha_1 - \frac{RC}{M}\right)} \qquad [78.19]$$

REFERENCES

(1) "Les méthodes nouvelles de la mécanique céleste" (New Methods in Celestial Mechanics), by H. Poincaré, Gauthier-Villars, Paris, Vol. 1, 1892, Chapters III and IV.

(2) "On Van der Pol's and Related Non-Linear Differential Equations," by J.A. Shohat, Journal of Applied Physics, Vol. 15, No. 7, July 1944, pp. 568-574.

(3) "Differentialgleichungen der Störungstheorie" (Differential Equations of the Theory of Perturbation), by And. Lindstedt, Mémoires de l'Académie Impériale des Sciences de St. Pétersbourg, Vol. XXXI, No. 4, 1883.

(4) "Theory of Oscillations," by A. Andronow and S. Chaikin, Moscow, (Russian), 1937, Chapters VII and VIII.

(5) "Introduction to Non-Linear Mechanics," by N. Kryloff and N. Bogoliuboff, Kieff, (Russian), 1937, Chapters X, XI, and XII.

(6) H. Poincaré, loc. cit., Chapter II.

(7) "Sur la théorie mathématique des auto-oscillations" (On the Mathematical Theory of Self-Excited Oscillations), by A. Andronow and A. Witt, Comptes Rendus, Paris, 1930.

(8) "Sur la théorie mathématique des systémes auto-oscillatoires à deux dégres de liberté" (On the Mathematical Theory of Self-Excited Systems with Two Degrees of Freedom), by A. Andronow and A. Witt, Journal of Technical Physics, USSR, (Russian), 1934.

(9) H. Poincaré, loc. cit., p. 179.

(10) "Dynamics of a System of Rigid Bodies," by E.J. Routh, London, 1905, Chapter VI.

(11) Über die Bedingungen unter welchen eine Gleichung nur Wurzeln mit negativen reellen Theilen besitzt" (On the Conditions under which an Equation Possesses Only Roots with Negative Real Parts), by A. Hurwitz, Mathematische Annalen, Vol. 46, 1895, p. 273.

(12) "Problème général de la stabilité du mouvement" (General Problemes of Stability of Motion), by M.A. Liapounoff, Annales de la Faculté des Sciences de Toulouse, Paris, Vol. 9, 1907.

(13) "On a Type of Oscillation Hysteresis in a Simple Triode Generator," by E.V. Appleton and B. Van der Pol, Philosophical Magazine, Vol. 42, 1921.

(14)   "Theory of Sound," by Lord Rayleigh, London, Vol. 1, 1894.

(15)   "On Oscillation Hysteresis in a Triode Generator," by B. Van der Pol, Philosophical Magazine, Vol. 43, 1922.

(16)   "Note sur la génération des oscillations entretenues" (Memoir on the Generation of Self-Excited Oscillations), by E. and H. Cartan, Annales des Postes Télégraphes et Téléphones, December 1925.

(17)   "Étude des oscillations entretenues" (Study of Self-Excited Oscillations), by A. Liénard, Revue Générale de l'Électricité, Vol. 23, 1928.

PART III

NON-LINEAR RESONANCE

79. INTRODUCTORY REMARKS

The object of Part III is to outline the present status of the theory of non-linear resonance. The phenomena of non-linear resonance are far more complicated and diversified than those of ordinary linear resonance, and it does not seem possible as yet to give a unified picture of the whole subject. Some of these phenomena appear to be more adequately discussed on the basis of the quasi-linear theory of Kryloff and Bogoliuboff, while others, on the contrary, fit better into the theory developed by Mandelstam and Papalexi, which is based on the earlier work of Poincaré.

For these reasons it was thought preferable to present separately the expositions of these two principal schools of thought without attempting to establish further generalizations at this time. It is apparent that this procedure inevitably reflects the somewhat unsettled state of the whole subject and leads to a certain overlapping of topics. The reader will undoubtedly observe this in connection with certain specific topics such as parametric excitation, entrainment of frequency, and others.

The first four chapters of Part III are devoted to an exposition of the theory of Kryloff and Bogoliuboff; the last three give an outline of the work done by the school of Mandelstam and Papalexi.

In addition to the intrinsic difference in the methods used by various writers, there also exists a considerable difference in the terminology they employ. An attempt was made to remedy this situation to some extent by designating as *internal resonance* the case when the divisors in the generalized response function become small. The term *external resonance* is reserved exclusively for the case when an external periodic excitation exists, as in the theory of ordinary linear resonance.

In the quasi-linear theory of Kryloff and Bogoliuboff the study is more or less equally divided between these two principal cases, whereas the work of the school of Mandelstam and Papalexi centers mainly about the phenomena of external resonance, which are illustrated by numerous experimental researches.

The reader will find it convenient to read Chapters X and XII of Part II before reading Chapters XIII, XIV, XV, and XVI of Part III. It is also suggested that he read Chapters I, III, and IV of Part I, and particularly

Chapter VIII of Part II, before reading Chapters XVII and XVIII, which are independent of the first four chapters of Part III.

Chapter XIX depends very little on any of the preceding chapters,
except possibly on the concept of representing solutions of differential equations by phase trajectories which is outlined in Section 3, Part I. The essence of Chapter XIX lies in the theory of differential equations with periodic
coefficients, outlined only briefly in Section 108.

It must be admitted that these attempts to establish junction points
between the exceedingly complicated phenomena of non-linear resonance and various existing theories are probably incomplete at present, and it is hoped
that this survey will serve as a stimulus for further generalizations.

CHAPTER XIII

SYSTEMS WITH SEVERAL DEGREES OF FREEDOM*

We now propose to study the behavior of quasi-linear systems with several degrees of freedom. For this purpose it is useful to review the so-called method of complex amplitudes used extensively in the theory of electric circuits. From this method the definitions of impedances and admittances of electric circuits can be generalized so that they also apply to mechanical systems. The further generalization necessary to pass from linear problems to quasi-linear ones is then relatively simple.

80. METHOD OF COMPLEX AMPLITUDES

In dealing with oscillatory phenomena, it is advantageous to use the exponential function $e^{j\omega t} = \cos \omega t + j \sin \omega t$, where $j = \sqrt{-1}$. A few well-known propositions, which will be useful later, are given below.

1. Multiplication by j of a sinusoidal function $f(t) = e^{j\omega t}$ advances its phase by $\pi/2$. This follows from Euler's identity $j = e^{j\frac{\pi}{2}}$; whence $je^{j\omega t} = e^{j\left(\omega t + \frac{\pi}{2}\right)}$. Likewise, multiplication by $-j$ retards the phase of $e^{j\omega t}$ by $\pi/2$.

2. Multiplication of $e^{j\omega t}$ by j^n, where n is an integer, advances or retards the phase of the vector $e^{j\omega t}$ by $n\pi/2$, according to whether n is a positive or a negative integer. This follows from the definition $j^n = j \cdot j \cdots j$ (n factors); each multiplication by j advances the rotation by $\pi/2$.

3. The derivative $df/dt = j\omega f$. Hence the derivative of a sinusoidal vector $f = ae^{j\omega t}$ consists in the operation $(j\omega)$ on the vector $ae^{j\omega t}$, which multiplies the amplitude a by ω and advances the phase by $\pi/2$. Likewise, $d^n f/dt^n = (j\omega)^n f$ is the operation which multiplies the amplitude by ω^n and advances the phase by $n\pi/2$.

Symbolically, $\delta^n = d^n/dt^n = (j\omega)^n = j^n\omega^n$. This holds only when a is a constant.

4. For a linear system of sinusoidal functions f, for example, $f = f_1 + f_2$, the operation $(j\omega)$ is additive, that is, $(j\omega)f = (j\omega)f_1 + (j\omega)f_2$.

5. If, instead of $(j\omega)$ or $(j\omega)^n$, one has a linear function $\phi(j)$, for example, $\phi(j) = A + Bj$, the operation $[\phi(j)]f = Af + jBf$. In this case the operation $\phi(j)$ produces two effects:

---

* The subject matter of this and of the following three chapters is taken from the treatise of Kryloff and Bogoliuboff, Reference (1).**

** Numbers in parentheses indicate references on page 130 of this report.

a. Multiplication of the amplitude vector f by A without changing its phase.

b. Multiplication of the amplitude by B with the incident rotation of the phase by $\pi/2$. The amplitude I of the new vector $[\phi(j)]f$ is thus complex, if the original amplitude a of the vector f is real.

6. More generally, if one has a relation between sinusoidal functions of the form

$$\phi_0(j)f_0(t) + \phi_1(j)f_1(t) + \cdots + \phi_n(j)f_n(t) = 0 \qquad [80.1]$$

there also exists an analogous relation

$$\phi_0(j)I_0 + \phi_1(j)I_1 + \cdots + \phi_n(j)I_n = 0 \qquad [80.2]$$

between their complex amplitudes $I_0, I_1, \cdots, I_n$.

81. ELEMENTS OF THE THEORY OF LINEAR CIRCUITS

In the theory of linear electric circuits one encounters differential equations of the form

$$\sum_{k=0}^{m} \alpha_k \frac{d^k I}{dt^k} = \sum_{k=0}^{n} \beta_k \frac{d^k E}{dt^k}$$

where I and E are the current and voltage in a given mesh, and α_k and β_k are constant parameters. This equation, written in terms of complex amplitudes, is

$$\sum_{k=0}^{m} \alpha_k(j\omega)^k I = \sum_{k=0}^{n} \beta_k(j\omega)^k E$$

From this we obtain

$$E = \frac{\displaystyle\sum_{k=0}^{m} \alpha_k(j\omega)^k}{\displaystyle\sum_{k=0}^{n} \beta_k(j\omega)^k} I = Z(j\omega) I \qquad [81.1]$$

and

$$I = \frac{\displaystyle\sum_{k=0}^{n} \beta_k(j\omega)^k}{\displaystyle\sum_{k=0}^{m} \alpha_k(j\omega)^k} E = Y(j\omega) E \qquad [81.2]$$

where

$$Z(j\omega) = \frac{\sum_{k=0}^{m} \alpha_k (j\omega)^k}{\sum_{k=0}^{n} \beta_k (j\omega)^k} \qquad [81.3]$$

is the complex impedance and

$$Y(j\omega) = \frac{\sum_{k=0}^{n} \beta_k (j\omega)^k}{\sum_{k=0}^{m} \alpha_k (j\omega)^k}$$

is the complex admittance of the mesh. From these equations it follows that

$$Z(j\omega) = \frac{1}{Y(j\omega)} \qquad [81.4]$$

Problems involving systems with one degree of freedom are thus reduced to the ultimate calculation of impedances or admittances, as the case may be.

For electric circuits this procedure is too well known to need emphasis here; consequently a few words about it will suffice. For an inductance L and a capacity C the values of the complex impedances are respectively $jL\omega$ and $1/jC\omega$; the resistance is a real quantity R. For a series circuit, the impedance equation is used; for a parallel one, the admittance equation. Thus, when L_1, R_1, and C_1 are in series,

$$Z_1 = R_1 + j\left(L_1\omega - \frac{1}{C_1\omega}\right)$$

For another series circuit (L_2, R_2, C_2) one has

$$Z_2 = R_2 + j\left(L_2\omega - \frac{1}{C_2\omega}\right)$$

If these two circuits are in parallel, the admittance is

$$Y = Y_1 + Y_2 = \frac{1}{Z_1} + \frac{1}{Z_2} = \frac{Z_1 + Z_2}{Z_1 Z_2}$$

and so on.

For systems with several degrees of freedom, there arises the question of coupling between these degrees of freedom. The coupling factor can be determined by analogy with electric-circuit theory.

Consider, for instance, a system with two degrees of freedom. The first circuit contains L_1, R_1, and an external "forcing" function. The forcing

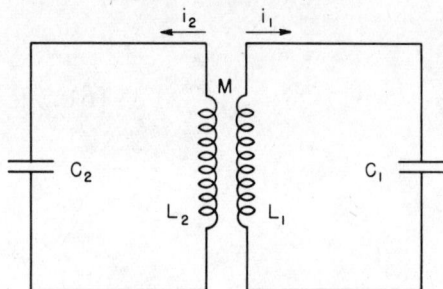

Figure 81.1

function is a sinusoidal electromotive force $E = E_0 e^{j\omega t}$. The second circuit contains L_2, R_2, and C_2. In addition, the two circuits are coupled together; M is the coefficient of mutual inductance. Kirchhoff's law applied to the first circuit gives

$$L_1 \frac{di_1}{dt} + R_1 i_1 - M \frac{di_2}{dt} = E_0 e^{j\omega t} \quad [81.5]$$

For the second circuit it gives

$$L_2 \frac{di_2}{dt} + R_2 i_2 + \frac{1}{C}\int i_2 \, dt + M \frac{di_1}{dt} = 0 \qquad [81.6]$$

Written in terms of the complex amplitudes, these equations are

$$(jL_1\omega + R_1)I_1 - jM\omega I_2 = E_0$$

$$jM\omega I_1 + \left(jL_2\omega + R_2 + \frac{1}{jC\omega}\right)I_2 = 0$$

whence

$$I_1 = E_0 \frac{R_2 + j\left(L_2\omega - \dfrac{1}{C\omega}\right)}{(R_1 + jL_1\omega)\left[R_2 + j\left(L_2\omega - \dfrac{1}{C\omega}\right)\right] + j^2 M^2 \omega^2} \qquad [81.7]$$

The cofactor of E_0 in this expression is the admittance $Y_1(j\omega)$ of the first circuit. If there is no coupling, that is, if $M = 0$, Equation [81.7] gives

$$I_1 = \frac{E_0}{R_1 + jL_1\omega}$$

As another application of the theory of linear circuits, consider two simple circuits (L_1, C_1) and (L_2, C_2) coupled inductively as shown in Figure 81.1. The complex equations are*

$$\left(L_1 j\omega + \frac{1}{C_1 j\omega}\right)i_1 - Mj\omega i_2 = 0$$

$$[81.8]$$

$$- Mj\omega i_1 + \left(L_2 j\omega + \frac{1}{C_2 j\omega}\right)i_2 = 0$$

The condition which expresses the consistency of the system [81.8] for values i_1 and i_2 other than the trivial ones, $i_1 = i_2 = 0$, is

---

* We follow the notation of Kryloff and Bogoliuboff in choosing the positive directions as shown in Figure 81.1.

$$\Delta(j\omega) = \left(L_1 j\omega + \frac{1}{C_1 j\omega}\right)\left(L_2 j\omega + \frac{1}{C_2 j\omega}\right) + M^2\omega^2 = 0 \qquad [81.9]$$

that is,

$$(L_1 C_1 \omega^2 - 1)(L_2 C_2 \omega^2 - 1) - M^2 C_1 C_2 \omega^4 = 0 \qquad [81.10]$$

Let

$$\omega_1^2 = \frac{1}{L_1 C_1}; \quad \omega_2^2 = \frac{1}{L_2 C_2}; \quad g^2 = \frac{M^2}{L_1 L_2}$$

This gives

$$\omega^4(1 - g^2) - (\omega_1^2 + \omega_2^2)\omega^2 + \omega_1^2 \omega_2^2 = 0 \qquad [81.11]$$

The oscillating circuits will have frequencies

$$\Omega_1^2 = \frac{(\omega_1^2 + \omega_2^2) + \sqrt{(\omega_1^2 - \omega_2^2)^2 + 4g^2 \omega_1^2 \omega_2^2}}{2(1 - g^2)} \qquad [81.12]$$

$$\Omega_2^2 = \frac{(\omega_1^2 + \omega_2^2) - \sqrt{(\omega_1^2 - \omega_2^2)^2 + 4g^2 \omega_1^2 \omega_2^2}}{2(1 - g^2)} \qquad [81.13]$$

differing somewhat from the natural frequencies ω_1 and ω_2 of each circuit.

82. ANALOGIES BETWEEN ELECTRICAL AND MECHANICAL SYSTEMS

Very often the establishment of a formal analogy between the differential equations expressing two different types of problems permits a formal transfer of known solutions of problems of one type to those of the other. The method of complex amplitudes developed in connection with electric circuits has a useful application in mechanical problems where generalized definitions of mechanical impedances and admittances are involved. In acoustics the notion of "acoustic impedance" also plays an important role.

The real usefulness of these generalizations occurs in connection with systems having several degrees of freedom. It is preferable, however, to establish an analogy first for a system having one degree of freedom.

The differential equation of a simple (L, C, R)-circuit acted upon by a sinusoidal electromotive force is

$$L\frac{di}{dt} + Ri + \frac{1}{C}\int_0^t i\,dt = E_0 e^{j\omega t} = E \qquad [82.1]$$

Consider, on the other hand, a mechanical system with one degree of freedom excited by an external sinusoidal force. Its equation is

$$m\frac{d^2 x}{dt^2} + h\frac{dx}{dt} + kx = F_0 e^{j\omega t} = F$$

When the new variable $v = \dfrac{dx}{dt}$ is introduced, this equation becomes

$$m \frac{dv}{dt} + hv + k \int_0^t v \, dt = F_0 e^{j\omega t} = F \qquad [82.2]$$

One observes that Equations [82.1] and [82.2] are of the same form and that the following corresponding quantities indicate the analogy between electrical and mechanical problems:

$$(i, v); \quad (L, m); \quad (R, h); \quad \left(\frac{1}{C}, k\right); \quad (E, F) \qquad [82.3]$$

The method of complex amplitudes in the electrical problem gives

$$I_0 = \frac{E_0}{\sqrt{R^2 + x^2}} \, e^{-j\phi_e} \qquad [82.4]$$

where $x = L\omega - \dfrac{1}{C\omega}$ is the reactance and $\phi_e = \tan^{-1}\left[\dfrac{L\omega - \dfrac{1}{C\omega}}{R}\right]$. The quantity

$$\frac{e^{-j\phi_e}}{\sqrt{R^2 + \left(L\omega - \dfrac{1}{C\omega}\right)^2}} = Y_e(j\omega)$$

is the *complex admittance* of the circuit. By the analogy [82.3], one obtains

$$v = \frac{F_0}{\sqrt{h^2 + \left(m\omega - \dfrac{k}{\omega}\right)^2}} \, e^{-j\phi_m} = \frac{F_0 \omega}{\sqrt{h^2\omega^2 + (m\omega^2 - k)^2}} \, e^{-j\phi_m} \qquad [82.5]$$

where $\phi_m = \tan^{-1} \dfrac{m\omega^2 - k}{h\omega}$. By further analogy, the quantity

$$\frac{e^{-j\phi_m}}{\sqrt{h^2\omega^2 + (m\omega^2 - k)^2}} = Y_m(j\omega)$$

is the *complex admittance* of the mechanical system. In both cases $\phi = 0$ at resonance, the variables I_0 and v are in phase with the exciting forces E_0 and F_0 respectively, and their amplitudes are limited by the dissipation factors R and L. The *complex impedances* are the inverse quantities of the admittances, that is, $Z(j\omega) = \dfrac{1}{Y(j\omega)}$.

One could proceed to establish an analogy between differential equations of the second order by differentiating Equation [82.1]. Here one would compare the differentiated equation [82.1] with that of the mechanical system. The condition of equivalence for these equations is

$$(i, x); \quad (L, m); \quad (R, h); \quad \left(\frac{1}{C}, k\right); \quad \left(\frac{dE}{dt}, F\right) \qquad [82.6]$$

It is seen that both the electrical and mechanical problems can be treated by the concept of admittances and impedances.

These electro-mechanical analogies can easily be established for systems with several degrees of freedom. Sometimes the establishment of an

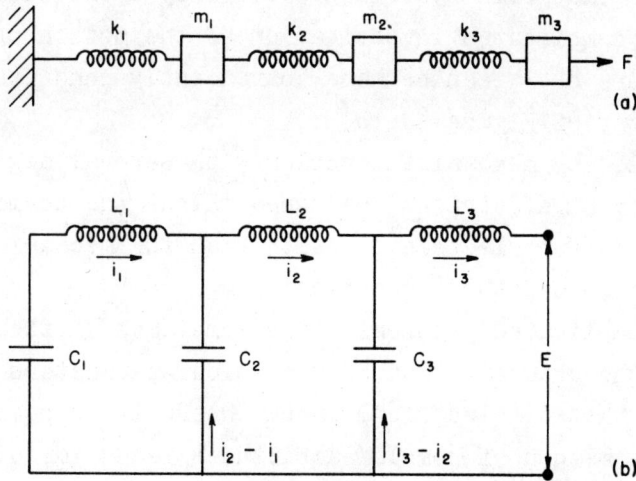

Figure 82.1

analogy with an electrical problem helps considerably in the solution of a mechanical problem. As an example, consider the mechanical system shown in Figure 82.1a, whose electrical analogue is indicated in Figure 82.1b. Designating the displacements of the masses m_1, m_2, and m_3 by x_1, x_2, and x_3 and the velocities by $\dot{x}_1 = v_1$, $\dot{x}_2 = v_2$, and $\dot{x}_3 = v_3$ respectively, we have, using the operational notation,

$$v_1 = j\omega x_1; \quad v_2 = j\omega x_2; \quad v_3 = j\omega x_3 \qquad [82.7]$$

The differential equations of the mechanical system are

$$m_1 j\omega v_1 + \frac{k_1}{j\omega} v_1 - \frac{k_2}{j\omega}(v_2 - v_1) = 0$$

$$m_2 j\omega v_2 + \frac{k_2}{j\omega}(v_2 - v_1) - \frac{k_3}{j\omega}(v_3 - v_2) = 0 \qquad [82.8]$$

$$m_3 j\omega v_3 + \frac{k_3}{j\omega}(v_3 - v_2) = F$$

In these equations, if one takes the velocity v as the dependent variable, the acceleration is clearly $j\omega v$ and the displacement is $v/j\omega$.

On the other hand, if, in the electric circuit of Figure 82.1b, the current i is the dependent variable, by applying Kirchhoff's law to the subsequent meshes of the circuit one gets

$$L_1 j\omega i_1 + \frac{1}{C_1 j\omega} i_1 - \frac{1}{C_2 j\omega}(i_2 - i_1) = 0$$

$$L_2 j\omega i_2 + \frac{1}{C_2 j\omega}(i_2 - i_1) - \frac{1}{C_3 j\omega}(i_3 - i_2) = 0 \qquad [82.9]$$

$$L_3 j\omega i_3 + \frac{1}{C_3 j\omega}(i_3 - i_2) = E$$

It is seen that both systems are formally identical. In this particular case a more complicated investigation of the motion of the mechanical system shown in Figure 82.1a can be more conveniently conducted by utilizing the electrical analogy of Figure 82.1b.

In general, any mechanical problem with several degrees of freedom can be represented by an electrical analogue. Since the terminology is more definitely established for electric circuits than for mechanical systems, it is always preferable to use the "electrical language."

In more complicated problems it is sometimes difficult to establish an analogy because the determination of mechanical parameters generally is more difficult than that of electrical ones. Where it is possible to establish an analogy, the method of complex amplitudes leads immediately to the establishment of steady-state conditions.

83. APPLICATION OF THE METHOD OF EQUIVALENT LINEARIZATION TO THE STEADY STATE OF A QUASI-LINEAR SYSTEM

With this reminder of the principal points of the theory of linear circuits, we can now proceed to establish a generalization of the Kryloff-Bogoliuboff theory applicable to circuits containing non-linear conductors of electricity. It will be assumed that the departure from linearity is small so that the theory of the first approximation describes the phenomena with sufficient accuracy. In what follows we shall make frequent use of the Principle of Equivalent Linearization, Chapter XII, so that the definitions of impedances and admittances can be extended to quasi-linear systems.

We shall consider first a linear dissipative circuit with constant parameters R, L, and C, the decrement of which is $\delta = -R/2L$. Let us assume that we introduce in series with this circuit a non-linear resistor having the characteristic $e = f(i)$. The variable resistance ρ of such a non-linear conductor is defined, as usual, by the relation $\rho = \dfrac{de}{di} = \dfrac{df(i)}{di}$. In accordance with the Principle of Equivalent Linearization, the non-linear conductor can be replaced by an equivalent linear one whose resistance R_e is

$$R_e = \frac{1}{\pi i_0} \int_0^{2\pi} f(i_0 \cos \phi) \cos \phi \, d\phi \qquad [83.1]$$

where i_0 is the quiescent value of i around which the oscillations are to be investigated. The complex equation of the circuit is

$$Lj\omega + R + \frac{1}{Cj\omega} + R_e = 0 \qquad [83.2]$$

Equating to zero the real and imaginary components of this equation, we obtain two equations:

$$L\omega - \frac{1}{C\omega} = 0 \quad \text{and} \quad R + R_e = 0 \qquad [83.3]$$

The first equation [83.3] determines the frequency and the second the amplitude of oscillations in a stationary state. From the second equation it is noted that oscillations are possible if $R_e < 0$. In the theory of linear circuits, $R_e = 0$, which requires that $R = 0$, that is, steady oscillations are possible only if the circuit has no resistance, which is obvious. It is to be noted that the method of equivalent linearization can only be applied when the resistance R is small enough to make the decrement $\delta = -R/2L$ small, in which case the oscillations are feebly damped and the system is quasi-linear and can be described by equations of the first approximation.

Let us now consider a linear circuit with admittance $A(j\omega)$, that is, with impedance $Z(j\omega) = \frac{1}{A(j\omega)}$, closed on a non-linear conductor with the equivalent admittance $S(a)$, where a is the amplitude. The circuit will consist, therefore, of two impedances $\frac{1}{A(j\omega)}$ and $\frac{1}{S(a)}$ in series so that the resultant impedance will be

$$Z_r(j\omega) = \frac{1}{A(j\omega)} + \frac{1}{S(a)} \qquad [83.4]$$

For steady-state oscillations, $Z_r(j\omega) = 0$, that is,

$$A(j\omega) + S(a) = 0 \qquad [83.5]$$

Again two equations are obtained by splitting the complex quantities into real and imaginary components. One of these equations determines the frequency and the other the amplitude of the stationary oscillations.

We shall now apply the method of complex amplitudes to the study of oscillations in electron-tube circuits. The non-linear conductor, the electron tube, is represented by an equation of the form

$$i_a = f(E)$$

where i_a is the anode or plate current and E is the control voltage. This equation can also be written as

$$i_a = S(a)\left[e_g + De_a\right] = S(a)e \qquad [83.6]$$

where e_g and e_a are the grid and the anode voltages, $D = 1/\mu$ is the factor of the anode reaction (here μ is the amplification factor of the tube), and $S(a)$ is the average transconductance,* a function of the amplitude a. The quantity $S(a)$ is given by the equation

$$S(a) = \frac{1}{\pi a} \int_0^{2\pi} f(E_0 + a\cos\phi)\cos\phi \, d\phi \qquad [83.7]$$

---

* The term *mutual conductance* is also employed.

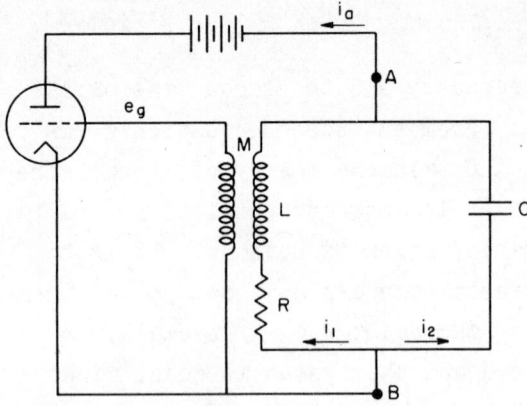

Figure 83.1

where E_0 is the quiescent point of the control voltage.

Let us consider the circuit shown in Figure 83.1 representing an electron-tube oscillator with inductive coupling. Designating by $Z_a(j\omega)$ the impedance of the circuit between the points A and B and by $M(j\omega)$ the mutual reactance and using other notations and positive directions as indicated in Figure 83.1, we have

$$e_a = - Z_a(j\omega) i_a; \quad e_g = M(j\omega) i_a \qquad [83.8]$$

From these equations and Equation [83.6] the admittance $A(j\omega)$ of the circuit is given by the expression

$$A(j\omega) = \frac{1}{M(j\omega) - DZ_a(j\omega)} \qquad [83.9]$$

In a self-excited state the total impedance vanishes, and by Equations [83.4] and [83.5] one must have

$$A(j\omega) - S(a) = 0 \qquad [83.10]$$

In other words, the admittance of the external circuit must be equal to the admittance, or transconductance, $S(a)$ of the electron tube.

Additional equations from which the conditions of the steady state can be established are obtained as follows. Let us introduce a complex number K defined by the relation

$$K = \frac{e_g}{-e_a} = \frac{M(j\omega)}{Z_a(j\omega)} \qquad [83.11]$$

From Equations [83.9], [83.10], and [83.11], we obtain

$$K = D + \frac{1}{S(a) Z_a(j\omega)} \qquad [83.12]$$

This equation is established by Barkhausen (2) and can be applied to the circuit shown in Figure 83.1. By a simple calculation we find first that

$$Z_a(j\omega) = \frac{R + jL\omega}{(1 - LC\omega^2) + jCR\omega} \qquad [83.13]$$

The voltage between the points A and B is $e_{AB} = Z_a(j\omega) i_a$ and the current i_1 in the LR-branch of the circuit is $i_1 = e_{AB}/(R + jL\omega) = i_a/[(1 - CL\omega^2) + jCR\omega]$. Hence the grid voltage e_g is

$$e_g = Mj\omega i_1 = \frac{Mj\omega}{(1 - LC\omega^2) + jCR\omega}\, i_a \qquad [83.14]$$

whence

$$K = \frac{e_g}{e_{AB}} = \frac{Mj\omega[(1 - LC\omega^2) + jCR\omega]}{[(1 - LC\omega^2) + jCR\omega](R + jL\omega)} = \frac{Mj\omega}{R + jL\omega} \qquad [83.15]$$

Substituting this value of K into Equation [83.12] and using Equation [83.13], one finds, after separating the real and the imaginary components, the following two equations:

$$S(M - DL) = CR \qquad [83.16]$$

$$1 - LC\omega^2 + SDR = 0 \qquad [83.17]$$

Since both D and R are generally very small, the quantity SDR is of the second order and can be neglected. One then finds from Equation [83.17] that the frequency of self-excited oscillations is practically that of the oscillating circuit, provided the amplification factor $\mu = 1/D$ is sufficiently large. Equation [83.16] determines the amplitude a_1 of the stationary self-excited oscillation, namely,

$$S(a_1) = \frac{1}{\pi a_1}\int_0^{2\pi} f(E_0 + a\cos\phi)\cos\phi\, d\phi = \frac{CR}{M - DL} \qquad [83.18]$$

Let us assume, for example, that the experimental function $i_a = f(E_0 + a\cos\phi)$ is of the form

$$i_a = f(E_0 + a\cos\phi) = i_0 + k_1 a\cos\phi + k_2(a\cos\phi)^2 + k_3(a\cos\phi)^3 + \cdots$$

where $i_0 = f(E_0)$ and k_1, k_2, $\cdots$ are constants. Substituting this expression into Equation [83.18], one gets

$$S(a) = \frac{1}{\pi a}\left[i_0\int_0^{2\pi}\cos\phi\, d\phi + k_1 a\int_0^{2\pi}\cos^2\phi\, d\phi + \right.$$

$$\left. + k_2 a^2\int_0^{2\pi}\cos^3\phi\, d\phi + k_3 a^3\int_0^{2\pi}\cos^4\phi\, d\phi + \cdots \right] \qquad [83.19]$$

The first and the third terms of this equation are zero. If we limit the expansion to the first four terms, Equation [83.19] gives

$$S(a) = k_1 + \frac{3}{4}k_3 a^2$$

whence, by Equation [83.16], the amplitude of the stationary oscillation is

$$a = \sqrt{\frac{4}{3k_3}\left(\frac{RC}{M} - k_1\right)} \qquad [83.20]$$

It is seen that the quadratic **term of** the polynomial approximating the experimental non-linear characteristic $i_a = f(E)$ does not contribute anything to
the expression for the amplitude a of the stationary oscillation. The amplitude is expressed only in terms of the coefficients k_1 and k_3 of the linear
and cubic terms and the parameters of the circuit, as was found previously by
other methods; see Section 54.

84. APPLICATION OF THE METHOD OF EQUIVALENT LINEARIZATION TO THE TRANSIENT STATE OF A QUASI-LINEAR SYSTEM

The method of complex amplitudes can also be generalized for the
transient state of a quasi-linear system. For this purpose it is necessary
to extend the definition of symbolic differentiation to the complex exponen-
tial functions e^{pt}, where $p = \delta + j\omega$. The quantity δ is the decrement if it
is negative and the increment if it is positive. The rule of symbolic differentiation remains the same as given in Section 80, Proposition 3, namely,

$$\frac{df}{dt} = p \cdot f; \qquad \frac{d^2f}{dt^2} = p^2 \cdot f; \quad \cdots$$

The vectorial interpretation of these operations is somewhat different. Thus,
for example, $\frac{df}{dt} = pf = (\delta + j\omega)f = (\delta f + j\omega f)$ means that the vector $\frac{df}{dt}$ consists now of two components, one $j\omega f$ leading the original vector f by $\pi/2$ and
the other δf in phase with f. It follows, therefore, that the vector $\frac{df}{dt}$ leads
the vector f by an angle $\phi = \tan^{-1}\frac{\omega}{\delta}$ which is less than $\pi/2$ if $\delta > 0$, that is,
if δ is an increment. If, however, $\delta < 0$, that is, if δ is a decrement,
$\phi = \tan^{-1}\frac{\omega}{-|\delta|}$ which is larger than $\pi/2$. The generalization for higher derivatives does not present any difficulties. If $\delta \to 0$, $\phi \to \pi/2$; if, however, the
condition of aperiodic damping is approached, $\omega \to 0$ and $\phi \to 0$, which means
that all higher derivative vectors approach the in-phase condition with the
real exponential function $f(t) = e^{\delta t}$.

For the transient state we must use the condition

$$\Delta(p) = 0 \qquad\qquad [84.1]$$

instead of the condition of consistency [81.9].

Consider, for example, the self-excitation of a simple (L,C,R)-
circuit, as shown in Figure 84.1, closed on a non-linear conductor N which has
the equivalent resistance $R_e(a)$.* In order to obtain a self-excitation of
this circuit, the total impedance must be zero, that is,

$$Z(p) + R_e = 0 \qquad\qquad [84.2]$$

where $Z(p)$ is the linear impedance, which we wish to consider in connection

---
* For convenience we will write R_e in place of $R_e(a)$ in the intermediate calculation.

with the transient state

$$p = -\delta + j\omega$$

when $\delta \neq 0$ but is small.*

The linearized impedance of the steady state is

$$Z_1(j\omega) + R_e = Lj\omega + (R + R_e) + \frac{1}{Cj\omega} = 0$$

Hence, for the transient state, we have to substitute p for $j\omega$. This gives

$$LCp^2 + (R + R_e)Cp + 1 = 0 \qquad [84.3]$$

Dividing by LC and putting $\frac{1}{LC} = \omega_0^2$, we have

$$p^2 + \frac{R + R_e}{L}p + \omega_0^2 = 0$$

whence

$$p = -\frac{R + R_e}{2L} \pm \sqrt{\omega_0^2 - \left(\frac{R + R_e}{2L}\right)^2}\, j = -\delta \pm j\omega \qquad [84.4]$$

where $\delta = \frac{R + R_e}{2L}$ is the decrement and ω is the frequency. Self-excitation from rest is possible if $R + R_e(0) < 0$, that is, if $R < -R_e(0)$. We shall call $R_0 = -R$ the critical value of the negative resistance and $\delta_0 = \frac{R}{2L}$ the linear decrement. In these notations we have

$$\delta = \delta_0\left[1 - \frac{R_e(a)}{R_0}\right] \qquad [84.5]$$

At the start, that is, when $a = 0$, one must have $\left|R_e(0)\right| > \left|R_0\right|$, that is, $\delta < 0$, in which case it follows from [84.4] that the amplitudes increase initially. The function $\left|R_e(a)\right|$ is a monotonically decreasing function of a so that for a certain value $a = a_1$, $R_e(a_1) = R_0$ and $\delta = 0$, which means that the oscillation reaches a stationary state. It is thus seen that the concept of equivalent resistance $R_e(a)$ permits formulating the condition of approach to the steady state by means of the variable decrement δ. When $a \to a_1$, for which $R_e(a) \to R_0$, $\delta \to 0$.

As a second example, consider the coupled system shown in Figure 84.2 in which N is a non-linear conductor characterized by the equivalent resistance $R_e(a)$ as in the first example. With the same assumptions and notations as in the preceding example, the linear impedance of the system is

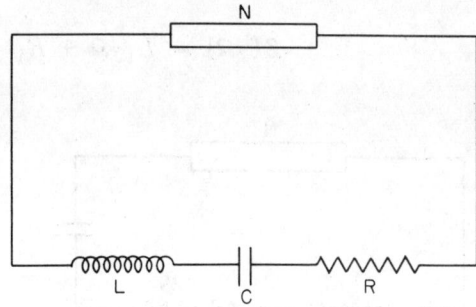

Figure 84.1

---

* In this expression, δ is the decrement if it is positive and the increment if it is negative; this corresponds to the notation of Kryloff and Bogoliuboff.

$$Z(j\Omega) = L_1 j\Omega + R_1 + \frac{1}{C_1 j\Omega} + \frac{M^2 C_2 j\Omega^3}{(1 - L_2 C_2 \Omega^2) + jR_2 C_2 \Omega} \qquad [84.6]$$

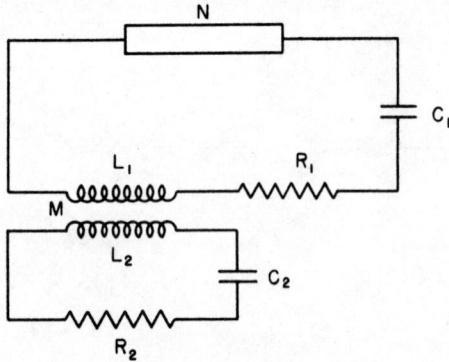

When the non-linear conductor N is present, we have to add $R_e(a)$ to R_1 in the preceding expression and replace $j\Omega$ by p in order to form the expression for the transient impedance $Z(p)$ during self-excitation, which we now propose to investigate. It is apparent that the quantity $Z(p)$ is generally of the form

$$Z(p) = \frac{A(p)}{B(p)} \qquad [84.7]$$

Figure 84.2

Since the condition for self-excitation is $Z(p) = 0$ and since $B(p) \neq 0$, we express this condition as

$$A(p) = \left[L_1 C_1 p^2 + (R_1 + R_e)C_1 p + 1\right]\left[L_2 C_2 p^2 + R_2 C_2 p + 1\right] - M^2 C_1 C_2 p^4 = 0 \quad [84.8]$$

Let

$$\frac{1}{L_1 C_1} = \omega_1^2; \quad \frac{1}{L_2 C_2} = \omega_2^2; \quad \frac{M}{\sqrt{L_1 L_2}} = g;$$

$$\rho_1 = (R_1 + R_e)C_1 \omega_1 = \frac{R_1 + R_e}{L_1 \omega_1}; \quad \rho_2 = R_2 C_2 \omega_2 = \frac{R_2}{L_2 \omega_2}$$

where ρ_1 and ρ_2 are small dimensionless factors of the first order. Equation [84.8] becomes

$$\left(\frac{p^2}{\omega_1^2} + \rho_1 \frac{p}{\omega_1} + 1\right)\left(\frac{p^2}{\omega_2^2} + \rho_2 \frac{p}{\omega_2} + 1\right) - g^2 \frac{p^4}{\omega_1^2 \omega_2^2} = 0 \qquad [84.9]$$

Since ρ_1 and ρ_2 are small, we can introduce a small parameter μ by setting $\rho_1 = \mu \xi_1$ and $\rho_2 = \mu \xi_2$. We thus obtain the following *characteristic equation* for the transient state:

$$\Delta(p,\mu) = \left(\frac{p^2}{\omega_1^2} + \mu \xi_1 \frac{p}{\omega_1} + 1\right)\left(\frac{p^2}{\omega_2^2} + \mu \xi_2 \frac{p}{\omega_2} + 1\right) - g^2 \frac{p^4}{\omega_1^2 \omega_2^2} = 0 \quad [84.10]$$

This equation can be solved by substituting for p a series expansion $p = p_0 + \mu p_1 + \mu^2 p_2 + \cdots$ and developing the function $\Delta(p,\mu)$ in a Taylor series around $(p_0, 0)$. By equating to zero the coefficients of like powers of μ, one obtains a system of equations from which the subsequent terms p_1, p_2, $\cdots$ can be calculated. These equations are

$$\Delta(p_0,0) = 0$$

$$\Delta_p(p_0,0)\,p_1 + \Delta_\mu(p_0,0) = 0 \qquad\qquad [84.11]$$

$$\Delta_p(p_0,0)\,p_2 + \Delta_{pp}(p_0,0)\,p_1^2 + 2\Delta_{p\mu}(p_0,0)\,p_1 + \Delta_{\mu\mu}(p_0,0) = 0$$

$$\cdots\cdots$$

From the first two equations one obtains p_0 and p_1, which give the first approximation

$$p = p_0 + \mu p_1 \qquad\qquad [84.12]$$

Introducing this value of p into Equation [84.10] and making use of Equations [81.12] and [81.13], one obtains the following equations

$$\frac{1}{1-g^2}\,\Delta(p,0) = \frac{(p^2 + \Omega_1^2)(p^2 + \Omega_2^2)}{\omega_1^2\,\omega_2^2}$$

$$\frac{1}{1-g^2}\,\Delta_p(p,0) = \frac{2p(2p^2 + \Omega_1^2 + \Omega_2^2)}{\omega_1^2\,\omega_2^2} \qquad\qquad [84.13]$$

$$\Delta_\mu(p,0) = \xi_1\,\frac{p}{\omega_1}\left(\frac{p^2}{\omega_2^2} + 1\right) + \xi_2\,\frac{p}{\omega_2}\left(\frac{p^2}{\omega_1^2} + 1\right)$$

It is apparent that, since we have here a coupled system possessing two distinct *coupled frequencies* Ω_1 and Ω_2, self-excitation may occur with either one of these frequencies. Thus one obtains two values for $p = p_0 + \mu p_1$, namely,

$$p = j\Omega_1 - \frac{1}{2}\rho_1\omega_1\frac{\Omega_1^2 - \omega_2^2}{\Omega_1^2 - \Omega_2^2}\frac{1}{1-g^2} - \frac{1}{2}\rho_2\omega_2\frac{\Omega_1^2 - \omega_1^2}{\Omega_1^2 - \Omega_2^2}\frac{1}{1-g^2}$$

$$[84.14]$$

$$p = j\Omega_2 - \frac{1}{2}\rho_1\omega_1\frac{\omega_2^2 - \Omega_2^2}{\Omega_1^2 - \Omega_2^2}\frac{1}{1-g^2} - \frac{1}{2}\rho_2\omega_2\frac{\omega_1^2 - \Omega_2^2}{\Omega_1^2 - \Omega_2^2}\frac{1}{1-g^2}$$

From these expressions it follows that the frequency and the decrement during the transient state are given by either pair of the following expressions:

$$\Omega = \Omega_1; \quad \delta_1 = \frac{1}{2(1-g^2)}\left(\rho_1\omega_1\frac{\Omega_1^2 - \omega_2^2}{\Omega_1^2 - \Omega_2^2} + \rho_2\omega_2\frac{\Omega_1^2 - \omega_1^2}{\Omega_1^2 - \Omega_2^2}\right) \quad [84.15]$$

$$\Omega = \Omega_2; \quad \delta_2 = \frac{1}{2(1-g^2)}\left(\rho_1\omega_1\frac{\omega_2^2 - \Omega_2^2}{\Omega_1^2 - \Omega_2^2} + \rho_2\omega_2\frac{\omega_1^2 - \Omega_2^2}{\Omega_1^2 - \Omega_2^2}\right) \quad [84.16]$$

It is seen that the frequencies of a non-linear system subject to a self-excitation to the order of approximation considered here are the same as those of the corresponding linear system, Equations [81.12] and [81.13], in which the dissipative parameters, both linear and non-linear, are neglected. Moreover, since neither Ω_1 nor Ω_2 depends on the amplitude, the system is isochronous.

The expression [84.15] for the decrement becomes

$$(1 - g^2)\delta_1(a) = \left(\frac{\Omega_1^2 - \omega_2^2}{\Omega_1^2 - \Omega_2^2}\right)\frac{R_1 + R_e(a)}{2L_1} + \left(\frac{\Omega_1^2 - \omega_1^2}{\Omega_1^2 - \Omega_2^2}\right)\frac{R_2}{2L_2} \qquad [84.17]$$

when ρ_1 and ρ_2 are replaced by their values. If $\delta_1(0) < 0$, self-excitation with frequency Ω_1 occurs. With the use of Equation [84.17] this condition of self-excitation with frequency Ω_1 can be written as

$$\left|R_e(0)\right| > \left|R_{01}\right| \qquad [84.18]$$

where R_{01} is the critical value of the equivalent resistance R_e. This critical value is

$$R_{01} = -\left(R_1 + R_2\frac{L_1}{L_2}\frac{\Omega_1^2 - \omega_1^2}{\Omega_1^2 - \omega_2^2}\right) \qquad [84.19]$$

With the use of [84.19], Equation [84.17] can be written

$$(1 - g^2)\delta_1(a) = \left(\frac{\Omega_1^2 - \omega_2^2}{\Omega_1^2 - \Omega_2^2}\frac{R_1}{2L_1} + \frac{\Omega_1^2 - \omega_1^2}{\Omega_1^2 - \Omega_2^2}\frac{R_2}{2L_2}\right)\left(1 - \frac{R_e(a)}{R_{01}}\right) \qquad [84.20]$$

The decrement $\delta_1(a_1) = 0$ when

$$R_e(a_1) = -\left(R_1 + R_2\frac{L_1}{L_2}\frac{\Omega_1^2 - \omega_1^2}{\Omega_1^2 - \omega_2^2}\right)$$

The stationary amplitude a_1 of the self-excited oscillation is then obtained from the explicit form of $R_e(a_1)$, as previously shown. Introducing the notation

$$(1 - g^2)\delta_{01}(a) = \frac{\Omega_1^2 - \omega_2^2}{\Omega_1^2 - \Omega_2^2}\frac{R_1}{2L_1} + \frac{\Omega_1^2 - \omega_1^2}{\Omega_1^2 - \Omega_2^2}\frac{R_2}{2L_2} \qquad [84.21]$$

we can write Equation [84.20] as

$$\delta_1(a) = \delta_{01}\left[1 - \frac{R_e(a)}{R_{01}}\right] \qquad [84.22]$$

and similarly

$$\delta_2(a) = \delta_{02}\left[1 - \frac{R_e(a)}{R_{02}}\right] \qquad [84.23]$$

where δ_{01} and δ_{02} are the decrements of the linear circuits with frequencies Ω_1 and Ω_2 and R_{01} and R_{02} are the corresponding critical values of the equivalent non-linear resistance $R_e(a)$. It is to be noted that the possibility of determining p_1 from the second equation [84.11] depends on the condition $\Delta_p(p_0, 0) \neq 0$, as follows from the theorem on implicit functions. On the other hand, the expression

$$\frac{1}{1 - g^2}\,\Delta_p(p_0,0) = \frac{2p_0(2p_0^2 + \Omega_1^2 + \Omega_2^2)}{\omega_1^2\omega_2^2}$$

becomes

$$-\frac{2j\Omega_1(\Omega_1^2 - \Omega_2^2)}{\omega_1^2\omega_2^2} \quad \text{or} \quad \frac{2j\Omega_2(\Omega_1^2 - \Omega_2^2)}{\omega_1^2\omega_2^2}$$

for $p_0 = j\Omega_1$ or $p_0 = j\Omega_2$ respectively. Hence, the condition $\Delta_p(p_0,0) \neq 0$ is fulfilled only when $\Omega_1 \neq \Omega_2$, that is, when both circuits *are not* tuned in resonance to the same frequency.

Whenever the circuits are tuned in resonance to the same frequency, the preceding method ceases to be applicable and a special procedure indicated in Section 86 will be necessary.

85. NON-RESONANT SELF-EXCITATION OF A QUASI-LINEAR SYSTEM

We shall now generalize the conclusions of the preceding section which were obtained for a particular non-linear system with two degrees of freedom.

The general condition of self-excitation of a quasi-linear system is, as previously,

$$Z(p,\mu) + \mu r_e(a) = 0 \qquad [85.1]$$

where $Z(p)$ is the transient impedance of the linear system and $\mu r_e(a) = R_e(a)$.

In general, the impedance can be represented by a rational function, namely,

$$Z(p,\mu) = \frac{A(p,\mu)}{B(p,\mu)} \qquad [85.2]$$

where $A(p,\mu)$ and $B(p,\mu)$ are certain polynomials prime to each other; see Equation [84.7]. For the system shown in Figure 84.2, the quantity $A(p,\mu)$ is given by Equation [84.10], and one finds

$$B(p,\mu) = Cp\left(\frac{p^2}{\omega_2^2} + \mu\xi_2\frac{p}{\omega_2} + 1\right) \qquad [85.3]$$

In the relation [85.2], the system is conservative if $\mu = 0$, and the impedance consists only of inductive and capacitive reactances. Moreover, the oscillations are undamped so that $p = j\Omega$ and Equation [85.2] becomes

$$Z(j\Omega) = \frac{A(j\Omega,0)}{B(j\Omega,0)} \qquad [85.4]$$

This expression is, therefore, purely imaginary, that is, it is an odd function of $j\Omega$. Hence, if $A(p,0)$ is even, $B(p,0)$ must be odd and vice versa. Since $B(p,0) \neq 0$, the condition for self-excitation is obviously

$$A(p,\mu) = 0 \qquad\qquad [85.5]$$

If the system is non-dissipative, $\mu = 0$, and we know that the decrement is then zero. We conclude therefore that the equation

$$A(p,0) = 0 \qquad\qquad [85.6]$$

has purely imaginary roots $p = j\Omega$. Let $p = j\Omega_0$ be one such root; then

$$A(p,0) = (p^2 + \Omega_0^2)\phi(p) \qquad\qquad [85.7]$$

where $\phi(j\Omega_0) \neq 0$. The quantity $A(p,\mu)$ can be expanded in a Taylor series around $\mu = 0$; when μ is very small we can write

$$A(p,\mu) = A(p,0) + \mu A_\mu(p,0) \qquad\qquad [85.8]$$

The first term, $A(p,0)$, contains the capacity and inductance terms; the second, $\mu A_\mu(p,0)$, the dissipative components. Since this term is proportional to μ, ohmic resistances for a series connection, or ohmic conductances for a parallel connection, appear in it linearly and homogeneously. It follows, therefore, that $A(p,0)$ is odd and $A_\mu(p,0)$ is even and vice versa. In view of this and of Equation [85.7], it is clear that $\dfrac{A_\mu(p,0)}{\phi(p,0)}$ and $\dfrac{B(p,0)}{\phi(p,0)}$ are odd, since, if $A(p,0)$ is even, $B(p,0)$ is odd and $\phi(p)$ is even.

The characteristic equation of a non-linear system is

$$\Delta(p,\mu) = A(p,\mu) + \mu B(p,\mu) r_e = 0 \qquad\qquad [85.9]$$

In order to solve this equation we assume a solution of the form

$$p = j\Omega_0 + \mu p_1 + \cdots \qquad\qquad [85.10]$$

By the theorem of implicit functions, this is possible since from Equation [85.7] we find

$$\left[A_p(p,0)\right]_{p = j\Omega_0} = 2j\Omega_0\phi(j\Omega_0) \neq 0$$

Using the second equation [84.11], we find

$$p = j\Omega_0 - \mu\,\frac{A_\mu(j\Omega_0,0) + B(j\Omega_0,0)\,r_e}{A_p(j\Omega_0,0)}$$

$$= j\Omega_0 - \mu\,\frac{A_\mu(j\Omega_0,0)}{2j\Omega_0\phi(j\Omega_0)} - \frac{B(j\Omega_0,0)R_e}{2j\Omega_0\phi(j\Omega_0)} \qquad\qquad [85.11]$$

In view of the fact that both A_μ/ϕ and B/ϕ are odd, we conclude that the quantities

$$\delta_0 = \mu\,\frac{A_\mu(j\Omega_0,0)}{2j\Omega_0\phi(j\Omega_0)} \qquad\text{and}\qquad k = \frac{B(j\Omega_0,0)}{2j\Omega_0\phi(j\Omega_0)} \qquad\qquad [85.12]$$

are real. From Equation [85.11] we obtain the frequency and the decrement, namely,

$$\Omega = \Omega_0 \quad \text{and} \quad \delta = \delta_0 + kR_e \qquad [85.13]$$

If this procedure is applied to the solution of the characteristic equation of the linear circuit

$$A(p,\mu) = 0 \qquad [85.14]$$

one obtains to the first order the expression

$$p = j\Omega_0 - \delta_0 \qquad [85.15]$$

From the second expression [85.13] it follows that the condition of self-excitation with frequency $\Omega = \Omega_0$ and $\delta(0) < 0$ reduces to the condition

$$R_e(0) < R_0 \qquad [85.16]$$

where $R_0 = -\frac{1}{k}\delta_0$ is the critical value of the equivalent resistance $R_e(a)$ at which the decrement δ vanishes and the oscillation becomes stationary.

In conclusion, one can state that, if Ω_0 and δ_0 are the frequency and decrement of a linear system and *if Ω_0 is not tuned in resonance* with other frequencies of the system, the frequency and the decrement of a quasi-linear system, linearized by the method of equivalent linearization, are

$$\Omega = \Omega_0$$

$$\delta = \delta_0\left[1 - \frac{R_e(a)}{R_0}\right] \qquad [85.17]$$

As was previously mentioned, the condition of quasi-linearity permits neglecting the dissipative parameters, which are assumed to be small quantities of the first order, as far as the frequency determination is concerned, since the error is of the second order, that is, of the order of μ^2. In other words, the quasi-linear systems in a non-resonant state are also quasi-isochronous.

86. RESONANT SELF-EXCITATION OF A QUASI-LINEAR SYSTEM

We shall now investigate a quasi-linear system in which the two frequencies Ω_1 and Ω_2 are adjusted so that they are the same. This condition shall be called the resonant self-excitation of a system with several degrees of freedom. For simplicity, we shall consider a system with two degrees of freedom of the kind previously investigated in connection with Figure 84.2. It is to be noted that in order to have the difference $\Omega_1 - \Omega_2$ of the two frequencies very small, say of the first order of smallness, it is necessary that the difference of the component, non-coupled frequencies ω_1 and ω_2 of each degree of freedom also be small and of the same order. This follows from Equations [81.12] and [81.13]. Moreover, the coefficient M of mutual inductance must also be small, that is, the coupling between the two degrees of freedom must be rather "loose." These conditions imply that

$$\frac{\omega_2}{\omega_1} = 1 + \mu P; \quad g = \mu Q \qquad [86.1]$$

Equation [84.9] can now be written

$$(x^2 + \mu \xi_1 x + 1)\left[x^2 + \mu(1 + \mu P)\xi_2 x + (1 + \mu P)^2\right] - \mu^2 Q^2 x^4 = 0 \quad [86.2]$$

where $x = p/\omega_1$. Substituting in this equation the power series solution $x = j + \mu x_1 + \cdots$ and equating the coefficients of equal powers of μ, one obtains the following equation for x_1:

$$(2jx_1 + j\xi_1)(2jx_1 + j\xi_2 + 2P) - Q^2 = 0$$

When rearranged, it becomes

$$4x_1^2 + 2x_1(\xi_1 + \xi_2 - 2jP) + Q^2 + \xi_1\xi_2 - 2jP\xi_1 = 0 \qquad [86.3]$$

Determining its roots, and using the notations $\xi_1 - \xi_2 = M$ and $Q^2 + P^2 = N$, one obtains to the second order the following expression for $x = j + \mu x_1$:

$$x = -\mu\left(\frac{\xi_1 + \xi_2}{4}\right) \pm \frac{\mu}{4\sqrt{2}} \sqrt{M^2 - 4N + \sqrt{16P^2M^2 + (M^2 - 4N)^2}} \; +$$

$$+ j\left[1 + \frac{P}{2} \pm \frac{\mu}{4\sqrt{2}} \sqrt{4N - M^2 + \sqrt{16P^2M^2 + (M^2 - 4N)^2}}\right] \qquad [86.4]$$

Putting

$$(R_e + R_1 - R_2)^2 C_1^2 \omega_1^2 - 4\left[g^2 - \left(1 - \frac{\omega_2}{\omega_1}\right)^2\right] = 2\eta$$

and

$$[86.5]$$

$$4(R_e + R_1 - R_2)^2 C_1^2 \omega_2^2 \left(1 - \frac{\omega_2}{\omega_1}\right)^2 = d^2$$

one obtains to the first order the following expression

$$p = \frac{R_1 + R_2 + R_e \mp L_1\omega_1\sqrt{\eta + \sqrt{d^2 + \eta^2}}}{4L_1} \; +$$

$$+ j\left[\omega_1 + \frac{2(\omega_2 - \omega_1) \pm \omega_1\sqrt{-\eta + \sqrt{d^2 + \eta^2}}}{4}\right] \qquad [86.6]$$

which gives the frequency Ω and the decrement δ as

$$\Omega = \Omega_1(a) = \frac{\omega_1 + \omega_2}{2} + \frac{\omega_1}{4}\sqrt{-\eta + \sqrt{d^2 + \eta^2}}$$

$$[86.7]$$

$$\delta = \delta_1(a) = \frac{R_1 + R_2 + R_e - L_1\omega_1\sqrt{\eta + \sqrt{d^2 + \eta^2}}}{4L_1}$$

or

$$\Omega = \Omega_2(a) = \frac{\omega_1 + \omega_2}{2} - \frac{\omega_1}{4}\sqrt{-\eta + \sqrt{d^2 + \eta^2}}$$

$$\delta = \delta_2(a) = \frac{R_1 + R_2 + R_e + L_1\omega_1\sqrt{\eta + \sqrt{d^2 + \eta^2}}}{4L_1}$$

[86.8]

The essential feature of these expressions is that both the frequency $\Omega(a)$ and the decrement $\delta(a)$ are *non-linear functions* of $R_e(a)$. This leads to the following important conclusion:

When the oscillatory system is tuned in resonance so that $\omega_1 \approx \omega_2 \approx \omega$, the system ceases to be isochronous.

Developing the expressions [86.7] and [86.8] in terms of the parameters of the system, we obtain the following two sets of expressions for $\Omega(a)$ and $\delta(a)$:

1. If $(R_e + R_1 - R_2)C_1\omega > 2g$, then

$$\Omega_1(a) = \omega; \quad \delta_1(a) = \frac{R_e + R_1 + R_2 - L_1\omega\sqrt{(R_e + R_1 - R_2)^2 C_1^2\omega^2 - 4g^2}}{4L_1}$$

and

[86.9]

$$\Omega_2(a) = \omega; \quad \delta_2(a) = \frac{R_e + R_1 + R_2 + L_1\omega\sqrt{(R_e + R_1 - R_2)^2 C_1^2\omega^2 - 4g^2}}{4L_1}$$

2. If $(R_e + R_1 - R_2)C_1\omega < 2g$, then

$$\Omega_1(a) = \omega\left[1 + \frac{1}{4}\sqrt{4g^2 - (R_e + R_1 - R_2)^2 C_1^2\omega^2}\right]; \quad \delta_1(a) = \frac{R_e + R_1 + R_2}{4L_1}$$

and

[86.10]

$$\Omega_2(a) = \omega\left[1 - \frac{1}{4}\sqrt{4g^2 - (R_e + R_1 - R_2)^2 C_1^2\omega^2}\right]; \quad \delta_2(a) = \frac{R_e + R_1 + R_2}{4L_1}$$

It is thus seen that the condition of resonance of a quasi-linear system with two degrees of freedom introduces a radical change in the behavior of the system. In a later chapter it will be shown that resonance in a multi-periodic system is characterized by another feature, namely, the differential equations of the first approximation do not permit a separation of variables although in a non-resonant condition such a separation is always possible and simplifies the problem appreciably.

CHAPTER XIV

SUBHARMONICS AND FREQUENCY DEMULTIPLICATION

87. COMBINATION TONES; SUBHARMONICS

The non-linearity of an oscillatory system accounts for the appearance of additional frequencies which we shall now investigate.

This phenomenon was first studied by Helmholtz (3) in connection with the theory of physiological acoustics. He discovered that the ear receives sounds which are not contained in the emitted acoustic radiation, and he has shown how the slightly funnel-shaped form of the tympanic membrane of the ear may account for unsymmetrical oscillations represented by a non-linear differential equation of the form

$$\ddot{x} + \omega_0^2 x = -\beta x^2 + X(t) \qquad [87.1]$$

where x is the displacement of the membrane and X is the exciting force produced by the periodically varying pressure of a sound wave. If the sound wave contains two frequencies, say ω_1 and ω_2, the function X is of the form $X = a_1 \cos \omega_1 t + a_2 \cos \omega_2 t$. It can be shown that the oscillation expressed by Equation [87.1] contains, in addition to the frequencies ω_1 and ω_2, the frequencies $\omega_1 - \omega_2$ and $\omega_1 + \omega_2$ which Helmholtz calls *combination tones*.

It is simpler to reach these conclusions from the well-known principles of modern radio technique. Consider a non-linear conductor of electricity, an electron tube, whose characteristic is

$$i_a = f(v) \qquad [87.2]$$

where i_a is the anode current and v is the grid potential. We shall be interested only in the alternating components of these quantities. It has been shown in preceding chapters that this experimental relation can always be expressed in the form

$$i_a = a_1 v + a_2 v^2 + a_3 v^3 + \cdots \qquad [87.3]$$

The number of terms in this series depends on the degree of the approximation desired, and it is shown (4) that in practice the coefficients decrease with sufficient rapidity to justify the retention of only a few terms. In order to simplify the argument, let us assume that the impressed grid voltage is of the form

$$v = k(\cos \omega_1 t + \cos \omega_2 t) \qquad [87.4]$$

that is, it is composed of two alternating voltages in series having the same amplitude k but two different frequencies ω_1 and ω_2. Substituting [87.4] into Equation [87.3], one obtains

$$i_a = a_1 k(\cos \omega_1 t + \cos \omega_2 t) + a_2 k^2 (\cos \omega_1 t + \cos \omega_2 t)^2 + a_3 k^3 (\cos \omega_1 t + \cos \omega_2 t)^3 \quad [87.5]$$

when the expansion is limited to the first three terms. The first term contains the original frequencies ω_1 and ω_2; the second gives the frequencies $2\omega_1$, $2\omega_2$, $\omega_1 + \omega_2$, and $\omega_1 - \omega_2$; the third term yields the frequencies ω_1, $3\omega_1$, ω_2, $3\omega_2$, $2\omega_1 + \omega_2$, $2\omega_1 - \omega_2$, $2\omega_2 + \omega_1$, and $2\omega_2 - \omega_1$. The current i_a will contain, therefore, the harmonics of the following frequencies:

$$\omega_1, \ \omega_2, \ 2\omega_1, \ 2\omega_2, \ 3\omega_1, \ 3\omega_2, \ \omega_1 + \omega_2, \ \omega_1 - \omega_2, \ 2\omega_1 + \omega_2, \ 2\omega_1 - \omega_2, \ 2\omega_2 + \omega_1, \ 2\omega_2 - \omega_1$$

Thus, for example, if $\omega_1 = 2\pi \times 100$ and $\omega_2 = 2\pi \times 120$, where $f_1 = 100$ cycles per second and $f_2 = 120$ cycles per second, the frequency spectrum of i_a will be composed of the following frequencies:

$$20, \ 80, \ |100, \ 120,| \ 140, \ 200, \ 220, \ 240, \ 300, \ 320, \ 360$$

It is seen that the combination frequencies spread out on both sides of the impressed frequencies, $f_1 = 100$ and $f_2 = 120$. In the study of this phenomenon, attention is usually centered on the frequencies lower than the impressed ones (in this case, $f = 20$ and $f = 80$); these lower frequencies are called *subharmonics*. The term "subharmonics," instead of the expression "combination harmonics," is sometimes applied, although perhaps improperly, to terms of the form

$$\omega_i = m\omega_1 + n\omega_2 \quad\quad\quad [87.6]$$

The problem of producing subharmonics in electric circuits is sometimes called the problem of *frequency demultiplication*.

In Equation [87.6], m and n are integers which depend upon the nature of the polynomial. Thus, for instance, in the previous example these combinations are (0,0); (1,0); (2,0); (3,0); (0,1); (0,2); (0,3); (1,1); (1,-1); (1,2); (1,-2); (2,1); (2,-1).

The terms (0,0) are constants arising from the trigonometric transformations.

As follows from the foregoing analysis, the combination frequencies are due exclusively to the non-linearity of the circuit. This can be demonstrated by the following experiment mentioned by H.J. Reich (4). The voltages from two audio-frequency oscillators are filtered so as to obtain two pure sinusoidal oscillations of angular frequencies ω_1 and ω_2, which are applied to the grid of an electron tube. The voltage across the anode resistance is applied to the input of a low-pass filter. The various combination frequencies can thus be heard in a telephone connected to the output of the filter. If the oscillators' frequencies are changed, the whole spectrum of the combination frequencies changes, but the relation [87.6] holds for any value of ω_1 or ω_2. If, instead of a low-pass filter, a high-pass filter is provided, the high-frequency part of the spectrum of the combination frequencies can also be recorded. The relation [87.6] is applicable throughout the whole spectrum. If an oscillating grid potential of the form $v = a_1 \cos \omega_1 t + a_2 \cos \omega_2 t$ is applied in the region where the electron-tube characteristic is fairly rectilinear, the spectrum of the combination frequencies fades away. This shows that the combination frequencies are due to the non-linearity of the circuit.

If a combination harmonic of amplitude $e_{n,m}$ is applied to a linear network of impedance $Z(j\Omega)$, the current $i_{n,m}$ due to this harmonic will be

$$i_{n,m} = \frac{e_{n,m}}{Z\left[j(n\Omega_1 + m\Omega_2)\right]} \cos\left[(n\Omega_1 + m\Omega_2)t + n\phi_1 + m\phi_2\right]^* \qquad [87.7]$$

88. EQUIVALENT LINEARIZATION FOR MULTIPERIODIC SYSTEMS

In the preceding chapter a quasi-linear system with two degrees of freedom was discussed. It was found that solutions in terms of frequency and decrement were given, not by one set of relations, but by two such sets. Thus, for example, we always have two pairs of relations

$$\Omega = \Omega_1(a); \quad \delta = \delta_1(a)$$

and

$$\Omega = \Omega_2(a); \quad \delta = \delta_2(a)$$

In still more complicated systems there may be a still greater number of pairs of solutions:

$$\Omega = \Omega_1(a); \quad \delta = \delta_1(a)$$
$$\cdots\cdots\cdots$$
$$\Omega = \Omega_n(a); \quad \delta = \delta_n(a)$$

On the basis of the method of the first approximation, Chapter X, this means that the most general oscillatory system is characterized by oscillations of the form

$$i = i_1 = a_1 \cos \psi_1$$
$$i = i_2 = a_2 \cos \psi_2$$
$$\cdots\cdots\cdots$$
$$i = i_n = a_n \cos \psi_n$$

* From now on we shall designate the component frequencies by capital letters Ω_1 and Ω_2, reserving the small letters ω_1 and ω_2 for the frequencies of uncoupled linear systems, as was done in the preceding chapter.

It is recalled that ψ, the *total phase*, in these expressions contains both the frequency Ω_k and the ordinary phase ϕ_k, as follows from the relation $\psi_k = \Omega_k t + \phi_k$.

The most general forms of the equations of the first approximation for both a_k and ψ_k are

$$\frac{da_k}{dt} = -\,\delta_k(a_k)\,a_k; \quad \frac{d\psi_k}{dt} = \Omega_k(a_k); \quad k = 1, 2, \cdots, n \qquad [88.1]$$

If the system is linear, the principle of superposition is applicable, that is,

$$i = i_1 + i_2 + \cdots + i_n = a_1 \cos\psi_1 + a_2 \cos\psi_2 + \cdots + a_n \cos\psi_n \qquad [88.2]$$

For non-linear systems this ceases to be applicable, and, if we wish to make use of the principle of superposition, we must introduce further definitions of the equivalent parameters of multiperiodic systems. In order to do this, it is sufficient to extend the Principle of Equivalent Linearization to systems where two distinct oscillations exist. This presupposes that the oscillations *are not* tuned in resonance with each other. We shall consider again the system shown in Figure 84.2 and note that its impedance across the terminals of the non-linear conductor N is

$$Z(j\Omega) = \frac{(\Omega_1^2 - \Omega^2 + 2j\delta_{01}\Omega)(\Omega_2^2 - \Omega^2 + 2j\delta_{02}\Omega)}{C j\Omega\omega_1^2(\omega_2^2 - \Omega^2 + 2j\rho_2\omega_2\Omega)} \qquad [88.3]$$

where Ω_1 and Ω_2 are the angular frequencies, and δ_{01} and δ_{02} are the decrements of the linear system given by Equations [81.12], [81.13], and [84.21], respectively, to the first order of small quantities. Equation [88.3] is obtained from Equation [84.6] by making use of Equations [84.10] and [84.14]. Since for quasi-linear systems the decrements δ_{01} and δ_{02} are small, one can put $\delta_{01} = \mu\zeta_1$; $\delta_{02} = \mu\zeta_2$, and we obtain

$$Z(j\Omega) = \frac{(\Omega_1^2 - \Omega^2 + 2j\zeta_1\mu\Omega)(\Omega_2^2 - \Omega^2 + 2j\zeta_2\mu\Omega)}{C j\Omega\omega_1^2(\omega_2^2 - \Omega^2 + 2j\mu\xi_2\omega_2\Omega)} \qquad [88.4]$$

where ζ_1, ζ_2, and ξ_2 are small. This impedance is impressed on a non-linear conductor having the characteristic

$$e = -F(i) = -\mu f(i) \qquad [88.5]$$

where μ emphasizes again the quasi-linearity of the example considered here. The function $f(i)$ can be approximated in practice by a polynomial. If $\mu = 0$, the system is linear and the principle of superposition holds, so that

$$i = i_1 + i_2 = a_1 \cos(\Omega_1 t + \phi_1) + a_2 \cos(\Omega_2 t + \phi_2) \qquad [88.6]$$

where a_1, a_2, ϕ_1, and ϕ_2 are constants.

If $\mu \neq 0$ but very small, one can still consider Equation [88.6] as approximately correct and substitute it in Equation [88.5]. Thus,

$$e = - \mu f(i) = - \mu f(i_1 + i_2) = - \mu f\left[a_1 \cos(\Omega_1 t + \phi_1) + a_2 \cos(\Omega_2 t + \phi_2)\right] \quad [88.7]$$

Consider now the function of the two variables ψ_1 and ψ_2, namely,

$$f(a_1 \cos \psi_1 + a_2 \cos \psi_2) = f(z)$$

Since $f(z)$ is a polynomial, it can be represented as a finite sum of harmonics of the type

$$A_{n,m} \cos(n\psi_1 + m\psi_2)$$

so that

$$f(a_1 \cos \psi_1 + a_2 \cos \psi_2) = \sum_n \sum_m A_{n,m} \cos(n\psi_1 + m\psi_2) \quad [88.8]$$

where the index n runs from zero through the positive integers and where m has positive integral values for $n = 0$ and runs through the negative integers for $n \neq 0$. For a polynomial of the third degree these values for m and n were given in the preceding section. From [88.7] and [88.8] it follows that

$$e = - \mu \sum_n \sum_m A_{n,m} \cos\left[(n\Omega_1 + m\Omega_2)t + n\phi_1 + m\phi_2\right] \quad [88.9]$$

Hence the corresponding combination harmonic $i_{n,m}$ of the current will be

$$i_{n,m} = - \frac{\mu A_{n,m}}{Z\left[j(n\Omega_1 + m\Omega_2)\right]} \cos\left[(n\Omega_1 + m\Omega_2)t + n\phi_1 + m\phi_2\right] \quad [88.10]$$

and the total current will be the sum of all these harmonics.

It is apparent that the amplitude of each combination harmonic will be

$$|i_{n,m}| = \frac{|\mu A_{n,m}|}{\left|Z\left[j(n\Omega_1 + m\Omega_2)\right]\right|}$$

Written explicitly, in view of [88.4], this expression becomes

$$[88.11]$$

$$|i_{n,m}| = \frac{\mu A_{n,m} C \omega_1^2 (n\Omega_1 + m\Omega_2)}{\sqrt{\left[\Omega_1^2 - (n\Omega_1 + m\Omega_2)^2\right]^2 + 4\mu^2 \xi_1^2 (n\Omega_1 + m\Omega_2)^2}} \sqrt{\frac{\left[\omega_2^2 - (n\Omega_1 + m\Omega_2)^2\right]^2 + 4\mu^2 \xi_1^2 (n\Omega_1 + m\Omega_2)^2}{\left[\Omega_2^2 - (n\Omega_1 + m\Omega_2)^2\right]^2 + 4\mu^2 \xi_2^2 (n\Omega_1 + m\Omega_2)^2}}$$

From this expression it is observed that, if for some values of n and m neither of the expressions $(n\Omega_1 + m\Omega_2)^2 - \Omega_1^2$ or $(n\Omega_1 + m\Omega_2)^2 - \Omega_2^2$ becomes small, the amplitudes $|i_{n,m}|$ will be small because of the small factor μ.

If, however, for a given pair of numbers (n and m), one of these expressions, or, which is the same, $n\Omega_1 + (m \pm 1)\Omega_2$ or $(n \pm 1)\Omega_1 + m\Omega_2$, becomes small and of the first order, or zero, both the numerator and the denominator in [88.11] become small and of the same order so that $|i_{n,m}|$ may be finite. This happens either for $n = 1$, $m = 0$ or for $n = 0$, $m = 1$.

It is seen from [88.9] that all harmonics of e are small except the two principal harmonics

$$- \mu A_{1,0} \cos(\Omega_1 t + \phi_1); \quad - \mu A_{0,1} \cos(\Omega_2 t + \phi_2) \qquad [88.12]$$

Hence, aside from the two corresponding harmonics of current, all others are very small and can be neglected. Thus we have

$$e = - \mu A_{1,0} \cos(\Omega_1 t + \phi_1) - \mu A_{0,1} \cos(\Omega_2 t + \phi_2) \qquad [88.13]$$

From Equations [88.5], [88.7], and [88.13], by the Principle of Equivalent Linearization, we obtain

$$\mu A_{1,0} = \frac{1}{2\pi^2} \int_0^{2\pi}\int_0^{2\pi} F(a_1 \cos\psi_1 + a_2 \cos\psi_2)\cos\psi_1 d\psi_1 d\psi_2$$

$$\mu A_{0,1} = \frac{1}{2\pi^2} \int_0^{2\pi}\int_0^{2\pi} F(a_1 \cos\psi_1 + a_2 \cos\psi_2)\cos\psi_2 d\psi_1 d\psi_2 \qquad [88.14]$$

Defining the equivalent non-linear parameters by the expressions

$$R_e' = \frac{1}{2\pi^2 a_1} \int_0^{2\pi}\int_0^{2\pi} F(a_1 \cos\psi_1 + a_2 \cos\psi_2)\cos\psi_1 d\psi_1 d\psi_2$$

and

$$R_e'' = \frac{1}{2\pi^2 a_2} \int_0^{2\pi}\int_0^{2\pi} F(a_1 \cos\psi_1 + a_2 \cos\psi_2)\cos\psi_2 d\psi_1 d\psi_2 \qquad [88.15]$$

one has

$$\mu A_{1,0} = R_e' a_1 \quad \text{and} \quad \mu A_{0,1} = R_e'' a_2$$

and, by [88.13],

$$e = - (R_e' i_1 + R_e'' i_2) \qquad [88.16]$$

This equation shows that in the example of non-resonance considered here the non-linear characteristic can be replaced by the corresponding linear one in which the variables i_1 and i_2 can be separated in the first approximation. This generalization of the Principle of Equivalent Linearization for a non-resonant system simplifies the problem because the variables can be separated.

We obtain the following systems of equations of the first approximation for the equivalent system:

$$\frac{da_1}{dt} = - \delta' a_1; \quad \frac{da_2}{dt} = - \delta'' a_2$$

$$\frac{d\psi_1}{dt} = \Omega'; \quad \frac{d\psi_2}{dt} = \Omega'' \qquad [88.17]$$

Since the total phases are $\psi_1 = \Omega_1 t + \phi_1$ and $\psi_2 = \Omega_2 t + \phi_2$, one can write the preceding equations in the form

$$\frac{da_1}{dt} = -\delta'a_1; \quad \frac{da_2}{dt} = -\delta''a_2$$

$$\frac{d\phi_1}{dt} = \Omega' - \Omega_1; \quad \frac{d\phi_2}{dt} = \Omega'' - \Omega_2 \qquad [88.18]$$

In view of [88.16], self-excitation of the equivalent linearized system can be represented by the equation

$$Z(j\Omega' - \delta')i_1 + Z(j\Omega'' - \delta'')i_2 + R_e'i_1 + R_e''i_2 = 0 \qquad [88.19]$$

whence

$$Z(j\Omega' - \delta') + R_e' = 0; \quad Z(j\Omega'' - \delta'') + R_e'' = 0 \qquad [88.20]$$

Because ϕ_1 and ϕ_2 are constants, one has from [84.23]

$$\Omega' = \Omega_1; \quad \Omega'' = \Omega_2; \quad \delta' = \delta_1\Big(1 - \frac{R_e'}{R_{01}}\Big); \quad \delta'' = \delta_2\Big(1 - \frac{R_e''}{R_{02}}\Big) \qquad [88.21]$$

where R_{01} and R_{02} are the critical values of the equivalent parameters R_e' and R_e'' corresponding to self-excitation with frequencies Ω_1 and Ω_2 respectively.

One concludes, therefore, that in the first approximation and in the absence of resonance,

$$i = a_1\cos(\Omega_1 t + \phi_1) + a_2\cos(\Omega_2 t + \phi_2) \qquad [88.22]$$

the principle of superposition still holds, and the stationary amplitudes a_1 and a_2 of the quasi-linear system are given by the system of differential equations in which the variables can be separated, namely,

$$\frac{da_1}{dt} = -\delta_1\Big(1 - \frac{R_e'}{R_{01}}\Big)a_1; \quad \frac{da_2}{dt} = -\delta_2\Big(1 - \frac{R_e''}{R_{02}}\Big)a_2 \qquad [88.23]$$

This result can be generalized for systems with n frequencies; however, this generalization will not be presented here.

89. INTERNAL SUBHARMONIC RESONANCE

In the theory of linear oscillations, an oscillating system is said to be in "resonance" when the frequency of the *external* exciting force coincides with the frequency of the system. In non-linear systems the situation, as was shown, is far more complicated.

We saw that a non-linear system with one degree of freedom acted upon by an exciting force with two or more component frequencies has a discrete spectrum of *combination frequencies* which are more numerous than the exciting frequencies.

On the other hand, a linear system with several degrees of freedom possesses the so-called *coupled frequencies*, the number of which is equal to that of the degrees of freedom. For non-linear systems with several degrees

of freedom, the situation becomes very complicated. In fact, if one considers
one particular circuit of the system that is coupled to other circuits, the
excitation of this circuit occurs through couplings and, by virtue of the non-
linearity, is resolved into combination frequencies which, in turn, react on
the other circuits and cause combination frequencies in these circuits if they
are non-linear. It must be noted, however, that not all frequencies may appear in the process of self-excitation but only those for which the initial
decrement $\delta_j(0) < 0$. Moreover, as long as the principal frequencies do not
coalesce, the method of equivalent linearization introduces a further simplification by providing a set of differential equations of the first approximation in which the variables can be separated.

A new complication arises, however, when two frequencies of the
spectrum are nearly the same and coalesce at the limit; we shall call this
internal resonance of the system. It occurs whenever two or more component
parts of the system are *tuned* to the same frequency. The word *internal* used
in this definition merely emphasizes the fact that the actuation is effected
through couplings without involving any externally impressed periodic force.

We shall consider again the system with two degrees of freedom shown
in Figure 84.2 which was the basis for our discussion of the non-resonant condition. The impedance of the system is

$$Z(j\Omega) = \frac{(\Omega_1^2 - \Omega^2 + 2j\zeta_1\mu\Omega)(\Omega_2^2 - \Omega^2 + 2j\zeta_2\mu\Omega)}{jC\omega_1^2\Omega(\omega_2^2 - \Omega^2 + 2j\mu\xi_2\omega_2\Omega)} \qquad [89.1]$$

This impedance is impressed on a non-linear element N with characteristic

$$e = -F(i) = -\mu f(i) \qquad [89.2]$$

We shall now assume that the ratio of the frequencies Ω_1 and Ω_2 of
the linear system is not far from being a rational number; this fact is expressed by the following relations:

$$\Omega_2 = \frac{r}{s}\Omega_1 + \mu\alpha \quad \text{with} \quad \frac{r}{s} \neq 0 \qquad [89.3]$$

where, without any loss of generality, r and s are relatively prime integers,
and α is a finite number so that $\mu\alpha$ is small and of the first order. It is
apparent that for $\mu = 0$ the system degenerates into a linear one with coupled
frequencies

$$\Omega_1 \quad \text{and} \quad \Omega_2 = \frac{r}{s}\Omega_1$$

In this case the principle of superposition holds; $i = i_1 + i_2$ where $i_1 = a_1 \cos \psi_1$ and $i_2 = a_2 \cos \psi_2$; ψ_1 and ψ_2, the *total phases*, are equal to
$\Omega_1 t + \phi_1$ and $\Omega_2 t + \phi_2$ respectively; and a_1, a_2, ϕ_1, and ϕ_2 are constants
determined by the initial conditions.

For $\mu \neq 0$ but very small we can still use the principle of superposition to the first order of approximation, as was just shown, and write

$$e = - \mu f\left[a_1 \cos(\Omega_1 t + \phi_1) + a_2 \cos\left(\frac{r}{s}\Omega_1 t + \phi_2\right)\right] \qquad [89.4]$$

The function f is periodic with period $\frac{2\pi s}{\Omega_1}$. Since we assume, on the other hand, that this function is approximated by a polynomial, it is possible to express the function by a limited number of terms of a Fourier series. Thus we obtain

$$f\left[a_1 \cos(\Omega_1 t + \phi_1) + a_2 \cos\left(\frac{r}{s}\Omega_1 t + \phi_2\right)\right] = \sum_{m>0}\left[A_m \cos \frac{m}{s}\Omega_1 t + B_m \sin \frac{m}{s}\Omega_1 t\right] \quad [89.5]$$

where A_m and B_m are certain functions of the variables a_1, a_2, ϕ_1, and ϕ_2. The harmonic I_m of the current will then be

$$I_m = \frac{- \mu\left[A_m \cos \frac{m}{s}\Omega_1 t + B_m \sin \frac{m}{s}\Omega_1 t\right]}{Z\left(j\frac{m}{s}\Omega_1\right)} \qquad [89.6]$$

Since the factor μ is small, all harmonics of the current are small except the two harmonics I_r and I_s, with frequencies $\frac{r}{s}\Omega_1$ and Ω_1, which remain finite in spite of the smallness of μ; see Equation [88.11]. If, therefore, one neglects in the first approximation all harmonics I_m for which $m \neq r$ and $m \neq s$, Expression [89.5] reduces to

$$e = - \mu\left(A_r \cos \frac{r}{s}\Omega_1 t + B_r \sin \frac{r}{s}\Omega_1 t\right) - \mu(A_s \cos \Omega_1 t + B_s \sin \Omega_1 t) \qquad [89.7]$$

The expressions in parentheses in this equation can be written

$$A_r \cos \frac{r}{s}\Omega_1 t + B_r \sin \frac{r}{s}\Omega_1 t = C_r \cos\left(\frac{r}{s}\Omega_1 t + \phi_2\right) + D_r \sin\left(\frac{r}{s}\Omega_1 t + \phi_2\right)$$

$$A_s \cos \Omega_1 t + B_s \sin \Omega_1 t = C_s \cos(\Omega_1 t + \phi_1) + D_s \sin(\Omega_1 t + \phi_1) \qquad [89.8]$$

where the constants C_r, D_r, C_s, and D_s are given by the Fourier procedure:

$$C_r = \frac{1}{\pi}\int_0^{2\pi} f\left(a_1 \cos\left[s\tau - \frac{1}{r}(s\phi_2 - r\phi_1)\right] + a_2 \cos r\tau\right)\cos r\tau \, d\tau$$

$$D_r = \frac{1}{\pi}\int_0^{2\pi} f\left(a_1 \cos\left[s\tau - \frac{1}{r}(s\phi_2 - r\phi_1)\right] + a_2 \cos r\tau\right)\sin r\tau \, d\tau$$

$$\qquad\qquad\qquad\qquad\qquad\qquad\qquad\qquad\qquad\qquad\qquad\qquad [89.9]$$

$$C_s = \frac{1}{\pi}\int_0^{2\pi} f\left(a_1 \cos s\tau + a_2 \cos\left[r\tau + \frac{1}{s}(s\phi_2 - r\phi_1)\right]\right)\cos s\tau \, d\tau$$

$$D_s = \frac{1}{\pi}\int_0^{2\pi} f\left(a_1 \cos s\tau + a_2 \cos\left[r\tau + \frac{1}{s}(s\phi_2 - r\phi_1)\right]\right)\sin s\tau \, d\tau$$

If we put $s\phi_2 - r\phi_1 = \theta$ and introduce the notations

$$R_e'' = \frac{1}{\pi a_2} \int_0^{2\pi} F\left[a_1 \cos\left(s\tau - \frac{\theta}{r}\right) + a_2 \cos r\tau\right] \cos r\tau\, d\tau$$

$$Y_e'' = -\frac{1}{\pi a_2} \int_0^{2\pi} F\left[a_1 \cos\left(s\tau - \frac{\theta}{r}\right) + a_2 \cos r\tau\right] \sin r\tau\, d\tau$$

[89.10]

$$R_e' = \frac{1}{\pi a_1} \int_0^{2\pi} F\left[a_1 \cos s\tau + a_2 \cos\left(r\tau + \frac{\theta}{s}\right)\right] \cos s\tau\, d\tau$$

$$Y_e' = -\frac{1}{\pi a_1} \int_0^{2\pi} F\left[a_1 \cos s\tau + a_2 \cos\left(r\tau + \frac{\theta}{s}\right)\right] \sin s\tau\, d\tau$$

the expressions in Equation [89.7] become

$$\mu\left(A_r \cos\frac{r}{s}\Omega_1 t + B_r \sin\frac{r}{s}\Omega_1 t\right) = R_e'' a_2 \cos\left(\frac{r}{s}\Omega_1 t + \phi_2\right) - Y_e'' a_2 \sin\left(\frac{r}{s}\Omega_1 t + \phi_2\right)$$

$$= (R_e'' + jY_e'')a_2 \cos\left(\frac{r}{s}\Omega_1 t + \phi_2\right) \qquad [89.11]$$

$$\mu(A_s \cos\Omega_1 t + B_s \sin\Omega_1 t) = R_e' a_1 \cos(\Omega_1 t + \phi_1) - Y_e' a_1 \sin(\Omega_1 t + \phi_1)$$

$$= (R_e' + jY_e')a_1 \cos(\Omega_1 t + \phi_1) \qquad [89.12]$$

When these values are substituted into Equation [89.7], it becomes

$$e = -\left[(R_e' + jY_e')i_1 + (R_e'' + jY_e'')i_2\right] \qquad [89.13]$$

It is seen that in systems having internal resonance the non-linear characteristic can be replaced by the equivalent linear one given by Equation [89.13]. The difference between resonant and non-resonant systems is that *in resonant systems the equivalent linear impedances are complex quantities, whereas in non-resonant systems they are real ones.*

This modification of the equivalent parameters for internal resonance introduces an essential difference in the form of the equations of the first approximation. For example, let Ω', Ω'', δ', and δ'' be the frequencies and decrements of the equivalent linear system. The equations of the first approximation are then

$$\frac{da_1}{dt} = -\delta' a_1; \quad \frac{da_2}{dt} = -\delta'' a_2$$

[89.14]

$$\frac{d\psi_1}{dt} = \Omega'; \quad \frac{d\psi_2}{dt} = \Omega''$$

where, by [88.6], $\psi_1 = \Omega_1 t + \phi_1$ and $\psi_2 = \Omega_2 t + \phi_2$ are the total phases. Equations [89.14] become

$$\frac{da_1}{dt} = -\,\delta'a_1; \quad \frac{da_2}{dt} = -\,\delta''a_2$$

$$\frac{d\phi_1}{dt} = \Omega' - \Omega_1; \quad \frac{d\phi_2}{dt} = \Omega'' - \Omega_2 \qquad [89.15]$$

For dynamical equilibrium the impedance drop and the impressed voltage must balance each other for both oscillations of the linearized systems; this gives

$$Z(j\Omega' - \delta')i_1 + Z(j\Omega'' - \delta'')i_2 + (R_e' + jY_e')i_1 + (R_e'' + jY_e'')i_2 = 0 \qquad [89.16]$$

Hence

$$Z(j\Omega' - \delta') + (R_e' + jY_e') = 0; \quad Z(j\Omega'' - \delta'') + (R_e'' + jY_e'') = 0 \qquad [89.17]$$

It is noted that these equations are the same as Equation [88.20] except that R_e is now replaced by $R_e + jY_e$. The algebraic work for Equations [89.16] and [89.17] is identical to that for Equation [88.20], provided one does not separate the real and the complex terms. Hence the solution of Equations [89.17] is the same as that of [85.17], which can be written as

$$p_i = \Omega_i + \delta_i\left[1 - \frac{R_e(a)}{R_{0i}}\right]$$

Without repeating the procedure, we can, therefore, write directly

$$\Omega' = \Omega_1 + \delta_1\frac{Y_e'}{R_{01}}; \quad \Omega'' = \Omega_2 + \delta_2\frac{Y_e''}{R_{02}} \qquad [89.18]$$

$$\delta' = \delta_1\left(1 - \frac{R_e'}{R_{01}}\right); \quad \delta'' = \delta_2\left(1 - \frac{R_e''}{R_{02}}\right) \qquad [89.19]$$

Hence, for the first approximation in a resonant system, one obtains

$$i = a_1\cos(\Omega_1 t + \phi_1) + a_2\cos\left(\frac{r}{s}\Omega_1 t + \phi_2\right) \qquad [89.20]$$

where a_1, a_2, ϕ_1, and ϕ_2 are given by the equations

$$\frac{da_1}{dt} = -\,\delta_1\left(1 - \frac{R_e'}{R_{01}}\right)a_1; \quad \frac{da_2}{dt} = -\,\delta_2\left(1 - \frac{R_e''}{R_{02}}\right)a_2$$

$$\frac{d\phi_1}{dt} = \frac{\delta_1}{R_{01}}Y_e'; \quad \frac{d\phi_2}{dt} = \Omega_2 - \frac{r}{s}\Omega_1 + \frac{\delta_2}{R_{02}}Y_e'' \qquad [89.21]$$

It is noted that the four equivalent parameters R_e', R_e'', Y_e', and Y_e'' appearing in these equations are now functions of only three variables a_1, a_2, and θ, as follows from [89.10]. The last two equations [89.21] can then be written

$$\frac{d\theta}{dt} = s\frac{d\phi_2}{dt} - r\frac{d\phi_1}{dt} = s\Omega_2 - r\Omega_1 + s\frac{\delta_2}{R_{02}}Y_e'' - r\frac{\delta_1}{R_{01}}Y_e' \qquad [89.22]$$

For a steady-state condition, a_1 = constant, a_2 = constant, and θ = constant, which gives

$$\left(1 - \frac{R_e{}'}{R_{01}}\right)a_1 = 0; \quad \left(1 - \frac{R_e{}''}{R_{02}}\right)a_2 = 0$$

$$[89.23]$$

$$s\Omega_2 - r\Omega_1 + s\frac{\delta_2}{R_{02}}Y_e{}'' - r\frac{\delta_1}{R_{01}}Y_e{}' = 0$$

The last equation can be written

$$s\left(\Omega_2 + \frac{\delta_2}{R_{02}}Y_e{}''\right) - r\left(\Omega_1 + \frac{\delta_1}{R_{01}}Y_e{}'\right) = s\Omega'' - r\Omega' = 0 \qquad [89.24]$$

where $\Omega' = \Omega_1 + \frac{\delta_1}{R_{01}}Y_e{}'$ and $\Omega'' = \Omega_2 + \frac{\delta_2}{R_{02}}Y_e{}''$.

Equation [89.24] shows that the stationary oscillation of the system occurs with two frequencies Ω' and Ω'' whose ratio is a rational number. In addition to these frequencies there exists a frequency spectrum corresponding to the harmonics of the order $\frac{m}{s}\Omega'$, as can be shown from the study of the refined first approximation, which we omit here.

90. SYNCHRONIZATION

In the previous notation the total phases are $\psi_1 = \Omega_1 t + \phi_1$ and $\psi_2 = \frac{r}{s}\Omega_1 t + \phi_2$, whence $\psi_2 - \frac{r}{s}\psi_1 = \phi_2 - \frac{r}{s}\phi_1 = \theta$. For a stationary state $d\theta/dt = 0$ and θ = constant, which gives

$$s\psi_2 - r\psi_1 = \theta = \text{constant} \qquad [90.1]$$

Thus the total phases are "locked in synchronism" with each other. The question now arises whether the condition [90.1] is stable. Since the four equivalent parameters $R_e{}'$, $R_e{}''$, $Y_e{}'$, and $Y_e{}''$ are functions of the three variables a_1, a_2, and θ, consider special values a_{10}, a_{20}, and θ_0 of these parameters corresponding to the stationary condition of the system. Following the method of variational equations, Chapter III, and considering arbitrary small increments Δa_1, Δa_2, and $\Delta\theta$ of the first order of small quantities, one obtains

$$\frac{d}{dt}\Delta a_1 = R_{a_1}{}'(a_{10},a_{20},\theta_0)\Delta a_1 + R_{a_2}{}'(a_{10},a_{20},\theta_0)\Delta a_2 + R_\theta{}'(a_{10},a_{20},\theta_0)\Delta\theta$$

$$\frac{d}{dt}\Delta a_2 = R_{a_1}{}''(a_{10},a_{20},\theta_0)\Delta a_1 + R_{a_2}{}''(a_{10},a_{20},\theta_0)\Delta a_2 + R_\theta{}''(a_{10},a_{20},\theta_0)\Delta\theta \quad [90.2]$$

$$\frac{d}{dt}\Delta\theta = F_{a_1}(a_{10},a_{20},\theta_0)\Delta a_1 + F_{a_2}(a_{10},a_{20},\theta_0)\Delta a_2 + F_\theta(a_{10},a_{20},\theta_0)\Delta\theta$$

where

$$R' = -\delta_1\left(1 - \frac{R_e'}{R_{01}}\right)a_1; \quad R'' = -\delta_2\left(1 - \frac{R_e''}{R_{01}}\right)a_2$$

and

[90.3]

$$F = s\Omega_2 - r\Omega_1 + s\frac{\delta_2}{R_{02}}Y_e'' - r\frac{\delta_1}{R_{01}}Y_e'$$

The question of stability is reduced to the investigation of the nature of the roots of the characteristic equation of the variational equations [90.2]. If all real parts of these roots are negative, the synchronized oscillations are stable; if any one of these parts is positive, the synchronization is unstable. Assume that the oscillations are stable; then, for sufficiently small departures of the parameters characterizing a disturbance in the synchronized condition [90.1], these departures satisfy the variational equations [90.2]. It is apparent that this is possible only for a certain range of Δa_1, Δa_2, and $\Delta\theta$ around the values a_{10}, a_{20}, and θ_0. If one exceeds this range, the conditions of stability may no longer be fulfilled.

The interval of variation of the parameters Δa_1, Δa_2, and $\Delta\theta$ which results in the stable condition of synchronized oscillations [90.1] is called the *zone of synchronization*. Non-linear systems are characterized by the presence of such a zone. It is absent in linear systems, or, in other words, one can say that linear systems are characterized by a zone of synchronization reduced to zero. It is thus seen that the phenomenon of synchronization is a characteristic property of non-linear internal resonance.

91. INTERNAL RESONANCE OF THE ORDER ONE

Consider now a particularly important case when $r = s$, that is, when $\Omega_1 \approx \Omega_2$, and $\omega_2/\omega_1 = 1 + \mu P$, and $g = \mu Q$; see Section 86. For $\mu = 0$, $\omega_1 = \omega_2 = \omega$ and for the first approximation we assume

$$i = a_1\cos(\omega t + \phi_1) + a_2\cos(\omega t + \phi_2) \qquad [91.1]$$

Putting $a_1\cos\phi_1 + a_2\cos\phi_2 = a\cos\phi$ and $a_1\sin\phi_1 + a_2\sin\phi_2 = a\sin\phi$, one has

$$a^2 = a_1^2 + a_2^2 + 2a_1a_2\cos(\phi_1 - \phi_2) \qquad [91.2]$$

Equation [91.1] can be written

$$i = a\cos(\omega t + \phi) \qquad [91.3]$$

Therefore, one has a simple relation

$$Z(j\omega) + R_e(a) = 0 \qquad [91.4]$$

It was shown in Section 86 that the frequencies $\Omega_1(a)$ and $\Omega_2(a)$ and the decrements $\delta_1(a)$ and $\delta_2(a)$ are given by Equations [86.9].

The equations of the first approximation for the amplitudes a_1 and a_2 and phases Ω_1 and Ω_2 in Equation [91.1] are therefore

$$\frac{da_1}{dt} = -\delta_1(a)a_1; \qquad \frac{da_2}{dt} = -\delta_2(a)a_2$$

$$\frac{d\phi_1}{dt} = \Omega_1(a) - \omega; \qquad \frac{d\phi_2}{dt} = \Omega_2(a) - \omega \qquad [91.5]$$

where a is given by Equation [91.2] and $\delta_1(a)$, $\delta_2(a)$, $\Omega_1(a)$, and $\Omega_2(a)$ are obtained from Equations [86.7] and [86.8]. It is apparent that, if $\delta_1(0) > 0$ and $\delta_2(0) > 0$, there will be no self-excitation. If, however, at least one of these quantities is negative, self-excitation from rest will take place. For a steady-state condition the resultant amplitude a is a constant, and from Equations [91.5]

$$a_1 = a_{10}e^{-\delta_1(a)t}; \qquad a_2 = a_{20}e^{-\delta_2(a)t}$$

$$\phi_1 = \phi_{10} + \Big[\Omega_1(a) - \omega\Big]t; \qquad \phi_2 = \phi_{20} + \Big[\Omega_2(a) - \omega\Big]t \qquad [91.6]$$

where a_{10}, a_{20}, ϕ_{10}, and ϕ_{20} are the integration constants. From Equation [91.2] one has

$$a^2 = a_{10}^2 e^{-2\delta_1(a)t} + a_{20}^2 e^{-2\delta_2(a)t} +$$

$$+ 2a_{10}a_{20}e^{-[\delta_1(a) + \delta_2(a)]t}\cos\Big(\Big[\Omega_2(a) - \Omega_1(a)\Big]t + \phi_{20} - \phi_{10}\Big) \qquad [91.7]$$

If $\delta_1(a) = 0$, then $a = a_{10} = a_1$; if $\delta_2(a) = 0$, then $a = a_{20} = a_2$. In the first case the oscillation will occur with frequency $\Omega_1(a)$ and its harmonics; in the second, with $\Omega_2(a)$ and its harmonics.

The oscillations in the first case will be stable if $\frac{\partial\delta_1}{\partial a} > 0$ and $\delta_2 > 0$, which means that the oscillation with frequency $\Omega_2(a)$ will die out. In the second case the oscillations will be stable if $\frac{\partial\delta_2}{\partial a} > 0$ and $\delta_1 > 0$, that is, the oscillation $\Omega_1(a)$ will die out.

For a resonant system, the investigation of the four equations [91.5] is reduced to an investigation of three equations; the first two give a_1 and a_2, and the third gives the phase difference $\theta = \phi_1 - \phi_2$.

92. METHOD OF EQUIVALENT LINEARIZATION IN QUASI-LINEAR SYSTEMS WITH SEVERAL FREQUENCIES

The principal points of the method of equivalent linearization were outlined in Chapter XII in connection with quasi-linear systems which have only one frequency. We now propose to generalize these conclusions so that they are applicable when, because of some couplings provided in the system, several frequencies are possible.

Let us assume that the oscillations are of the form

$$x = x_1 + \cdots + x_n \qquad [92.1]$$

where $x_1 = a_1 \cos (\omega_1 t + \phi_1), \cdots , x_n = a_n \cos (\omega_n t + \phi_n)$. Substituting Equation [92.1] into the expression for the characteristic of a non-linear conductor

$$y = F(x) \qquad [92.2]$$

one obtains, in general, a Fourier series. Let us keep in this series only those terms which contain the original frequencies $\omega_1, \cdots , \omega_n$ and let $y_1, \cdots , y_n$ be these terms. Since any term y_i will have the same frequency as the corresponding term x_i, we can write $y_i = S_i x_i$ so that Expression [92.2] becomes

$$y = y_1 + \cdots + y_n = S_1 x_1 + \cdots + S_n x_n \qquad [92.3]$$

It is apparent that this procedure leads to the *definition* of the equivalent parameters $S_1, \cdots , S_n$ on the basis of the Principle of Harmonic Balance, Section 77. One notes also that the non-linear expression [92.2] has been replaced by an equivalent linear one [92.3]. Moreover, it is also clear that by adopting this procedure the terms expressing combination frequencies have been omitted inasmuch as the frequencies of these terms are generally different from the original frequencies $\omega_1, \cdots , \omega_n$ appearing in Expression [92.3].

After the frequencies ω_{ie} and the decrements δ_{ie} of the equivalent linear system have been determined, the equations of the first approximation so obtained can be written in the form

$$\frac{da_1}{dt} = - \delta_{1e} a_1; \quad \cdots ; \quad \frac{da_n}{dt} = - \delta_{ne} a_n \qquad [92.4]$$

$$\frac{d\phi_1}{dt} = \omega_{1e} - \omega_1; \quad \cdots ; \quad \frac{d\phi_n}{dt} = \omega_{ne} - \omega_n \qquad [92.5]$$

In order to improve the accuracy of the approximation, the terms with combination harmonics omitted in the first approximation are added on the right side of these equations and appear as external forcing terms. When there are regular forcing terms, they are added to the harmonics just mentioned. Since the equation is now linear, there is no difficulty in carrying this procedure further.

In setting up the original differential equations, it is essential to introduce non-linear terms with a small parameter μ so that for $\mu = 0$ one has a linear system without damping.

In the equations of the first approximation only the terms containing the first power of the parameter μ are retained.

Let us apply these considerations to a linear system characterized by the impedance $Z(j\omega)$; the relation between the current and voltage is then $e = Z(j\omega)i$.

If the impedance is of the form $Z(j\omega) = \dfrac{P(j\omega)}{Q(j\omega)}$, the preceding relation becomes

$$Q(j\omega)e = P(j\omega)i \qquad [92.6]$$

Since for a steady state the operator $j\omega$ is d/dt, the preceding expression can also be written

$$Q\left(\frac{d}{dt}\right)e = P\left(\frac{d}{dt}\right)i \qquad [92.7]$$

As was shown in Section 84, Equation [92.7] is also valid for a transient state. In non-linear systems, as we saw, the current and voltage have a non-linear relation

$$e = -F(i) = -\mu f(i)$$

so that Equation [92.7] becomes

$$P\left(\frac{d}{dt}, \mu\right)i = -\mu Q\left(\frac{d}{dt}\right)f(i) \qquad [92.8]$$

When $\mu = 0$ one has a linear differential equation

$$P\left(\frac{d}{dt}, 0\right)i = 0$$

Thus, for example, instead of Equations [88.4] and [88.5], we can write

$$[92.9]$$

$$\left(\frac{d^2}{dt^2} + 2\mu\xi_1\frac{d}{dt} + \Omega_1^2\right)\left(\frac{d^2}{dt^2} + 2\mu\xi_2\frac{d}{dt} + \Omega_2^2\right)i = -\mu C\omega_1^2\frac{d}{dt}\left(\frac{d^2}{dt^2} + 2\mu\xi_1\omega_2\frac{d}{dt} + \omega_2^2\right)f(i)$$

which is of the same form as [92.8].

Since we know that for linear systems, that is, for systems in which $\mu = 0$, this equation has two coupled frequencies, let us try to form a non-linear solution ($\mu \neq 0$) in the form

$$i = a_1\cos\psi_1 + a_2\cos\psi_2 + \mu z_1(a_1,a_2,\psi_1,\psi_2) + \mu^2 z_2(a_1,a_2,\psi_1,\psi_2) + \cdots \quad [92.10]$$

where z_1, z_2, $\cdots$ are periodic functions with period 2π and the functions a_1, a_2, ψ_1, and ψ_2 satisfy expressions of the form

$$\frac{da_1}{dt} = \mu X_{11}(a_1,a_2) + \mu^2 X_{12}(a_1,a_2) + \cdots$$

$$\frac{da_2}{dt} = \mu X_{21}(a_1,a_2) + \mu^2 X_{22}(a_1,a_2) + \cdots$$

$$[92.11]$$

$$\frac{d\psi_1}{dt} = \Omega_1 + \mu Y_{11}(a_1,a_2) + \mu^2 Y_{12}(a_1,a_2) + \cdots$$

$$\frac{d\psi_2}{dt} = \Omega_2 + \mu Y_{21}(a_1,a_2) + \mu^2 Y_{22}(a_1,a_2) + \cdots$$

Substituting Expression [92.10] into Equation [92.9] and taking into account Equations [92.11], we can develop the result of the substitution into a power series of the parameter μ. Equating the coefficients of equal powers of μ, one obtains the expressions for z_1, z_2, $\cdots$; X_{11}, X_{12}, $\cdots$; X_{21}, X_{22}, $\cdots$; Y_{11}, Y_{12}, $\cdots$; and Y_{21}, Y_{22}, $\cdots$.

Carrying out these calculations for terms containing the first power of μ, that is, for z_1, X_{11}, X_{21}, Y_{11}, and Y_{21}, one observes that the equations of the first approximation so obtained are precisely those which were obtained directly by the method of equivalent linearization. If, however, one retains the first three terms in Equation [92.10], the calculation results in what have previously been called equations of the improved first approximation, Section 68, and so on for approximations of higher orders.

To summarize these conclusions, it can be stated that the method of equivalent linearization, which was more or less postulated in Part II, can be justified on the basis of the preceding analysis and can be generalized for approximations of higher orders. It can be shown by following the argument just outlined that it is possible to form linearized differential equations whose solutions satisfy the original differential equations with accuracy of the order μ, μ^2, $\cdots$. For a more detailed proof of this proposition, the reader is referred to the Kryloff-Bogoliuboff text, Reference (1), pages 241 to 246.

CHAPTER XV

EXTERNAL PERIODIC EXCITATION OF QUASI-LINEAR SYSTEMS

In preceding chapters we have been concerned with the phenomena of self-excitation of quasi-linear systems of the *autonomous* type, that is, quasi-linear systems in which the independent variable t, meaning time, does not appear explicitly in the differential equations. We shall now indicate how the Kryloff-Bogoliuboff theory of quasi-linear systems can be applied to systems having an external periodic excitation. We shall return to this question later in connection with the Mandelstam-Papalexi method based on the theory of Poincaré.

93. EQUATIONS OF THE FIRST APPROXIMATION FOR
    A PERIODIC NON-RESONANT EXCITATION

The quasi-linear differential equation for a system with an external excitation has the form

$$m\ddot{x} + kx = \mu f(t, x, \dot{x}) \qquad [93.1]$$

in which the time t appears explicitly.

We shall consider only the case where $f(t, x, \dot{x})$ can be written in the form

$$f(t, x, \dot{x}) = f_0(x, \dot{x}) + \sum_{n=0}^{N} \left[f_{n1}(x, \dot{x}) \cos \gamma_n t + f_{n2}(x, \dot{x}) \sin \gamma_n t \right] \qquad [93.2]$$

where f_0, f_{n1}, and f_{n2} are certain polynomials in x and $\dot{x}$.

In the terminology of electric-circuit theory, the motion represented by Equation [93.2] may be considered a current produced by an electromotive force $e = \mu f(t, x, \dot{x})$ applied to a linear impedance $Z(j\omega_0) = mj\omega_0 + \dfrac{k}{j\omega_0}$. It was mentioned in Chapter XIII that in electrical problems x corresponds to the charge in the capacitor and $\dot{x}$ to the current.

When $\mu = 0$, the system [93.1] becomes a linear one whose solution is

$$x = a \sin(\omega_0 t + \phi)$$

$$\dot{x} = a\omega_0 \cos(\omega_0 t + \phi) \qquad [93.3]$$

where $\omega_0 = \sqrt{k/m}$ and ϕ are two constants of integration. When $\mu \neq 0$ but sufficiently small, the expressions [93.3] appear as *generating solutions* (compare with the method of Poincaré in Chapter VIII) with which we start the approximation. One may consider these expressions as an approximation of *zero* order. Our purpose will be to establish an approximation of the *first* order which will characterize the quasi-linear system with a degree of accuracy of the order of μ^2.

The non-linear term becomes

$$e = \mu f\left[t, a \sin(\omega_0 t + \phi), a\omega_0 \cos(\omega_0 t + \phi)\right] \qquad [93.4]$$

Since the functions f_0, f_{n1}, and f_{n2} are polynomials, their Fourier expansions are of the form

$$f_0(a \sin\psi, a\omega_0 \cos\psi) = \sum_{k \geqq 0}^{N'}\left[g_k(a) \cos k\psi + h_k(a) \sin k\psi\right]$$

$$f_{n1}(a \sin\psi, a\omega_0 \cos\psi) = \sum_{k \geqq 0}^{N'}\left[g_{n1,k}(a) \cos k\psi + h_{n1,k}(a) \sin k\psi\right] \qquad [93.5]$$

$$f_{n2}(a \sin\psi, a\omega_0 \cos\psi) = \sum_{k \geqq 0}^{N'}\left[g_{n2,k}(a) \cos k\psi + h_{n2,k}(a) \sin k\psi\right]$$

Using these expressions and also the expansion [93.2], one can write the non-linear term [93.4] as

$$e = \mu \sum_{k=0}^{N'}\left[g_k(a) \cos k(\omega_0 t + \phi) + h_k(a) \sin k(\omega_0 t + \phi)\right] +$$

$$+ \frac{\mu}{2} \sum_{n=0}^{N} \sum_{k=0}^{N'}\left[h_{n1,k}(a) + g_{n2,k}(a)\right] \sin\left[(k\omega_0 + \gamma_n)t + k\phi\right] +$$

$$+ \frac{\mu}{2} \sum_{n=0}^{N} \sum_{k=0}^{N'}\left[g_{n1,k}(a) - h_{n2,k}(a)\right] \cos\left[(k\omega_0 + \gamma_n)t + k\phi\right] +$$

$$+ \frac{\mu}{2} \sum_{n=0}^{N} \sum_{k=0}^{N'}\left[g_{n1,k}(a) + h_{n2,k}(a)\right] \cos\left[(k\omega_0 - \gamma_n)t + k\phi\right] +$$

$$+ \frac{\mu}{2} \sum_{n=0}^{N} \sum_{k=0}^{N'}\left[h_{n1,k}(a) - g_{n2,k}(a)\right] \sin\left[(k\omega_0 - \gamma_n)t + k\phi\right] \qquad [93.6]$$

It is noted that the frequencies $k\omega_0 + \gamma_n$ and $k\omega_0 - \gamma_n$ appearing in these expressions are *combination frequencies* like those we have previously encountered.

We shall limit our study in this section to systems in which none of the combination frequencies approaches or is equal to the frequency ω_0. In other words

$$\left[k\omega_0 + \gamma_n\right] \neq \omega_0 \quad \text{and} \quad \left[k\omega_0 - \gamma_n\right] \neq \omega_0$$

As before, we call this case the *non-resonant case*. From the form of Expression [93.6] one ascertains that the only harmonic having the frequency ω_0 is the harmonic

$$e_1 = \mu g_1(a) \cos(\omega_0 t + \phi) + \mu h_1(a) \sin(\omega_0 t + \phi) \qquad [93.7]$$

Using this expression together with the second equation [93.3], one has

$$Z_e = \frac{e_1}{i} = \frac{\mu}{a\omega_0}\left[g_1(a) - h_1(a)j\right] \qquad [93.8]$$

Hence, to the first order, the non-linear element of the system can be replaced by the equivalent linear one so that the symbolic equation of the quasi-linear system becomes

$$Z - Z_e = 0 \qquad [93.9]$$

Written explicitly, this equation is

$$mp + \frac{k}{p} = \frac{\mu}{a\omega_0}\left[g_1(a) - h_1(a)j\right] \qquad [93.10]$$

where $p = -\delta + j\omega$, δ being the decrement and ω the frequency of the equivalent linear system. Substituting this value of p into Equation [93.10], one has

$$(-\delta + j\omega)^2 + \omega_0^2 = \frac{\mu}{m\omega_0 a}\left[g_1(a) - h_1(a)j\right](-\delta + j\omega) \qquad [93.11]$$

whence, to the first order, one obtains

$$\delta = -\frac{\mu}{2m\omega_0 a}g_1(a); \qquad \omega = \omega_0 - \frac{\mu}{2m\omega_0 a}h_1(a) \qquad [93.12]$$

By substituting these values into the equations of the first approximation

$$\frac{da}{dt} = -\delta a \quad \text{and} \quad \frac{d\phi}{dt} = \omega - \omega_0$$

one obtains

$$\frac{da}{dt} = \frac{\mu}{2m\omega_0}g_1(a); \qquad \frac{d\phi}{dt} = -\frac{\mu}{2m\omega_0 a}h_1(a) \qquad [93.13]$$

By the introduction of the *total phase* $\psi = \omega_0 t + \phi$, these equations become

$$\frac{da}{dt} = \frac{\mu}{2m\omega_0}g_1(a); \qquad \frac{d\psi}{dt} = \omega_0 - \frac{\mu}{2m\omega_0 a}h_1(a) = \omega(a) \qquad [93.14]$$

It is thus seen that the solution to the first approximation is still of the form

$$x = a\sin\psi \qquad [93.15]$$

where a and ψ are given by Equations [93.14].

By analogy with the definition of the linear decrement, it is logical to introduce now a quantity $\overline{\lambda}$, the equivalent decrement, defined by the equation

$$\overline{\lambda} = -\frac{\mu}{a\omega_0}g_1(a) \qquad [93.16]$$

Since $g_1(a)$ is the **first coefficient of the Fourier expansion**, its explicit value is

$$g_1(a) = \frac{1}{\pi} \int_0^{2\pi} f_0(a \sin\psi, \, a\omega_0 \cos\psi) \cos\psi \, d\psi \qquad [93.17]$$

whence

$$\overline{\lambda} = -\frac{\mu}{a\omega_0 \pi} \int_0^{2\pi} f_0(a \sin\psi, \, a\omega_0 \cos\psi) \cos\psi \, d\psi \qquad [93.18]$$

Following the procedure explained in Section 75, one obtains

$$k_e' = -\frac{\mu}{\pi a} \int_0^{2\pi} f_0(a \sin\psi, \, a\omega_0 \cos\psi) \sin\psi \, d\psi \qquad [93.19]$$

and to the first order $\omega^2 = \dfrac{k + k_e'}{m}$. The equations of the first approximation then acquire the familiar form

$$\frac{da}{dt} = -\frac{\overline{\lambda}}{2m} a; \quad \frac{d\psi}{dt} = \omega = \sqrt{\frac{k + k_e'}{m}} \qquad [93.20]$$

If one differentiates the solution $x = a \sin\psi$ twice, takes into account Equations [93.20], and substitutes x and $\ddot{x}$ into Equation [93.1], one finds that the solution $x = a \sin\psi$ satisfies the linearized equation

$$m\ddot{x} + \overline{\lambda}\dot{x} + (k + k_e')x = 0 \qquad [93.21]$$

to within a factor of the order of μ^2.

It should be noted that in the equation of the first approximation the dependence of the "forcing function" on time does not appear explicitly. This is due to the fact that, for the formation of these equations, only the term $f_0(x, \dot{x})$ of Expansion [93.2] has been retained. This term is expressed by the equation

$$f_0(x, \dot{x}) = \lim_{t \to \infty} \frac{1}{T} \int_0^T f(\tau, x, \dot{x}) \, d\tau$$

In other words, the first approximation deals with the average value of the forcing function with respect to time, and the instantaneous behavior of that function is felt only in approximations of higher orders.

The rest of the discussion is centered about the linear equation [93.21]. Thus, for example, the stationary state is reached when

$$\lambda(a_0) = -\frac{\mu}{a\omega_0 \pi} \int_0^{2\pi} f_0(a \sin\psi, \, a\omega_0 \cos\psi) \cos\psi \, d\psi = 0 \qquad [93.22]$$

This corresponds to Equation [46.22] of the theory of Poincaré or to the first of the "abbreviated equations" [52.9] of the theory of Van der Pol.

The stationary state is stable if $\left(\dfrac{\partial\lambda}{\partial a}\right)_{a=a_0} > 0$ and unstable if $\left(\dfrac{\partial\lambda}{\partial a}\right)_{a=a_0} < 0$.

Self-excitation may develop from rest if $\overline{\lambda}(0) < 0$; if, however, $\overline{\lambda}(0) > 0$, no self-excitation takes place.

94. FIRST-ORDER SOLUTION OF VAN DER POL'S EQUATION WITH FORCING TERM

It has been shown that the operation of a self-excited thermionic generator with inductive coupling can be expressed by an equation of the Van der Pol type, that is,

$$\ddot{y} + y - \mu(1 - y^2)\dot{y} = 0 \qquad [94.1]$$

If an alternating electromotive force $E = E_0 \sin \alpha t$ of constant frequency is provided in the grid circuit shown in Figure 94.1, the differential equation [94.1] acquires a "forcing term" and becomes

$$\ddot{y} + y - \mu(1 - y^2)\dot{y} = E_0 \sin \alpha t \qquad [94.2]$$

If we introduce a new variable x, defined by the equation $y = x +$ $+ U \sin \alpha t$, where $U = \dfrac{E_0}{1 - \alpha^2}$, Equation [94.2] becomes

$$\ddot{x} + x = \mu\left[1 - (x + U\sin\alpha t)^2\right]\left[\dot{x} + U\alpha\cos\alpha t\right] \qquad [94.3]$$

In this equation

$$f(t, x, \dot{x}) = \left[1 - (x + U\sin\alpha t)^2\right]\left[\dot{x} + U\alpha\cos\alpha t\right] \qquad [94.4]$$

Developing the right side of this equation and collecting terms not depending explicitly on t, one has

$$f_0(x, \dot{x}) = \left(1 - x^2 - \frac{U^2}{2}\right)\dot{x} \qquad [94.5]$$

If we let $m = 1$ and $k = 1$ in Equation [93.1], then we can take as generating solutions $x = a \sin \phi$ and $\dot{x} = a \cos \phi$, since $\omega_0 = 1$. Substituting these solutions into [94.5] and carrying out the integration indicated by [93.18], one obtains

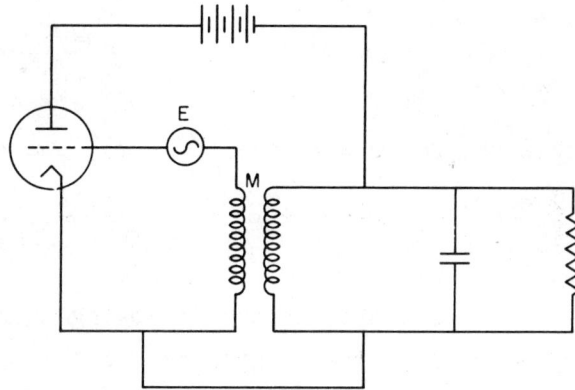

Figure 94.1

$$\bar{\lambda} = -\mu\left(1 - \frac{a^2}{4} - \frac{U^2}{2}\right) \qquad [94.6]$$

The equation of the first approximation therefore becomes

$$\frac{da}{dt} = +\frac{\mu}{2}\left(1 - \frac{a^2}{4} - \frac{U^2}{2}\right)a \qquad [94.7]$$

This equation shows that for $U^2 < 2$ there exists a trivial solution $a = 0$ which, however, is unstable. In fact, for a very small initial departure, the quantity in parentheses is positive, which indicates that the amplitude begins to increase. The stationary amplitude a_1 is reached when

$$a = a_1 = 2 \sqrt{1 - \frac{U^2}{2}} \tag{94.8}$$

If $U^2 > 2$, there is no self-excitation, and the trivial solution $a = 0$ is stable. The value

$$U^2 = \frac{E_0{}^2}{(1 - \alpha^2)^2} = 2$$

is thus a critical threshold separating two zones: in one zone, where $U^2 < 2$, the system becomes self-excited; in the other, where $U^2 > 2$, the external periodic excitation with frequency α prevents self-excitation.

95. IMPROVED FIRST APPROXIMATION FOR A NON-RESONANT EXTERNAL EXCITATION OF A QUASI-LINEAR SYSTEM

Equation [93.6] gives the expression for a non-linear force in terms of the Fourier coefficients for different combination harmonics.

Using the terminology of electric-circuit theory, one can say that, if an electromotive force $e = e_0 \sin (\Omega t + \phi)$ is impressed on a linear imped-ance $Z = mj\omega + \frac{k}{j\omega}$, the steady-state current due to this forcing term will be

$$\frac{e_0}{mj\Omega + \dfrac{k}{j\Omega}} \sin (\Omega t + \phi) = \frac{e_0 j\Omega}{m(\omega_0{}^2 - \Omega^2)} \sin (\Omega t + \phi) = \frac{e_0 \Omega}{m(\omega_0{}^2 - \Omega^2)} \cos (\Omega t + \phi)$$

Likewise, for $e = e_0 \cos (\Omega t + \phi)$, the forced oscillation is

$$\frac{e_0}{mj\Omega + \dfrac{k}{j\Omega}} \cos (\Omega t + \phi) = \frac{- e_0 j\Omega}{m(\Omega^2 - \omega_0^2)} \cos (\Omega t + \phi) = \frac{e_0 \Omega}{m(\Omega^2 - \omega_0^2)} \sin (\Omega t + \phi)$$

One obtains the following equations for x by dividing Equation [93.6] by the linear impedance of the system:

$$x = a \sin \psi + \frac{\mu g_0}{k} + \frac{\mu}{m} \sum_{k=2}^{N'} \frac{g_k \cos k\psi + h_k \sin k\psi}{(1 - k^2) \omega_0^2} +$$

$$+ \frac{\mu}{2m} \sum_{n=0}^{N} \sum_{k=0}^{N'} \frac{(g_{n1,k} - h_{n2,k}) \cos (k\psi + \gamma_n t)}{\omega_0^2 - k(\omega_0 + \gamma_n)^2} + \frac{\mu}{2m} \sum_{n=0}^{N} \sum_{k=0}^{N'} \frac{(g_{n1,k} + h_{n2,k}) \cos (k\psi + \gamma_n t)}{\omega_0^2 - (k\omega_0 + \gamma_n)^2} +$$

$$+ \frac{\mu}{2m} \sum_{n=0}^{N} \sum_{k=0}^{N'} \frac{(g_{n1,k} + h_{n2,k}) \cos (k\psi - \gamma_n t)}{\omega_0^2 - (k\omega_0 - \gamma_n)^2} + \frac{\mu}{2m} \sum_{n=0}^{N} \sum_{k=0}^{N'} \frac{(g_{n2,k} + h_{n1,k}) \sin (k\psi + \gamma_n t)}{\omega_0^2 - (k\omega_0 + \gamma_n)^2} +$$

$$+ \frac{\mu}{2m} \sum_{n=0}^{N} \sum_{k=0}^{N'} \frac{(g_{n1,k} - h_{n2,k}) \sin (k\psi - \gamma_n t)}{\omega_0^2 - (k\omega_0 - \gamma_n)^2} \tag{95.1}$$

A similar expression can be written for $\dot{x}$. From Expression [95.1] it follows that resonance occurs whenever one of the divisors becomes either zero or a small quantity of the first order. Under such circumstances the smallness of the numerator due to the factor μ is offset by the smallness of the denominator, so that the resulting term remains finite.

It can also be seen from Expression [95.1] that the dependent variable $x(t)$ consists of three kinds of oscillations, namely:

1. Free or *autoperiodic* oscillation, $a \sin \psi = a \sin [\omega(a)t + \phi]$.

2. Forced or *heteroperiodic* oscillation with frequencies γ_n given by the terms in which $k = 0$.

3. The spectrum of combination oscillations with frequencies $k\omega(a) \pm \gamma_n$.

One could proceed with building approximations of higher orders in which the divisors would be of the form $\omega_0^2 - (k\omega_0 + b_1\lambda_1 + \cdots + b_n\lambda_n)^2$ and apply the preceding argument. However, the formation of these approximations is complicated and adds nothing new to the qualitative aspects contained in the improved first approximation [95.1].

In the following discussion, we prefer to use the terms "autoperiodic" and "heteroperiodic" instead of "free" and "forced," for reasons which will appear later.

96. HETEROPERIODIC AND AUTOPERIODIC STATES OF NON-LINEAR SYSTEMS; ASYNCHRONOUS EXCITATION AND QUENCHING

We shall now consider Equation [95.1] when the autoperiodic oscillation is absent, that is, when $a \equiv 0$. In such a case

$$g_k = h_k = 0; \qquad k = 1, 2, \cdots$$

$$g_{n1,k} = 0; \quad g_{n2,k} = 0; \quad h_{n1,k} = 0; \quad h_{n2,k} = 0; \qquad k = 1, 2, \cdots$$

This follows from the fact that the numbers g_k, $\cdots$ for $k > 0$, which we have just asserted to be zero, are merely the non-constant terms in the Fourier expansions of [93.5]. Now for $a = 0$ all the expressions on the left side of these equations reduce to their constant terms. This same fact is true of their Fourier expansions, and hence all coefficients of the cosine and sine terms in these expansions are zero.

If we put $g_{n1,0} = A_n$ and $h_{n2,0} = B_n$, Expression [95.1] reduces to

$$x = \frac{\mu}{m} \sum_{n=0}^{N} \frac{A_n \cos \gamma_n t + B_n \sin \gamma_n t}{\omega_0^2 - \gamma_n^2} + \frac{\mu}{k} g_0(0,0) \qquad [96.1]$$

Hence, for $a = 0$, only heteroperiodic oscillations exist with externally applied frequencies $\gamma_1, \gamma_2, \cdots, \gamma_N$. In Section 94 it was shown that for

$$U^2 = \left(\frac{E_0}{1 - \alpha^2}\right)^2 > 2$$

the heteroperiodic state is the only one possible.

Consider the following differential equation encountered in acoustics:

$$m\ddot{y} + \lambda_1 \dot{y} + ky + \delta_1 y^2 = E_1 \sin\alpha_1 t + E_2 \sin(\alpha_2 t + \beta) \qquad [96.2]$$

where m, λ_1, and k are positive constants. Moreover, λ_1 and δ_1 are small, so that we can introduce a small parameter μ by writing

$$\lambda_1 = \mu\lambda; \qquad \delta_1 = \mu\delta \qquad [96.3]$$

In order to make Equation [96.2] of the same form as [93.1], one can introduce a new variable x defined by the equation

$$y = x + \frac{E_1 \sin\alpha_1 t}{m(\omega_0^2 - \alpha_1^2)} + \frac{E_2 \sin(\alpha_2 t + \beta)}{m(\omega_0^2 - \alpha_2^2)} \qquad [96.4]$$

This change of the variable gives

$$m\ddot{x} + kx = \mu\left\{\left[-\lambda\dot{x} - \frac{\lambda E_1 \alpha_1 \cos\alpha_1 t}{m(\omega_0^2 - \alpha_1^2)} - \frac{\lambda E_2 \alpha_2 \cos(\alpha_2 t + \beta)}{m(\omega_0^2 - \alpha_2^2)}\right] - \right.$$

$$\left. - \delta\left[k + \frac{E_1 \sin\alpha_1 t}{m(\omega_0^2 - \alpha_1^2)} + \frac{E_2 \sin(\alpha_2 t + \beta)}{m(\omega_0^2 - \alpha_2^2)}\right]^2\right\} \qquad [96.5]$$

Here $\overline{\lambda} = \mu\lambda > 0$. Hence, by Equation [93.20], the autoperiodic oscillation dies out and only the heteroperiodic state is possible. By Equation [96.1] one obtains the following expression for the heteroperiodic oscillation:

$$x = \frac{\mu\lambda E_1 \alpha_1 \cos\alpha_1 t}{m^2(\omega_0^2 - \alpha_1^2)^2} - \frac{\mu\lambda E_2 \alpha_2 \cos(\alpha_2 t + \beta)}{m^2(\omega_0^2 - \alpha_2^2)^2} - \frac{\mu\delta E_1^2}{2k[m(\omega_0^2 - \alpha_1^2)]^2} - \qquad [96.6]$$

$$- \frac{\mu\delta E_2^2}{2k[m(\omega_0^2 - \alpha_2^2)]^2} + \frac{\mu\delta E_1^2 \cos 2\alpha_1 t}{2m[m(\omega_0^2 - \alpha_1^2)]^2(\omega_0^2 - 4\alpha_1^2)} + \frac{\mu\delta E_2^2 \cos 2(\alpha_2 t + \beta)}{2m[m(\omega_0^2 - \alpha_2^2)]^2(\omega_0^2 - 4\alpha_2^2)} +$$

$$+ \frac{\mu\delta E_1 E_2 \cos[(\alpha_2 - \alpha_1)t + \beta]}{m^3(\omega_0^2 - \alpha_1^2)(\omega_0^2 - \alpha_2^2)[\omega_0^2 - (\alpha_2 - \alpha_1)^2]} + \frac{\mu\delta E_1 E_2 \cos[(\alpha_2 + \alpha_1)t + \beta]}{m^3(\omega_0^2 - \alpha_1^2)(\omega_0^2 - \alpha_2^2)[\omega_0^2 - (\alpha_2 + \alpha_1)^2]}$$

It is seen that the heteroperiodic oscillation consists of harmonics of the fundamental frequencies α_1 and α_2 and also of the combination frequencies $2\alpha_1$, $2\alpha_2$, $\alpha_1 + \alpha_2$, and $\alpha_1 - \alpha_2$. The frequency zero (the third and the fourth terms) also appears in the spectrum.

As another, more complicated example in which both heteroperiodic and autoperiodic oscillations appear, we shall consider an electron-tube oscillator acted upon by an extraneous voltage of frequency α in addition to the feed-back voltage e. The anode current is

$$i_a = f(E_0 + F\cos\alpha t + e) \qquad [96.7]$$

Let the frequency of the oscillating circuit be ω_0. In the first approximation, the preceding expression becomes

$$i_a = f\left[E_0 + F\cos\alpha t + a\cos(\omega_0 t + \phi)\right] \qquad [96.8]$$

where a and ϕ are the amplitude and phase of the autoperiodic oscillation of the voltage applied to the grid.

In order to apply the method of equivalent linearization, the non-linear conductor $i_a = f(e_g)$ must be replaced by a linear one $i_a = Se_g$, where the equivalent parameter S must be so chosen that the fundamental harmonic of [96.8] is equal to the harmonic $Sa\cos(\omega_0 t + \phi)$. By the Principle of Harmonic Balance, Section 77,

$$S = \frac{1}{2a\pi^2}\int_0^{2\pi}\int_0^{2\pi} f(E_0 + F\cos\tau_1 + a_2\cos\tau_2)\cos\tau_2 \, d\tau_1 \, d\tau_2 \qquad [96.9]$$

It was shown in Chapter XIII that in the linearized scheme in which the non-linear conductor is replaced by an equivalent linear one,

$$j\omega - \delta = j\omega_0 - \delta_0\left(1 - \frac{S}{S_1}\right) \qquad [96.10]$$

where ω_0 is the frequency and δ_0 is the decrement of the linear circuit closed on the non-linear conductor linearized by the transconductance S. The quantity S_1 is the critical transconductance, that is, a particular value of the transconductance S for which the decrement δ vanishes and the oscillation becomes stationary.

It is apparent that, if the external excitation $F\cos\alpha t$ is absent, the value of S is somewhat different from its value in Equation [96.9]. In fact, for an autoperiodic excitation the equivalent transconductance is given by Equation [83.7], viz.,

$$S(a) = \frac{1}{\pi a}\int_0^{2\pi} f(E_0 + a\cos\phi)\cos\phi \, d\phi$$

In order to use this equation, it is sufficient to replace E_0 by $E_0 + F\cos\alpha t$ and to average it again over the period 2π. If the autoperiodic frequency ω_0 is high (for example, radio frequency) and the heteroperiodic frequency α is low (for example, audio frequency), the equivalent transconductance $S(a)$ given by Equation [83.7] is a slowly varying function with frequency α. If the value of $S(a)$ oscillates with frequency α in the neighborhood of the critical value of self-excitation (autoperiodic frequency) and the amplitude F of the heteroperiodic frequency is sufficiently large to pass out of the zone of self-excitation, it is apparent that the appearance and disappearance of the autoperiodic state will also be periodic with the period $T_H = \frac{2\pi}{\alpha}$ of the heteroperiodic oscillation. The reader will recognize the characteristic behavior of the so-called superregenerative circuit.

If, however, the heteroperiodic frequency is considerably higher than the autoperiodic one, its effect will be felt in the virtual modification of the critical transconductance of the electron tube. Depending on the form of the characteristic, this effect will sometimes manifest itself in the appearance of an autoperiodic self-excitation and sometimes in the extinction of an existing autoperiodic oscillation. These phenomena are sometimes referred to as *asynchronous excitation* or *asynchronous quenching* of an autoperiodic oscillation by a heteroperiodic one (5). The conditions for such asynchronous action are easily established by following the procedure indicated by Equation [96.9] in which one integration, say $d\tau_1$, is carried out with respect to the heteroperiodic period and the other $d\tau_2$ with respect to the autoperiodic one.

As an example (5), consider an electron-tube oscillator with a nonlinear characteristic given by the polynomial

$$i_a = f(x) = \alpha x + \beta x^2 + \gamma x^3 + \delta x^4 + \epsilon x^5 \qquad [96.11]$$

It has been shown that this expression approximates sufficiently well both the soft and the hard characteristics. For a soft characteristic, it is sufficient to put $\delta = \epsilon = 0$, whereas for a hard one, the full polynomial should be used. Assume that the grid voltage x is of the form

$$x = a\cos\phi + b\cos\psi \qquad [96.12]$$

where a and ϕ are the autoperiodic variables and b and ψ the heteroperiodic ones. Replacing x in Expression [96.11] by its value [96.12] and carrying out the integrations indicated by [96.9], viz.,

$$S(a,b) = \frac{1}{2a\pi^2} \int_0^{2\pi}\int_0^{2\pi} f(a\cos\phi + b\cos\psi)\cos\phi\, d\phi\, d\psi \qquad [96.13]$$

one obtains the following expression

$$S(a,b) = \alpha + \frac{3}{4}\gamma a^2 + \frac{3}{2}\gamma b^2 + \frac{5}{8}\epsilon a^4 + \frac{15}{4}\epsilon a^2 b^2 + \frac{15}{8}\epsilon b^4 \qquad [96.14]$$

If the heteroperiodic excitation is absent, that is, if $b = 0$,

$$S(a,0) = \alpha + \frac{3}{4}\gamma a^2 + \frac{5}{8}\epsilon a^4 \qquad [96.15]$$

which is the expression for the transconductance S of an autoperiodic state. More specifically, if the characteristic is soft, that is, if $\gamma < 0$ and $\delta = \epsilon = 0$, the stationary condition is

$$S(a_0,0) = \alpha - \frac{3}{4}|\gamma|a_0^2 = 0 \qquad [96.16]$$

which gives

$$a_0 = \sqrt{\frac{4}{3}\frac{\alpha}{|\gamma|}} \qquad [96.17]$$

which was obtained previously by the method of Poincaré, see Section 54.*
      The condition for soft self-excitation in the absence of a hetero-periodic frequency is

$$S(0,0) = \alpha > S(a,0) \qquad [96.18]$$

If, however, the heteroperiodic frequency is present, that is, $b \neq 0$, the initial value of the transconductance is

$$S(0,b) = \alpha + \frac{3}{2}\gamma b^2 \qquad [96.19]$$

Since $\gamma < 0$, $S(0,b) < S(0,0)$, which means that the presence of the heteroperiodic frequency may prevent the occurrence of self-excitation. Therefore one concludes that, for a normally soft characteristic, asynchronous quenching of the autoperiodic frequency by the heteroperiodic one occurs, a fact which was mentioned at the end of Section 94.
      For a hard characteristic ($\epsilon < 0$ and α, β, γ, and $\delta > 0$) in the absence of the heteroperiodic excitation, the transconductance is

$$S(a,0) = \alpha + \frac{3}{4}\gamma a^2 - \frac{5}{8}|\epsilon|a^4 \qquad [96.20]$$

This expression considered as a function of a^2 is a maximum when

$$a^2 = \frac{3\gamma}{5|\epsilon|}$$

The maximum value of $S(a,0)$ is then

$$S_{max}(a,0) = \alpha + \frac{9}{40}\frac{\gamma}{|\epsilon|} \qquad [96.21]$$

One can obtain asynchronous self-excitation ($b \neq 0$) if

$$S(0,0) - S_{max}(a,0) = \frac{3}{2}\gamma b^2 + \frac{15}{8}\epsilon b^4 + \frac{9}{40}\frac{\gamma^2}{\epsilon} > 0 \qquad [96.22]$$

that is, if

$$\frac{3}{2}\gamma b^2 > \frac{15}{8}|\epsilon|b^4 + \frac{9}{40}\frac{\gamma^2}{|\epsilon|} \qquad [96.23]$$

This inequality can be fulfilled if the quantity b^2 lies in the interval

$$\frac{1}{5}\frac{\gamma}{|\epsilon|} < b^2 < \frac{3}{5}\frac{\gamma}{|\epsilon|} \qquad [96.24]$$

---

* It should be observed that the notation here differs from that of Section 54.

The subject of asynchronous action on a self-excited system can be summarized as follows:

a. If the characteristic is *soft*, the heteroperiodic frequency may result only in quenching the autoperiodic oscillation and not in causing its appearance.

b. If the characteristic is *hard*, the heteroperiodic frequency may cause self-excitation of the autoperiodic oscillation provided the amplitude of the heteroperiodic frequency lies in the interval indicated by the inequalities [96.24].

c. In all cases, the heteroperiodic action manifests itself in a virtual modification of the transconductance by which the conditions of self-excitation are influenced one way or the other according to the form of the non-linear characteristic.

CHAPTER XVI

NON-LINEAR EXTERNAL RESONANCE

97. EQUATIONS OF THE FIRST APPROXIMATION FOR AN EXTERNALLY EXCITED RESONANT SYSTEM

We shall now investigate the conditions under which certain harmonics in the combination-frequency spectrum become large compared to others when a quasi-linear dynamical system is excited by an external heteroperiodic frequency. We shall call this *external resonance* in contrast to internal resonance, which characterized a similar system without an external excitation.

For simplicity, we confine our attention to systems having one degree of freedom and fractional-order resonance. In such systems

$$\omega_0 = \frac{r}{s}\,\alpha \qquad\qquad [97.1]$$

where r and s are relatively prime. Unless otherwise stated we also assume that $s > 1$, because $s = 1$ corresponds essentially to ordinary resonance. In the "neighborhood" of resonance

$$\omega = \frac{r}{s}\,\alpha + \mu Q \qquad\qquad [97.2]$$

where μ is small.

Let us consider an electron-tube oscillator whose non-linear element, the electron tube, has a characteristic $i_a = f(e)$. Let the autoperiodic oscillation be

$$e = a\cos(\omega_0 t + \phi) = a\cos\left(\frac{r}{s}\,\alpha t + \phi\right)$$

The anode current i_a is given in terms of the grid voltage by the expression

$$i_a = f\left[E_0 + F\cos\alpha t + a\cos\left(\frac{r}{s}\,\alpha t + \phi\right)\right] \qquad\qquad [97.3]$$

In this expression the quantity a is the amplitude of the autoperiodic oscillation, $\frac{r}{s}\alpha$ is its frequency, and F and α are the corresponding quantities for the heteroperiodic oscillation introduced in the grid circuit, for instance, through an inductive coupling.

We begin by linearizing the non-linear element of the system by writing

$$i_a = Se \qquad\qquad [97.4]$$

where S is the equivalent transconductance, a function of the amplitude a of the autoperiodic oscillation. For simplicity we will write S instead of $S(a)$.

It is recalled, see Section 77, that, according to the Principle of Harmonic Balance, the fundamental harmonic of the non-linear periodic quantity

[97.3] is equal to the linearized oscillation [97.4]. By a Fourier series we obtain the following expression for this harmonic:

$$\frac{\alpha}{\pi s}\int_0^{\frac{2\pi s}{\alpha}} f\left[E_0 + F\cos\alpha\tau + a\cos\left(\frac{r}{s}\alpha\tau + \phi\right)\right]\left[\cos\left(\frac{r}{s}\alpha\tau + \phi\right)\cos\left(\frac{r}{s}\alpha t + \phi\right) + \right.$$

$$\left. + \sin\left(\frac{r}{s}\alpha\tau + \phi\right)\sin\left(\frac{r}{s}\alpha t + \phi\right)\right]d\tau \qquad [97.5]$$

This expression can be written in the form

$$S_r\, a\cos\left(\frac{r}{s}\alpha t + \phi\right) - S_i\, a\sin\left(\frac{r}{s}\alpha t + \phi\right) \qquad [97.6]$$

where

$$S_r = S_r(a,\phi) = \frac{1}{\pi a}\int_0^{2\pi} f\left[E_0 + F\cos\left(s\tau - \frac{s}{r}\phi\right) + a\cos r\tau\right]\cos r\tau\, d\tau$$

$$[97.7]$$

$$S_i = S_i(a,\phi) = -\frac{1}{\pi a}\int_0^{2\pi} f\left[E_0 + F\cos\left(s\tau - \frac{s}{r}\phi\right) + a\cos r\tau\right]\sin r\tau\, d\tau$$

Equation [97.6] can be written as

$$Sa\cos\left(\frac{r}{s}\alpha t + \phi\right) = (S_r + jS_i)\, a\cos\left(\frac{r}{s}\alpha t + \phi\right) \qquad [97.8]$$

It is seen that in a resonant system the transconductance S is a complex quantity

$$S = S_r + jS_i \qquad [97.9]$$

whereas in a non-resonant system it is real. Moreover, the formal procedure remains the same as in Section 89, the only difference being that instead of impedances we are now dealing with admittances since transconductance is an admittance. Using Equation [96.10] for the fundamental harmonic [97.8] and separating the real and the imaginary parts, one gets

$$\omega = \omega_0 + \delta_0\frac{S_i}{S_0}\;;\quad \delta = \delta_0\left(1 - \frac{S_r}{S_0}\right) \qquad [97.10]$$

where S_0, as before, designates the critical value of the transconductance S. If we put $\frac{r}{s}\alpha t + \phi = \psi$, the equations of the first approximation become

$$\frac{da}{dt} = -\delta_0\left(1 - \frac{S_r}{S_0}\right)a;\quad \frac{d\phi}{dt} = \omega_0 - \frac{r}{s}\alpha + \delta_0\frac{S_i}{S_0} \qquad [97.11]$$

The variables in these equations cannot be separated since both S_r and S_i are now functions of a and ϕ. On the other hand, since these equations are of the type investigated by Poincaré, we can assert that in the (a,ϕ)-plane the only stationary motions are either positions of equilibrium, that is, singular points of the system [97.11], or stationary motions of the limit-cycle type.

The first case is characterized by the approach of a and ϕ to certain fixed values a_0 and ϕ_0 when $t \to \infty$. Thus we have

$$\left[1 - \frac{S_r(a_0, \phi_0)}{S_0}\right] a_0 = 0; \qquad \omega_0 - \frac{r}{s}\alpha + \delta_0 \frac{S_i(a_0, \phi_0)}{S_0} = \omega - \frac{r}{s}\alpha = 0 \quad [97.12]$$

The oscillation ultimately reaches a frequency ω which is exactly equal to $\frac{r}{s}\alpha$; this means that the frequencies ω and α become "locked" in a certain rational relation. We may call this *synchronization* of the autoperiodic oscillation with the heteroperiodic one. Thus there exists one single frequency, and the stationary oscillation is

$$a_0 \cos\left(\omega t + \phi\right) = a_0 \cos\left(\frac{r}{s}\alpha t + \phi\right)$$

In the second case both $a(t)$ and $\phi(t)$ are periodic and have the same period as the autoperiodic solution so that the ultimate oscillation consists of the two frequencies. In other words, there are "beats" of autoperiodic and heteroperiodic frequencies. We shall consider this subject in greater detail in Chapter XVIII.

It is possible to show* that, when $r \to \infty$ and $s \to \infty$, $S_i \to 0$ and S_r approaches the value given by Equation [96.9], so that for large values of r and s the resonant case degenerates into the non-resonant one, which has already been investigated. Hence, the typical features of fractional-order resonance appear when r and s are relatively small integers.

Let us consider the following example. We assume that the function $f(E_0 + u)$ can be approximated by a polynomial of the third degree:

$$f(E_0 + u) = f(E_0) + S_1 u + S_2 u^2 - S_3 u^3 \qquad [97.13]$$

where S_1, S_2, and S_3 are positive. Assume further that $r = 1$ and $s = 2$, which gives $\omega_0 = \alpha/2$. Placing $u = F \cos \alpha t + a \cos\left(\frac{r}{s}\alpha t + \phi\right)$ in [97.13], we obtain

$$S_r = S_1 + \frac{3}{2} S_3 F^2 + \frac{1}{2} S_2 F \cos 2\phi - \frac{3}{4} S_3 a^2; \qquad S_i = -\frac{1}{2} S_2 F \sin 2\phi \quad [97.14]$$

Equations [97.11] become

$$\frac{da}{dt} = \frac{\delta_0}{S_0}\left(S_1 - S_0 - \frac{3}{2} S_3 F^2 + \frac{1}{2} S_2 F \cos 2\phi\right) a - \frac{3}{4} \frac{\delta_0 S_3}{S_0} a^3$$

$$[97.15]$$

$$\frac{d\phi}{dt} = \omega_0 - \frac{\alpha}{2} - \frac{\delta_0 S_2 F}{2 S_0} \sin 2\phi$$

The second equation [97.15] admits separation of variables and can be integrated. Putting

---

* The proof of this proposition can be found in the Kryloff-Bogoliuboff text "Introduction to Non-Linear Mechanics," Reference (1), pages 270 and 271.

$$\Delta\omega = \left|\omega_0 - \frac{\alpha}{2}\right| \quad \text{and} \quad \frac{\delta_0 S_2 F}{2 S_0} = \lambda$$

one has two cases: Case 1, $\Delta\omega < \lambda$ and Case 2, $\Delta\omega > \lambda$.

In Case 1 it is apparent that $\phi(t)_{t \to \infty} \to \phi_0$, where ϕ_0 is given by the expression

$$2\phi_0 = \sin^{-1}\left(\frac{2 S_0 \Delta\omega}{\delta_0 S_2 F}\right) \qquad [97.16]$$

One can select for $2\phi_0$ the principal determination, that is, $\sin 2\phi_0 > 0$; $\cos 2\phi_0 > 0$. Let us consider the asymptotic behavior of the solution of the first equation [97.15] as $\phi \to \phi_0$. If, for brevity, we put

$$\frac{\delta_0}{S_0}\left(S_1 - S_0 - \frac{3}{2}S_3 F^2 + \frac{1}{2}S_2 F \cos 2\phi_0\right) = A; \quad \frac{3}{4}\frac{\delta_0}{S_0}S_3 = B$$

the first equation [97.15] is

$$\frac{da}{dt} = Aa - Ba^3 \qquad [97.17]$$

When $A < 0$, and since a is always positive, the derivative da/dt is always negative and hence a cannot tend to any limit other than zero. Thus $a = 0$ is the only stable stationary amplitude. If, however, $A > 0$, one finds that the point $a = 0$ is unstable. The stationary autoperiodic oscillation, which can be shown to be stable, see Section 65, is then

$$a = a_0 = \sqrt{\frac{4}{3 S_3}\left(S_1 - S_0 - \frac{3}{2}S_3 F^2 + \frac{1}{2}S_2 F \cos 2\phi_0\right)} \qquad [97.18]$$

Since $\phi \to \phi_0$ when $t \to \infty$, we conclude that there will be a synchronous autoperiodic oscillation.

In Case 2, when $\Delta\omega > \lambda$, the second equation [97.15] gives

$$\frac{d\phi}{\Delta\omega - \lambda \sin 2\phi} = \frac{d\phi}{\Delta\omega\left(1 - \frac{\lambda}{\Delta\omega}\sin 2\phi\right)} = \frac{d\phi}{\Delta\omega}\left(1 + \frac{\lambda}{\Delta\omega}\sin 2\phi\right) = dt \quad [97.19]$$

Integrating this expression, one obtains

$$\phi - \phi_0 - \frac{\lambda}{2\Delta\omega}\cos 2\phi = \Delta\omega t$$

that is,

$$\phi = \Delta\omega t + \phi_0 + \frac{\lambda}{2\Delta\omega}\cos 2\phi$$

where ϕ_0 is an arbitrary constant. In view of the smallness of λ this can be written as

$$\phi = (\Delta\omega t + \phi_0) + \frac{\lambda}{2\Delta\omega}\cos 2(\Delta\omega t + \phi_0) \qquad [97.20]$$

Substituting this value of ϕ into the first equation [97.15], one obtains a differential equation with periodic coefficients.

It is noted that this equation admits a trivial solution $a = 0$, which expresses the condition of a heteroperiodic state. The stability of this solution depends on the sign of the expression

$$S_1 - S_0 - \frac{3}{2} S_3 F^2 + \frac{1}{2} S_2 F \overline{\cos 2\phi}$$

where $\overline{\cos 2\phi}$ is the average of $\cos 2\phi$ per period, that is,

$$\overline{\cos 2\phi} = \frac{1}{T} \int_0^T \cos 2\phi \, dt \qquad [97.21]$$

$$\int_0^T \cos 2\phi \, dt = \int_0^{2\pi} \cos 2\phi \frac{dt}{d\phi} \, d\phi = \frac{1}{2} \int_0^{2\pi} \frac{\cos 2\phi}{\Delta\omega - \lambda \sin 2\phi} \, d(2\phi)$$

$$= -\frac{1}{2\Delta\omega k^2} \int_0^\pi \frac{d(1 - k^2 \sin \psi)}{1 - k^2 \sin \psi} = -\frac{1}{2\Delta\omega k^2} \log(1 - k^2 u)\Big|_{u=0}^{u=0} = 0$$

thus $\overline{\cos 2\phi} = 0$, and the preceding expression becomes

$$S_1 - S_0 - \frac{3}{2} S_3 F^2 = C \qquad [97.22]$$

If $C < 0$, the first equation [97.13] shows that the heteroperiodic state $a = 0$ is stable; if, however, $C > 0$, the heteroperiodic state is unstable and autoperiodic excitation sets in.

98. FRACTIONAL-ORDER RESONANCE

We shall consider Equations [97.11] again in the more general case of fractional-order resonance. It was shown that a trivial solution $a = 0$ exists which characterizes the heteroperiodic state. We will now investigate the stability of the solution $a = 0$; for that purpose we develop the integrands appearing in the functions S_r and S_i in terms of the small quantity a, around the point $E_0 + F \cos \left(s\tau - \frac{s}{r}\phi\right)$ in Equations [97.7]. This gives the first terms of Taylor's expansion for these functions, namely:

$$S_r = \frac{1}{\pi} \int_0^{2\pi} f_a \left[E_0 + F \cos \left(s\tau - \frac{s}{r}\phi\right)\right] \cos^2 r\tau \, d\tau$$

$$\qquad [98.1]$$

$$S_i = \frac{1}{2\pi} \int_0^{2\pi} f_a \left[E_0 + F \cos \left(s\tau - \frac{s}{r}\phi\right)\right] \sin 2r\tau \, d\tau$$

With $\tau = t + \dfrac{\phi}{r}$, these expressions reduce to

$$S_r = \frac{1}{2\pi} \int_0^{2\pi} f_a \left[E_0 + F \cos st\right]\left[1 + \cos(2rt + 2\phi)\right] dt$$

$$S_i = -\frac{1}{2\pi} \int_0^{2\pi} f_a \left[E_0 + F \cos st\right] \sin(2rt + 2\phi) \, dt$$

because of the periodicity of the integrands. Since

$$\int_0^{2\pi} f_a(E_0 + F\cos st)\sin 2rt \; dt = 0$$

these relations reduce to

$$S_r = \frac{1}{2\pi}\int_0^{2\pi} f_a\big[E_0 + F\cos st\big]\big[1 + \cos 2rt \cos 2\phi\big]\; dt$$

$$S_i = -\frac{1}{2\pi}\int_0^{2\pi} f_a\big[E_0 + F\cos st\big]\cos 2rt \;\sin 2\phi \; dt$$

If we set

$$\frac{1}{2\pi}\int_0^{2\pi} f_a\big[E_0 + F\cos st\big]\; dt = N_0$$

and   [98.2]

$$\frac{1}{2\pi}\int_0^{2\pi} f_a\big[E_0 + F\cos st\big]\cos 2rt \; dt = N_1$$

Equations [98.1] become

$$S_r = N_0 + N_1 \cos 2\phi$$

$$S_i = -N_1 \sin 2\phi$$ [98.3]

With these values for S_r and S_i, Equations [97.11] become

$$\frac{da}{dt} = \delta_0\Big(\frac{N_0}{S_0} - 1\Big)a + \frac{\delta_0 N_1}{S_0} a \cos 2\phi$$

[98.4]

$$\frac{d\phi}{dt} = \Big(\omega_0 - \frac{r}{s}\alpha\Big) - \frac{\delta_0 N_1}{S_0} \sin 2\phi$$

The nature of the solutions of these equations establishes the conditions for the stability or instability of the autoperiodic oscillation. If the only stable autoperiodic solution is $a = 0$, only heteroperiodic oscillations are possible. Equations [98.4] with periodic coefficients can be reduced to a system with constant coefficients by introducing the new variables $u = a \cos\phi$ and $v = a \sin\phi$. With these new variables we have

$$\frac{du}{dt} = \frac{da}{dt}\cos\phi - a\sin\phi\frac{d\phi}{dt} \quad \text{and} \quad \frac{dv}{dt} = \frac{da}{dt}\sin\phi + a\cos\phi\frac{d\phi}{dt}$$

Substituting in these equations $\frac{da}{dt}$ and $\frac{d\phi}{dt}$ from Equations [98.4] and rearranging, one gets

$$\frac{du}{dt} = \delta_0\Big(\frac{N_0 + N_1}{S_0} - 1\Big)u - \Big(\omega_0 - \frac{r}{s}\alpha\Big)v = Au - Bv$$

[98.5]

$$\frac{dv}{dt} = \Big(\omega_0 - \frac{r}{s}\alpha\Big)u + \delta_0\Big(\frac{N_0 - N_1}{S_0} - 1\Big)v = Bu + Cv$$

These equations have non-trivial solutions if

$$\begin{vmatrix} (-p + A) & -B \\ B & (-p + C) \end{vmatrix} = 0 \qquad [98.6]$$

Hence the solution $a = 0$ is stable if the roots p_1 and p_2 of [98.6] have negative real parts. Written explicitly, these roots are

$$p_{1,2} = \delta_0 \left(\frac{N_0}{S_0} - 1 \right) \pm \sqrt{\left(\delta_0 \frac{N_1}{S_0} \right)^2 - \left(\omega_0 - \frac{r}{s} \alpha \right)^2} \qquad [98.7]$$

According to whether the quantity under the radical is positive or negative, the roots will be real or conjugate complex. Replacing N_1 by its value [98.2] gives

$$\left| \omega_0 - \frac{r}{s} \alpha \right| > \frac{\delta_0}{2\pi S_0} \left| \int_0^{2\pi} f_a(E_0 + F \cos s\tau) \cos 2r\tau \, d\tau \right| \qquad [98.8]$$

$$\left| \omega_0 - \frac{r}{s} \alpha \right| < \frac{\delta_0}{2\pi S_0} \left| \int_0^{2\pi} f_a(E_0 + F \cos s\tau) \cos 2r\tau \, d\tau \right| \qquad [98.9]$$

In Equation [98.8], the roots are conjugate complex, and self-excitation is possible if $N_0 > S_0$, that is, if

$$\frac{1}{2\pi} \int_0^{2\pi} f_a(E_0 + F \cos \tau) \, d\tau > S_0 \qquad [98.10]$$

In Equation [98.9], the roots are real, and self-excitation is possible when at least one root is positive. One finds that this condition is

$$(N_0 - S_0)^2 + N_1^2 > \left[\frac{\omega_0 - \frac{r}{s} \alpha}{\delta_0} \right]^2 S_0^2 \qquad [98.11]$$

with $N_0 > S_0$.

If one takes a still stronger inequality by dropping the term $(N_0 - S_0)^2$ in [98.11], one obtains a sufficient condition for self-excitation:

$$\frac{s}{r} \left(\omega_0 - \left| \delta_0 \frac{N_1}{S_0} \right| \right) < \alpha < \frac{s}{r} \left(\omega_0 + \left| \delta_0 \frac{N_1}{S_0} \right| \right) \qquad [98.12]$$

This means that the autoperiodic state always sets in when the external frequency α lies in the interval defined by [98.12], which requires that

$$N_1 = \frac{1}{2\pi} \int_0^{2\pi} f_a(E_0 + F \cos s\tau) \cos 2r\tau \, d\tau \neq 0 \qquad [98.13]$$

This condition is fulfilled only when $2r/s = k$, where k is an integer. Since systems where r/s is an integer have been eliminated because they do not possess subharmonic solutions, one can assert that the condition for the existence of self-excitation of the autoperiodic state excited by the extraneous frequency α is

$$\frac{r}{s} = \frac{2q+1}{2} \qquad [98.14]$$

where $q = 0, 1, 2, \cdots$.

     If the amplitude F of the externally applied force is very small, one can further simplify the expression [98.13] and write

$$N_1 = \frac{F f_{aF}(E_0)}{2\pi} \int_0^{2\pi} \cos s\tau \cos 2r\tau \, d\tau \qquad [98.15]$$

where $f_{aF}(E_0)$ designates the derivative of f_a with respect to F taken at the point E_0. From this expression it follows that

$$N_1 = 0 \quad \text{for} \quad s \neq 2r$$

$$\qquad\qquad\qquad\qquad\qquad [98.16]$$

$$N_1 = \frac{F f_{aF}(E_0)}{2} \quad \text{for} \quad s = 2r$$

which means that in the zone of self-excitation defined by [98.12] only *fundamental fractional resonance* of the order one-half can exist, in which case

$$\frac{r}{s} = \frac{1}{2}; \quad \omega_0 = \frac{\alpha}{2} \qquad [98.17]$$

This fact was noted by Lord Rayleigh in his experiments with oscillating systems. He observed that, if one of the parameters (L,m) or $(1/C,k)$, in the notation of Chapter XIII, oscillates with a frequency twice as large as the frequency of the system, the system will oscillate with half the frequency of the parameter.

99. PARAMETRIC EXCITATION

     Parametric excitation of a system is defined as the condition of self-excitation caused by a periodic variation of a parameter of the system. Although this subject is discussed in Chapter XIX from a different point of view, it is preferable to give an outline of the phenomenon here in order not to interrupt the argument of Kryloff and Bogoliuboff which we are following.

     Let us consider the circuit shown in Figure 99.1. It consists of a very small resistance R, a constant inductance L, a non-linear inductance $L_1(i)$ containing a saturated iron core, and a variable capacitor C arranged to produce a fluctuating capacity with frequency α around its average value C_0 according to the law

$$C = C_0(1 + \rho \sin \alpha t)$$

where ρC_0 is the amplitude of the fluctuating capacity and $\rho \ll 1$. If we assume that R is very small and that $L_1(i) \ll L$, the problem is clearly within the scope of the quasi-linear theory. Let us also assume that the circuit is tuned so that

$$\omega_0 = \frac{1}{\sqrt{LC_0}} \approx \frac{\alpha}{2} \qquad [99.1]$$

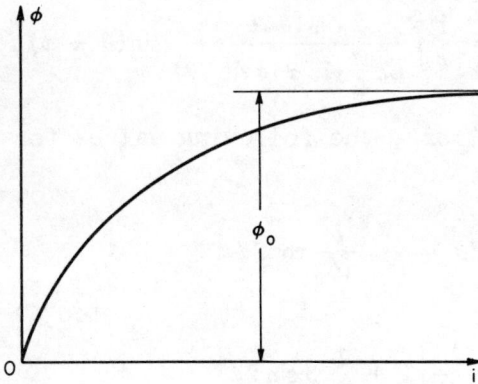

Figure 99.1

This condition will result in fractional-order resonance of the order one-half, as was just shown, and the steady-state current will be of the form

$$i = a \sin\left(\frac{\alpha}{2} t + \phi\right) \qquad [99.2]$$

In this problem we have, in addition to the constant parameters R and L, one periodically varying parameter $C = C_0(1 + \rho \sin \alpha t)$ and one non-linear parameter $L_1(i)$. We can apply the Principle of Equivalent Linearization to the non-linear parameter L_1 and write

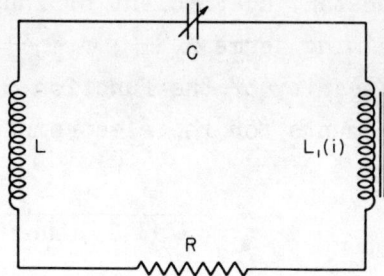

Figure 99.2

$$L_1(a) = \frac{1}{a\pi} \int_0^{2\pi} L'(a \sin \phi) \sin \phi \, d\phi \qquad [99.3]$$

It is recalled that the coefficient of inductance L is defined in all cases by the relation $\phi = Li$, where ϕ is the flux linkages of the coil carrying the current i. When the coil is wound on an iron core, the function $\phi(i)$ has the appearance shown in Figure 99.2, when we neglect the effect of hysteresis and the inflection point near the origin in order to simplify the argument. It is apparent from the above definition that the coefficient of inductance L is a monotonically decreasing function of i in the presence of magnetic saturation. Approximating the function $\phi(i)$ by the expression $\phi(i) = \phi_0(1 - e^{-\lambda i})$, one has the following expression for $L(i)$:

$$L(i) = \phi_0\left(\lambda - \frac{\lambda^2}{2} i + \frac{\lambda^3}{6} i^2 - \cdots\right) \qquad [99.4]$$

It is seen from this expression that

$$\frac{dL(i)}{di} = \phi_0\left(-\frac{\lambda^2}{2} + \frac{\lambda^3}{3} i - \cdots\right)$$

is negative. The argument is obviously valid for any point around which the expansion is made. It is also apparent that the term $\phi_0\lambda = L_0$ represents the constant coefficient of inductance of the coil without an iron core; the remaining terms $\phi_0 \frac{\lambda^2 i}{2}$; $\phi_0 \frac{\lambda^3 i^2}{6}$; $\cdots$ are variable terms resulting from the non-linearity of the function $\phi(i)$. The variable parameter $C = C_0(1 + \rho \sin \alpha t)$ accounts for the electromotive force

$$e = -\frac{1}{C_0(1 + \rho \sin \alpha t)} \int_0^t i\, dt = -\frac{1}{C_0(1 + \rho \sin \alpha t)} \int_0^t a \sin\left(\frac{\alpha}{2} t + \phi\right) dt$$

$$= \frac{a \cos\left(\frac{\alpha}{2} t + \phi\right)}{C_0 \frac{\alpha}{2}(1 + \rho \sin \alpha t)} \qquad [99.5]$$

By the Principle of Harmonic Balance, Section 77, the fundamental harmonic of this expression must be equal to the voltage drop of the current i, given by [99.2], across the impedance $Z_e = r_e + j x_e$, where Z_e is the equivalent impedance of the circuit.

Since the Fourier coefficients of the first harmonic $a_1 \cos\left(\frac{\alpha}{2} t + \phi\right)$ $+ b_1 \sin\left(\frac{\alpha}{2} t + \phi\right)$ of the periodic function [99.4] are

$$a_1 = \frac{1}{\pi}\int_0^{2\pi} \frac{a \cos(\theta + \phi)}{C_0 \frac{\alpha}{2}(1 + \rho \sin 2\theta)} \cos(\theta + \phi)\, d\theta; \qquad b_1 = \frac{1}{\pi}\int_0^{2\pi} \frac{a \cos(\theta + \phi)}{C_0 \frac{\alpha}{2}(1 + \rho \sin 2\theta)} \sin(\theta + \phi)\, d\theta$$

one finds, after a few elementary transformations, the following values for r_e and x_e:

$$r_e = \frac{1}{\pi \frac{\alpha}{2}}\int_0^{2\pi} \frac{\sin(\theta + \phi)\cos(\theta + \phi)}{C_0(1 + \rho \sin 2\theta)}\, d\theta = -\frac{\rho}{\alpha C_0} \cos 2\phi$$

$$\qquad [99.6]$$

$$x_e = \frac{1}{\pi \frac{\alpha}{2}}\int_0^{2\pi} \frac{\cos^2(\theta + \phi)}{C_0(1 + \rho \sin 2\theta)}\, d\theta = \frac{2}{\alpha C_0}\left[1 + \frac{1}{2}\rho \sin 2\phi\right]$$

It is thus seen that a variable capacity results in the appearance of a variable impedance Z_e characterized by components r_e and x_e given by [99.6]. The circuit acts as if it had an equivalent capacity

$$C_e = \frac{C_0}{1 + \frac{\rho}{2}\sin 2\phi} \approx C_0\left(1 - \frac{\rho}{2}\sin 2\phi\right) \qquad [99.7]$$

We have seen that the equivalent system consists of an inductance $L + L_1$, a resistance $R - \frac{\rho}{\alpha C_0} \cos 2\phi$, and a capacity $C_0(1 + \frac{\rho}{2} \sin 2\phi)$. The equivalent parameters thus appear as functions of the phase angle ϕ. The decrement and frequency of the equivalent system are

$$\delta = \frac{R - \frac{\rho}{\alpha C_0} \cos 2\phi}{2(L + L_1)} \approx \frac{R}{2L} - \frac{\rho \omega_0}{4} \cos 2\phi$$

$$\omega = \frac{1}{\sqrt{(L + L_1)C}} \approx \omega_0 \left[1 - \frac{L_1(a)}{2L} + \frac{\rho}{4} \sin 2\phi \right]$$

[99.8]

whence the equations of the first approximation are

$$\frac{da}{dt} = \left(\frac{\omega_0 \rho}{4} \cos 2\phi - \frac{R}{2L} \right) a; \quad \frac{d\phi}{dt} = \left(\omega_0 - \frac{L_1(a)}{2L} \omega_0 - \frac{\alpha}{2} \right) + \frac{\omega_0 \rho}{4} \sin 2\phi \quad [99.9]$$

Expanding the function $\frac{L_1(a)}{2L} \omega_0$, which appears in the second equation, in a Taylor's series around the value $a = 0$, we get

$$\frac{d\phi}{dt} = \left(\omega_0 - \frac{L_1(0)}{2L} \omega_0 - \frac{\alpha}{2} \right) + \frac{\omega_0 \rho}{4} \sin 2\phi - \frac{a}{2L} L_1'(0) - \cdots$$

If we let

$$\frac{\omega_0 \rho}{4} = m; \quad \frac{R}{2L} = n; \quad \omega_0 - \frac{L_1(0)}{2L} \omega_0 - \frac{\alpha}{2} = p$$

Equations [99.9] become

$$\frac{da}{dt} = (m \cos 2\phi - n)a; \quad \frac{d\phi}{dt} = p + m \sin 2\phi - \frac{a}{2L} L_1'(0) \quad [99.10]$$

Let us examine the behavior of the system when $a = 0$. The singular points occur when

$$m \sin 2\phi + p = 0 \quad\quad [99.11]$$

Let $2\phi_0$ be one of the roots, which we will assume to be in the first quadrant ($\sin 2\phi_0 > 0$; $\cos 2\phi_0 > 0$). Applying the Poincaré-Liapounoff criteria of stability and designating the small perturbation of the amplitude by ξ and the perturbation in the phase angle around ϕ_0 by η, we have the following variational equations

$$\frac{d\xi}{dt} = (m \cos 2\phi_0 - n)\xi$$

[99.12]

$$\frac{d\eta}{dt} = \left(-\frac{L_1'(0)}{2L} \right) \xi + (2m \cos 2\phi_0)\eta - 2m \cos 2\phi_0 \cdot \phi_0$$

The last constant term in the second equation clearly does not have any effect on stability and amounts to a shift of the origin in the (ξ, η)-plane. The characteristic equation of the system [99.12] is then

$$S^2 - (3m \cos 2\phi_0 - n)S + 2m \cos 2\phi_0(m \cos 2\phi_0 - n) = 0 \quad [99.13]$$

For self-excitation it is necessary that the free term as well as the coefficient of S be positive. In this case the singularity is either an unstable nodal point or an unstable focal point. Since we have assumed that $2\phi_0$ is in the first quadrant, these conditions require that

$$\cos 2\phi_0 > \frac{n}{m}$$

$$\cos 2\phi_0 > \frac{n}{3m}$$

[99.14]

The first inequality is stronger than the second and should be used. On the other hand, for real values of the argument, one must have

$$\frac{n}{m} = \frac{2R}{L\omega_0 \rho} < 1$$

[99.15]

This merely imposes the additional condition that the index of modulation ρ should be below a certain critical value given by [99.15]. From the first inequality [99.14] and the condition [99.11] we have

$$p^2 = m^2 \sin^2 2\phi_0 = m^2(1 - \cos^2 2\phi_0)$$

that is,

$$m^2 \cos^2 2\phi_0 = m^2 - p^2$$

whence

$$p^2 + n^2 < m^2$$

Substituting the values of m, n, and p, we obtain the condition of self-excitation which was derived by Kryloff and Bogoliuboff:

$$\left(2 - \frac{L_1(0)}{L} - \frac{\alpha}{\omega_0}\right)^2 < \frac{\rho^2}{4} - \frac{R^2}{L^2 \omega_0^2}$$

[99.16]

Self-excitation does not occur if the sign of this inequality is reversed. The stationary condition is obtained when $da/dt = d\phi/dt = 0$ in Equations [99.9]. If we designate the stationary amplitude by a_1 and the phase angle by ϕ_1, we get

$$\cos 2\phi_1 = \frac{2R}{L\omega_0 \rho}$$

From the second equation [99.9] we have

$$L_1(a_1) = L\left(2 - \frac{\alpha}{\omega_0} + \frac{\rho}{2} \sin 2\phi_1\right)$$

[99.17]

This equation gives the amplitude a_1 of the stationary oscillation since $2\phi_1$ is known and since the function $L_1(a)$ is given by Equation [99.3].

For the stability of a stationary state one can again apply the Poincaré-Liapounoff criteria, see Chapter III, to the differential equations [99.9] by expanding the functions $\cos 2\phi$, $\sin 2\phi$, and $L_1(a)$ in a Taylor series around fixed values ϕ_1 and a_1 and by introducing the perturbation variables ξ and η given by equations $\phi = \phi_1 + \xi$ and $a = a_1 + \eta$. Proceeding in this manner, one obtains the following variational equations:

$$\frac{d\eta}{dt} = \eta(m\cos 2\phi_1 - n) + \xi(-2ma_1\sin 2\phi_1)$$

[99.18]

$$\frac{d\xi}{dt} = \eta[-qL_1'(a_1)] + \xi(2m\cos 2\phi_1)$$

where

$$m = \frac{\omega_0\rho}{4}; \quad n = \frac{R}{2L}; \quad q = \frac{\omega_0}{2L}$$

It is to be noted that $L_1'(a_1)$ is negative, since the non-linear inductance decreases when a_1 increases. The characteristic equation of the system [99.13] is

$$\lambda^2 - (3m\cos 2\phi_1 - n)\lambda + \left[(m\cos 2\phi_1 - n)2m\cos 2\phi_1 + 2mS\sin 2\phi_1\right] = 0$$

where $S = a_1 q |L_1'(a_1)| > 0$. Conditions for a stable stationary solution are clearly

$$3m\cos 2\phi_1 - n < 0 \quad \text{and} \quad m\cos^2 2\phi_1 - n\cos 2\phi_1 + S\sin 2\phi_1 > 0 \quad [99.19]$$

From the first condition $\cos 2\phi_1 < \frac{n}{3m}$. From the second

$$\cos 2\phi_1(m\cos 2\phi_1 - n) > -S\sin 2\phi_1$$

If the angle $2\phi_1$ is in the first quadrant ($\sin 2\phi_1 > 0$; $\cos 2\phi_1 > 0$), the preceding inequality can be replaced by a stronger one

$$\cos 2\phi_1(m\cos 2\phi_1 - n) > 0$$

[99.20]

whence

$$\cos 2\phi_1 > \frac{n}{m}$$

Comparing this with the previous one, namely, $\cos 2\phi_1 < \frac{n}{3m}$, we see that these two conditions are not consistent. This means that a stable stationary solution cannot exist when $2\phi_1$ is in the interval $0 < 2\phi_1 < \frac{\pi}{2}$.

If one now considers the interval $\frac{\pi}{2} < 2\phi_1 < \pi$, that is, $\cos 2\phi_1 < 0$, $\sin 2\phi_1 > 0$, it is observed that both conditions, namely, $3m\cos 2\phi_1 - n < 0$ and $m\cos 2\phi_1 - n < 0$, are fulfilled. The argument can easily be carried out for the remaining two quadrants. This means that stable stationary solutions may exist for certain definite ranges of the phase angle.

100. STABILITY OF NON-LINEAR EXTERNAL RESONANCE; JUMPS

We shall now investigate the so-called *jump phenomenon* observed in non-linear systems acted upon by an external periodic excitation. We will consider the usual quasi-linear equation

$$m\ddot{x} + kx = \mu f(\alpha t, x, \dot{x})$$

[100.1]

where $f(\alpha t, x, \dot{x})$ is a non-linear periodic function of t with period $\frac{2\pi}{\alpha}$. In the neighborhood of external resonance we have the relation

$$\omega_0 = \frac{r}{s}\alpha + \mu Q \qquad [100.2]$$

where $\omega_0 = \sqrt{\frac{k}{m}}$ is the undamped frequency and r and s are relatively prime integers. The term μQ is a small quantity of the first order. The mechanical interpretation of Equation [100.1] is obvious. We can apply the method of equivalent linearization, Chapter XII, and for this purpose we seek a solution of the form

$$x = a \sin\left(\frac{r}{s}\alpha t + \phi\right) \qquad [100.3]$$

According to this method, the non-linear exciting force

$$F = \mu f(\alpha t, x, \dot{x}) \qquad [100.4]$$

is to be replaced by the equivalent linear one

$$F = -k_1 x - \lambda_1 \dot{x} \qquad [100.5]$$

The *equivalent parameters* k_1 and λ_1 are obtained by equating the fundamental harmonic of the expression

$$F = \mu f(\alpha t, x, \dot{x}) = \mu f\left[\alpha t,\ a\sin\left(\frac{r}{s}\alpha t + \phi\right),\ a\frac{r}{s}\alpha\cos\left(\frac{r}{s}\alpha t + \phi\right)\right] \qquad [100.6]$$

to the linearized terms

$$F = -k_1 x - \lambda_1 \dot{x} = -k_1 a\sin\left(\frac{r}{s}\alpha t + \phi\right) - \lambda_1 a\frac{r}{s}\alpha\cos\left(\frac{r}{s}\alpha t + \phi\right) \qquad [100.7]$$

The equivalent parameters k_1 and λ_1 are given by the Fourier coefficients of the first harmonic, namely,

$$k_1 = -\frac{\mu}{\pi a}\int_0^{2\pi} f\left(s\tau - \frac{s}{r}\phi,\ a\sin r\tau,\ a\frac{r}{s}\alpha\cos r\tau\right)\sin r\tau\, d\tau \qquad [100.8]$$

$$\lambda_1 = -\frac{\mu}{\pi a}\left(\frac{s}{r\alpha}\right)\int_0^{2\pi} f\left(s\tau - \frac{s}{r}\phi,\ a\sin r\tau,\ a\frac{r}{s}\alpha\cos r\tau\right)\cos r\tau\, d\tau$$

In view of Equation [100.2] these equations can be written as

$$k_1 = -\frac{\mu}{\pi a}\int_0^{2\pi} f\left(s\tau - \frac{s}{r}\phi,\ a\sin r\tau,\ a\omega_0\cos r\tau\right)\sin r\tau\, d\tau \qquad [100.9]$$

$$\lambda_1 = -\frac{\mu}{\pi\omega_0 a}\int_0^{2\pi} f\left(s\tau - \frac{s}{r}\phi,\ a\sin r\tau,\ a\omega_0\cos r\tau\right)\cos r\tau\, d\tau$$

The parameters of the equivalent linearized system are

$$\delta = \frac{\lambda_1}{2m}; \qquad \omega = \sqrt{\frac{k+k_1}{m}} \approx \omega_0\left(1 + \frac{k_1}{2k}\right) \qquad [100.10]$$

and the equations of the first approximation appear in the form

$$\frac{da}{dt} = -\frac{\lambda_1}{2m}a; \quad \frac{d\phi}{dt} = \omega - \frac{r}{s}\alpha = \omega_0 - \frac{r}{s}\alpha + \omega_0\frac{k_1}{2k} \qquad [100.11]$$

Replacing in these equations k_1 and λ_1 by their values in [100.9], one obtains two differential equations of the first order sufficient to determine the two quantities a and ϕ.

As an example of the application of these results, we will consider a rod of length l on which is impressed an axial periodic force $F = H \sin \alpha t$.

The partial differential equation for the transverse vibrations of the rod is

$$EI\frac{\partial^4 y}{\partial x^4} + \frac{\gamma A}{g}\frac{\partial^2 y}{\partial t^2} + H\sin\alpha t\frac{\partial^2 y}{\partial x^2} = 0 \qquad [100.12]$$

where y is the lateral deflection,

EI is the rigidity of the rod,

γ is the weight of the rod per unit volume,

A is the cross-sectional area of the rod, and

g is the force of gravity, 32.2 feet per second squared.

Assuming as boundary conditions

$$y(0) = y(l) = y_{xx}(0) = y_{xx}(l) = 0 \qquad [100.13]$$

and seeking a solution of the form

$$y = z(t)\sin\pi\frac{x}{l} \qquad [100.14]$$

one finds, upon the substitution of [100.14] into [100.12], the following differential equation

$$\frac{\gamma A}{g}\ddot{z} + EI\frac{\pi^4}{l^4}\left(1 - \frac{l^2 H}{EI\pi^2}\sin\alpha t\right)z = 0 \qquad [100.15]$$

If we let

$$\omega_0^2 = \frac{EI\pi^4 g}{\gamma A l^4}; \quad F_{cr} = \frac{EI\pi^2}{l^2}; \quad \rho = \frac{H}{F_{cr}}$$

where ω_0 is the fundamental frequency of the transverse oscillation of the rod and F_{cr} is the critical Euler's load, Equation [100.15] becomes

$$\ddot{z} + \omega_0(1 - \rho\sin\alpha t)z = 0 \qquad [100.16]$$

We are looking for a subharmonic oscillation of the order one-half, when $\omega_0 \approx \alpha/2$. The solution is then of the form

$$z = a\sin\left(\frac{\alpha}{2}t + \phi\right) \qquad [100.17]$$

where a and ϕ satisfy the equations of the first approximation, viz.,

$$\frac{da}{dt} = \frac{1}{4}\,\rho a \omega_0 \cos 2\phi$$

$$\frac{d\phi}{dt} = \omega_0 - \frac{\alpha}{2} - \frac{1}{4}\,\rho \omega_0 \sin 2\phi$$

[100.18]

Comparing these equations with Equations [99.9] of the circuit excited by a periodically varying capacity, we note that they appear as a particular case of the latter, namely, the case when $L_1(a) = 0$ and $R = 0$. We can therefore use the condition of self-excitation [99.16], which gives here

$$\left| 2 - \frac{\alpha}{\omega_0} \right| < \frac{\rho}{2}$$

[100.19]

Let us now consider fundamental non-linear resonance, that is, $r = s$. The non-linear function appearing in Equation [100.1] is of the form

$$\mu f(\alpha t, x, \dot{x}) = -\,f(x, \dot{x}) + E \sin \alpha t$$

[100.20]

We have $\omega_0 \approx \alpha$. The quasi-linear equation then becomes

$$m\ddot{x} + kx + f(x, \dot{x}) = E \sin \alpha t$$

[100.21]

We are seeking a solution of the form

$$x = a \sin(\alpha t + \phi)$$

[100.22]

The linearized equations of the first approximation are

$$\frac{da}{dt} = -\,\frac{\lambda_1}{2m}\,a$$

$$\frac{d\phi}{dt} = \sqrt{\frac{k + k_1}{m}} - \alpha$$

[100.23]

where the equivalent parameters λ_1 and k_1 are given by the equations

$$\lambda_1 = \frac{1}{\pi a \omega_0}\int_0^{2\pi}\left[f(a \sin \tau,\ a \omega_0 \cos \tau) - E \sin(\tau - \phi)\right] \cos \tau\, d\tau$$

[100.24]

$$k_1 = \frac{1}{\pi a}\int_0^{2\pi}\left[f(a \sin \tau,\ a \omega_0 \cos \tau) - E \sin(\tau - \phi)\right] \sin \tau\, d\tau$$

If we put

$$\lambda_e = \frac{1}{\pi a \omega_0}\int_0^{2\pi} f(a \sin \tau,\ a \omega_0 \cos \tau) \cos \tau\, d\tau$$

[100.25]

$$k_e = k + \frac{1}{\pi a}\int_0^{2\pi} f(a \sin \tau,\ a \omega_0 \cos \tau) \sin \tau\, d\tau$$

it is noted that the coefficients $\lambda_e(a)$ and $k_e(a)$ correspond to the absence of the external periodic excitation $E \sin \alpha t$. In view of Equations [100.24] we can write

$$\frac{\lambda_1}{2m} = \frac{\lambda_e}{2m} + \frac{E}{2ma\omega_0} \sin \phi \approx \frac{\lambda_e}{2m} + \frac{E}{2ma\alpha} \sin \phi = \delta_e + \frac{E}{2ma\alpha} \sin \phi \quad [100.26]$$

where $\delta_e = \frac{\lambda_e}{2m}$.

Similarly,

$$\sqrt{\frac{k + k_1}{m}} - \alpha \approx \frac{1}{2\alpha}\left(\frac{k + k_1}{m} - \alpha^2\right) = \frac{1}{2\alpha}\left(\frac{k_e}{m} - \alpha^2 - \frac{E}{ma} \cos \phi\right)$$

$$= \frac{1}{2\alpha}\left(\omega_e^2 - \alpha^2 - \frac{E}{ma} \cos \phi\right) \qquad [100.27]$$

where $\omega_e = \sqrt{k/m}$. The quantities δ_e and ω_e are the equivalent parameters for the non-linear oscillations of the system in the absence of an external periodic force.

Substituting these values of λ_1 and $\sqrt{\frac{k + k_1}{m}}$ in Equations [100.23], one obtains the following expressions of the first approximation:

$$\frac{da}{dt} = -\delta_e a - \frac{E}{2m\alpha} \sin \phi$$

$$2\alpha \frac{d\phi}{dt} = \omega_e^2 - \alpha^2 - \frac{E}{ma} \cos \phi \qquad [100.28]$$

The stationary amplitude a is obtained from these equations:

$$- E \sin \phi = 2m\alpha a \delta_e$$

$$E \cos \phi = ma(\omega_e^2 - \alpha^2) \qquad [100.29]$$

whence

$$a = \frac{E}{m\sqrt{(\omega_e^2 - \alpha^2)^2 + 4\delta_e^2 \alpha^2}} \qquad [100.30]$$

It is observed that the stationary amplitude is given to the first order of approximation by exactly the same relation which gives the forced amplitude of a linear system, except that the equivalent parameters are to be used instead of the constant linear parameters.

Although these results, which were derived from the equations of the first approximation at a glance, do not seem to yield anything new, it will be shown now that the important difference between linear resonance and non-linear resonance lies in the conditions of stability. More specifically, it will be shown that, whereas the linear oscillation is stable throughout the whole neighborhood around the point of resonance, the non-linear oscillation is stable only in certain regions.

If we set

$$R(a,\phi) = -\frac{E}{m}\sin\phi - 2\alpha a \delta_e$$

[100.31]

$$\psi(a,\phi) = (\omega_e^2 - \alpha^2)a - \frac{E}{m}\cos\phi$$

Equations [100.28] become

$$2\alpha \frac{da}{dt} = R(a,\phi)$$

[100.32]

$$2\alpha a \frac{d\phi}{dt} = \psi(a,\phi)$$

The stationary state is given by the equations

$$R(a,\phi) = 0; \quad \psi(a,\phi) = 0$$

[100.33]

In order to investigate the stability of the stationary state we must form variational equations. If we designate the perturbations in a and ϕ by δa and $\delta\phi$, respectively, the variational equations are

$$2\alpha \frac{d\delta a}{dt} = R_a \delta a + R_\phi \delta\phi$$

[100.34]

$$2\alpha a \frac{d\delta\phi}{dt} = \psi_a \delta a + \psi_\phi \delta\phi$$

The characteristic equation, see Chapter III, of the system [100.34] is

$$aS^2 - (aR_a + \psi_\phi)S + (R_a\psi_\phi - R_\phi\psi_a) = 0$$

[100.35]

The conditions for stability are clearly

$$aR_a + \psi_\phi < 0; \quad R_a\psi_\phi - R_\phi\psi_a > 0$$

[100.36]

Using Equations [100.29] and [100.31], one has

$$aR_a + \psi_\phi = -2\alpha a \frac{\partial(a\delta_e)}{\partial a} - 2a\alpha\delta_e = -2\alpha \frac{\partial(a^2\delta_e)}{\partial a}$$

[100.37]

On the other hand, we have

$$2\alpha a^2 \delta_e = \frac{a^2\lambda_e}{m} = \frac{a\alpha}{m\omega_0}\frac{1}{\pi}\int_0^{2\pi} f(a\sin\tau,\, a\omega_0\cos\tau)\cos\tau\, d\tau$$

[100.38]

Let us consider the quantity

$$W(a) = \frac{1}{2\pi} a\omega_0 \int_0^{2\pi} f(a\sin\tau,\, a\omega_0\cos\tau)\cos\tau\, d\tau$$

$$= \frac{\omega_0}{2\pi}\int_0^{\frac{2\pi}{\omega_0}} f\big[a\sin(\omega_0 t + \phi),\, a\omega_0\cos(\omega_0 t + \phi)\big]a\omega_0\cos(\omega_0 t + \phi)\, dt \quad [100.39]$$

It is apparent from this expression that the quantity $W(a)$ represents the average power dissipated by the non-linear force $f(x,\dot{x})$ during the oscillation $x = a \sin(\omega_0 t + \phi)$. Hence, for the usual law of friction, $W(a)$ increases with a so that $W_a(a) > 0$. In this case the first condition [100.36] is always fulfilled, as follows from Equation [100.38] and from the condition $W_a(a) > 0$.

Hence the stability of the stationary state depends on the fulfillment of the second condition [100.36].

Differentiating the functions $R(a,\phi)$ and $\psi(a,\phi)$ with respect to α, we have

$$R_a \frac{da}{d\alpha} + R_\phi \frac{d\phi}{d\alpha} = -R_\alpha$$

$$\psi_a \frac{da}{d\alpha} + \psi_\phi \frac{d\phi}{d\alpha} = -\psi_\alpha$$

whence

$$R_a \psi_\phi - \psi_a R_\phi = \psi_\alpha R_\phi - R_\alpha \psi_\phi \qquad [100.40]$$

From Equation [100.31] we have

$$R_\phi = -\frac{E}{m}\cos\phi; \quad R_\alpha = -2a\delta_e; \quad \psi_\phi = \frac{E}{m}\sin\phi; \quad \psi_\alpha = -2\alpha a \quad [100.41]$$

which gives

$$\psi_\alpha R_\phi - R_\alpha \psi_\phi = 2a\frac{E}{m}(\alpha\cos\phi + \delta_e\sin\phi)$$

From Equations [100.29]

$$\frac{E}{m}(\alpha\cos\phi + \delta_e\sin\phi) = \alpha(\omega_e^2 - \alpha^2)a - 2\alpha\delta_e^2 a$$

hence

$$\psi_\alpha R_\phi - R_\alpha \psi_\phi = 2\alpha a^2[(\omega_e^2 - \alpha^2) - 2\delta_e^2]$$

so that

$$(R_a \psi_\phi - \psi_a R_\phi)\frac{da}{d\alpha} = 2\alpha\omega^2[(\omega_e^2 - \alpha^2) - 2\delta_e^2]$$

The second condition [100.36] can be written in the form

$$\frac{da}{dt} > 0 \quad \text{if} \quad \omega_e^2 > \alpha^2 + 2\delta_e^2$$

$$\frac{da}{dt} < 0 \quad \text{if} \quad \omega_e^2 < \alpha^2 + 2\delta_e^2 \qquad [100.42]$$

Since the term δ_e^2 is small and of the second order, it can be neglected, so the conditions of stability become

$$\frac{da}{dt} > 0 \quad \text{if} \quad \omega_e > \alpha$$

$$\frac{da}{dt} < 0 \quad \text{if} \quad \omega_e < \alpha \qquad [100.43]$$

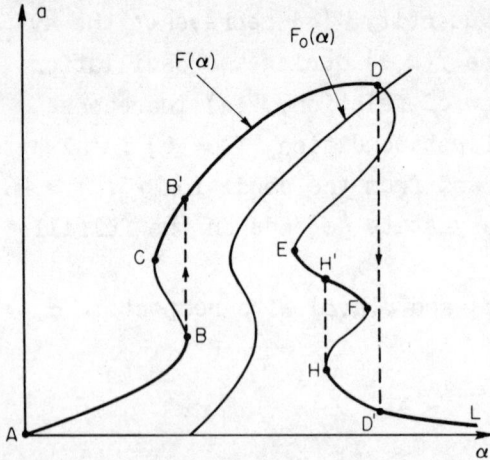

Figure 100.1

These conditions for stability and, hence, for the existence of stationary oscillations, can be represented graphically in a simple manner. Let us trace the curve $a = F(\alpha)$ determined by Equation [100.30], which can be written as

$$\frac{E^2}{m^2} = a^2\left[(\omega_e^2 - \alpha^2)^2 + 4\delta^2\alpha^2\right]$$

Furthermore, let $a = F_0(\alpha)$ be the curve corresponding to the exact resonance $\omega_e(a) = \alpha$. Assume that these curves have the shape shown in Figure 100.1. On the portion of the curve $F(\alpha)$ situated to the left of the curve $F_0(\alpha)$, the condition of stability exists in intervals such as AB, CD, $\cdots$, where the amplitude a increases with increasing frequency α. On the parts of the curve $F(\alpha)$ situated to the right of $F_0(\alpha)$, on the contrary, stability exists in intervals such as EF, HL, $\cdots$, in which the amplitude a decreases with increasing frequency α. These peculiar conditions of stability of non-linear external resonance cause the appearance of *jumps* similar to those which we have already investigated in Part II in connection with the phenomena of hard self-excitation. Thus, for example, if we excite a non-linear system from rest by a gradually increasing frequency, the stable branch AB will be traversed. At the point B, however, this stable zone ends and the amplitude suddenly jumps up to the point B', after which for a continuously increasing frequency of the external excitation the branch B'D will be followed. At the point D the stable region on this branch ends, so that the amplitude drops from D to D'. For a further increase of the frequency of the external periodic excitation the branch D'L will be traversed.

If, however, the frequency is decreased, the amplitude will not pass through the same stages it traversed during the period when the frequency was steadily increasing. Thus, for example, if the frequency is decreased from the value corresponding to the point L, the region D'H will be traversed in a stable manner. This region, as was just mentioned, was missed during the period when the frequency was steadily increasing. If the frequency continues to decrease, the amplitude will jump abruptly from the value H to the value H' and a further change will occur along the branch H'E, and so on.

These phenomena of *resonance hysteresis* may be more or less complicated, depending on the form of the curves $F(\alpha)$ and $F_0(\alpha)$; they are usually accompanied by quasi-discontinuous jumps and hence by similar discontinuities in the energy input into the oscillating system supplied by the external periodic source of energy.

As a special example, consider a non-linear system whose non-linearity is limited only to x, that is, its non-linear function is of the form $f(x)$. In practice, this corresponds to a system with a non-linear spring constant. From Equations [100.25] and [100.26], it is apparent that $\delta_e = 0$, and from the second equation [100.25] we get

$$\omega_e^2 = \frac{1}{m}\left[k + \frac{1}{\pi a}\int_0^{2\pi} f(a \sin \tau) \sin \tau \, d\tau \right] \qquad [100.44]$$

so that Equation [100.30] gives

$$\alpha = \pm \frac{E}{m a_0} + \omega_e(a_0) \qquad [100.45]$$

From Equations [100.29] it follows that, for the plus sign, $\phi = \pi$; for the minus sign, $\phi = 0$. From [100.45] one can build the curve $a = F(\alpha)$. It is noted that if $\omega_e(a)$ varies with a, for instance according to the relation

$$\omega_e(a_0) = \omega_0 + \lambda a_0^2 \qquad \text{when} \qquad \lambda \neq 0$$

the amplitude cannot increase indefinitely for any α. This circumstance is another typical feature of an undamped non-linear resonance.

Interesting examples of jump phenomena have been obtained recently by Ludeke (6) in his experimental work on non-linear mechanical systems. By varying the non-linearity of the springs, different response curves were obtained. Figure 100.2 shows the experimental and theoretical resonance curves obtained for a particular non-linear spring of the "increasing stiffness" type. The theoretical curve was obtained by a graphical method (7) the details of which we omit here.

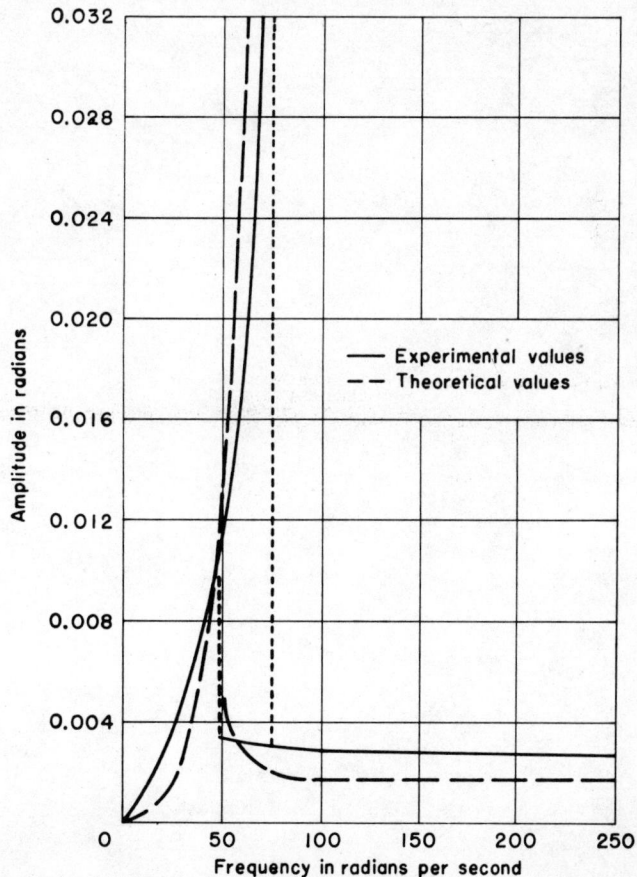

Figure 100.2

      The results of this section and of Section 99 were obtained on the basis of linearized equations of the first approximation. In Chapter XIX the study of the effect of a periodically varying parameter will be resumed, but from a different viewpoint; there we will use differential equations with periodic coefficients.

CHAPTER XVII

SUBHARMONIC RESONANCE ON THE BASIS OF THE THEORY OF POINCARÉ

101. METHOD OF MANDELSTAM AND PAPALEXI

The preceding four chapters of this report have been devoted to a survey of the theory developed by Kryloff and Bogoliuboff. We now propose to review an alternative theory developed by Mandelstam and Papalexi (8) and derived from the classical theory of Poincaré, which was discussed in Chapter VIII. The essence of the Mandelstam-Papalexi method lies in extending Poincaré's theory to systems having an external periodic excitation. Certain advantages arise from this argument. First, the questions of the existence and stability of solutions are treated in a relatively simple manner. Secondly, the description of the behavior of a system in terms of its characteristic parameters is also relatively simple. Finally, the manipulation with generalized impedances and admittances used by Kryloff and Bogoliuboff is replaced here by the analytical method, which is probably a more familiar approach to the subject. It is noteworthy that the theory given in this chapter was found to be a useful tool in connection with the numerous experimental researches conducted by the group of scientists under the leadership of Mandelstam and Papalexi.

102. RESONANCE OF THE ORDER n; DIFFERENTIAL EQUATIONS IN DIMENSIONLESS FORM

The following analysis is a discussion of differential equations of the form

$$\ddot{x} + x = \mu f(t, x, \dot{x}) \qquad [102.1]$$

where the non-linear function $f(t, x, \dot{x})$ now depends explicitly on the time t. More specifically, in what follows we shall consider the equation

$$\ddot{x} + x = \mu f(x, \dot{x}) + \lambda_0 \sin n\tau \qquad [102.2]$$

in which we let the argument of the periodic "forcing" function be $n\tau$ instead of τ in order to prepare for the study of subharmonic resonance of the order $1/n$. Many circuits of electron-tube oscillators can be represented by equations having the same form as [102.2], but we shall not enter into these generalizations here.

We shall consider the standard circuit shown in Figure 102.1 representing an electron-tube oscillator with an inductive coupling M. The externally applied electromotive force $E = E_0 \sin \omega t$ is inserted either in the anode circuit between M and N or in the grid circuit between P and Q. It has been shown that, if the effects of the anode reaction and the grid current are neglected, the differential equation of the circuit is

$$CL \frac{d^2 i}{dt^2} + CR \frac{di}{dt} + i = i_a + C \frac{dE}{dt} \qquad [102.3]$$

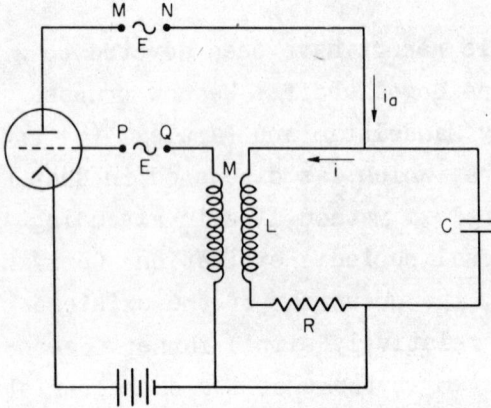

Figure 102.1

where $i_a = f(V_s)$ is a non-linear function representing the anode current i_a as a function of the grid voltage V_s. It is apparent that $V_s = M \frac{di}{dt}$, where M is the coefficient of mutual inductance between the anode and grid circuits. It is convenient to transform Equation [102.3] into dimensionless form.

We introduce the following dimensionless variables:

$$\tau = \frac{t\omega}{n}; \qquad I = \frac{i}{I_0}; \qquad I_a = \frac{i_a}{I_0}$$

where I_0 is the saturation anode current, occurring for a sufficiently high grid voltage V_0. The change of the independent variable gives

$$\frac{di}{dt} = \frac{di}{d\tau} \frac{d\tau}{dt} = \frac{di}{d\tau} \frac{\omega}{n}$$

$$\frac{d^2 i}{dt^2} = \frac{d}{dt}\left(\frac{di}{dt}\right) = \frac{d}{d\tau}\left(\frac{di}{dt}\right)\frac{d\tau}{dt} = \frac{d^2 i}{d\tau^2} \frac{\omega^2}{n^2}$$

$$\frac{dE}{dt} = \frac{dE}{d\tau} \frac{d\tau}{dt} = \frac{dE}{d\tau} \frac{\omega}{n} \qquad [102.4]$$

In the new variable, moreover, $E = E_0 \sin \omega t$ becomes $E = E_0 \sin n\tau$; hence, $\frac{dE}{dt} = E_0 n \cos n\tau$ and, by [102.4],

$$\frac{dE}{dt} = E_0 \omega \cos n\tau$$

Equation [102.3] becomes

$$CL \frac{\omega^2}{n^2} \frac{d^2 i}{d\tau^2} + CR \frac{\omega}{n} \frac{di}{d\tau} + i = i_a + CE_0 \omega \cos n\tau$$

If the "dimensionless current" $I = \frac{i}{I_0}$ is introduced, the previous equation becomes

$$CL \frac{\omega^2}{n^2} \frac{d^2 I}{d\tau^2} + CR \frac{\omega}{n} \frac{dI}{d\tau} + I = I_a + \frac{CE_0 \omega}{I_0} \cos n\tau \qquad [102.5]$$

If we assume that the resistance R of the oscillating circuit is small, the autoperiodic frequency of the circuit is equal to its undamped frequency $\omega_0 = 1/\sqrt{LC}$ to the first order. If the impressed frequency ω is in the neighborhood of the frequency $n\omega_0$ of the oscillating circuit, that is, if

$$CL\,\frac{\omega^2}{n^2} \;=\; \frac{\omega^2}{\omega_0^2 n^2} \;=\; 1 + \xi \qquad\qquad [102.6]$$

where $\xi \ll 1$, the coefficient of $dI/d\tau$ can be written

$$\frac{CR\omega}{n} \;=\; \frac{CLR\omega^2 n}{n^2 L\omega} \;=\; \frac{\omega^2}{n^2 \omega_0^2}\,\frac{Rn}{L\omega} \;=\; (1 + \xi)\,\frac{Rn}{L\omega}$$

Equation [102.5] then becomes

$$(1 + \xi)\frac{d^2 I}{d\tau^2} \;+\; (1 + \xi)\frac{Rn}{L\omega}\frac{dI}{d\tau} \;+\; I \;=\; I_a \;+\; \frac{CE_0\omega}{I_0}\cos n\tau$$

If we divide this equation by $(1 + \xi)$, noting that

$$\frac{1}{1 + \xi} \;=\; \frac{1 + \xi - \xi}{1 + \xi} \;=\; 1 - \frac{\xi}{1 + \xi}$$

we obtain

$$\frac{d^2 I}{d\tau^2} \;+\; \frac{Rn}{L\omega}\frac{dI}{d\tau} \;+\; I \;=\; \frac{\xi}{1 + \xi}\,I \;+\; \frac{1}{1 + \xi}\,I_a \;+\; \frac{CE_0\omega}{I_0(1 + \xi)}\cos n\tau \quad [102.7]$$

Since $I_a = \dfrac{i_a}{I_0} = f\!\left(\dfrac{V_s}{V_0}\,V_0\right)$ where V_0 is the saturation voltage defined by the equation $V_0 = MI_0\omega/n$, the "dimensionless voltage"

$$\frac{V_s}{V_0} \;=\; \frac{M\dfrac{di}{d\tau}\dfrac{\omega}{n}}{MI_0\dfrac{\omega}{n}} \;=\; \frac{dI}{d\tau}$$

so that

$$I_a \;=\; f\!\left(\frac{V_s}{V_0}\right) \;=\; f_1\!\left(\frac{dI}{d\tau}\right) \qquad\qquad [102.8]$$

Setting $\dfrac{Rn}{L\omega} = 2\theta$ in Equation [102.7] and rearranging, we have

$$\frac{d^2 I}{d\tau^2} \;+\; I \;=\; \frac{1}{1 + \xi}\,f_1\!\left(\frac{dI}{d\tau}\right) \;-\; 2\theta\frac{dI}{d\tau} \;+\; \frac{\xi}{1 + \xi}\,I \;+\; Q\cos n\tau$$

where

$$Q \;=\; \frac{CE_0\omega}{I_0(1 + \xi)} \;=\; \frac{CLE_0\omega}{I_0 L(1 + \xi)} \;=\; \frac{E_0 n^2}{I_0 L\omega}$$

Letting

$$\left[\frac{1}{1 + \xi}\,f_1\!\left(\frac{dI}{d\tau}\right) \;-\; 2\theta\frac{dI}{d\tau}\right] \;=\; F\!\left(\frac{dI}{d\tau}\right) \qquad\qquad [102.9]$$

one obtains

$$\frac{d^2 I}{d\tau^2} \;+\; I \;=\; F\!\left(\frac{dI}{d\tau}\right) \;+\; \frac{\xi}{1 + \xi}\,I \;+\; Q\cos n\tau$$

Differentiating this equation with respect to τ, and putting $dI/d\tau = x$, we obtain

$$\ddot{x} \;+\; x \;=\; F'(x)\dot{x} \;+\; \frac{\xi}{1 + \xi}\,x \;+\; \lambda_0 \sin n\tau \qquad\qquad [102.10]$$

where $\lambda_0 = -Qn$. Equation [102.10] has the same form as [102.2].

103. PERIODIC SOLUTIONS OF A QUASI-LINEAR EQUATION WITH A FORCING TERM

From the theory of Poincaré, Chapter VIII, it follows that a quasi-linear equation

$$\ddot{x} + x = \mu f(x, \dot{x}) \qquad [103.1]$$

with $\mu = 0$ admits an infinity of periodic solutions represented in the phase plane by a continuum of concentric circles with the origin as center. For $\mu \neq 0$, but small, periodic solutions may still exist in the neighborhood of *certain* circles, the *generating solutions*. In the rest of the phase plane no periodic solutions exist, but the phase trajectories are spirals winding onto the closed trajectories, the limit cycles, which exist in the neighborhood of the generating solutions.

For Equation [102.2] the situation is similar, for when $\mu = 0$ there exists an infinity of such linear solutions of the form

$$x = a \sin \tau - b \cos \tau + \frac{\lambda_0}{1 - n^2} \sin n\tau \qquad [103.2]$$

The fundamental problem is the determination of the functions $a(\mu)$ and $b(\mu)$ which will yield periodic solutions for the non-linear case, that is, when $\mu \neq 0$ but is small.

If, when $\mu \to 0$, these constants reduce to a_0 and b_0 respectively, that is,

$$a(\mu)_{\mu \to 0} \to a_0; \qquad b(\mu)_{\mu \to 0} \to b_0 \qquad [103.3]$$

the corresponding solution of the linearized equation is called the principal or fundamental solution.

In order to establish the conditions under which the expression [103.2] is the principal solution of Equation [102.2], it is necessary first to determine the limit values [103.3] of a and b for $\mu \to 0$ and then to ascertain that the solution so obtained is stable in the sense of Liapounoff. In this section we shall be concerned with the first part of this problem.

If the new variable

$$z = x - \frac{\lambda_0}{1 - n^2} \sin n\tau \qquad [103.4]$$

is substituted into [102.2], that equation becomes

$$\ddot{z} + z = \mu f\left(z + \frac{\lambda_0}{1 - n^2} \sin n\tau, \ \dot{z} + \frac{n\lambda_0}{1 - n^2} \cos n\tau\right) \qquad [103.5]$$

Introducing into this equation the variables u and v defined by the equations

$$u = \dot{z} \cos \tau + z \sin \tau$$

$$v = \dot{z} \sin \tau - z \cos \tau \qquad [103.6]$$

we find

$$\dot{u} = (\ddot{z} + z)\cos\tau = \mu\psi(u,v,\tau)\cos\tau$$

$$\dot{v} = (\ddot{z} + z)\sin\tau = \mu\psi(u,v,\tau)\sin\tau$$

[103.7]

where

$$\psi(u,v,\tau) = f\left(u\sin\tau - v\cos\tau + \frac{\lambda_0}{1-n^2}\sin n\tau, \ u\cos\tau + v\sin\tau + \frac{n\lambda_0}{1-n^2}\cos n\tau\right)$$

The function $\psi(u,v,\tau)$ is periodic with period 2π. From Equations [103.4] and [103.6] one obtains

$$x = u\sin\tau - v\cos\tau + \frac{\lambda_0}{1-n^2}\sin n\tau \qquad [103.8]$$

Since this expression is of the same form as [103.2], the principal solution of Equation [102.2] will be found when $u_0 = a$ and $v_0 = b$ for $\mu \to 0$.

We can now apply the procedure of Poincaré by assuming that, when $\mu \ll 1$, the quantities u and v for $\tau = 0$ differ but little from a and b, that is,

$$u_{\tau=0} = a + \alpha; \qquad v_{\tau=0} = b + \beta \qquad [103.9]$$

where α and β are small numbers. From Equations [103.7] one obtains

$$u = u_{\tau=0} + \mu\int_0^\tau \psi(u,v,\tau)\cos\tau \, d\tau$$

[103.10]

$$v = v_{\tau=0} + \mu\int_0^\tau \psi(u,v,\tau)\sin\tau \, d\tau$$

The functions u and v, on the other hand, can be expanded in terms of the small parameters μ, α, and β; this, in view of [103.9], gives

$$u = a + \alpha + \mu C_1(\tau) + \mu\alpha D_1(\tau) + \mu\beta E_1(\tau) + \mu^2 G_1(\tau) + \cdots$$

$$v = b + \beta + \mu C_2(\tau) + \mu\alpha D_2(\tau) + \mu\beta E_2(\tau) + \mu^2 G_2(\tau) + \cdots$$

[103.11]

where the dots designate terms of higher orders containing μ^3, μ^4, $\cdots$. Comparing these expansions with [103.10], one finds

$$C_1(\tau) = \int_0^\tau \psi(a,b,\tau)\cos\tau \, d\tau; \qquad C_2(\tau) = \int_0^\tau \psi(a,b,\tau)\sin\tau \, d\tau \qquad [103.12]$$

and also

$$D_1(\tau) = \int_0^\tau \left[\frac{d\psi}{du}\right]\cos\tau \, d\tau; \qquad E_1(\tau) = \int_0^\tau \left[\frac{d\psi}{dv}\right]\cos\tau \, d\tau$$

[103.13]

$$D_2(\tau) = \int_0^\tau \left[\frac{d\psi}{du}\right]\sin\tau \, d\tau; \qquad E_2(\tau) = \int_0^\tau \left[\frac{d\psi}{dv}\right]\sin\tau \, d\tau$$

where the symbols $\left[\dfrac{d\psi}{du}\right]$ and $\left[\dfrac{d\psi}{dv}\right]$ designate the partial derivatives $\dfrac{\partial\psi}{\partial u}$ and $\dfrac{\partial\psi}{\partial v}$ in which $\mu = \alpha = \beta = 0$.

If u and v are periodic, it is clear that $u(2\pi) - u(0) = 0$ and $v(2\pi) - v(0) = 0$; in view of [103.11], this implies that

$$C_1(2\pi) + \alpha D_1(2\pi) + \beta E_1(2\pi) + \mu G_1(2\pi) + \cdots = 0$$
$$C_2(2\pi) + \alpha D_2(2\pi) + \beta E_2(2\pi) + \mu G_2(2\pi) + \cdots = 0$$

[103.14]

The problem of determining a and b in Equations [103.2], when μ is small and hence when $\alpha(\mu)$ and $\beta(\mu)$ are small, therefore is one of finding values of α and β which will satisfy Equations [103.14] and which will reduce to zero when $\mu = 0$.

Since there are two equations, it is possible to determine α and β as functions of μ, provided

$$C_1(2\pi) = \int_0^{2\pi} \psi(a,b,\tau)\cos\tau\,d\tau = 0; \quad C_2(2\pi) = \int_0^{2\pi} \psi(a,b,\tau)\sin\tau\,d\tau = 0 \quad [103.15]$$

These equations give the first-order solution for a and b, since other terms in [103.14] contain small factors α, β, and μ.

For solutions valid to the second order, the equations

$$\alpha D_1(2\pi) + \beta E_1(2\pi) + \mu G_1(2\pi) + \cdots = 0$$
$$\alpha D_2(2\pi) + \beta E_2(2\pi) + \mu G_2(2\pi) + \cdots = 0$$

[103.16]

must be satisfied for any arbitrary but small μ. These equations admit single-valued solutions with α and β approaching zero as μ approaches 0 if

$$\Delta = \begin{vmatrix} D_1(2\pi) & E_1(2\pi) \\ D_2(2\pi) & E_2(2\pi) \end{vmatrix} \neq 0$$

[103.17]

Hence the problem of determining the limit values of the coefficients a and b in Equation [103.2] when $\mu \to 0$ is solved by Equations [103.16] provided the condition [103.17] is satisfied.

104. STABILITY OF PERIODIC SOLUTIONS

The condition for stability of periodic solutions can be obtained by utilizing the variational equations of Poincaré. If we introduce in Equations [103.7] the quantities $u = u_0 + \eta$ and $v = v_0 + \xi$, where u_0 and v_0 are periodic with period 2π and η and ξ are small perturbations, and develop the function $\psi(u,v,\tau)$ in a Taylor series around the values u_0 and v_0, we obtain the variational equations

$$\frac{d\eta}{d\tau} = (\mu\psi_u \cos\tau)\eta + (\mu\psi_v \cos\tau)\xi$$

[104.1]

$$\frac{d\xi}{d\tau} = (\mu\psi_u \sin\tau)\eta + (\mu\psi_v \sin\tau)\xi$$

since the functions u_0 and v_0 satisfy Equations [103.7]. Equations [104.1] have periodic coefficients. Suppose that $\eta_1(\tau)$, $\xi_1(\tau)$ and $\eta_2(\tau)$, $\xi_2(\tau)$ are two sets of solutions forming a fundamental system. One can assume the initial conditions $\eta_1(0) = 1$, $\xi_1(0) = 0$ and $\eta_2(0) = 0$, $\xi_2(0) = 1$. Since $\eta_1(\tau + 2\pi)$, $\xi_1(\tau + 2\pi)$, $\cdots$ are also solutions, one can write

$$\eta_1(\tau + 2\pi) = a\eta_1(\tau) + b\eta_2(\tau); \quad \xi_1(\tau + 2\pi) = a\xi_1(\tau) + b\xi_2(\tau)$$

[104.2]

$$\eta_2(\tau + 2\pi) = c\eta_1(\tau) + d\eta_2(\tau); \quad \xi_2(\tau + 2\pi) = c\xi_1(\tau) + d\xi_2(\tau)$$

Whence, for $\tau = 0$, in view of the initial conditions,

$$\eta_1(2\pi) = a; \quad \xi_1(2\pi) = b; \quad \eta_2(2\pi) = c; \quad \xi_2(2\pi) = d \quad [104.3]$$

It is possible to select a fundamental system so as to reduce [104.2] to a canonical form where $\eta_1(\tau + 2\pi) = S_1\eta_1(\tau) \cdots$. The formation of such a system depends on the solution of the characteristic equation

$$F(S) = \begin{vmatrix} a - S & b \\ c & d - S \end{vmatrix} = \begin{vmatrix} \eta_1(2\pi) - S & \xi_1(2\pi) \\ \eta_2(2\pi) & \xi_2(2\pi) - S \end{vmatrix} = 0 \quad [104.4]$$

This can be written as

$$F(S) = S^2 + pS + q = 0 \quad [104.5]$$

with

$$p = -\left[\eta_1(2\pi) + \xi_2(2\pi)\right] \quad \text{and} \quad q = \left[\eta_1(2\pi)\xi_2(2\pi) - \eta_2(2\pi)\xi_1(2\pi)\right] \quad [104.6]$$

The parameter μ in [104.1] is supposed to be fixed; thus, if $\mu = 0$, $\frac{d\eta}{d\tau} = \frac{d\xi}{d\tau} = 0$, so that η and ξ remain equal to their initial values, namely,

$$\eta_1(\tau) = \xi_2(\tau) = 1; \quad \eta_2(\tau) = \xi_1(\tau) = 0 \quad [104.7]$$

Hence, for $\mu = 0$, $p = -2$ and $q = +1$. For $\mu \neq 0$ but small, we conclude, therefore, that $p < 0$ and $q > 0$. The system is stable if the real parts of the characteristic exponents h_1 and h_2 (see Section 27) are negative, which implies that $|e^{2\pi h_1}| < 1$ and $|e^{2\pi h_2}| < 1$, that is, the moduli of the roots S_1 and S_2 are less than unity. Equation [104.5] has roots with absolute values less than unity only if

$$p > -2; \quad 1 + p + q > 0 \quad [104.8]$$

which follows from the equations

$$1 + p + q = (S_1 - 1)(S_2 - 1); \quad p = -(S_1 + S_2) \quad [104.9]$$

On the other hand, for $\mu = 0$, $p = -2$ and $q = +1$, as was shown. Hence, the conditions of stability [104.8] can be satisfied for small positive values of μ only when the first non-vanishing derivatives of p and $p + q$ with respect to μ are positive for $\mu = 0$.

In order to calculate these derivatives, replace η and ξ in Equations [104.1] by η_1 and ξ_1 and integrate between 0 and 2π. This gives

$$\eta_1(2\pi) - \eta_1(0) = \eta_1(2\pi) - 1 = \mu \int_0^{2\pi} \psi_u \eta_1 \cos \tau \, d\tau + \mu \int_0^{2\pi} \psi_v \xi_1 \cos \tau \, d\tau$$

[104.10]

$$\xi_1(2\pi) - \xi_1(0) = \xi_1(2\pi) = \mu \int_0^{2\pi} \psi_u \eta_1 \sin \tau \, d\tau + \mu \int_0^{2\pi} \psi_v \xi_1 \sin \tau \, d\tau$$

Differentiating these equations with respect to μ, one obtains

$$\frac{d\eta_1(2\pi)}{d\mu} = \int_0^{2\pi} (\psi_u \eta_1 \cos \tau + \psi_v \xi_1 \cos \tau) \, d\tau + \mu \int_0^{2\pi} \left(\psi_u \frac{d\eta_1}{d\mu} \cos \tau + \psi_v \frac{d\xi_1}{d\mu} \cos \tau \right) d\tau$$

[104.11]

$$\frac{d\xi_1(2\pi)}{d\mu} = \int_0^{2\pi} (\psi_u \eta_1 \sin \tau + \psi_v \xi_1 \sin \tau) \, d\tau + \mu \int_0^{2\pi} \left(\psi_u \frac{d\eta_1}{d\mu} \sin \tau + \psi_v \frac{d\xi_1}{d\mu} \sin \tau \right) d\tau$$

Passing to the limit $\mu = 0$ and taking into account [104.7], one gets

$$\left[\frac{d\eta_1(2\pi)}{d\mu} \right]_{\mu=0} = \int_0^{2\pi} \psi_u \cos \tau \, d\tau = D_1(2\pi); \qquad \left[\frac{d\xi_1(2\pi)}{d\mu} \right]_{\mu=0} = \int_0^{2\pi} \psi_u \sin \tau \, d\tau = D_2(2\pi)$$

[104.12]

$$\left[\frac{d\eta_2(2\pi)}{d\mu} \right]_{\mu=0} = \int_0^{2\pi} \psi_v \cos \tau \, d\tau = E_1(2\pi); \qquad \left[\frac{d\xi_2(2\pi)}{d\mu} \right]_{\mu=0} = \int_0^{2\pi} \psi_v \sin \tau \, d\tau = E_2(2\pi)$$

From [104.6] and [104.12] one obtains

$$\left(\frac{dp}{d\mu} \right)_{\mu=0} = - \left[D_1(2\pi) + E_2(2\pi) \right]; \qquad \left[\frac{d(p+q)}{d\mu} \right]_{\mu=0} = 0;$$

[104.13]

$$\left[\frac{d^2(p+q)}{d\mu^2} \right]_{\mu=0} = 2 \begin{vmatrix} D_1(2\pi) & D_2(2\pi) \\ E_1(2\pi) & E_2(2\pi) \end{vmatrix}$$

This leads finally to the following conditions of stability*

$$D_1(2\pi) + E_2(2\pi) < 0 \quad \text{and} \quad \begin{vmatrix} D_1(2\pi) & D_2(2\pi) \\ E_1(2\pi) & E_2(2\pi) \end{vmatrix} > 0 \qquad [104.14]$$

_____

* Conditions [104.14] have been formulated by Mandelstam and Papalexi (8). The proof given here was developed by Professor W. Hurevicz.

105. SUBHARMONIC RESONANCE OF THE ORDER ONE-HALF FOR A SOFT SELF-EXCITATION

We shall apply the theory outlined in the two preceding sections to the important practical case when $n = 2$. This case has already been investigated in Chapter XVI by the quasi-linear method of Kryloff and Bogoliuboff.

We employ the usual polynomial approximation for the non-linear element of the system, the electron tube, that is,

$$i_a = f(V_s) = i_{a_0} + a_1'V_s + a_2'V_s^2 + a_3'V_s^3 + a_4'V_s^4 + a_5'V_s^5 \qquad [105.1]$$

In Section 51 it was shown that for a soft self-excitation the approximation can be limited to the first four terms, that is, $a_4' = a_5' = 0$, whereas for a hard self-excitation the full polynomial [105.1] must be used. We have also seen that the important terms are those containing the odd powers of V_s, but for greater generality we shall use the full expression [105.1]. Using the notation of Section 102 and designating the "dimensionless" grid voltage $\frac{V_s}{V_0} = x = \frac{dI}{d\tau}$, one has

$$I_a = f_1(x) = I_{a_0} + a_1 x + a_2 x^2 + a_3 x^3 + a_4 x^4 + a_5 x^5 \qquad [105.2]$$

Using Expression [102.8], one obtains the following expression for $\mu f(x, \dot{x})$ in [102.2]:

$$\mu f(x, \dot{x}) = \frac{1}{1 + \xi}\left(\left[a_1 - 2\theta(1 + \xi) + \right. \right.$$
$$\left. \left. + 2a_2 x + 3a_3 x^2 + 4a_4 x^3 + 5a_5 x^4\right]\dot{x} + \xi x\right) \qquad [105.3]$$

Since in practice the coefficient a_2 is very small, we can put

$$\frac{a_2}{1 + \xi} = \mu; \quad \frac{a_1 - 2\theta(1 + \xi)}{a_2} = k; \quad A_3 = \frac{3a_3}{a_2}; \quad A_4 = \frac{4a_4}{a_2}; \quad A_5 = \frac{5a_5}{a_2}$$

Equation [105.3] then becomes

$$f(x, \dot{x}) = (k + 2x + A_3 x^2 + A_4 x^3 + A_5 x^4)\dot{x} + \frac{\xi}{a_2}x \qquad [105.4]$$

For $n = 2$, Expression [103.2] is

$$x = a \sin\tau - b\cos\tau - \frac{\lambda_0}{3}\sin 2\tau = X\sin(\tau - \phi) - \frac{\lambda_0}{3}\sin 2\tau \qquad [105.5]$$

In this section we shall consider systems having soft self-excitation, that is, systems in which $A_4 = A_5 = 0$. In order to determine the limit values [103.3] for a and b, one must solve the equations

$$\int_0^{2\pi} \psi(a, b, \tau)\cos\tau \, d\tau = 0 \quad \text{and} \quad \int_0^{2\pi} \psi(a, b, \tau)\sin\tau \, d\tau = 0$$

Since the function $\psi(a, b, \tau)$ is, by definition, $f(x, \dot{x})$, in which x has the value [105.5], we obtain

$$\int_0^{2\pi} \psi(a,b,\tau)\cos\tau\,d\tau = \int_0^{2\pi}(k + 2x + A_3 x^2)\,\dot{x}\cos\tau\,d\tau + \frac{\xi}{a_2}\int_0^{2\pi}x\cos\tau\,d\tau$$

[105.6]

$$\int_0^{2\pi} \psi(a,b,\tau)\sin\tau\,d\tau = \int_0^{2\pi}(k + 2x + A_3 x^2)\,\dot{x}\sin\tau\,d\tau + \frac{\xi}{a_2}\int_0^{2\pi}x\sin\tau\,d\tau$$

Carrying out this substitution and the integrations, one finally obtains

$$a\left[k + \frac{A_3}{4}\left(a^2 + b^2 + \frac{2\lambda_0^2}{9}\right)\right] = b\left(-\frac{\lambda_0}{3} + \frac{\xi}{a_2}\right)$$

[105.7]

$$b\left[k + \frac{A_3}{4}\left(a^2 + b^2 + \frac{2\lambda_0^2}{9}\right)\right] = -a\left(\frac{\lambda_0}{3} + \frac{\xi}{a_2}\right)$$

From these expressions one obtains the square of the amplitude X of the principal solution

$$X^2 = a^2 + b^2 = -\frac{2}{9}\lambda_0^2 - \frac{4}{A_3}\left[k \pm \sqrt{\frac{\lambda_0^2}{9} - \frac{\xi^2}{a_2^2}}\right]$$

[105.8]

and the phase

$$\phi = \tan^{-1}\frac{b}{a} = \tan^{-1}\sqrt{\frac{\dfrac{\lambda_0}{3} + \dfrac{\xi}{a_2}}{\dfrac{\lambda_0}{3} - \dfrac{\xi}{a_2}}}$$

[105.9]

The principal solution corresponds to real values of X, that is, to values of X such that $X^2 > 0$. Since the term $-\frac{2}{9}\lambda_0^2$ in [105.8] is always negative, it is apparent that this condition is fulfilled if the second term on the right of [105.8] is positive and is greater than the value $\frac{2}{9}\lambda_0^2$. Hence, if A_3 and k are negative, only the plus sign can be taken before the radical. If, however, $A_3 < 0$ and $k > 0$, the condition $X^2 > 0$ may be fulfilled for either sign of the radical. All depends, of course, on the magnitude of A_3, k, and $\frac{\xi}{a_2}$, that is, on the magnitude of the constants of the circuit.

Fulfillment of the condition $X^2 > 0$, however, does not mean that the principal solution exists in practice. Its existence implies that the oscillation be *stable*, which requires that the conditions [104.14] be satisfied. In Equations [103.13], which determine the functions $D_1(\tau)$, $D_2(\tau)$, $E_1(\tau)$, and $E_2(\tau)$, appear the expressions $\left[\dfrac{d\psi}{du}\right]$ and $\left[\dfrac{d\psi}{dv}\right]$ previously defined, that is,

$$\left[\frac{d\psi}{du}\right] = \frac{\partial f}{\partial x}\frac{\partial x}{\partial u} + \frac{\partial f}{\partial \dot{x}}\frac{\partial \dot{x}}{\partial u}; \qquad \left[\frac{d\psi}{dv}\right] = \frac{\partial f}{\partial x}\frac{\partial x}{\partial v} + \frac{\partial f}{\partial \dot{x}}\frac{\partial \dot{x}}{\partial v}$$

[105.10]

where

$$x = u\sin\tau - v\cos\tau - \frac{\lambda_0}{3}\sin 2\tau; \qquad \dot{x} = u\cos\tau + v\sin\tau - \frac{2\lambda_0}{3}\cos 2\tau$$

Hence

$$\frac{\partial x}{\partial u} = \sin\tau; \qquad \frac{\partial \dot{x}}{\partial u} = \cos\tau; \qquad \frac{\partial x}{\partial v} = -\cos\tau; \qquad \frac{\partial \dot{x}}{\partial v} = \sin\tau$$

This gives

$$D_1(2\pi) = \int_0^{2\pi} \frac{\partial f}{\partial x} \sin\tau \cos\tau \, d\tau + \int_0^{2\pi} \frac{\partial f}{\partial \dot{x}} \cos^2\tau \, d\tau$$

$$E_1(2\pi) = \int_0^{2\pi} \frac{\partial f}{\partial x} \cos^2\tau \, d\tau + \int_0^{2\pi} \frac{\partial f}{\partial \dot{x}} \sin\tau \cos\tau \, d\tau$$

$$D_2(2\pi) = \int_0^{2\pi} \frac{\partial f}{\partial x} \sin^2\tau \, d\tau + \int_0^{2\pi} \frac{\partial f}{\partial \dot{x}} \sin\tau \cos\tau \, d\tau$$

$$E_2(2\pi) = -\int_0^{2\pi} \frac{\partial f}{\partial x} \sin\tau \cos\tau \, d\tau + \int_0^{2\pi} \frac{\partial f}{\partial \dot{x}} \sin^2\tau \, d\tau$$

[105.11]

Moreover, from [105.4], one has

$$\frac{\partial f}{\partial x} = 2(1 + A_3 x)\dot{x} + \frac{\xi}{a_2}; \qquad \frac{\partial f}{\partial \dot{x}} = k + 2x + A_3 x^2 \qquad [105.12]$$

The criteria of stability [104.14] can be applied now both to the principal solution [105.5] and to the heteroperiodic one, in which $a = b = 0$. Carrying out the calculations [104.14] in which $D_1(2\pi)$, $\cdots$ are replaced by their expressions [105.11] and [105.12] for both the principal and heteroperiodic solutions, one finds that the conditions for stability, and hence for the existence of the principal solution, are

$$k + \frac{A_3}{2}\left(X^2 + \frac{\lambda_0^2}{9}\right) < 0; \qquad A_3\left[k + \frac{A_3}{4}\left(X^2 + \frac{2\lambda_0^2}{9}\right)\right] > 0 \quad [105.13]$$

For the heteroperiodic solution, they are

$$k + A_3\frac{\lambda_0^2}{18} < 0; \qquad \left(k + A_3\frac{\lambda_0^2}{18}\right) + \frac{\xi^2}{a_2^2} - \frac{\lambda_0^2}{9} > 0 \qquad [105.14]$$

The last inequalities, in view of [105.8], reduce to

$$\mp\sqrt{\frac{\lambda_0^2}{9} - \frac{\xi^2}{a_2^2}} + \frac{A_3}{4}X^2 < 0; \qquad A_3\left[\mp\sqrt{\frac{\lambda_0^2}{9} - \frac{\xi^2}{a_2^2}}\right] > 0 \qquad [105.15]$$

These inequalities are satisfied if $A_3 < 0$ and the minus sign is taken before the radical. We re-emphasize here the important point which has previously been noted in Section 51, that is, for a soft self-excitation, the coefficient of the cubic term in the polynomial approximation of the non-linear characteristic must be *negative*. Under these conditions Expression [105.8] for the square of the amplitude X becomes

$$X^2 = +\frac{4}{|A_3|}\left[k + \sqrt{\frac{\lambda_0^2}{9} - \frac{\xi^2}{a_2^2}} + A_3\frac{\lambda_0^2}{18}\right] \qquad [105.16]$$

Since $k = \dfrac{a_1 - 2\theta(1 + \xi)}{a_2}$, where $2\theta = Rn/L\omega$, it is seen that when $k > 0$ the energy input from the electron tube outweighs the dissipation of energy in the circuit, whereas when $k < 0$ the dissipation of energy exceeds the input. From Equation [105.16] it is observed that the existence of a stable amplitude when $k < 0$ depends on the values of other parameters. Physically this means that the self-excitation of a system which is not normally self-excited ($\lambda_0 = 0$) can be produced by the effect of the externally applied electromotive force ($\lambda_0 \neq 0$). If $\lambda_0 = 0$, the quantity ξ does not exist and one has $X^2 = \dfrac{4k_0}{|A_3|}$, which coincides with the equation previously obtained from the theory of Poincaré.

Comparing the condition of stability of the principal solution with that of the heteroperiodic solution, one finds from [105.16]

$$\frac{\xi^2}{a_2^2} \leqq \frac{\lambda_0^2}{9} - \left(k - \frac{|A_3|\lambda_0^2}{18} \right)^2 \qquad [105.17]$$

On the other hand, from [105.15] one finds

$$\frac{\xi^2}{a_2^2} > \frac{\lambda_0^2}{9} - \left(k - \frac{|A_3|\lambda_0^2}{18} \right)^2 \qquad [105.18]$$

It is thus seen that one solution appears at the point where the other disappears and vice versa, so that there is no interval in which both exist at the same time. From the equation

$$\frac{\xi^2}{a_2^2} = \frac{\lambda_0^2}{9} - \left(k - \frac{|A_3|\lambda_0^2}{18} \right)^2 \qquad [105.19]$$

where

$$k = \frac{a_1 - 2\theta}{a_2} - \frac{2\theta\xi}{a_2} = k_0 - \frac{2\theta\xi}{a_2}$$

one can obtain two values ξ' and ξ'' determining the limits of stability. These limits determine the zone of discrepancy $\Delta\xi = \xi'' - \xi'$ between ω and $n\omega_0$ within which a stable principal solution exists. One obtains the following expression for $\Delta\xi$ valid to the second order of the quantity θ:

$$\Delta\xi = \xi'' - \xi' = 2a_2 \sqrt{ \frac{\lambda_0^2}{9} \left(1 - k_0 A_3 - \frac{A_3^2 \lambda_0^2}{36} \right) - k_0^2 } \qquad [105.20]$$

Considering $\Delta\xi$ as a function of λ_0, it is seen that for

$$\frac{\lambda_0^2}{9} \geqq \frac{2}{A_3^2} \left[1 - k_0 A_3 - \sqrt{1 - 2k_0 A_3} \right] \qquad [105.21]$$

$\Delta\xi$ is real, hence the zone $\xi'' - \xi'$ exists. Beginning with the value of λ_0 given by the equality sign in [105.21], the real values for $\Delta\xi$ appear and $\Delta\xi$ increases up to a maximum value

$$\Delta\xi_{\max} = \frac{2a_2}{|A_3|} \sqrt{1 - 2k_0 A_3} \qquad [105.22]$$

when the amplitude λ_0 of the externally applied excitation reaches the value

$$\frac{\lambda_0^2}{9} = \frac{2(1 - k_0 A_3)}{A_3^2} \qquad [105.23]$$

For a further increase of λ_0, the interval $\Delta\xi$ decreases and becomes zero when

$$\frac{\lambda_0^2}{9} = \frac{2}{A_3^2}\left[1 - k_0 A_3 + \sqrt{1 - 2k_0 A_3}\right] \qquad [105.24]$$

If one continues to increase λ_0, the interval $\Delta\xi$ becomes imaginary, that is, it ceases to exist.

Summing up, one can say that the external periodic excitation having a frequency ω which differs somewhat from twice the frequency ω_0 to which the oscillating circuit is tuned is capable of producing oscillations in the circuit provided the coefficient $\xi = \frac{\omega^2 - 2\omega_0^2}{2\omega_0^2}$ remains inside the interval corresponding to values of λ_0 in the interval

$$\frac{2}{A_3^2}\left[1 - k_0 A_3 - \sqrt{1 - 2k_0 A_3}\right] \leqq \frac{\lambda_0^2}{9} \leqq \frac{2}{A_3^2}\left[1 - k_0 A_3 + \sqrt{1 - 2k_0 A_3}\right]$$

106. NATURE OF SUBHARMONIC RESONANCE OF THE ORDER ONE-HALF FOR AN UNDEREXCITED SYSTEM

In the preceding section the conditions for the existence and stability of the principal solution were established without specifying the sign of the quantity

$$k = \frac{a_1 - 2\theta(1 + \xi)}{a_2} = k_0 - \frac{2\theta\xi}{a_2}$$

As has been mentioned, this quantity characterizes the stability of the system in the neighborhood of equilibrium, when the effect of the terms containing the small quantity x (see Equation [105.3]) is negligible. Hence when $k < 0$ at the point of equilibrium ($x = 0$) the system is stable, and when $k > 0$ it is unstable. These conditions correspond to the existence of either a stable ($k < 0$) or unstable ($k > 0$) singularity in a self-excited system without an external force. When subharmonic external resonance is present, the situation is different in that even when $k < 0$ the principal subharmonic oscillation may arise if the amplitude of the external periodic oscillation is contained in the zone $\Delta\xi$ specified in Section 105.

In this section we shall investigate a system where $k < 0$, that is, a system which is stable without an external excitation. We call such a system an *underexcited* one. If such a system is subjected to an external excitation with frequency ω differing from $2\omega_0$ by a considerable amount, only a relatively small heteroperiodic oscillation will be present. If, however, ω approaches $2\omega_0$ so as to be within the limits of the zone $\Delta\xi$, the principal oscillation will suddenly appear and will have *exactly* the frequency $\omega/2$. If the parameter ξ is varied, the frequency of the principal oscillation will

always be $\omega/2$, but it is worth noting that the variation of $\xi = \frac{\omega^2 - 2\omega_0^2}{2\omega_0^2}$ can
be accomplished in two different manners, that is, by varying either ω or ω_0.
If ω is varied, the frequency of the subharmonic oscillation will follow the
variations of ω, since it is always $\omega/2$; if ω_0 is varied, the frequency of the
subharmonic oscillation will remain constant. It is thus seen that when the
principal oscillation exists its frequency is always $1/2$ (or $1/n$ for subharmonic resonance of the nth order) of the externally applied frequency ω, but
the range within which it exists is influenced by ξ, that is, by both ω and ω_0
simultaneously. Moreover, the range $\Delta\xi$ is a function of the amplitude λ_0, as
was shown at the end of Section 105.

The phenomenon of subharmonic resonance of the order one-half (or,
more generally, of the order $1/n$) presents features radically different from
those of ordinary linear resonance. It is sufficient to investigate the behavior of the function X^2 given by Equation [105.16]. Since the range within
which the principal solution exists as well as the amplitude X of this solution depend on ξ and not on ω and ω_0 individually, it is convenient to take
the quantity ξ as the independent variable instead of ω as is customary for
linear systems.

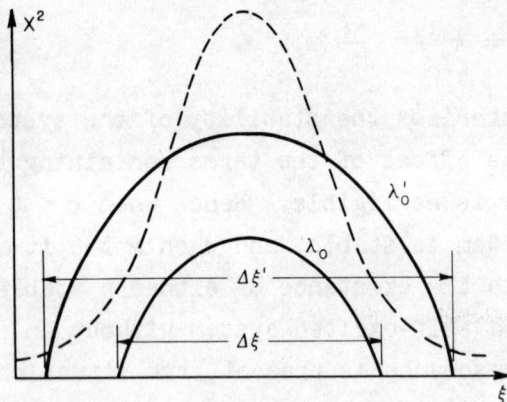

Figure 106.1

If one plots the results previously obtained concerning the ranges
$\Delta\xi$ depending on the amplitude λ_0 of the
external excitation, one obtains the
curves shown in Figure 106.1, which were
corroborated experimentally by physicists of the Mandelstam-Papalexi school.
It is observed that this phenomenon of
subharmonic resonance differs radically
from classical linear resonance, which
has the appearance shown by the dotted
line. The phenomenon is entirely different when $k > 0$.

107. SUBHARMONIC RESONANCE OF THE ORDER ONE-HALF
FOR A HARD SELF-EXCITATION

The procedure remains the same as in Section 105 except that now we
have to introduce Expression [105.4] with $A_4 \neq 0$ and $A_5 \neq 0$. Carrying out the
calculations, one obtains, instead of Expressions [105.7], the following ones:

$$a\left[k + \frac{A_3}{4}\left(X^2 + \frac{2\lambda_0^2}{9}\right) + \frac{A_5}{8}\left(X^4 + \frac{\lambda_0^4}{27} + \frac{\lambda_0^2}{9}\left[5X^2 + 4b^2\right]\right)\right]$$

$$= b\left[-\frac{\lambda_0}{3} + \frac{\xi}{a_2} - \frac{A_4}{4}\frac{\lambda_0}{3}\left(X^2 + \frac{\lambda_0^2}{6} + 2b^2\right)\right]$$

[107.1]

$$b\left[k + \frac{A_3}{4}\left(X^2 + \frac{2\lambda_0^2}{9}\right) + \frac{A_5}{8}\left(X^4 + \frac{\lambda_0^4}{27} + \frac{\lambda_0^2}{9}\left[5X^2 + 4a^2\right]\right)\right]$$

$$= a\left[-\frac{\lambda_0}{3} - \frac{\xi}{a_2} - \frac{A_4}{4}\frac{\lambda_0}{3}\left(X^2 + \frac{\lambda_0^2}{6} + 2b^2\right)\right]$$

Discussion of the conditions of stability in Equations [107.1] is too complicated. One notes that in practice the coefficient A_4 of asymmetry is very small and can be neglected. One can further simplify the problem by assuming that the square of the amplitude of the principal solution is much larger than the forcing term, that is, $X^2 \gg \frac{\lambda_0^2}{9}$. With these simplifications, one obtains the expression

$$\frac{A_5}{8}X^4 + \frac{A_3}{4}X^2 + k \pm \sqrt{\frac{\lambda_0^2}{9} - \frac{\xi^2}{a_2^2}} = 0 \qquad [107.2]$$

Applying the same procedure as that followed in Section 105, one finds the inequalities

$$(A_5 X^2 + A_3)\frac{X^2}{4} \pm \sqrt{\frac{\lambda_0^2}{9} - \frac{\xi^2}{a_2^2}} < 0; \quad (A_5 X^2 + A_3)\left(\mp\sqrt{\frac{\lambda_0^2}{9} - \frac{\xi^2}{a_2^2}}\right) > 0 \quad [107.3]$$

These inequalities can be satisfied simultaneously if $A_5 X^2 + A_3 < 0$ and the minus sign is taken before the radical.

The stable solution for X^2 is then given by the equation

$$X^2 = -\frac{A_3}{A_5} \pm \sqrt{\frac{A_3^2}{A_5^2} - \frac{8}{A_5}\left(k + \sqrt{\frac{\lambda_0^2}{9} - \frac{\xi^2}{a_2^2}}\right)} \qquad [107.4]$$

Equation [105.9] for ϕ is also applicable here.

If the external excitation is absent ($\lambda_0 = 0$ and $\xi = 0$)

$$X^2 = -\frac{A_3}{A_5} \pm \sqrt{\frac{A_3^2}{A_5^2} - \frac{8k}{A_5}} \qquad [107.5]$$

The condition $A_5 X^2 + A_3 < 0$ implies that systems where both A_3 and A_5 are greater than zero are to be excluded. Hence the following combinations of signs are possible:

1. $A_5 < 0, A_3 < 0$;   2. $A_5 > 0, A_3 < 0$;   3. $A_5 < 0, A_3 > 0$

In the first two cases

$$X^2 = -\left|\frac{A_3}{A_5}\right| + \sqrt{\left(\frac{A_3}{A_5}\right)^2 + \frac{8k}{|A_5|}} \quad \text{or} \quad X^2 = \left|\frac{A_3}{A_5}\right| - \sqrt{\left(\frac{A_3}{A_5}\right)^2 - \frac{8k}{|A_5|}} \quad [107.6]$$

X^2 can be positive only when $k > 0$, that is, when the system is self-excited. These two cases therefore characterize soft self-excitation in that the amplitude increases with k beginning when $k = 0$.

The third case yields different results, however. It is noted that, if $A_3 > 0$ and $A_5 < 0$, the characteristic of the non-linear conductor, the electron tube, exhibits an inflection point for a certain value of the amplitude (see Section 51). In this case

$$X^2 = + \left| \frac{A_3}{A_5} \right| + \sqrt{\left(\frac{A_3}{A_5} \right)^2 + \frac{8k}{|A_5|}} \qquad [107.7]$$

It is observed that in this case one can also have $k < 0$, which means that a periodic oscillation may occur in an underexcited system. In order that no self-excitation be possible one must have

$$|k| > \frac{A_3{}^2}{8|A_5|} \qquad [107.8]$$

It can be shown, however, that in the interval

$$\frac{A_3{}^2}{6|A_5|} > |k| > \frac{A_3{}^2}{8|A_5|} \qquad [107.9]$$

the heteroperiodic oscillation is unstable. Thus in the interval [107.9] neither the principal nor the heteroperiodic oscillation exists. This implies that $|k|$ must be greater than $A_3{}^2/6|A_5|$ in order to obtain resonance of the order one-half.

Proceeding in the manner indicated at the end of Section 105 and omitting the intermediate calculations, we obtain the following results.

By requiring that X^2 given by [107.4] be real, one finds that there exist two intervals $\Delta\xi_x$ (for a stable principal oscillation) and $\Delta\xi_\lambda$ (for a stable heteroperiodic oscillation) with the condition

$$\Delta\xi_x > \Delta\xi_\lambda \qquad [107.10]$$

which shows that in a certain region these intervals overlap. Hence there exists a zone in which both a subharmonic and a heteroperiodic oscillation may exist at the same time. It is recalled that for a soft self-excitation these intervals do not overlap, so that the oscillation of one type appears at the point where that of the other type disappears.

Moreover, from Equation [107.4] it is apparent that the positive quantity X^2 is composed of two essentially positive parts. One of these parts $\left(-\frac{A_3}{A_5} \right)$ is constant since it depends on the characteristic of the non-linear element. Hence, if X^2 is considered as a function of ξ, it is noted that the curve $X^2(\xi)$ cannot become zero either at the beginning or at the end of the interval in which X^2 exists, but has to start from, and end at, a constant

value $\left(-\frac{A_3}{A_5}\right)$. This feature is characteristic of the phenomenon of hard self-
excitation, as has been pointed out in
Section 51. This is illustrated by
Figure 107.1, where the "discrepancy" ξ
is assumed to vary while the externally
applied amplitude λ_0 remains constant.
For $\xi < 0$ and for $|\xi|$ sufficiently large,
there will be no principal oscillation
and only a relatively weak heteroperi-
odic oscillation until the value $\xi = \xi_\lambda'$
is reached; at this point a powerful
oscillation of subharmonic resonance of

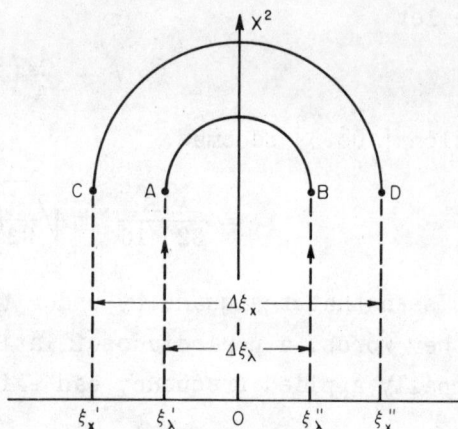

Figure 107.1

the order one-half will set in abruptly, see Point A in Figure 107.1. With a
further increase of ξ, the amplitude X increases relatively slowly, passing
through a rather flat maximum. For $\xi = \xi_x''$ the subharmonic oscillation will
suddenly disappear. If, however, one starts with large positive values of ξ
and decreases them gradually, the subharmonic oscillation will start at the
point $\xi = \xi_\lambda''$ and will disappear at C for $\xi = \xi_x'$. In other words, for increasing ξ, the principal oscillation starts abruptly at A and ends abruptly
at D; for decreasing ξ, it starts at B and ends at C in the same abrupt manner. The sudden jump during both the appearance and disappearance of the
oscillation is numerically equal to $\left(-\frac{A_3}{A_5}\right)$.

108. SUBHARMONIC RESONANCE OF THE ORDER ONE-THIRD

For $n = 3$ the principal oscillation [103.2] becomes

$$x = a \sin \tau + b \cos \tau - \frac{\lambda_0}{8} \sin 3\tau \qquad [108.1]$$

Proceeding in the manner explained in Section 105, one obtains the following
expressions (compare with Equations [105.7]):

$$a\left[k + \frac{A_3}{4}\left(X^2 + \frac{\lambda_0^2}{32}\right)\right] + \frac{\xi}{a_2} b = -(a^2 - b^2)\frac{\lambda_0 A_3}{32}$$

$$[108.2]$$

$$b\left[k + \frac{A_3}{4}\left(X^2 + \frac{\lambda_0^2}{32}\right)\right] - \frac{\xi}{a_2} a = + 2ab\frac{\lambda_0 A_3}{32}$$

Squaring, adding, and rearranging, one obtains

$$X^2\left\{\left[k + \frac{A_3}{4}\left(X^2 + \frac{\lambda_0^2}{32}\right)\right]^2 + \frac{\xi^2}{a_2^2}\right\} = \frac{\lambda_0^2 A_3^2}{32^2} X^4$$

Leaving out the trivial solution $X = 0$, we have

$$\left[k + \frac{A_3}{4}\left(X^2 + \frac{\lambda_0^2}{32}\right)\right]^2 + \frac{\xi^2}{a_2^2} = \left(\frac{\lambda_0 A_3}{32}\right)^2 X^2 \qquad [108.3]$$

If we let

$$k + \frac{A_3}{4}\left(X^2 + \frac{\lambda_0^2}{32}\right) = Y$$

Equation [108.3] becomes

$$Y = \frac{\lambda_0^2 A_3}{32 \cdot 16} \pm \sqrt{\frac{-7\lambda_0^4 A_3^4}{32^2 \cdot 16^2} + \frac{\lambda_0^2 k}{32 \cdot 8}\,|A_3| - \frac{\xi^2}{a_2^2}} \qquad [108.4]$$

It is seen that the quantity under the radical can be positive only if $k > 0$. In other words, a periodic oscillation with a frequency of one-third of the externally applied frequency can exist only if the system is self-excited.

109. EXPERIMENTAL RESULTS

The preceding theoretical considerations can be verified by the following experiment. An ordinary self-excited electron-tube oscillator is inductively coupled to a circuit containing an electromotive force with frequency ω. The oscillating circuit is tuned so that it has a frequency of approximately $\omega/2$. The oscillator has first been adjusted to a condition of soft self-excitation, that is, self-excitation starts from zero at a critical value of the coupling k if one gradually changes the feed-back coupling. When the critical condition is thus established, the coupling is decreased below that critical value ($k < 0$). Under such circumstances, the oscillator remains underexcited. If the external excitation of frequency ω is now introduced, the previously discussed phenomena of resonance of the order one-half make their appearance. If the discrepancy ξ remains outside the interval $\Delta\xi$ (Equation [105.20]), the circuit exhibits a vanishingly small heteroperiodic oscillation with a frequency the same as that of the external excitation. As soon as ξ enters the interval $\Delta\xi_1 = \xi_1'' - \xi_1'$, an intense subharmonic oscillation with frequency $\omega/2$ sets in at $\xi = \xi_1'$; this oscillation passes through a maximum for a value of ξ in the interval $\Delta\xi_1$ and disappears at $\xi = \xi_1''$, as shown by Curve 1 in Figure 109.1. If one now reproduces the phenomenon for a somewhat smaller value λ_{0_2} of the amplitude of the external excitation, one obtains Curve 2, which has a smaller maximum than Curve 1. For a sufficiently large value of λ_0 the subharmonic resonance disappears entirely, which is in accordance with Equation [105.24]. It should be noted that in these experiments the oscillator remains below the point of self-excitation if the external electromotive force is withdrawn.

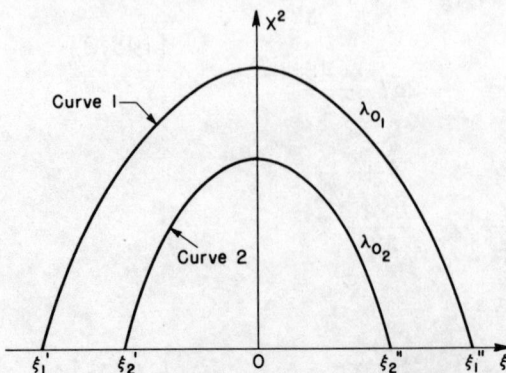

Figure 109.1

CHAPTER XVIII

ENTRAINMENT OF FREQUENCY

110. INTRODUCTORY REMARKS

If a periodic electromotive force of frequency ω is applied to an oscillator tuned to a frequency ω_0, one observes the well-known effect of beats, or heterodyning, which can be heard through a headphone in a circuit inductively coupled to the oscillator. As the difference between the two frequencies decreases, the pitch of the sound decreases, and from linear theory one may expect that the beat frequency should decrease indefinitely as $|\omega - \omega_0| \to 0$. In reality, the sound in the headphone disappears suddenly at a certain value of the difference $(\omega - \omega_0)$, and it is found that the oscillator frequency ω_0 falls in synchronism with, or is *entrained* by, the external frequency ω within a certain band of frequencies. This phenomenon is called *entrainment of frequency*, and the band of frequency in which the entrainment occurs is called the band or the *zone of entrainment*. Figure 110.1 represents the difference $|\omega - \omega_0|$ plotted against the external frequency ω; the interval $\Delta\omega$ is the zone of entrainment in which both frequencies coalesce and there exists only one frequency ω. On the basis of linear theory, the difference $|\omega - \omega_0|$ should be zero for only one value of $\omega = \omega_0$, as shown by the broken lines.

The phenomenon of entrainment of frequency is a manifestation of the non-linearity of the system and cannot be accounted for by linear theory. This effect was apparently recognized long ago, but its theory was not developed until recently. Thus, for example, Van der Pol, who developed the theory of the phenomenon (9), observes that "the synchronous timekeeping of two clocks hung on the same wall was already known to Huygens." Before Van der Pol, Lord Rayleigh (10) observed a similar effect in connection with acoustic oscillations. Vincent (11), Möller (12), and Appleton (13) have also investigated the phenomenon. In recent years Russian physicists have analyzed the phenomenon in the light of modern methods of non-linear mechanics, so that at present the matter seems to be well understood and offers an interesting field of research, particularly in connection with the problem of synchronizing oscillating systems.

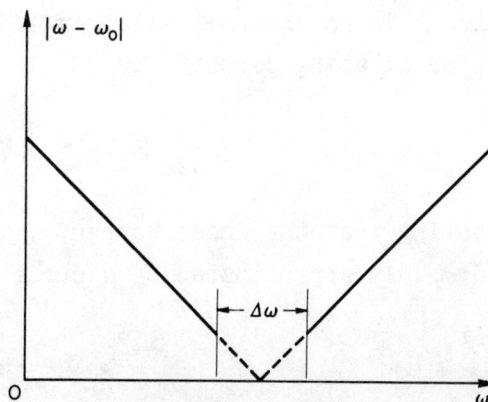

Figure 110.1

The entrainment phenomenon has been analyzed in Chapter XVI on the basis of the quasi-linear theory of Kryloff and Bogoliuboff, but it is preferable to treat this matter in more detail, starting from the discussion of Van der Pol and concluding the analysis with the topological method of Andronow and Witt.

Electron-tube circuits, as usual, offer a simple way of obtaining the differential equations from which conclusions regarding the phenomenon of entrainment can be formed. It must be noted, however, that the entrainment effect is a general property of non-linear systems acted on by a periodic excitation with a frequency in the neighborhood of the autoperiodic frequency of the system. Acoustic entrainment is also sufficiently well explored at present.

As far as is known, no special studies of mechanical entrainment have been made so far, but the following example is worth mentioning. If one actuates a mechanical pendulum by a periodic non-linear torque, one obtains beats if the two frequencies are sufficiently far apart; these beats can easily be observed as the envelope of oscillations recorded on a moving chart. If the frequency ω of the exciting moment approaches ω_0, the frequency of the pendulum, the period on the envelope becomes longer. At a certain point, the envelope suddenly becomes a straight line parallel to the motion of the recording paper, and beyond this point no further beats are observed. The non-linearity of the torque in this case is generally due to the kinematics of the mechanism which drives the pendulum by springs attached to a crank.

One may assume, therefore, that the phenomenon of frequency entrainment arises whenever there is a non-linearity in the differential equation of a system subject to an external periodic excitation with frequency sufficiently near the autoperiodic frequency of the system.

111. DIFFERENTIAL EQUATIONS OF VAN DER POL

The differential equation of the circuit shown in Figure 111.1, in which E is an external electromotive force with fixed frequency ω_1 inserted in the oscillating circuit, is

$$L\frac{di}{dt} + Ri + \frac{1}{C}\int_0^t i\,dt - M\frac{di_a}{dt_o} = E_0 \sin \omega_1 t \qquad [111.1]$$

Assuming that the anode current i_a, considered as a function of the grid voltage e_g, is approximated by a cubic parabola, we have

$$i_a = f(e_g) = Se_g\left(1 - \frac{e_g^2}{3V_s^2}\right) \qquad [111.2]$$

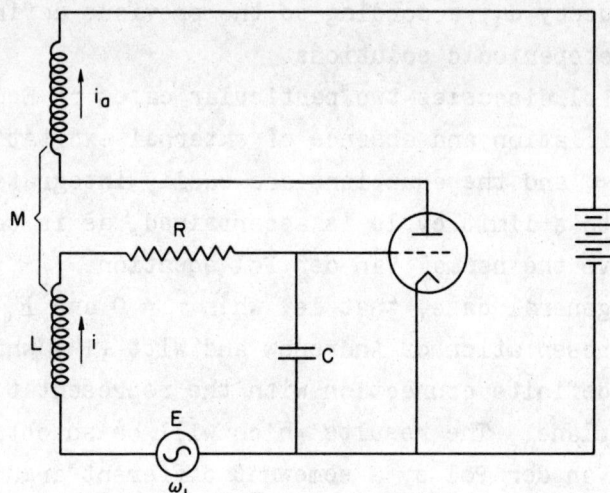

Figure 111.1

where V_s is the "saturation voltage," which was defined in Section 51, and S is the transconductance of the electron tube. As usual, we shall neglect the grid current and the anode reaction. Introducing the notations

$$v = \frac{e_g}{V_s} = \frac{\int_0^t i \, dt}{C V_s}; \quad \alpha = \frac{MS}{LC} - \frac{R}{L}; \quad \gamma = \frac{1}{3} \frac{MS}{LC}; \quad B = \frac{E_0}{V_s}; \quad \omega_0^2 = \frac{1}{LC}$$

we obtain

$$\ddot{v} - \alpha \dot{v} + \gamma \dot{v}^3 + \omega_0^2 v = B \omega_0^2 \sin \omega_1 t \qquad [111.3]$$

It is noted that the left side of this equation is of the same general type as Equation [44.1].

Van der Pol assumes as the solution of this equation the expression

$$v = b_1 \sin \omega_1 t + b_2 \cos \omega_1 t \qquad [111.4]$$

where b_1 and b_2 are certain slowly varying functions of time. Substituting this expression into [111.3], equating like coefficients, and neglecting second derivatives, we obtain

$$2\dot{b}_1 + z b_2 - \alpha b_1 \left(1 - \frac{b^2}{a_0^2}\right) = 0$$

$$\qquad [111.5]$$

$$2\dot{b}_2 - z b_1 - \alpha b_2 \left(1 - \frac{b^2}{a_0^2}\right) = -B \omega_0^2$$

where

$$z = 2(\omega_0 - \omega_1); \quad b^2 = b_1^2 + b_2^2; \quad a_0^2 = \frac{\alpha}{\frac{3}{4} \gamma} \qquad [111.6]$$

It is apparent that, if b_1 and b_2 were constant, the solution v would be periodic with frequency ω_1; according to the previous definition we would call such solutions heteroperiodic solutions.

Van der Pol discusses two particular cases of Equations [111.5], namely, linear oscillation and absence of external excitation. In the first case $\gamma = 0$, $a_0^2 = \infty$, and the equations are easily integrated. In the second case the approach to a limit cycle is ascertained, as is to be expected since in this case we have the normal Van der Pol equation.

For the general case, that is, when $\gamma \neq 0$ and $E_0 \sin \omega_1 t \neq 0$, we shall follow the presentation of Andronow and Witt (14) which will permit establishing a more definite connection with the representation of the phenomenon in the phase plane. The results which will be so obtained coincide with those obtained by Van der Pol by a somewhat different argument (9).

It is noted that Equations [111.5] are of the form studied by Poincaré, that is,

$$\frac{db_1}{dt} = P(b_1, b_2); \qquad \frac{db_2}{dt} = Q(b_1, b_2)$$

if b_1 and b_2 are taken as the variables of the phase plane; thus the conditions for a stationary oscillation, $b_1 =$ constant and $b_2 =$ constant, reduce to $P(b_1, b_2) = Q(b_1, b_2) = 0$. Hence the singular points of the system [111.5] give precisely the condition for the heteroperiodic state with a single frequency ω_1. In the neighborhood of the singular points, b_1 and b_2 are slowly varying quantities. This may be expressed by saying that the solution [111.4] is an amplitude-modulated function, the period of modulation approaching infinity as the frequencies ω_0 and ω_1 approach each other.

It is seen that the whole procedure is now reduced to the investigation of the singular points of the differential equations [111.5].

112. REPRESENTATION OF THE PHENOMENON IN THE PHASE PLANE

If we introduce the notations

$$x = \frac{b_1}{a_0}; \qquad y = \frac{b_2}{a_0}; \qquad a = \frac{z}{\alpha}; \qquad A = -\frac{B\omega_0}{a_0 \alpha}; \qquad r^2 = x^2 + y^2; \qquad \tau = \frac{t\alpha}{2} \quad [112.1]$$

Equations [111.5] become

$$\frac{dx}{d\tau} = x(1 - r^2) - ay$$

$$[112.2]$$

$$\frac{dy}{d\tau} = ax + y(1 - r^2) + A$$

The equation of the phase trajectories is

$$\frac{dy}{dx} = \frac{A + ax + y(1 - r^2)}{-ay + x(1 - r^2)} \qquad [112.3]$$

To investigate the nature of the singular point (x_0, y_0) we use the standard procedure given in Chapter III. If we let

$$x = x_0 + \xi; \quad y = y_0 + \eta \qquad\qquad [112.4]$$

the differential equations [112.2] become

$$\frac{d\xi}{d\tau} = P(\xi, \eta) = m\xi + n\eta + \text{terms with } \xi^2, \eta^2, \cdots$$

$$[112.5]$$

$$\frac{d\eta}{d\tau} = Q(\xi, \eta) = p\xi + q\eta + \text{terms with } \xi^2, \eta^2, \cdots$$

The nature of the singular point (x_0, y_0) is given by the form of the roots of the characteristic equation

$$S^2 - (m + q)S + (mq - np) = 0 \qquad\qquad [112.6]$$

For a stable singular point it is necessary to ascertain first that the singularity is not a saddle point, which implies that $(mq - np)$ should be positive. If this necessary condition is fulfilled, then the condition of stability is that the term $(m + q)$ should be negative. This implies that the real part of the roots should be negative; thus one has either a stable nodal point when the roots S_1 and S_2 are real or a stable focal point when S_1 and S_2 are conjugate complex. If the system [112.2] has stable singular points, the motion approaches an oscillation with a single frequency ω_1 since both b_1 and b_2 tend to become constant for $t \to \infty$.

If the system [112.2] possesses a limit cycle, the functions x and y, and hence also ξ and η, are periodic with period 2π. The quantities b_1 and b_2 are also periodic, which means that the Van der Pol solution [111.4] for this system represents beats between the heteroperiodic and autoperiodic oscillations.

We know from the theorem of Bendixson, Chapter IV, that any non-closed trajectory which neither goes to infinity nor approaches the singular points winds itself on a limit cycle. This limit cycle is stable for $t \to +\infty$ and unstable for $t \to -\infty$. From a practical standpoint only the stable limit cycles are of interest; we know from Section 25 that in the interior of such cycles there exist, generally, $2n + 1$ singularities whose sum of indices is always +1. This means that, if the number of saddle points is n, the number of singularities with index +1 is necessarily $n + 1$ so as to make the sum of the indices +1.

The "coordinates" (x_0, y_0) of the singular point are given by the equations

$$x_0 = -\frac{a\rho}{A}; \quad y_0 = -\frac{\rho(1 - \rho)}{A} \qquad\qquad [112.7]$$

where $\rho = r_0^2$ is determined by the equation

$$a^2\rho + \rho(1 - \rho^2) = A^2 \qquad\qquad [112.8]$$

For a fixed A, Equation [112.8] represents in the (ρ, a)-plane a curve of the third degree which gives the "amplitudes" $\sqrt{\rho} = r_0$ of the singular points for any $a = 2(\omega_0 - \omega_1)/\alpha$. The quantity A is the parameter of the family of the curves [112.8]. Any point of the (ρ, a)-plane represents a singular point of the differential equations [112.2] for a given value of the parameter A. The nature of the singular points in the (ρ, a)-plane depends on the nature of the roots of Equation [112.6].

113. NATURE AND DISTRIBUTION OF SINGULARITIES; TRANSIENT STATE OF ENTRAINMENT

The curves represented by Equation [112.8] have the appearance shown in Figure 113.1. For sufficiently small values of the parameter A the curve consists of two branches, M_1 and M_1'; the figure shows these branches for $A^2 = 0.1$. For an increasing A the branch M_1 increases in size, and the branch M_1' rises until both branches join as shown by the curve M. If A is further increased, there exists only one branch M_2 shown for $A^2 = 1$. It is noted that

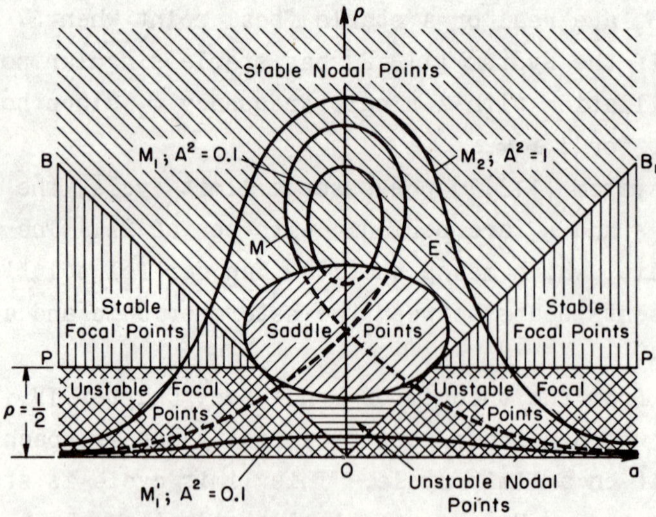

Figure 113.1

the curves M of the family exist only above the a-axis and are symmetrical with respect to the ρ-axis. If one substitutes Expression [112.4] into Equations [112.2], one obtains Equations [112.5] with the following values of the coefficients m, n, p, and q:

$$\frac{d\xi}{dt} = \xi\left[(1 - \rho) - 2x_0^2\right] + \eta\left[-(a + 2x_0y_0)\right] + \text{terms in } \xi^2, \eta^2, \cdots$$

$$[113.1]$$

$$\frac{d\eta}{dt} = \xi\left[a - 2x_0y_0\right] + \eta\left[(1 - \rho) - 2y_0^2\right] + \text{terms in } \xi^2, \eta^2, \cdots$$

where x_0 and y_0 are given by Equations [112.7]. Thus the characteristic equation of the system [113.1] is

$$S^2 - 2(1 - 2\rho)S + \left[(1 - \rho)(1 - 3\rho) + a^2\right] = 0 \qquad [113.2]$$

From this equation one can determine the zones of separation of the roots of various types as was shown in Chapter III. These zones, when drawn in the same (ρ,a)-plane as Figure 113.1 in which the curves [112.8] representing the loci of singular points are drawn, will indicate the nature of singularities in that plane.

We note first that the region of saddle points is determined by the inequality

$$(1 - \rho)(1 - 3\rho) + a^2 < 0 \qquad [113.3]$$

for, with this condition, the roots are real and of opposite sign. The curve

$$(1 - \rho)(1 - 3\rho) + a^2 = 0$$

is an ellipse E with its center situated on the ρ-axis, and Condition [113.3] means that the region of saddle points is situated inside this ellipse. The quantity under the radical sign in the expression for the roots S_1 and S_2 of [113.2] is $\rho^2 - a^2$. Hence the straight lines B and B_1, expressed by

$$\rho + a = 0 \quad \text{and} \quad \rho - a = 0$$

which bisect the first and the second quadrants represent the divides between the real roots and the complex ones. These lines are tangent to the ellipse at $\rho = 1/2$. Inside the angle BOB_1 formed by these lines lies the zone of nodal points and saddle points; outside it, the zone of focal points. The area inside the ellipse, as was shown, is the zone of distribution of saddle points.

The condition for negative real parts and hence for stability is clearly

$$(1 - 2\rho) < 0$$

Hence the line PP' of the equation $\rho = 1/2$ is the divide separating the roots with negative real parts (stable singularities) from those with positive real parts (unstable singularities). The former lie above that line; the latter, below it. This completes the picture of the distribution of the various singularities in the (ρ,a)-plane. From [112.8] one has

$$a = \pm \sqrt{\frac{A^2}{\rho} - (1 - \rho)^2}$$

For $a = 0$ the ordinate of the curve is given by the equation

$$\rho^3 - 2\rho^2 + \rho - A^2 = 0 \qquad [113.4]$$

The condition for the reality of the three roots is $A^2 < 4/27$. For $A^2 > 4/27$, there exists one real root, and two conjugate complex roots which are of no interest here.

For $0 < a^2 < a_1^2$, where a_1 is the abscissa of the point of intersection of the curve [112.8] with the ellipse $(1 - \rho)(1 - 3\rho) + a^2 = 0$, Equation [112.8] has three roots of which only one is stable as can be seen from Figure 113.1. For $a_1^2 < a^2 < +\infty$, there exists only one unstable root. Hence, only in the region $0 < a^2 < a_1^2$ can the Van der Pol solution [111.4] approach a stationary periodic solution with the heteroperiodic frequency ω_1, since only in that interval does there exist a stable singularity so that the coefficients b_1 and b_2 in the Van der Pol equations [111.5] approach fixed values as $t \to \infty$.

From Equations [112.2] it follows that the trajectories are directed radially inward for sufficiently large values of r^2. Hence, if only one unstable singularity exists, we can assert by the Bendixson theorem that a limit cycle exists and hence an autoperiodic oscillation ω_0 beating with the external frequency ω_1. Hence, whenever $a^2 > a_1^2$, which corresponds to the existence of a single unstable singularity, the solution [111.4] of Van der Pol has slowly varying coefficients b_1 and b_2 characterizing the heterodyning of the two frequencies ω_0 and ω_1. If, however, $a^2 < a_1^2$, one singularity is stable with index +1, and the other two are unstable. No limit cycle exists in this case, and the stable singularity gives rise to a stationary heteroperiodic oscillation, as previously mentioned.

The topological study of the trajectories of the Van der Pol equations [112.2] in the zone of entrainment can be pursued by constructing the family of curves [112.8] for different values of the parameters with superimposed regions of distribution of the various singular points, as shown in Figure 113.1. A topological analysis of this kind was carried out by Gaponow (15) on the basis of the general considerations of Chapter IV, where singularities and limit cycles are considered as either sources (if they are unstable) or sinks (if they are stable) for the "flow" of trajectories in the phase plane. Such an analysis gives some idea of the transient state of the entrainment phenomenon under various conditions. Without going into the details of this analysis, since they have been given in Part I, it is sufficient to indicate a few interesting results.

In pure entrainment, when only a single stable singularity exists, the trajectories approach it in the usual manner

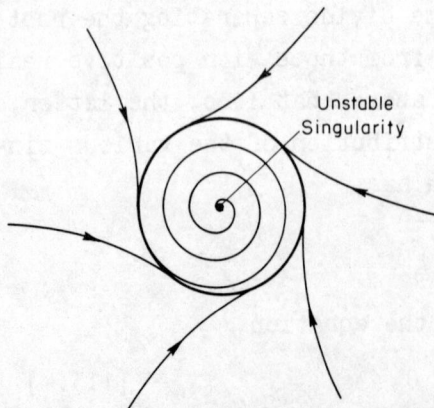

Unstable Singularity

Figure 113.2

depending on whether the singularity lies in the region of stable nodal points or in that of stable focal points. When one unstable singularity exists, in view of the fact that for large values of r Equations [112.2] indicate the inward flow of trajectories, the Bendixson theorem indicates that a stable limit cycle exists, as shown in Figure 113.2. This condition, as was just mentioned, corresponds to the quasiperiodic Van der Pol solution [111.4] when heteroperiodic and autoperiodic frequencies exist and no entrainment takes place.

According to the form of curves [112.8] and the different location of the regions of stability (or instability),

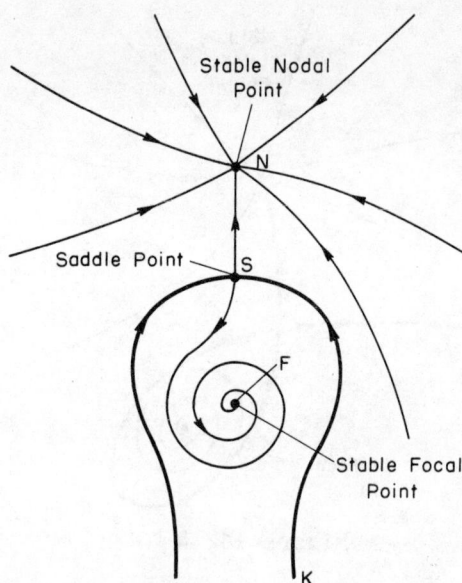

Figure 113.3

more complicated situations may arise, as was shown by Gaponow. Thus, for instance, for certain values of the parameters resulting in a particular shape of the curve [112.8] and for a certain range of $a = 2(\omega_0 - \omega_1)/\alpha$, one may have three singular points, namely, a stable nodal point, a saddle point, and a stable focal point. The flow of trajectories for this situation is shown in Figure 113.3. Since there is a saddle point S, there also exists a separatrix K formed in the neighborhood of S by the stable asymptotes of the saddle point S. There is one singular trajectory SN issuing from S along its unstable asymptote and approaching the nodal point N. The focal point F is approached by a singular trajectory issuing from the other unstable asymptote of S. At a large distance from the singularities the trajectories are inwardly directed as shown. Depending on the form of the separatrix, the trajectories may approach either the nodal point or the focal point. Their approach to the nodal point will be aperiodic from a definite direction; their approach to the focal point will be in the manner of a spiral, which indicates an oscillatory damped motion.

Another possibility is the combination of a stable nodal point, a saddle point, and an unstable focal point. This configuration is shown in Figure 113.4. The separatrix forms a closed loop with the unstable focal point in its interior. The trajectories arriving from distant points of the phase plane approach the stable nodal point.

A number of other combinations are possible, particularly when two singular points coalesce so as to form a singularity of a higher order. Here the approach to the state of entrainment may be relatively complicated. This

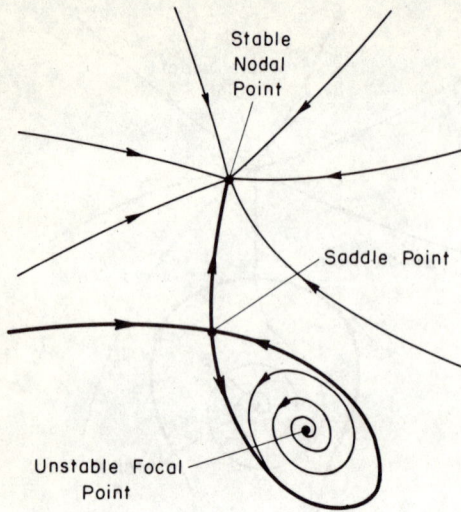

Figure 113.4

coalescence of singular points occurs whenever the line $a = a_1$ in Figure 113.1 becomes tangent to the curve of singular points defined by Equation [112.8].

This transient state of the entrainment process can be studied oscillographically by analyzing the form of the envelopes of the oscillations. When entrainment is reached (16), the envelope becomes a straight line.

114. STEADY STATE OF ENTRAINMENT

During entrainment the heteroperiodic and the autoperiodic oscillations become "locked," and the former imposes its frequency on the latter. In the Van der Pol solution [111.4] the quantities b_1 and b_2 then become constant and one can write

$$v = b_1 \sin \omega_1 t + b_2 \cos \omega_1 t = \sqrt{b_1^2 + b_2^2} \left[\sin \omega_1 t \cos \phi + \cos \omega_1 t \sin \phi \right]$$

$$= b \sin(\omega_1 t + \phi) \qquad [114.1]$$

where

$$\frac{b_1}{\sqrt{b_1^2 + b_2^2}} = \frac{b_1}{b} = \cos \phi; \quad \frac{b_2}{\sqrt{b_1^2 + b_2^2}} = \frac{b_2}{b} = \sin \phi; \quad b = \sqrt{b_1^2 + b_2^2}$$

and where b is the amplitude and ϕ the phase of the oscillation relative to the externally applied voltage. One has

$$\tan \phi = \frac{b_2}{b_1} = \frac{y_0}{x_0} = \frac{1 - \rho}{a} = \frac{(1 - r_0^2)\alpha}{2(\omega_0 - \omega_1)} \qquad [114.2]$$

where a and ρ are the coordinates of the stable singular point in the (ρ, a)-plane. The amplitude b of the oscillation is

$$b = \sqrt{b_1^2 + b_2^2} = a_0 \sqrt{x_0^2 + y_0^2} = \sqrt{\frac{4}{3} \frac{\alpha}{\gamma}} \frac{\rho}{a} \sqrt{a^2 + (1 - \rho)^2} = k \sqrt{\frac{4}{3} \frac{\alpha}{\gamma}} \qquad [114.3]$$

where $k = \frac{\rho}{a} \sqrt{a^2 + (1 - \rho^2)}$ is a factor depending on the difference of frequencies $\omega_0 - \omega_1$ and the ordinate ρ of the stable singular point. It is noted that the quantity

$$a_0 = \sqrt{\frac{4}{3} \frac{\alpha}{\gamma}} \qquad [114.4]$$

is the amplitude of the generating solution of Poincaré; compare with Equation [54.5]. It is thus seen that the autoperiodic amplitude a_0 is affected by the entrainment factor k during the steady state of the phenomenon.

115. ACOUSTIC ENTRAINMENT OF FREQUENCY

The preceding theory of entrainment was established in connection with an electron-tube circuit where experimentation is relatively simple and results can be established in terms of known parameters of the circuit and of the electron tube.

As was mentioned in Section 110, the phenomenon of acoustic entrainment was discussed by Lord Rayleigh in his investigation on sound. More specifically, he says that if two organ pipes of slightly different frequencies are placed near each other, the beats disappear and both pipes oscillate at the same frequency. Later he reproduced an analogous experiment with electrically driven tuning forks of slightly different frequencies; the entrainment effect is evident if the tuning forks are "coupled" by an acoustic resonator.

A recent study of this effect was made by K. Theodorchik and E. Chaikin (17) at the suggestion of Mandelstam and Papalexi. Without going into details, it is sufficient to mention briefly the experimental arrangement used. Figure 115.1 shows an electron-tube oscillator; in its anode circuit a telephone T is inserted and in its grid circuit a microphone M. The telephone and the microphone are also coupled acoustically by two armatures A_1 and A_2

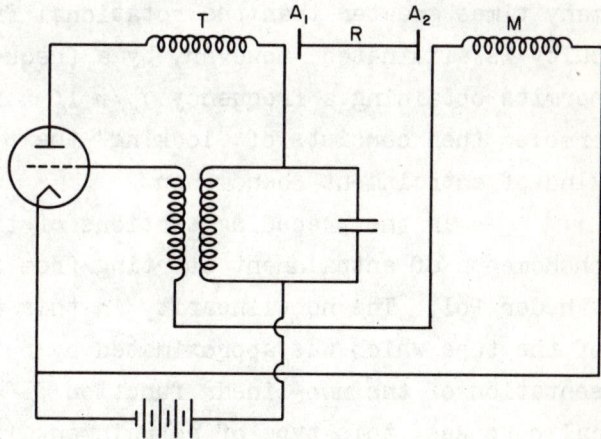

Figure 115.1

fixed to the same rod R. The rod is centralized by a spring and provided with a damper which is not shown. The mechanical system A_1RA_2 is described by a linear differential equation of the second order having a frequency ω. The oscillator is a non-linear self-excited system with frequency ω_0 on the limit cycle. If the difference $\omega - \omega_0$ is appreciable, one finds that there are beats in the system, indicating the presence of both frequencies ω_0 and ω. If the value of this difference is decreased, one finds that both frequencies coalesce into a single frequency ω which corresponds to the external frequency mentioned in Section 110. The "non-linear frequency" ω_0 is thus entrained by the external one ω, and it is found that the ratio $\frac{\omega - \omega_0}{\omega}$ of the zone of entrainment is proportional to the ratio a/a_0 where a is the amplitude of the oscillations of the mechanical system driven by the acoustic pressure emitted by the telephone, and a_0 is the amplitude of the autoperiodic oscillation in the electron-tube oscillator.

This method has been applied in measuring acoustic intensity by observing the magnitude of the band of entrainment, knowing a_0, and determining the proportionality factor by calibration.

116. OTHER FORMS OF ENTRAINMENT

The phenomenon of entrainment, as we have already indicated, has important applications in problems in which it is desirable to obtain synchronization of frequencies. For example, the problem of maintaining the speed of an electric motor with a high degree of accuracy can be solved by synchronizing the motor's frequency with the standard frequency of a quartz oscillator, which can be maintained with great accuracy. If such synchronization can be obtained, the motor speed can be maintained with the same accuracy. In this particular example, the frequency f_q of the quartz oscillator is generally many times greater than the rotational frequency f_m of the motor. This difficulty is eliminated, however, by a frequency-demultiplication network, which permits obtaining a frequency f_q/n if n is the demultiplication factor. The problem then consists of "locking" the two frequencies f_q/n and f_m by some kind of entrainment phenomenon.

In the preceding sections of this chapter we have investigated the phenomenon of entrainment starting from a particular circuit investigated by Van der Pol. The non-linearity in this circuit is due to the characteristic of the tube which was approximated by retaining the cubic term in the representation of the non-linear function $i_a = f(e_g)$ by a polynomial. For practical purposes, this type of entrainment is difficult to obtain because of the small zone of entrainment and also because it is difficult to modify the characteristic of an electron tube so as to produce more favorable conditions for entrainment. In view of this, numerous schemes have recently been developed in which the zone of entrainment is artificially made large by suitable circuits. In this manner one obtains a kind of *artificially produced entrainment* which is more adequate for practical purposes than the simple type investigated by Van der Pol.

As an illustration we shall investigate one such scheme suggested by Kaden (18) and shown in Figure 116.1. We shall omit the mathematical analysis of the circuit, since it follows the argument previously explained, and will give only an elementary explanation of its behavior. The electron tube V_1 operates as an oscillator with frequency ω_1 having C_1 and L_1 as its oscillating circuit. The coefficient of inductance L_1 can be varied within certain limits because the coil L_1 is wound on an iron core whose state of magnetic saturation can be varied by changing the direct current i flowing through the coil G wound on the middle leg of the magnetic circuit M as shown. There are

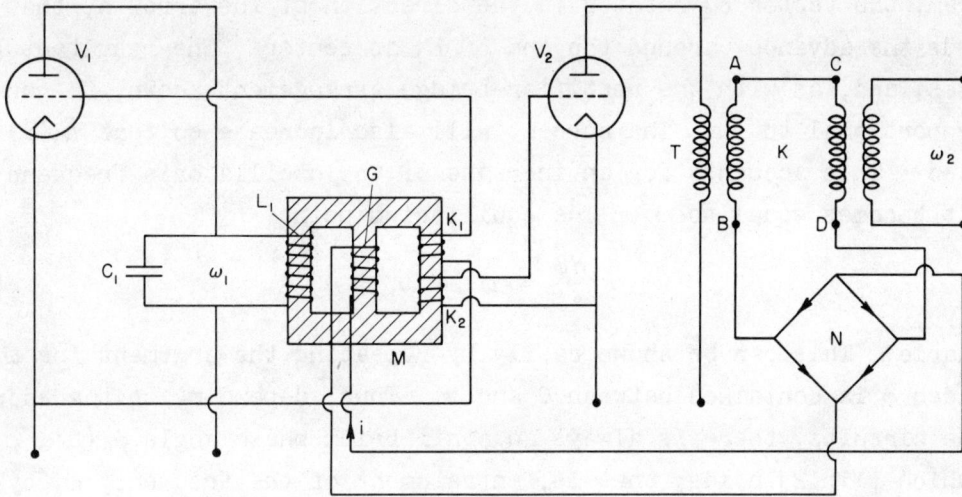

Figure 116.1

two other coils: K_1, which produces a feed-back voltage to the grid of V_1 which merely maintains the oscillation with frequency ω_1, and the coil K_2 transmitting the oscillation at that frequency to the second tube V_2 working as an amplifier. The output of V_2 through a transformer is coupled with the branch AB of the synchronizing network K. The network K also has a second branch CD into which the external frequency ω_2 is inductively transferred. The synchronizing network BACD is closed on a bridge N formed by rectifying elements; the direction of rectification is shown by the arrows. The diagonal points of the bridge N are closed on the saturation coil G of the iron-core reactor. In the circuit BACD there are two induced voltages: E_1 with frequency ω_1 induced in the AB-branch, and E_2 with frequency ω_2 induced in the CD-branch. We shall consider the case when the difference $\omega_2 - \omega_1 = \Delta\omega$ is small. The vector diagram is shown in Figure 116.2; the vector E_1 can be assumed to be fixed; E_2 rotates with frequency $\Delta\omega$ in one direction or the other, depending on the sign of the difference $\omega_2 - \omega_1$. The resultant vector E_r is the voltage between B and D and, to a certain scale, it represents the rectified current i flowing through the coil G.

The frequency $\omega_1 = 1/\sqrt{L_1(i)C_1}$ where $L_1(i)$ is a non-linear function of i decreasing with increasing i. It is apparent that, if $\omega_2 \neq \omega_1$, one has the relation

$$\frac{d\phi}{dt} = \omega_2 - \omega_1 = \Delta\omega \qquad [116.1]$$

Assume, for instance, that initially $\Delta\omega > 0$, which means that the extraneous frequency ω_2 is greater than the frequency ω_1 of the oscillator. In the vector

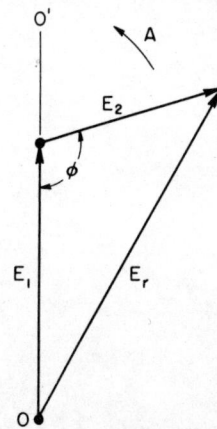

Figure 116.2

diagram, the vector E_2 rotates in the direction of the arrow A, that is, towards the advance, around the end of E_1 as center. The resultant E_r increases, and, as with the rectifier-bridge arrangement shown, the current i is proportional to E_r. The current will also increase so that $L_1(i)$ will be reduced. This accounts for an increase of the oscillator's frequency ω_1 until it becomes equal to ω_2. The equilibrium point

$$\frac{d\phi}{dt} = \omega_2 - \omega_1 = 0 \qquad\qquad [116.2]$$

is stable. This can be shown easily by repeating the argument for $\omega_2 < \omega_1$ provided ϕ is contained between 0 and π. Thus, depending on the adjustment of the circuits, there is always an equilibrium phase angle ϕ_0 $(0 < \phi_0 < \pi)$ for which [116.2] holds; that is, entrainment of the frequency ω_1 by the external frequency ω_2 is artificially produced.

If the frequencies ω_1 and ω_2 are far apart, the vector E_2 rotates rapidly with respect to the fixed vector E_1, and in view of the finite time constants of the circuits the magnetic saturation control may not be sufficiently rapid to adjust the frequency ω_1 so as to "lock" it in synchronism with the frequency ω_2. One would then have beats due to the existence of both frequencies ω_1 and ω_2.

In the example given here the entrainment phenomenon is possible because of the non-linearity of the parameter $L_1(i)$. If the parameter L_1 were constant, that is, in the absence of the saturable iron core, it would be impossible to obtain the synchronization of the two frequencies ω_1 and ω_2, and the zone of entrainment would be absent.

CHAPTER XIX

PARAMETRIC EXCITATION

117. HETEROPARAMETRIC AND AUTOPARAMETRIC EXCITATION

In Section 99 it was shown that it is possible to obtain self-excitation of subharmonic oscillations by varying periodically a parameter of the system. In this chapter we shall investigate this phenomenon, called parametric excitation, from a somewhat different point of view and will introduce certain generalizations.

It is noteworthy that the phenomenon of parametric excitation has been known for many years. Thus, for example, Lord Rayleigh describes in Reference (10) an old experiment of Melde (19) which he reproduces and analyzes. In this experiment a stretched string is attached to a prong of a tuning fork vibrating in the direction of the string; it is observed that periodic variations of frequency f in the string's tension account for the appearance of transverse vibrations of the string with a frequency of $f/2$. Later, M. Brillouin (20) and H. Poincaré (21) investigated a similar effect in electric circuits. Quite recently certain Russian physicists under the leadership of Mandelstam and Papalexi (22) investigated these phenomena in greater detail; we propose to give a brief outline of these researches.

It is useful to define two types of parametric excitation, heteroparametric and autoparametric. In heteroparametric excitation, self-excitation is caused by the variation of a parameter expressed as an explicit function of time. In autoparametric excitation the variation of the parameter depends directly on some physical quantity and thus is an implicit periodic function of time.

The vibrations of the string in Lord Rayleigh's experiment are clearly heteroparametric in that the variation of the parameter is produced by a tuning fork having a definite frequency. Parametric excitation occurs here with a frequency equal to one-half the external frequency of the tuning fork. The same remark applies to the circuit described in Section 99 where the capacity is modulated as an explicit function of time.

On the other hand, as has been shown on numerous occasions, self-excitation of electron-tube circuits can be traced to the fluctuating transconductance of the tube caused by the oscillatory process itself. In all electron-tube circuits the periodic variation of the parameter, the transconductance, appears as an explicit function of the physical quantity which characterizes the process, for instance, the grid voltage, and depends only *implicitly* on time. Self-excitation of electron-tube circuits therefore belongs to the autoparametric type. The concept of autoparametric excitation is not particularly interesting because most excitations of the autoparametric type can be treated by the standard method of Poincaré.

With heteroparametric excitation, however, the situation is different. Since one or several parameters of the system appear as explicit periodic functions of time, the problem is reduced to the solution of differential equations with periodic coefficients, that is, equations of the Mathieu-Hill type; more specifically, the condition of self-excitation of the system is equivalent to the existence of unstable solutions of such equations, which means that an initially small departure increases because of the periodic variation of a parameter.

It must be noted that, although the theory of the Mathieu-Hill equation is necessary for the establishment of the conditions of heteroperiodic excitation, there is nothing in that theory which would permit determining the amplitude of the ultimate steady state. This difficulty arises from the fact that the known types of Mathieu-Hill equations are *linear* equations and, as such, possess unstable solutions increasing indefinitely in their unstable region. In order to establish a theory of heteroparametric excitation approaching a definite steady state, one should apply some kind of non-linear differential equation with periodic coefficients. Unfortunately, no theory involving non-linear equations with periodic coefficients exists at present.

These theoretical difficulties limit a further analysis of heteroparametric excitation. It is interesting to note that Mandelstam and Papalexi, who developed a heteroparametric generator, an electric machine described in Section 124, were able to demonstrate that, in the absence of non-linearities in the circuit, the voltage builds up indefinitely until the insulation is punctured. On the contrary, by providing a non-linear element in the circuit, the voltage builds up to a finite value, and the generator functions in a stable manner. In spite of these theoretical limitations, equations with periodic coefficients can be used to determine the conditions of heteroparametric excitation in a general manner, as will be shown.

118. DIFFERENTIAL EQUATIONS WITH PERIODIC COEFFICIENTS

Consider a differential equation with periodic coefficients (23)

$$\ddot{z} + 2p(t)\dot{z} + q(t)z = 0 \qquad [118.1]$$

where $p(t) = p(t + 2\pi)$ and $q(t) = q(t + 2\pi)$. If we introduce a new variable x defined by the equation

$$z = xe^{-\int pdt} \qquad [118.2]$$

Equation [118.1] becomes

$$\ddot{x} + M(t)x = 0 \qquad [118.3]$$

where $M(t) = q - p^2 - \dot{p}$ is a periodic function.

In practice one frequently encounters the following expressions for $M(t)$:

1. $M(t) = \omega_0^2 + \alpha_0^2 \cos kt$, in which case Equation [118.3] is called the Mathieu equation, or

2. $M(t)$ is a Fourier series, $\omega_0^2 + A_1 \cos kt + A_2 \cos 2kt + \cdots + B_1 \sin kt + B_2 \sin 2kt + \cdots$, in which case [118.3] is called the Hill equation.

Since the theory of the Hill equation is similar to that of the Mathieu equation, it is sufficient to consider the latter. The Mathieu equation

$$\ddot{x} + (\omega_0^2 + \alpha_0^2 \cos k\tau) x = 0 \qquad [118.4]$$

by a change of the independent variable $t = k\tau$ can be reduced to the form

$$\ddot{x} + (\omega^2 + \alpha^2 \cos t) x = 0 \qquad [118.5]$$

where $\omega k = \omega_0$ and $\alpha k = \alpha_0$. The essential feature of the Mathieu equation [118.5] is that, although the function $M(t) = \omega^2 + \alpha^2 \cos t$ is periodic, its solutions are not necessarily periodic although under certain conditions they may be periodic. If they are periodic, the solutions are given in terms of the so-called Mathieu functions (23). Since Equation [118.5] is linear, one can assert that, if one knows two particular solutions f_1 and f_2 forming a fundamental system, the general solution will be of the form

$$F = A_1 f_1 + A_2 f_2 \qquad [118.6]$$

where A_1 and A_2 are arbitrary constants. Moreover, since $f_1(t + 2\pi)$ and $f_2(t + 2\pi)$ are also solutions, one can express them in terms of $f_1(t)$ and $f_2(t)$ by equations of the form

$$f_1(t + 2\pi) = a f_1(t) + b f_2(t)$$
$$f_2(t + 2\pi) = c f_1(t) + d f_2(t) \qquad [118.7]$$

From [118.6] one has also

$$F(t + 2\pi) = A_1 f_1(t + 2\pi) + A_2 f_2(t + 2\pi) \qquad [118.8]$$

From the theorem of Floquet (24) we know that there is a solution F such that

$$F(t + 2\pi) = A_1 f_1(t + 2\pi) + A_2 f_2(t + 2\pi) = \sigma F(t) \qquad [118.9]$$

If we select the following initial conditions,

$$f_1(0) = 0; \quad f_1'(0) = 1; \quad f_2(0) = 1; \quad f_2'(0) = 0 \qquad [118.10]$$

we observe that the Wronskian

$$\begin{vmatrix} f_1(0) & f_2(0) \\ f_1'(0) & f_2'(0) \end{vmatrix} \neq 0$$

and thus the system of solutions f_1 and f_2 is fundamental. From Equations [118.7] one gets for $t = 0$

$$f_1(2\pi) = b; \quad f_2(2\pi) = d; \quad f_1'(2\pi) = a; \quad f_2'(2\pi) = c \qquad [118.11]$$

From [118.9] one obtains

$$F(t + 2\pi) = A_1(af_1 + bf_2) + A_2(cf_1 + df_2) \qquad [118.12]$$

Since f_1 and f_2 are the solutions of [118.5], clearly

$$f_1'' + M(t)f_1 = 0; \quad f_2'' + M(t)f_2 = 0$$

whence $f_1''/f_1 = f_2''/f_2$ and, therefore, $f_1''f_2 - f_2''f_1 = 0$, that is,

$$f_1'f_2 - f_2'f_1 = h = \text{constant} \qquad [118.13]$$

The value of h is

$$h = f_1'(0)f_2(0) - f_2'(0)f_1(0) = f_1'(2\pi)f_2(2\pi) - f_2'(2\pi)f_1(2\pi) \qquad [118.14]$$

which, by [118.10] and [118.11], becomes

$$1 = ad - bc \qquad [118.15]$$

From Equations [118.9] and [118.12] in view of the initial conditions [118.11] one gets

$$A_1(a - \sigma) + A_2c = 0$$
$$A_1b + A_2(d - \sigma) = 0 \qquad [118.16]$$

Thus, in view of [118.15], the condition for the non-trivial solution of the system [118.16] is

$$\sigma^2 - (a + d)\sigma + (ad - bc) = \sigma^2 - (a + d)\sigma + 1 = 0 \qquad [118.17]$$

The roots of the characteristic equation [118.17] are

$$\sigma_{1,2} = \frac{a + d}{2} \pm \sqrt{\left(\frac{a + d}{2}\right)^2 - 1} = \frac{a + d}{2} \pm j\sqrt{1 - \frac{(a + d)^2}{4}} \qquad [118.18]$$

If we put $\frac{a + d}{2} = \cos 2\pi\mu$, this equation becomes

$$\sigma_{1,2} = \cos 2\pi\mu \pm j\sin 2\pi\mu = e^{\pm j2\pi\mu} \qquad [118.19]$$

If $\frac{a + d}{2} < 1$, $\cos 2\pi\mu$ is real; hence, μ is also real, and σ is complex with modulus equal to one. This characterizes stability, both of equilibrium and of the stationary motion, from the very definition of σ, Equation [118.9]. If $\frac{a + d}{2} > 1$, μ is imaginary; hence, σ is real, and there is a root greater than one which indicates instability. If $\frac{a + d}{2} = 1$, $\mu = 0$, and hence $\sigma = 1$; this should be considered as the beginning of the unstable range of the Mathieu equation.

Taking into account the values [118.11], one can write

$$\cos 2\pi\mu = \frac{1}{2}(a + d) = \frac{1}{2}\left[f_1'(2\pi) + f_2(2\pi)\right] \qquad [118.20]$$

119. STABLE AND UNSTABLE REGIONS OF THE MATHIEU EQUATION

Let $f = \cos \gamma t$ and $\phi = \frac{1}{\gamma} \sin \gamma t$ be a pair of fundamental solutions in the interval $0 \leq t \leq \pi$ with initial conditions $f(0) = 1$, $\phi(0) = 0$, $f'(0) = 0$, and $\phi'(0) = 1$, and let

$$g(t) = C \sin \delta t + D \cos \delta t; \quad h(t) = E \sin \delta t + F \cos \delta t \qquad [119.1]$$

be a pair of fundamental solutions in the interval $\pi \leq t \leq 2\pi$, where $\gamma = \sqrt{\omega^2 + \alpha^2}$ and $\delta = \sqrt{\omega^2 - \alpha^2}$. Fitting these functions together at $t = \pi$, we obtain

$$f(\pi) = g(\pi) \quad \text{or} \quad \cos \gamma\pi = C \sin \delta\pi + D \cos \delta\pi$$

$$f'(\pi) = g'(\pi) \quad \text{or} \quad -\gamma \sin \gamma\pi = C\delta \cos \delta\pi - D\delta \sin \delta\pi$$

$$\phi(\pi) = h(\pi) \quad \text{or} \quad \frac{1}{\gamma} \sin \gamma\pi = E \sin \delta\pi + F \cos \delta\pi \qquad [119.2]$$

$$\phi'(\pi) = h'(\pi) \quad \text{or} \quad \cos \gamma\pi = E\delta \cos \delta\pi - F\delta \sin \delta\pi$$

From these equations we can determine the four constants A, B, C, and D and thus determine

$$\cos 2\pi\mu = \frac{f(2\pi) + \phi'(2\pi)}{2} = \frac{g(2\pi) + h'(2\pi)}{2} \qquad [119.3]$$

One finds that for $\omega^2 > \alpha^2 > 0$,

$$\cos 2\pi\mu = \cos \pi\gamma \cos \pi\delta - \frac{1}{2}\left(\frac{\gamma}{\delta} + \frac{\delta}{\gamma}\right) \sin \pi\gamma \sin \pi\delta \qquad [119.4]$$

and for $\omega^2 < \alpha^2$,

$$\cos 2\pi\mu = \cos \pi\gamma \cosh \pi\eta - \frac{1}{2}\left(\frac{\gamma}{\eta} - \frac{\eta}{\gamma}\right) \sin \pi\gamma \sinh \pi\eta \qquad [119.5]$$

where $\eta = \sqrt{\alpha^2 - \omega^2}$.

From these equations one may plot curves in the (ω^2, α^2)-plane which are the boundaries between the regions of unstable motion (shown in white in Figure 119.1) and of stable motion (shown by shading). This discussion is taken from an article by Van der Pol and Strutt (25). These authors discuss the character of the stable and unstable regions for various values of the two parameters α^2 and ω^2 and derive the following conclusions:

1. The unstable regions cover a larger area than the stable ones.

2. Below the 45-degree line in the first quadrant the motion is, in general, stable. Here $\alpha^2 < \omega^2$, the stepwise "ripple" appearing in Figure 119.1

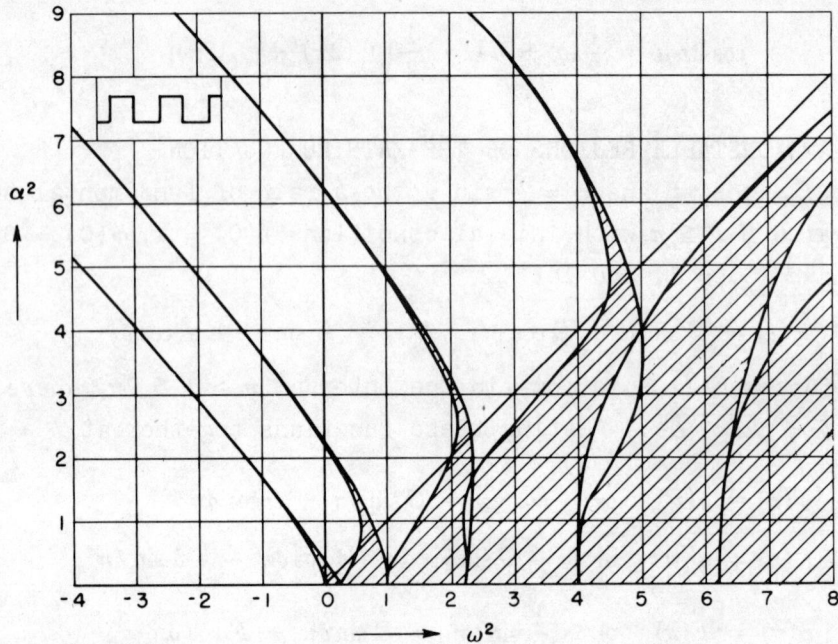

Figure 119.1

does not touch the zero line, and the coefficient of x in the Mathieu equation remains positive. Thus, without the ripple, one would always have stable motion. Under certain conditions the ripple renders the motion unstable.

3. Above and to the left of the 45-degree line the motion is generally unstable; the stable areas which exist are relatively small. Without the ripple the motion is unstable in this region so that the ripple under certain conditions transforms the instability into stability.

The last conclusion is illustrated experimentally by a reversed pendulum whose support undergoes a periodic vertical motion. It is found that, for a certain band of frequencies and for a certain amplitude of the motion of the support in the vertical direction, the unstable pendulum exhibits stability.

In what follows we shall be interested particularly in the unstable solutions of differential equations with periodic coefficients and will extend the discussion a little further to ascertain whether self-excitation will exist under various conditions of frequency and phase of the ripple relative to the fundamental oscillation of the system.

Instead of following the analytical argument of Van der Pol and Strutt, we will investigate the behavior of the phase trajectories, which will enable us to gain a more intuitive understanding of the phenomenon of hetero-parametric excitation.

120. PHYSICAL NATURE OF SOLUTIONS

From the preceding analysis it follows that in certain regions of the (ω^2, α^2)-plane the solutions of the Mathieu-Hill equation are unstable. These regions of instability have not as yet been explored to any extent because the aim of previous analytical studies has been the establishment of conditions of stability which resulted in the Mathieu functions, with which we are not concerned here. On the contrary, for parametric self-excitation, in which we are interested here, the unstable regions present greater interest. Although by introducing the Mathieu-Hill equation we lose the familiar ground of the theory of Poincaré, that is, it is impossible to eliminate time between the two differential equations of the first order, the procedure is more direct, as will be shown. The main limitation of this method, as was already mentioned, is the fact that since the Mathieu-Hill equation is linear, there is no indication whatever as to how the gradually increasing oscillations of the unstable region reach a steady state. To determine this it would be necessary to investigate a non-linear equation of the Mathieu-Hill type, but, as we pointed out, no theory of such equations exists at present. Since we are unable to proceed analytically with a non-linear Mathieu-Hill equation, it is still possible to form a certain physical idea as to what happens in the unstable region of solutions of this equation by the following argument of Mandelstam.

Assume that we have a non-dissipative oscillating circuit with a capacity which varies periodically between the two limits C_{max} and C_{min}. Let the capacitor have initially, that is, when $t = 0$, a certain charge q; the circuit has no current. Since there is no essential difference between the solutions of the Mathieu equation and those of the Hill equation with the function

$$M(t) = \omega^2 + \frac{4}{\pi}\alpha^2\left(\cos t - \frac{1}{3}\cos 3t + \frac{1}{5}\cos 5t - \cdots\right) \qquad [120.1]$$

representing a rectangular ripple, see Section 119, we can adopt the argument of Van der Pol and Strutt and consider abrupt variations of capacity from C_{max} to C_{min}, and vice versa, occurring periodically.

Assume, therefore, that for $t = 0$ the capacity is suddenly decreased by $\Delta C = C_{max} - C_{min}$. Since the whole energy stored in the circuit is purely electrostatic, it is apparent that the impulsive work done during this sudden decrease of capacity is

$$\frac{\Delta C}{2C^2}q^2 \qquad [120.2]$$

This amount of energy is thus added to the initial weak electrostatic energy existing in the capacitor prior to the instant $t = 0$. The capacitor will then begin to discharge through the circuit and a current will appear. Assume now that one-quarter period later, when the capacitor is totally discharged and the energy is entirely electromagnetic $(Li^2/2)$, we restore abruptly the original value of the capacity C_{max} by giving the increment $+\Delta C$ to the capacity. In so doing no work will be performed since the electrostatic energy is zero at this instant. However, from the fact that during the preceding operation the electrostatic and, hence, the total energy of the system has received an increment $\frac{\Delta C}{2C^2} q^2$, it is apparent that it is still present in the system which has been assumed to be conservative. If one-quarter period later we repeat the procedure made at $t = 0$, that is, reduce the capacity by the amount ΔC, another increment of the electrostatic energy will be added, and so on for subsequent abrupt changes ΔC of capacity occurring periodically every quarter period of the circuit. It is thus seen that energy is injected into the system periodically at the instants $t = 2n\frac{T}{4}$, n being an integer, when the capacity is suddenly changed by the amount $-\Delta C$; the restoration of the capacity $(+\Delta C)$ to its maximum value occurs at the instants $t = (2n + 1)\frac{T}{4}$ without involving any work. It is observed that the period of variation of the capacity is one-half the period of the free oscillatory phenomenon.

The argument remains the same if, instead of capacity variations, inductance variations $\pm \Delta L$ are used. The timing of the ripple for inductance variations is exactly the same as for capacity variations, namely, the coefficient of the inductance is decreased $(-\Delta L)$ at the instants 0, $T/2$, $\cdots$, and increased $(+\Delta L)$ at the instants $T/4$, $3T/4$, $\cdots$. To the same timing, however, there will correspond a diametrically opposite effect, that is, at the instants $T/4$, $3T/4$, $\cdots$, when L is increased, there will be an addition of energy since the whole energy is electromagnetic at these instants; whereas at 0, $T/2$, $\cdots$, when L is decreased, no work will be done since the electromagnetic energy is zero.

121. TOPOLOGY OF THE HILL-MEISSNER EQUATION

The Hill equation with the rectangular ripple expressed by Equation [120.1] was used by Meissner in his analysis of vibrations arising in driving rods of electric locomotives (26) and was found useful by other investigators (25). Very frequently this particular form of Hill's equation is designated as the Hill-Meissner equation; we will inquire further into the nature of its solutions. The usefulness of the Hill-Meissner equation lies in the particular form of its periodic coefficient, the ripple, which permits a simple discussion of its trajectories in the phase plane. It is apparent that the trajectories of the Hill-Meissner equation differ somewhat from those of the Mathieu equation, but it is likely that, at least qualitatively, there is not much difference between the shapes of integral curves for both equations, as was pointed out by Strutt (27) and as follows from experimental evidence. It is to be understood, however, that no direct quantitative comparison of the unstable solutions of equations of both types has been attempted so far, and the above assumption seems to be a plausible hypothesis convenient for a qualitative analysis of the phenomenon.

With these remarks in mind, we shall write the Hill-Meissner equation in the form

$$\ddot{x} + (a^2 \pm b^2)x = 0 \qquad [121.1]$$

which means that we consider alternately the two equations

$$\ddot{x} + (a^2 + b^2)x = 0; \qquad \ddot{x} + (a^2 - b^2)x = 0 \qquad [121.2]$$

during each half period π of the ripple, with the understanding that the solutions have to be continuous on physical grounds although not necessarily analytic at the points at which the changes from $(a^2 + b^2)$ to $(a^2 - b^2)$, or vice versa, occur. We will assume that $a^2 > b^2$ inasmuch as we will be concerned with the problem of *modulation* of the quantity a^2 by a rectangular ripple $\pm b^2$.

We will now elaborate somewhat the example of heteroparametric excitation discussed in the preceding section and write the differential equation of the non-dissipative circuit in the form

$$L_0 \frac{d^2q}{dt^2} + \frac{1}{C}q = 0 \qquad [121.3]$$

where L_0 is the inductance, C is the capacity, and q is the quantity of electricity stored in the capacitor. Let us assume that the capacity C varies between $C_{max} = C_0 + \Delta C$ and $C_{min} = C_0 - \Delta C$ in a stepwise manner. The preceding equation can then be written as

$$\ddot{q} + \frac{1}{L_0 C_0 (1 \pm \gamma_c)}q = 0 \qquad [121.4]$$

where $\gamma_c = \Delta C/C_0$ is the index of the stepwise modulation. If $1/L_0 C_0 = \omega_0^2$ and if we assume that $\gamma_c \ll 1$, without any loss of generality Equation [121.4] becomes

$$\ddot{q} + (1 \mp \gamma_c)\omega_0^2 q = 0 \qquad [121.5]$$

This equation, as was just explained, should be considered as an alternate sequence of the two equations

$$\ddot{q} + (1 + \gamma_c)\omega_0^2 q = 0; \qquad \ddot{q} + (1 - \gamma_c)\omega_0^2 q = 0 \qquad [121.6]$$

A trivial change of the independent variable $t = \tau/\omega_0$ transforms these equations into the form

$$\frac{d^2q}{d\tau^2} + \alpha_1^2 q = 0; \qquad \frac{d^2q}{d\tau^2} + \alpha_2^2 q = 0 \qquad [121.7]$$

where $\alpha_1^2 = 1 + \gamma_c$ and $\alpha_2^2 = 1 - \gamma_c$. The two equations replace each other at the "frequency" of the ripple $\pm \Delta C$.

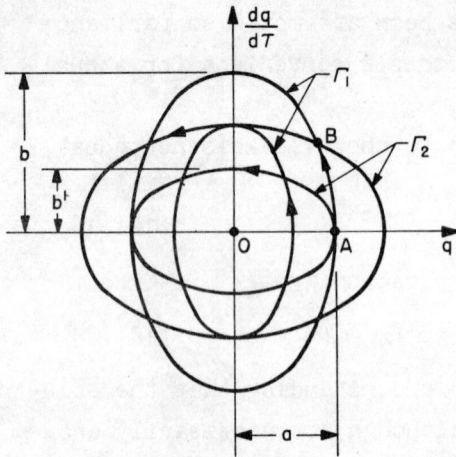

Figure 121.1

Since no confusion is to be feared, we shall designate by $\dot{q}$ and $\ddot{q}$ the derivatives with respect to the new variable τ, the angular time.

Let us transfer the problem into the phase plane of the variables q and $\dot{q}$. The solutions $q(\tau)$ will then be represented by the integral curves, or *phase trajectories*, of Equations [121.7], and the dynamical process described by these equations will be represented by the *motion* of the *representative point* on these trajectories; see Part I.

For $\gamma_c = 0$ and $\alpha_1^2 = \alpha_2^2 = 1$, the trajectories of Equations [121.7] form a continuous family Γ_0 of concentric circles with the origin as center. If $\gamma_c \neq 0$, the trajectories form continuous families Γ_1 and Γ_2 of concentric homothetic ellipses shown in Figure 121.1. The family Γ_1 corresponding to $\alpha_1^2 > 1$ has a constant ratio $b/a = \alpha_1^2 = 1 + \gamma_c$ of semiaxes; the family Γ_2 has a ratio $b'/a = \alpha_2^2 = 1 - \gamma_c$. The family Γ_1 corresponds to the reduced value $C_0 - \Delta C$ of the capacity and Γ_2 to the increased value $C_0 + \Delta C$. The origin O is the singular point of Equations [121.7]. The two families Γ_1 and Γ_2 thus serve as a kind of reference system determining the motion in the phase plane. For example, if for $t = 0$ certain initial conditions, say $(q_0, 0)$, are given and the value of C is prescribed, for example, $C = C_0 - \Delta C$, the process is depicted by the motion starting from the point A corresponding to the initial conditions and moving along the ellipse of the family Γ_1 passing through A. If at a later instant $t = t_1$, corresponding to the point B on the ellipse, the capacity is changed and is then $C = C_0 + \Delta C$, the representative point will pass onto the elliptic trajectory belonging to the family Γ_2 passing through B and will continue to move on that trajectory until the next change ($C = C_0 - \Delta C$), and so on.

This representation of the solutions $q(\tau)$ of Equations [121.7] by phase trajectories is a convenient way of ascertaining the various circumstances of heteroparametric self-excitation. As an example, let us consider self-excitation when a capacity ripple, discussed in Section 120, is present. Let us start from a point $A(q_0, 0)$, see Figure 121.2, after the capacity has been reduced ($C = C_0 - \Delta C$). The representative point will move on the arc AB of the elliptic trajectory of the family Γ_1. At the point B ($q = 0$, $\dot{q} = \text{max}$) the capacity is increased ($C = C_0 + \Delta C$), and the arc BC of the family Γ_2 is followed. At the point C the capacity is reduced, and the next arc CD is of

the family Γ_1, and so on. After a
period 2π one reaches the point E
corresponding to $q_{2\pi} > q_0$ which
shows that the energy content of
the system has been increased.

It must be noted that
the phenomenon is reversible; in
fact, if we replace the words
"capacity is decreased" by "capacity is increased," and vice versa,
in the argument of Section 120, it
is apparent that instead of *adding*
energy by capacity variations, energy will be withdrawn by these
variations. Physically this means

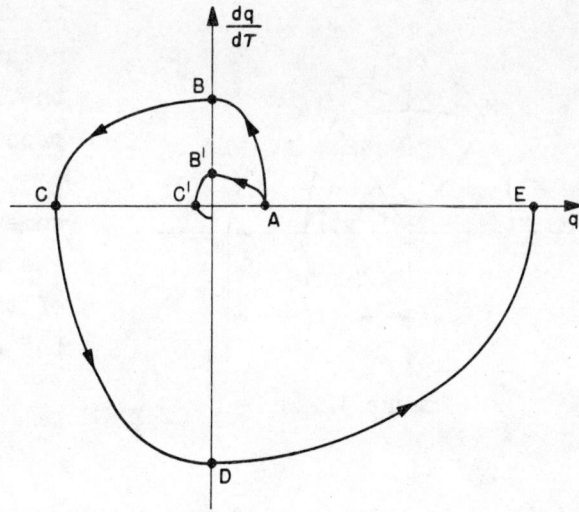

Figure 121.2

that, instead of *injecting* energy into the system by providing external impulsive work which will overcome the electrostatic forces, energy will be *withdrawn* because the electrostatic forces will do the impulsive work and will
thus diminish the energy content of the system. This situation is shown by
the trajectory $AB'C' \cdots$ in Figure 121.2. If, starting from the point A, as
before, the capacity is increased $(+ \Delta C)$, at B' decreased, at C' increased,
and so on, a convergent spiral will result which represents withdrawal of
energy.

In this example the trajectories are spirals made up of elliptic
arcs; these spirals have continuous tangents at every point, although there
are discontinuities in the curvature at the points B, C, D, E, $\cdots$, at which
the changes of capacity occur. In other words the trajectories of the Hill-
Meissner equation with which we are concerned here are *piecewise analytic
curves*, possessing continuous first derivatives but discontinuous second derivatives at points where a loss of analyticity occurs. In a more general
case analyzed in the following section the piecewise analytic trajectories
may have discontinuous first derivatives at certain points.

122. DEPENDENCE OF HETEROPARAMETRIC EXCITATION ON FREQUENCY
AND PHASE OF THE PARAMETER VARIATION

In the preceding section we studied a special case in which the discontinuous changes in the rectangular ripple occurred at the instants when the
representative point crossed the coordinate axes of the $(x,\dot{x})$-plane and the
frequency of the ripple was twice that of the circuit. This case, which is
the one studied by the early investigators, is also the one most frequently
encountered in practice. We will now outline a more general method of approach

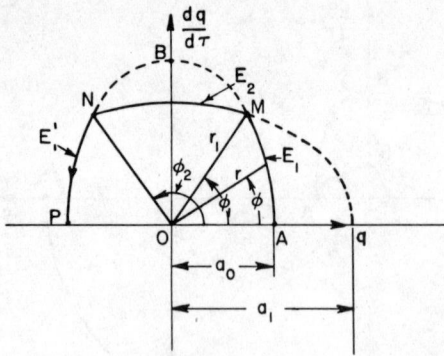

Figure 122.1

to this problem by considering different relative frequencies and phase angles of the ripple with respect to the oscillatory process in the circuit.

For this purpose we shall extend somewhat the study of the preceding section. The radius vector r of a phase trajectory of the family Γ_1, for example, is given by the equation

$$r = \frac{a_0}{\sqrt{\cos^2\phi + \dfrac{1}{\alpha_1^2}\sin\phi}} \qquad [122.1]$$

where ϕ is the angle of the radius vector; $a_0 = OA$, the semiaxis on the x-axis; and $\alpha_1^2 = 1 + \gamma_c$ as before. If the change of capacity occurs at some point M, see Figure 122.1, whose coordinates are $x_1 = r_1\cos\phi_1$ and $y_1 = r_1\sin\phi_1$, where r_1 corresponds to the angle ϕ_1, the arc of the family Γ_2 corresponding to $C = C_0 + \Delta C$ will begin at the point M and will continue to the point $N(r_2,\phi_2)$ at which a change of capacity from $C_0 + \Delta C$ to $C_0 - \Delta C$ occurs and a new arc NP of the family Γ_1 will be traversed. If we start from a given point of the phase plane and assume a particular subdivision of angles $\phi_2 - \phi_1$, $\phi_3 - \phi_2$, $\cdots$, it can be shown (28) that the subsequent major semiaxes a_1, a_2, $\cdots$ of the elliptic trajectories can be calculated by an elementary recurrence procedure. Thus, for example, starting from the point A in Figure 122.1, one obtains after N changes of capacity the following expressions for the major semiaxis a_N:

$$a_N = a_{2\nu} = a_0\frac{f_1 f_3\cdots f_{2\nu-1}}{f_2 f_4\cdots f_{2\nu}} \qquad [122.2]$$

$$a_N = a_{2\nu+1} = a_0\frac{\alpha_1}{\alpha_2}\frac{f_1 f_3\cdots f_{2\nu+1}}{f_2 f_4\cdots f_{2\nu}} \qquad [122.3]$$

where

$$f_i(\phi_i) = \sqrt{\frac{\alpha_2^2 + \tan^2\phi_i}{\alpha_1^2 + \tan^2\phi_i}} \qquad [122.4]$$

From the properties of the functions $f_i(\phi_i)$ it is apparent that

$$f_i(\phi_i) = f_i(-\phi_i) = f_i(\phi_i + \pi) = f_i(-\phi_i + \pi) \qquad [122.5]$$

The only case of practical interest is that in which all intervals are equal and are fractions of $2k\pi$, where k is an integer. We shall call the intervals in this mode of subdivision the *equiphase intervals* inasmuch as the phase plane is divided into equal sectors. If N is the number of changes of capacity in one period (2π) of the process, the phase angles for $N = 4$ will be

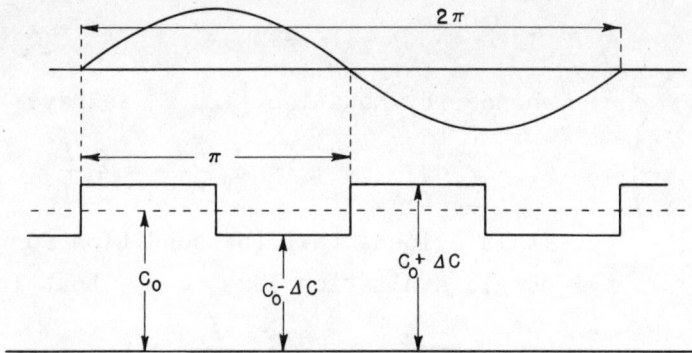

Figure 122.2

ϕ_0, $\phi_1 = \phi_0 + \frac{\pi}{2}$, $\phi_2 = \phi_0 + \frac{2\pi}{2}$, $\phi_3 = \phi_0 + \frac{3\pi}{2}$, and $\phi_4 = \phi_0$. We may call ϕ_0 the *phase angle* of the ripple and the number N the relative frequency of the ripple. Figure 122.2 shows the relative position of the ripple, with $N = 4$ and a certain arbitrary angle ϕ_0, with respect to the free oscillation of the system.

It is to be noted that in a more detailed investigation of this phenomenon one has to take into account the fact that the equiphase intervals are not equitime intervals, that is, intervals of equal time, because of the non-uniformity of the motion of the representative point on the elliptic trajectories. Although this circumstance can be taken into account by defining certain functions $g_i(\phi_i)$ similar to the functions $f_i(\phi_i)$ just introduced, we shall not elaborate on this subject here but will investigate the principal features of heteroparametric excitation on the basis of the equiphase intervals. There is sufficient justification for this because in the most important practical cases, when the changes of capacity occur on the coordinate axes of the phase diagram, both types of intervals coincide; when they do not, the introduction of equitime intervals, while complicating the calculations somewhat, does not change the qualitative aspect of the phenomenon of heteroparametric excitation.

It is convenient to consider the following four groups of numbers N. 1. $N = 4\nu$;   2. $N = (2\nu + 1)2$;   3. $N = 2\nu + 1$;   4. $N = p/q$, where $\nu = 1, 2, 3, \cdots$, and p and q are relatively prime. In the first three groups N is an integer, and in the last it is a rational fraction. This covers all cases of practical interest.

1. First group: $N = 4, 8, 12, \cdots$

Let us consider the first case, $N = 4$, which has previously been studied by an elementary method. We shall now apply the general method involving the use of the functions $f_i(\phi_i)$. The intervals are clearly ϕ_0, $\phi_1 = \phi_0 + \frac{\pi}{2}$, $\phi_2 = \phi_0 + \frac{2\pi}{2}$, $\phi_3 = \phi_0 + \frac{3\pi}{2}$, and $\phi_4 = \phi_0$. By the properties [122.5]

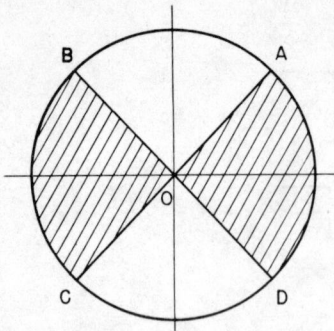

of the functions $f_i(\phi_i)$ it is apparent that

$$f_0 = f_2 = f_4; \quad f_1 = f_3$$

whence, by Equation [122.2] we have

$$a_4 = a_0 \frac{f_1 f_3}{f_2 f_4} = a_0 \frac{f_1^2}{f_0^2} \qquad [122.6]$$

It is evident that the condition for a heteroparametric excitation is $a_4 > a_0$, that is,

$$\frac{f_1^2}{f_0^2} \geqq 1$$

Figure 122.3

If we substitute for f_1 and f_2 their values from
Equation [122.4], it is easy to discuss the conditions for self-excitation of
the heteroparametric oscillations. We will omit these elementary calculations
and merely indicate the conclusions. The zones of the phase angle ϕ_0 in which
self-excitation occurs are located within the shaded sectors shown in Figure
122.3. In the non-shaded sectors, self-excitation does not occur. The lines
AC and BD form the critical phase angles ϕ_0 for which self-excitation appears
or disappears. The maximum increase of the amplitudes per cycle occurs for
$\phi_0 = 0$ and $\phi_0 = \pi$. For these values of ϕ_0 one has the relation

$$a_4 = \frac{\alpha_1^2}{\alpha_2^2} a_0 = \frac{1+\gamma}{1-\gamma} a_0 \qquad [122.7]$$

2. Second group: $N = 6, 10, 14, 18, \cdots$

Consider, for instance, the case when $N = 6$. By Equation [122.2]

$$a_6 = a_0 \frac{f_1 f_3 f_5}{f_2 f_4 f_6} \qquad [122.8]$$

and, for the intervals in question, $f_0 = f_3 = f_6$, $f_1 = f_4$, and $f_2 = f_5$, which
shows that $a_6 = a_0$ for all values of ϕ_0. Hence, for this particular frequency
of the ripple, parametric excitation is impossible.

3. Third group: $N = 3, 5, 7, 9, \cdots$

Let us take the case $N = 3$. Since N is odd, we apply Equation
[122.3] and obtain

$$a_3 = a_0 \frac{\alpha_1}{\alpha_2} \frac{f_1 f_3}{f_2}$$

From the form of the subdivisions and from Equation [122.5], $f_3 = f_0$. Hence,
the condition for self-excitation will be

$$\frac{\alpha_1}{\alpha_2} \frac{f_1 f_0}{f_2} \geqq 1 \qquad [122.9]$$

By introducing for f_0, f_1, and f_2 their values from Equations [122.4] and carrying out the calculations, one finds that no self-excitation is possible in this case.

4. Fourth group: $N = p/q$

One easily ascertains that as far as self-excitation is concerned most fractions p/q are either of no interest or fall within the scope of the groups previously investigated. The only cases in which heteroparametric excitation occurs are those in which $N = 4/3, 4/5, 4/7, \cdots$; $8/3, 8/5, \cdots$, corresponding to the intervals $\Delta\phi = 3\pi/2, 5\pi/2, 7\pi/2, \cdots$, which fall into the first group.

123. HETEROPARAMETRIC EXCITATION OF A DISSIPATIVE SYSTEM

If a system is dissipative, it is apparent that the injection of energy communicated by the variation of a parameter must, on the average, exceed the energy dissipated by the system. This, as we shall see, will lead to an additional condition.

Let us consider the equation

$$L_0\ddot{q} + R_0\dot{q} + \frac{1}{C}q = 0 \qquad [123.1]$$

of a dissipative electric circuit in which we assume that the capacity C is modulated by a ripple $\pm \Delta C$ so that $C = C_0 \pm \Delta C$.

If we divide by L_0 and put $R_0/L_0 = 2p_0$ and

$$\frac{1}{L_0 C_0 (1 \pm \gamma_c)} = \omega_0^2 (1 \mp \gamma_c)$$

Equation [123.1] becomes

$$\ddot{q} + 2p_0\dot{q} + \omega_0^2(1 \mp \gamma_c)q = 0 \qquad [123.2]$$

When the new variable Q defined by the equation

$$q = Qe^{-\int p_0 dt} \qquad [123.3]$$

is introduced, Equation [123.2] becomes

$$\ddot{Q} + \omega_1^2(1 \mp \delta)Q = 0 \qquad [123.4]$$

Changing the independent variable from t to $\tau = \omega_1 t$, one obtains

$$\frac{d^2Q}{d\tau^2} + (1 \mp \delta)Q = 0 \qquad [123.5]$$

As mentioned previously, this equation is equivalent to the alternate sequence of the following two equations replacing each other at each discontinuous change of capacity:

$$\frac{d^2Q}{d\tau^2} + \alpha_1^2 Q = 0; \quad \frac{d^2Q}{d\tau^2} + \alpha_2^2 Q = 0 \qquad [123.6]$$

where

$$\alpha_1^2 = 1 + \delta = 1 + \frac{\omega_0^2}{\omega_1^2}\gamma_c; \quad \alpha_2^2 = 1 - \delta = 1 - \frac{\omega_0^2}{\omega_1^2}\gamma_c \qquad [123.7]$$

The plus sign in the first equation [123.7] corresponds to $C = C_0 - \Delta C$. Equations [123.6] have the same form as Equations [121.7], so that the conclusions reached for those equations are applicable here except that Equations [123.6] contain the dependent variable Q whereas Equations [121.7] contain the variable q; the two variables are related by Equation [123.3]. The trajectories of Equations [123.6] are either convergent or divergent piecewise analytic spirals formed by elliptic arcs, the closed trajectories, appearing as a threshold between the two forms of spirals. For a closed trajectory Q is bounded; hence, by [123.3] q decreases monotonically. This means that convergent spirals in the $(q,\frac{dq}{d\tau})$-plane correspond to the closed trajectories in the $(Q,\frac{dQ}{d\tau})$-plane so that no self-excitation is possible. It is obvious that in order to have parametric excitation, the amplitude q must increase monotonically, or at least be constant, which requires that

$$Q = Q_0 e^{+\int p_1 dt} \qquad [123.8]$$

where $p_1 \geqq p_0$. This means that the trajectories in the $(Q,\frac{dQ}{d\tau})$-plane must be divergent spirals with the absolute value of the average negative decrement $|p_1|$ greater than, or at least equal to, the positive decrement $p_0 = R_0/2L_0$ of the dissipative circuit (R_0, L_0, C_0). Physically this means precisely the condition stated at the beginning of this section, namely, the energy injections into the circuit by the ripple $\pm \Delta C$ must, on the average, be greater than the energy dissipation.

On the other hand, since for a dissipative circuit with constant parameters (R_0, L_0, C_0) the decrement is $p_0 = R_0/2L_0$, the ratio of the amplitudes after one turn 2π in the phase plane is

$$\frac{q_{2\pi}}{q_0} = e^{-p_0 2\pi} \qquad [123.9]$$

In the optimum case of parametric excitation ($N = 4$, $\phi_0 = 0$), from Equation [122.7] one has

$$\frac{q_{2\pi}}{q_0} = \frac{\alpha_1^2}{\alpha_2^2} = e^{+p_1 2\pi}$$

which defines the increment

$$p_1 = \frac{1}{2\pi} \log \frac{\alpha_1^2}{\alpha_2^2} \qquad [123.10]$$

Expressing the condition for parametric excitation, namely, $p_1 \geqq p_0$, and substituting for α_1^2, α_2^2, and p_0 their values, one gets

$$\gamma_c \geqq \frac{\omega_0^2 - p_0^2}{\omega_0^2} \frac{e^{\mu_0} - 1}{e^{\mu_0} + 1} = \gamma_c' \qquad [123.11]$$

where $\mu_0 = \pi R_0 / L_0 \omega_0$. Since α_1^2 and α_2^2 are to be positive and $\alpha_1^2 > \alpha_2^2$, one obtains the other limit for γ_c. This gives

$$\gamma_c \leqq \frac{\omega_0^2 - p_0^2}{\omega_0^2} = \gamma_c'' \qquad [123.12]$$

From these expressions it follows that γ_c must be in the interval

$$\gamma_c' \leqq \gamma_c \leqq \gamma_c'' \qquad [123.13]$$

in order to obtain heteroparametric excitation. When $R_0 = 0$, we have $\mu_0 = 0$ and $p_0 = 0$ which gives the interval $(0,1)$. This interval decreases when R_0 increases and becomes zero when $\omega_0^2 - p_0^2 = \omega_1^2 = 0$, that is, when $R_0 = 2\sqrt{L_0/C_0}$. The last expression is the condition for critical damping. It is therefore impossible to obtain parametric excitation of a critically damped, or overdamped, circuit.

As was previously mentioned, heteroparametric excitation can be obtained by a variable inductance, instead of a variable capacity. For a non-dissipative circuit the conditions of heteroparametric excitation are identical except for the phase of energy injections, as was mentioned at the end of Section 120. This similarity in the effects resulting from the variation of capacity and inductance arises from the fact that both these factors enter symmetrically into the expression $\omega_0^2 = 1/L_0 C_0$ for the frequency.

For a dissipative circuit the situation is different in that the capacity enters only into the expression for the damped frequency $\omega_1^2 = \omega_0^2 - p_0^2$ (through ω_0^2) and does not appear in the decrement $p_0 = R_0/2L_0$. The inductance L_0 appears both in the expressions for the frequency and for the decrement. Hence, *a priori*, one may expect different results in both cases.

One can develop the theory of inductance modulation in exactly the same manner in which we have outlined the effect of capacity modulation. The only difference lies in the fact that for the inductance ripple instead of an *interval* in which the *index of modulation* γ_c must remain in order to obtain self-excitation, the condition for self-excitation is given by an inequality. It is also noteworthy that in the preceding discussions it was assumed that $\gamma \ll 1$, which enabled us to simplify the expressions by writing $\frac{1}{1 + \gamma} \approx 1 - \gamma$. By waiving this restriction, the calculations are considerably more complicated but the qualitative picture of the phenomenon remains substantially the same.

124. HETEROPARAMETRIC MACHINE OF MANDELSTAM AND PAPALEXI

A differential equation with periodic coefficients of the form

$$L(t)\ddot{x} + R(t)\dot{x} + C(t)x = 0 \qquad [124.1]$$

can be reduced to an equation of the Mathieu-Hill type. It follows that the effect of a parametric excitation can be obtained by periodically varying one of the parameters L, C, or R. The variation of the parameters L and C has been studied sufficiently in preceding sections. As to the parameter R, it must be noted that only those parametric variations which extend alternately into the region of *negative resistance* are capable of producing parametric excitation. We shall not go into this matter here, as it is clear that on physical grounds negative resistance means the supply of energy from an outside source.

Mandelstam and Papalexi (22) developed an interesting generator of electrical energy, which they called a "heteroparametric machine." The arrangement consisted of a series of coils located on the periphery of a stationary disk; the inductance of these coils was varied by the periodic passage of teeth and slots on a rotating disk parallel to the stationary disk. The frequency of the inductance variation thus obtained was of the order of 2000 cycles per second.

In a circuit of this kind devoid of any source of energy other than the kinetic energy of the wheel, electrical oscillations of exactly half the frequency of the parameter variation were observed. For a linear system, corresponding to a linear Mathieu equation, the oscillations rapidly reached high amplitudes of about 1500 volts which caused a puncture of the insulation; later on, by adding a non-linear element in the circuit, the authors succeeded in obtaining stable performance of the machine.

The factor of modulation during these tests was of the order of 40 per cent, and the power developed was about 4 kilowatts. The non-linearity by which the oscillations were stabilized was obtained by means of a saturated-core reactor; an auxiliary d-c winding served the purpose of displacing the stable point on the characteristic and of adjusting the stable voltage to a desired value.

Similar experiments were produced with a periodically varying capacity. The variable capacitor consisted of 25 aluminum disks with peripheral holes rotating between a corresponding number of similar stationary disks. The variable capacitor in these tests was shunted by a constant oil capacitor. The non-linearity necessary for the stabilization of oscillations was obtained by neon tubes which permitted maintaining the voltage at about 600 to 700 volts. Without the neon tubes the phenomenon is governed by a linear Mathieu equation, and the voltage rises rapidly to between 2000 and 3000 volts and the insulation is punctured. If one changes the parameters of the oscillating

373

circuit so as to deviate from the condition of exact fractional-order resonance, the amplitudes of the parametrically excited oscillations decrease, all
other conditions being equal, until finally the excitation suddenly disappears
at a certain critical threshold as was analyzed theoretically in Section 123.

125. SUBHARMONIC RESONANCE ON THE BASIS OF THE MATHIEU-HILL EQUATION

In order to complete the study of heteroparametric excitation, we
shall now show that the differential equation [102.2] of subharmonic external
resonance which we have discussed in Chapter XVII on the basis of the theory
of Poincaré can be reduced to an equation of the Mathieu-Hill type. For that
purpose, instead of following the method of Poincaré by introducing small perturbations α and β, Equation [103.9], in the value of the parameters u and v,
we shall now introduce a small perturbation ρ in the value of the periodic
solution $x_0(\tau)$ of Equation [102.2] since we know that it possesses periodic
solutions. Putting

$$x = x_0(\tau) + \rho \qquad [125.1]$$

and substituting it into Equation [102.2], we get, after expanding $f(x,\dot{x})$ in a
Taylor series,

$$\ddot{x}_0 + x_0 + \ddot{\rho} + \rho = \mu f(x_0,\dot{x}_0) + \lambda_0 \sin n\tau + \rho\mu f_{x_0}(x_0,\dot{x}_0) + \dot{\rho}\mu f_{\dot{x}_0}(x_0,\dot{x}_0) \qquad [125.2]$$

Since x_0 satisfies Equation [102.2], we obtain

$$\ddot{\rho} + \rho = \rho\mu f_{x_0}(x_0,\dot{x}_0) + \dot{\rho}\mu f_{\dot{x}_0}(x_0,\dot{x}_0) \qquad [125.3]$$

where $f_{x_0}(x_0,\dot{x}_0)$ and $f_{\dot{x}_0}(x_0,\dot{x}_0)$ are known functions of x_0 and $\dot{x}_0$ and, hence,
known periodic functions of time. Equation [125.3] is therefore an equation
with periodic coefficients. If we use the substitution [118.2] which in this
case is

$$\rho = z e^{\frac{\mu}{2}\int f_{\dot{x}_0}(x_0,\dot{x}_0)d\tau} \qquad [125.4]$$

Equation [125.3] becomes

$$\ddot{z} + \left[1 - \mu f_{\dot{x}_0} + \frac{\mu}{2}\frac{d}{d\tau}(f_{\dot{x}_0}) - \frac{\mu^2}{2}(f_{\dot{x}_0})^2\right]z = 0 \qquad [125.5]$$

Since the quantity in brackets is a periodic function of time, this equation
is of the Mathieu-Hill type whose general solution is

$$z = e^{\mu k_1 \tau}\phi_1(\tau) + e^{\mu k_2 \tau}\phi_2(\tau) \qquad [125.6]$$

where ϕ_1 and ϕ_2 are periodic with period 2π and k_1 and k_2 are the characteristic exponents of the general theory. The question of the stability of the
motion can be discussed by the method indicated in Sections 118 and 119 if
one knows the explicit form of the function $f(x_0,\dot{x}_0)$.

126. AUTOPARAMETRIC EXCITATION

Throughout this chapter we have been concerned with heteroparametric excitation because in a great majority of practical cases self-excitation as well as the steady state of non-linear oscillations can be discussed more conveniently on the basis of the theory of Poincaré than by treating it as autoparametric excitation.

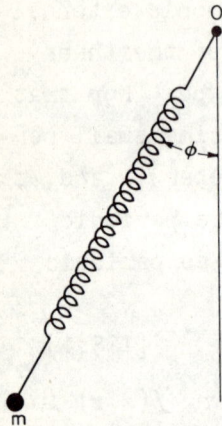

In some special problems, however, the concept of autoparametric excitation of oscillations may be convenient. In this section we propose to apply this method to an interesting problem of an elastic pendulum investigated by Gorelik and Witt (29). These authors investigated the motion of a physical pendulum suspended on a spring and capable of oscillating in a plane, as shown in Figure 126.1. Let m be the mass of the bob, l_0 the length of the pendulum in the absence of the dynamical load, r its length under load, k the spring constant, and g the acceleration of gravity. Obviously the system possesses two degrees of freedom, namely, the angle ϕ of the pendulum and the elongation z of the spring.

Figure 126.1

In order to investigate the condition for autoparametric excitation, we write the Lagrangian equations of motion for both degrees of freedom. The kinetic energy of the pendulum is

$$T = \frac{m}{2}(\dot{r}^2 + r^2\dot{\phi}^2) \qquad [126.1]$$

and its potential energy is

$$V = \frac{k}{2}(r - l_0)^2 - mgr\left(1 - \frac{\phi^2}{2}\right) \qquad [126.2]$$

where $1 - \frac{\phi^2}{2} \approx \cos\phi$. The first term of V corresponds to the elasticity of the suspension and the second to gravity. If we introduce a new constant

$$l = r_0 + \frac{mg}{k} \qquad [126.3]$$

and a new variable

$$z = \frac{r - l}{l} \qquad [126.4]$$

Expressions [126.1] and [126.2] become

$$T = \frac{ml^2}{2}(\dot{z}^2 + \dot{\phi}^2 + 2z\dot{\phi}^2) \qquad [126.5]$$

$$V = \frac{ml^2}{2}\left(\frac{k}{m}z^2 + \frac{g}{l}\phi^2 + \frac{g}{l}z\phi^2\right) \qquad [126.6]$$

where z and ϕ are assumed to be small of the first order and we retain terms up to and including those of the third order.

The Lagrangian equations are

$$\ddot{z} + \frac{k}{m}z + \left(\frac{g}{2l}\phi^2 - \dot{\phi}^2\right) = 0$$

$$\ddot{\phi} + \frac{g}{l}\phi + \left(\frac{g}{l}z\phi + 2\dot{z}\dot{\phi} + 2z\ddot{\phi}\right) = 0$$

[126.7]

It is seen that, if the terms in the parentheses of these equations are zero, the first equation will represent a simple harmonic oscillation in the z degree of freedom with frequency $\omega_z = \sqrt{k/m}$, and the second equation will give a similar oscillation in the ϕ degree of freedom with frequency $\omega_\phi = \sqrt{g/l}$. These terms represent a *non-linear coupling* between the two degrees of freedom; we will now investigate this condition.

It is to be noted that in the general case when $\omega_z \neq \frac{p}{q}\omega_\phi$ the non-linear coupling does not contribute anything of particular interest.

An interesting case arises when $\omega_z = 2\omega_\phi$. Assume that the spring has been stretched and released at $t = 0$ so that $\phi = 0$ initially. The initial motion will, therefore, be

$$z = z_0 \cos \omega_z t$$

[126.8]

Substituting this value of z into the second equation [126.7] and regrouping the terms, one has

$$(1 + 2z_0 \cos \omega_z t)\ddot{\phi} - (2\omega_z \sin \omega_z t)\dot{\phi} + \omega_\phi^2(1 + z_0 \cos \omega_z t)\phi = 0 \qquad [126.9]$$

which is a differential equation with periodic coefficients and can be reduced to the form of the Mathieu equation. Since $\omega_z = 2\omega_\phi$, it is observed that the periodic variation of the coefficients occurs at twice the frequency of the oscillation in the ϕ degree of freedom. If the parameters of the Mathieu equation to which Equation [126.9] can be reduced are such as to correspond to the unstable region, the oscillation in the ϕ degree of freedom will gradually build up.

This curious phenomenon of autoparametric self-excitation was actually observed by Gorelik and Witt. However, in view of the fact that this system is conservative, it is apparent that the building-up of the oscillation in the ϕ degree of freedom implies a decrease of the original oscillation [126.8] in the z degree of freedom. In this manner the occurrence of the initial oscillation in the z degree of freedom is transferred into the ϕ degree of freedom through the instrumentality of the autoparametric non-linear coupling between both degrees of freedom.

One could, of course, start from the ϕ degree of freedom by releasing the pendulum from an angle $\phi = \phi_0$ for $t = 0$ which would give the oscillation

$$\phi = \phi_0 \cos \omega_\phi t \qquad [126.10]$$

Substituting this expression into the first equation [126.7], one has

$$\ddot{z} + \omega_z^2 z = \frac{\omega_\phi^2 \phi_0}{4}(1 - 3\cos 2\omega_\phi t) \qquad [126.11]$$

This is the equation of a simple harmonic oscillator with frequency ω_z acted on by a periodic external excitation with frequency $2\omega_\phi = \omega_z$. Hence, in the z degree of freedom there will be ordinary linear resonance by which the z-oscillation will gradually increase while the ϕ-oscillation will gradually decay, since the system is conservative.

It is to be noted that in both cases the phenomenon manifests itself in the fact that the energy appearing initially in one degree of freedom is eventually transferred into the other degree of freedom. There exists, however, an asymmetry in the phenomenon depending on whether one starts with the oscillation [126.8] or [126.10]. If the initial oscillation is [126.8], the excitation of the oscillation in the ϕ degree of freedom occurs through the instrumentality of the unstable solution of the Mathieu equation, whereas if the initial oscillation is [126.10], the autoparametric excitation manifests itself in classical linear resonance with which the z-oscillation builds up. This difference, however, is incidental to the particular scheme employed and is of no further importance insofar as in the second case the autoparametric excitation is still present in the form of the centrifugal force whose frequency is *twice* the frequency of the oscillation in the ϕ degree of freedom.

It is noteworthy that in both cases the frequency with which the parameter varies is double that with which the self-excited oscillation occurs. If one starts the oscillation in the z degree of freedom this is apparent because $\omega_z = 2\omega_\phi$. If, however, one starts the oscillation in the ϕ degree of freedom, it is noted that the variation of the z-parameter takes place under the effect of the centrifugal force so that in both cases the condition of autoparametric excitation is fulfilled and the "pumping" of energy from one degree of freedom into the other is reciprocal.

Another interesting experiment similar to that of Melde was made recently by Sekerska (22), who passed an alternating current of 50-cycle frequency through a stretched metallic wire capable of oscillating laterally with a frequency of 50 cycles. It is observed that if the wire is initially at rest the passage of alternating current eventually builds up the lateral vibration of the string. The explanation of this phenomenon is that the thermal effect of a current of 50-cycle frequency occurs at a frequency of 100 cycles which causes a periodic variation of the parameter, the coefficient of elasticity, at that frequency, and this, through the instrumentality of the autoparametric excitation, produces self-excitation of lateral oscillations with half the frequency of the parameter variation.

These phenomena occur not only for the ratio $\omega_r/\omega = 2/1$, where ω_r is the frequency at which a parameter varies and ω is the frequency of self-excited autoparametric oscillation, but also for the ratios 2/2, 2/3, $\cdots$. Migulin (30) investigated, both theoretically and experimentally, these phenomena when this ratio has the value 2/3 and found that the resonance curves then resemble those obtained by Mandelstam and Papalexi, Chapter XVII, in their studies of subharmonic resonance of the nth order. As a matter of fact, the phenomena of subharmonic resonance and those of autoparametric excitation are closely related to each other and merely represent different aspects of the same physical phenomenon.

REFERENCES

(1) "Introduction to Non-Linear Mechanics," by N. Kryloff and N. Bogoliuboff, Kieff, (Russian), 1937.

(2) "Lehrbuch der Elektronenröhren" (Manual of Electronic Tubes), by G.H. Barkhausen, S. Hirzel, Leipzig, Germany, Fourth Edition, 1931-1937.

(3) "Sensations of Tone," by H. Helmholtz, Longmans, Green, and Co., London, England, English Translation, Third Edition, 1895.

(4) "Principles of Electron Tubes," by H.J. Reich, McGraw-Hill Book Co., New York, N.Y., First Edition, 1941, Chapter 3.

(5) "Asynchronous Action on Self-Excited Oscillatory Systems," by J.B. Kobsarev, Journal of Technical Physics, USSR, (Russian), Vol. 3, 1933.

(6) "An Experimental Investigation of Forced Vibrations in a Mechanical System Having a Non-Linear Restoring Force," by C.A. Ludeke, to appear in the Journal of Applied Physics, July 1946.

(7) "Mechanical Vibrations," by J.P. Den Hartog, McGraw-Hill Book Co., New York, N.Y., 1940, p. 403.

(8) "Über Resonanzerscheinungen bei Frequenzteilung" (On Resonance Phenomena in Frequency Demultiplication), by L. Mandelstam and N. Papalexi, Zeitschrift für Physik, Vol. 73, 1932.

(9) "Forced Oscillations in a Circuit with Non-Linear Resistance," by B. Van der Pol, Philosophical Magazine, Vol. 3, Number 13, January 1927.

(10) "On Maintained Vibrations," by Lord Rayleigh, Philosophical Magazine, 5th Series, Vol. 15, April 1883.

(11) "On Some Experiments in Which Two Neighboring Maintained Circuits Affect a Resonating Circuit," by J.H. Vincent, Proceedings of the Physical Society, London, England, Vol. 32, Part 2, February 1919.

(12) "Über störungsfreien Gleichstromempfang mit dem Schwingaudion" (On Non-Disturbed D-C Reception with an Autodyne), by H.G. Möller, Zeitschrift für drahtlose Telegraphie und Telephonie, Vol. 17, April 1921.

(13) "The Automatic Synchronization of Triode Oscillators," by E.V. Appleton, Proceedings of the Cambridge Philosophical Society, London, England, Vol. 21, November 1922.

(14) "Zur Theorie des Mitnehmens von Van der Pol" (On Van der Pol's Theory of Entrainment), by A. Andronow and A. Witt, Archiv für Elektrotechnik, Vol. 24, 1930.

(15) "Theory of Entrainment in the Case of a Soft Characteristic," by V.I. Gaponow, Journal of Technical Physics, USSR, (Russian), Vol. 5, 1935.

(16) "Einstellungs- und Schwebungsprozesse bei der Mitnahme" (Tuning or Beat Phenomena in Entrainment), by P. Rjasin, Journal of Technical Physics, USSR, (Russian), Vol. 5, 1935.

(17) "Acoustical Entrainment," by K. Theodorchik and E. Chaikin, Journal of Technical Physics, USSR, (Russian), Vol. 2, 1932.

(18) "Frequenzmesser nach dem Kompensationsverfahren" (Frequency Meter Designed According to the Compensation Method), by H. Kaden, Elektrische Nachrichtentechnik, Vol. 16, 1939.

(19) "Über die Erregung stehender Wellen eines fadenförmigen Körpers" (On the Excitation of Standing Waves in a Filiform Body), by F. Melde, Poggendorff's Annalen der Physik, Vol. 109, 1860, p. 193.

(20) "Theorié d'un alternateur auto-excitateur" (Theory of a Self-Exciting Oscillator), by M. Brillouin, Éclairage Électrique, Vol. XI, April 1897.

(21) "Sur quelques théorèmes généraux de l'électrotechnique" (On Some General Theorems of Electrical Engineering), by H. Poincaré, Éclairage Électrique, Vol. 50, March 1907.

(22) "Exposé des recherches récentes sur les oscillations non-linéaires" (Outline of Recent Research on Non-Linear Oscillations), by L. Mandelstam and N. Papalexi, Journal of Technical Physics, USSR, 1934. A complete bibliography on parametric excitation is appended to this reference.

(23) "Modern Analysis," by E.T. Whittaker and G.N. Watson, Cambridge University Press, 1927, Chapter XIX.

(24) "Sur les équations différentielles linéaires à coefficients périodiques" (On Linear Differential Equations with Periodic Coefficients), by G. Floquet, Annales de l'École Normale Supérieure, Vol. XII, 1883.

(25) "On the Stability of the Solutions of Mathieu's Equation," by B. Van der Pol and M.J.O. Strutt, Philosophical Magazine, 7th Series, Vol. V, January-June, 1928.

(26) "Über Schüttelerscheinungen in Systemen mit periodisch veränderlicher Elastizität" (On Vibrations in Systems with Periodically Varying Elasticity), by E. Meissner, Schweizerische Bauzeitung, Vol. 72, 1918.

(27) "Lamé'sche, Mathieu'sche und verwandte Funktionen" (On Lamé, Mathieu and Related Functions), by M.J.O. Strutt, J. Springer, Berlin, Germany, 1932.

(28) "On Parametric Excitation," by N. Minorsky, Journal of the Franklin Institute, Vol. 240, Number 1, July 1945.

(29) "Schwingungen eines elastischen Pendels als Beispiel für zwei parametrisch gebundene lineare Schwingungsysteme" (Oscillations of an Elastic Pendulum as an Example for Two Parametrically United Linear Vibratory Systems), by G. Gorelik and A. Witt, Journal of Technical Physics, USSR, Vol. 3, 1933, p. 294.

(30) "Resonance Effects in a Non-Linear System with Two Degrees of Freedom," by V. Migulin, Journal of Technical Physics, USSR, (Russian), Vol. 4, Number 2, 1937.

PART IV

RELAXATION OSCILLATIONS*

127. INTRODUCTORY REMARKS

The term *relaxation oscillations*, introduced by Van der Pol (1)† (2) and commonly used at present, generally designates self-excited oscillations exhibiting quasi-discontinuous features. Because of the importance of such oscillations in applications in connection with the so-called "sweep circuits" in electronics, television, and allied fields, an extensive literature exists on this subject, References (3) through (9). Ph. LeCorbeiller (10) gives an interesting survey of various devices, both mechanical and electrical, by which these phenomena can be demonstrated; some of these devices have been known for centuries.

The characteristic feature of these phenomena is that a certain physical quantity (such as coordinate, velocity, etc., in mechanical problems, and charge, current, etc., in electrical problems) exists on two levels, remaining on each level alternately for a relatively long time but passing from one level to the other so rapidly that in the idealized representation the passage may be considered as instantaneous. A few examples taken from the paper by LeCorbeiller will illustrate these phenomena.

Figure 127.1 shows a device consisting of a container C, of the form shown, fastened to a support R capable of rotating about an axis A, perpendicular to the plane of the paper, and provided with a weight W sufficient to hold the system against the stop S. The container is slowly filled with water, and at the instant when the moment due to the weight of the water becomes greater than the moment due to the weight W, the system tumbles over against another stop S'. The container then empties, and the weight W brings the system back against the stop S, after which the filling period begins again, and so on. In this system the two levels, previously mentioned, are the angles θ and θ' at which the system is constrained by the stops

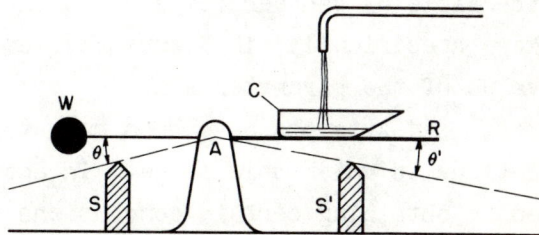

Figure 127.1

* The text of Part IV follows the presentation in "Theory of Oscillations," by Andronow and Chaikin, Moscow, (Russian), 1937. A complete bibliography on the subject of relaxation oscillations appears in this volume.

† Numbers in parentheses indicate references on page 66 of this report.

S and S' respectively, and the representation of this system in the (θ, t)-plane appears as a periodic rectangular ripple with the length of its horizontal stretches determined by the rates of filling and of evacuation of C.

Another familiar example is the charging of a capacitor shunted by a gaseous conductor such as a neon lamp. During the charging period the capacitor's voltage gradually rises. At the point of ionization of the gaseous conductor, the neon lamp flashes and the capacitor is suddenly discharged, whereupon the gaseous conduction ceases abruptly and the charging period begins anew. Here, again, there are two levels, the voltage V_1 immediately before the discharge strikes and the voltage V_2 immediately after the extinction of the discharge. The transition from V_2 to V_1 is gradual, but the inverse transition from V_1 to V_2 is quasi-discontinuous. A phenomenon of this kind is represented in the (V, t)-plane by a so-called "saw-tooth" curve.

It was shown in Section 37, Part I, that a similar situation exists for large values of the parameter μ in the Van der Pol equation. Figure 37.1c shows quasi-discontinuous changes in the variable $x(t)$ between the two regions in which it changes but little.

When these periodic phenomena are represented in the phase plane of the variable undergoing rapid changes, they appear as closed curves with regions of very large curvature, such as the curves shown in Figures 37.2c and 37.3c. By idealizing these very rapid changes as discontinuous changes, closed trajectories of this kind become *piecewise analytic curves* "closed" by the discontinuous stretches.

Available analytical methods are inadequate for a rigorous treatment of these phenomena. In fact, all analytical methods presuppose that the parameter μ appearing in the basic quasi-linear equation

$$\ddot{x} + x = \mu f(x, \dot{x}) \qquad [127.1]$$

is very small. On the contrary, in some of these oscillations, which are expressible by Van der Pol's differential equation, this parameter is large. More specifically, in Figures 37.1c, 37.2c, and 37.3c, referred to above, the value of the parameter μ is 10.

Attempts have been made to extend the analytical methods to oscillations in which μ is large. In Section 36 it was shown that Liénard succeeded in obtaining certain conclusions regarding the qualitative aspect of the phase trajectories when μ was very large. N. Levinson (11) extended the proof of the existence of closed trajectories to cover oscillations in which μ is not small. In a recent publication (12) J.A. Shohat has indicated a form of series expansion formally satisfying the Van der Pol equation when μ is large. These various attempts, however, did not result in any complete analytical theory comparable to the one which has been studied in Part II in connection with oscillations in which μ is small.

Moreover, as will appear below, not all known relaxation oscillations seem to belong to the group of equations [127.1] of which the Van der Pol equation is a particular example. More specifically, it will be shown in Chapter XXI that relaxation oscillations are frequently observed in systems which are amenable to representation by differential equations of the *first* order which do not admit any analytic periodic solutions for the simple reason that these equations do not possess singularities, without which no closed analytic trajectories can exist; see Section 25. These difficulties led the school of physicists under the leadership of L. Mandelstam and N. Papalexi to evolve a theory, called by its authors the *discontinuous theory of relaxation oscillations*, whose exposition and applications will form the principal topic of Part IV.

The use of the concept of mathematical discontinuities for the purpose of describing a rapidly changing dynamical process, at least during certain instants of its evolution in time, is not new. It is recalled that the classical theory of mechanical impacts uses precisely the discontinuous method by assuming an infinitely small duration of the impact process during which the dynamics of the process is entirely ignored, and the "initial" and "terminal" conditions are correlated on the basis of certain *additional information* not contained in the differential equations themselves. This permits obtaining the correct overall effect of the impact without knowledge of its details. For an elastic impact, such additional information is supplied by the theorems of momentum and kinetic energy; to this information is added, for non-elastic impacts, the so-called *coefficient of restitution*, an empirical factor characterizing the loss of energy during the impact. This coefficient depends on the material of which the colliding bodies are composed.

One can imagine a discontinuous periodic motion generated by impacts from the following example given by Andronow and Chaikin (13). Let us assume that a perfectly elastic ball rolls without friction on a horizontal plane and strikes elastic walls WW perpendicular to the direction of its motion, as shown in Figure 127.2a. With the usual discontinuous treatment of mechanical impacts, the phase

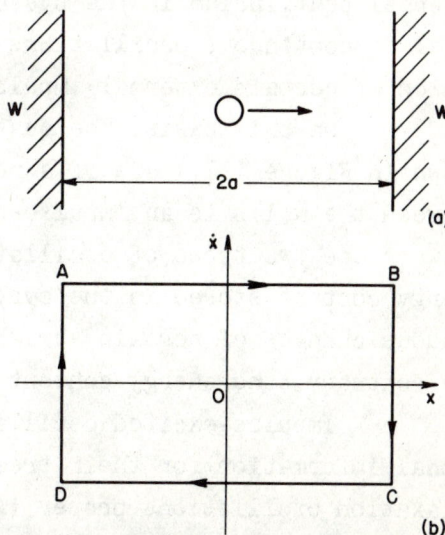

Figure 127.2

trajectory of such motion is represented by a "closed curve" ABCDA, a rectangle. On the branches AB and CD the motion is continuous with the constant velocities $\dot{x} = \pm v_0$, respectively; on the branches BC and DA, on the contrary, it is discontinuous.

In the systems of Figures 127.1 and 127.2 we encounter periodic phenomena having certain quasi-discontinuous features. The nature of these discontinuities in the two systems is, however, different. For the ball striking the walls there exists a definite external actuation, the reaction of the constraint, the wall, applied to the dynamical system, the ball; this actuation is properly "timed" by the distance $2a$ between the walls which determines the "period" of the motion. On the contrary, no external impact excitation exists during the discontinuities in the motion of the container shown in Figure 127.1. These discontinuities are due rather to a sudden loss of equilibrium between the moment M_W of the constant weight and that of the container M_C, occurring at a certain critical value, $M_C = M_W$. The change of equilibrium position from θ to θ' is not instantaneous, of course, but in comparison with the long periods of filling and evacuation of the container it may be considered as such in the idealized picture of the phenomenon. We can improve the idealization by making the moment of inertia of the system (W,C) relatively small; this will render the short time interval during which θ varies still shorter, which, in turn, makes the relative time intervals of filling and of evacuation still longer.

We find it expedient to define as *relaxation oscillations* those quasi-discontinuous oscillations in which the rapid changes between certain levels of a physical quantity occur as the result of the loss of a certain internal equilibrium in the system, and as *impulse-excited oscillations* those quasi-discontinuous oscillations in which these rapid changes are due to the action of certain external impulsive causes.

On this basis, the quasi-discontinuous oscillations of the container shown in Figure 127.1 are of a relaxation type, whereas the ball rebounding between the walls is an impulse-excited phenomenon. The essential difference between the two types of oscillations is that in relaxation oscillations the energy content stored in the system remains constant during the quasi-discontinuous changes of certain variables, whereas in impulse-excited systems, on the contrary, the energy content changes abruptly.

Impulse-excited oscillations do not require any particular additional information for their treatment, as will be seen in Chapter XXIV. For relaxation oscillations proper (see Chapters XXI, XXII, and XXIII) it is necessary to specify the conditions under which the discontinuities are bound to occur in a system; it will be shown that the basic assumption given in

Section 130 provides a criterion sufficiently broad to cover all known types of relaxation oscillations.

Finally, inasmuch as the representation of a rapidly changing process by a mathematical discontinuity is always an idealization, it becomes necessary to analyze the conditions under which this idealization is justified in practice. In analyzing the behavior of the device shown in Figure 127.1, we have noted that the change from the angle θ to the angle θ' may be considered as quasi-discontinuous. The smaller the moment of inertia of the system, the more accurate is the approximation. In mechanical systems, such as the examples described above, it is obviously difficult to extend the hypothesis by assuming that the moment of inertia is zero, but in electrical systems neglect of one of the oscillatory parameters is a common practice. In both types of systems, instead of a "full" differential equation of the second order, the abbreviated or *degenerate* equation of the first order is frequently employed. By using degenerate equations, numerous problems can be treated as discontinuous in the phase plane; this appreciably simplifies their solution.

A simple example will show the application of degenerate equations for this purpose. Let us consider an oscillating circuit shown in Figure 127.3 comprising an inductance L, a capacity C, and resistors R and r as shown. The circuit may be closed on a source of d-c voltage by a switch S. It is useful to specify certain idealizations which appear somewhat trivial but which will be found to be of considerable importance in what follows.

We assume first that the left branch of the circuit ALRB has no capacity and that the right branch ACrB has no inductance. In other words, we neglect the effect of small, parasitic, distributed capacities in the inductance L and resistance R; likewise, we neglect the effect of a small inductance accompanying the flow of current in the branch ACrB.

The second assumption will be that the opening and closing of S is instantaneous, that is, occurs in an infinitely small time interval ($t - 0$, $t + 0$).

Let us assume that we open and close the switch S at some frequency. The process will then be represented by a sequence of very long intervals, when S is either closed or opened, separated by infinitely short intervals of closing and opening. During the long intervals there will generally be a

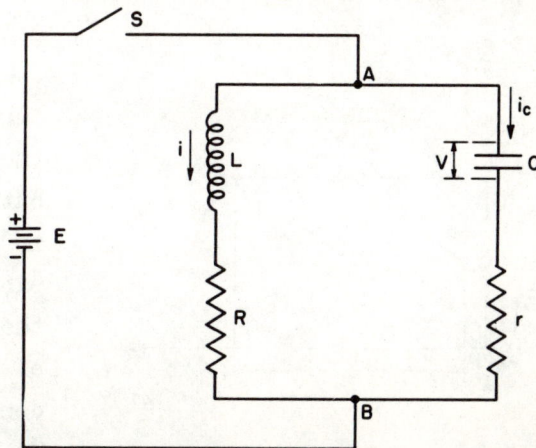

Figure 127.3

certain oscillatory process in the circuit $(L, C, R + r)$ describable by a differential equation of the second order whose phase trajectories are spirals converging toward a focal point, as we know from Section 5. The closing or opening of S will disturb this process by introducing a certain transient. Without any loss of generality we may consider the first closing of S at $t_0 = 0$ and assume that for $t < t_0$ the circuit was "dead." It is noted that, at the instant of closing, the two circuits ALRB and ACrB are *in parallel*, and the differential equations are

$$L \frac{di}{dt} + Ri = E; \qquad rC \frac{dV}{dt} + V = E \qquad\qquad [127.2]$$

where $E = 0$ for $t \leqq t_0$ and $E = $ constant for $t \geqq t_0$. With these assumptions one finds that

$$i = \frac{E}{R}\left(1 - e^{-\frac{R}{L}t}\right); \qquad \frac{di}{dt} = \frac{E}{L}e^{-\frac{R}{L}t}$$

$$[127.3]$$

$$V = E\left(1 - e^{-\frac{1}{rC}t}\right); \qquad \frac{dV}{dt} = \frac{E}{rC}$$

It is seen that for $t = t_0$ the solutions of Equations [127.2], $i(t)$ and $V(t)$, are continuous but not analytic in the sense that their first derivatives undergo discontinuous jumps $\left(\frac{di}{dt}\right)_0 = \frac{E}{L}$; $\left(\frac{dV}{dt}\right)_0 = \frac{E}{rC}$. Noting that $i_c = C\frac{dV}{dt}$ we can take instead of $\frac{dV}{dt}$ the variable i_c and state that under the assumed idealizations the functions $\frac{di}{dt}$ and i_c undergo discontinuities $\frac{E}{L}$ and $\frac{E}{r}$, respectively. If one takes the plane of the variables $\left(\frac{di}{dt}, i_c\right)$, the process occurring at $t = t_0$ is represented by a discontinuous jump of the representative point from the origin to the point A whose coordinates are $\frac{E}{r}$ and $\frac{E}{L}$; see Figure 127.4. After the initial discontinuity the subsequent motion of the representative point will follow a continuous trajectory AB which, as the transient dies out, will eventually approach a damped oscillatory motion represented by a convergent spiral. If, at a later instant $t = t_1$, the switch is opened, another jump will occur, but this jump will generally not bring the representative point back to the origin but to some other point A", and so on. It is thus seen that in the phase plane of these particular variables $\left(\frac{di}{dt}, i_c\right)$ the history of the system will be represented by a sequence of disconnected, spiral arcs "joined" by discontinuous stretches such as OA, BA', $\cdots$. We thus obtain a *piecewise analytic representation* of such a phenomenon.

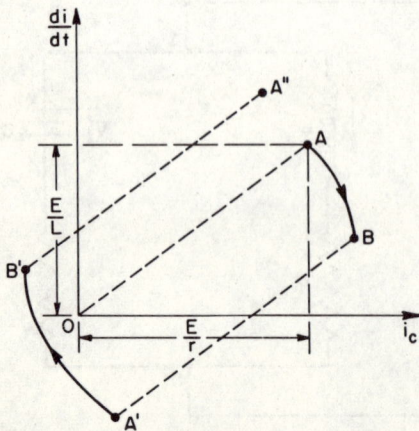

Figure 127.4

It is important to emphasize once more that such a representation of a quasi-discontinuous phenomenon by discontinuities in the phase plane of certain variables is possible only because we have introduced certain idealizations into the problem.

a. We consider the time interval during which rapid changes occur as an infinitely short interval.

b. The effect of the parasitic parameters is neglected, which enables us to deal with the *degenerate* equations [127.2] of the first order instead of the full equations of the second order.

c. We have selected the dynamical variables $\frac{di}{dt}$ and i_c which are capable of undergoing discontinuities under Assumption b.

The necessity for Assumptions a and b is obvious. As for Assumption c, it is clear that if one selected some other variables, for example, i and V instead of $\frac{di}{dt}$ and i_c, discontinuous representation in such a phase plane would be lost since these variables are continuous.

In the preceding discussion we have tacitly assumed an impulse-excited phenomenon as previously defined. For a pure relaxation phenomenon we must answer an additional question, namely, how to determine the instants (in the time representation) or the points (in the phase-plane representation) at which the discontinuity occurs in a system of this kind.

It is impossible to go beyond this point without formulating some kind of *a priori* assumption, as will be explained in Section 130.

CHAPTER XX

FUNDAMENTALS OF THE DISCONTINUOUS THEORY OF RELAXATION OSCILLATIONS

128. SOLUTIONS OF A DIFFERENTIAL EQUATION IN THE
NEIGHBORHOOD OF A POINT OF DEGENERATION

We now propose to investigate the nature of the solutions of a differential equation of the second order with constant coefficients, for example,

$$a\ddot{x} + b\dot{x} + kx = 0 \qquad [128.1]$$

when one of the coefficients approaches zero. In an electrical problem, $a = L$, $b = R$, and $k = 1/C$; in a mechanical one, $a = m$ (mass), b is the coefficient of "velocity damping," and k is the spring constant.

First, if b approaches zero, one readily sees that the oscillatory damped motion approaches the oscillatory undamped motion. We saw that in the phase plane the solutions of [128.1] with $b \neq 0$ but small are spirals approaching a stable focal point; this remains true as b approaches zero. For $b = 0$, the origin is a vortex point and the trajectories are closed. It is thus seen that there is a definite difference between the qualitative aspect of trajectories when b is very small and that when b is equal to zero. From a practical standpoint, however, there is hardly any difference between the two cases; no discontinuities of any kind exist in the solutions.

Of greater practical interest are the cases when either $a \to 0$ or $k \to 0$. We shall examine first the case when $a \to 0$. It is apparent that when $a = 0$ Equation [128.1] becomes an equation of the first order and its solution is given in terms of *one* constant of integration, namely,

$$x = x_0 e^{-\frac{k}{b}t} \qquad [128.2]$$

where x_0 is that constant. By differentiating [128.2] we obtain

$$\dot{x} = -\frac{k}{b}x_0 e^{-\frac{k}{b}t} = -\frac{k}{b}x \qquad [128.3]$$

It is seen that the coordinate x and the velocity $\dot{x}$ are not independent but are related by Equation [128.3]. In other words, in the phase plane the trajectories of Equation [128.2] are reduced to a single line $y = -\frac{k}{b}x$, and the rest of the plane is not involved. This fact can be expressed by stating that the phase space of a differential equation of the first order is *uni-dimensional*, that is, it is a *phase line* instead of a phase plane.

The limit case, $a = 0$, never actually occurs in practice since in any electrical system containing resistance and capacity there is always a small residual or "parasitic" inductance. Likewise, mechanical systems without inertia are only idealizations. For these reasons it is preferable to investigate the effect of a small coefficient a in the solution of Equation

[128.1] rather than to drop this coefficient in the differential equation itself.

The solution of [128.1] is

$$x = C_1 e^{r_1 t} + C_2 e^{r_2 t} \tag{128.4}$$

where C_1 and C_2 are the constants of integration and r_1 and r_2 are the roots of the characteristic equation

$$ar^2 + br + k = 0$$

If the initial conditions $t = 0$, $x = x_0$, and $\dot{x} = \dot{x}_0$ are given, one obtains

$$x_0 = C_1 + C_2; \qquad \dot{x}_0 = C_1 r_1 + C_2 r_2 \tag{128.5}$$

from which one obtains the values of C_1 and C_2:

$$C_1 = \frac{x_0 r_2 - \dot{x}_0}{r_2 - r_1} \quad \text{and} \quad C_2 = \frac{x_0 r_1 - \dot{x}_0}{r_1 - r_2} \tag{128.6}$$

where

$$r_{1,2} = -\frac{b}{2a} \pm \sqrt{\frac{b^2}{4a^2} - \frac{k}{a}} \approx -\frac{b}{2a} \pm \frac{b}{2a}\left(1 - \frac{2ak}{b^2}\right) \tag{128.7}$$

In this expression only one term is retained in the expansion of the square root, since a is small. This gives

$$r_1 = -\frac{k}{b} \quad \text{and} \quad r_2 = -\frac{b}{a} + \frac{k}{b} \approx -\frac{b}{a} \tag{128.8}$$

If the values [128.6] of the constants and [128.8] of the approximate expressions for the roots r_1 and r_2 are substituted in Equation [128.4], the approximate solution $x_1(t)$ of [128.1] is in the form

$$x_1(t) = x_0\left[e^{-\frac{k}{b}t} - \frac{ak}{b^2}e^{-\frac{b}{a}t}\right] + \frac{a}{b}\dot{x}_0\left[e^{-\frac{k}{b}t} - e^{-\frac{b}{a}t}\right] \tag{128.9}$$

It is to be noted that the solution $x_1(t)$ is an approximate one because the expansion of the square root has been limited to the first two terms; this is justified by the assumed smallness of a.

On the other hand, for $a = 0$ the solution of Equation [128.1] of the second order becomes the same as that of the equation of the first order given by [128.2]. To emphasize the fact that the solution [128.2] is the same as that of Equation [128.1] when *complete degeneration* occurs, that is, when $a = 0$, we will write it as

$$\bar{x}(t) = x_0 e^{-\frac{k}{b}t} \tag{128.2}$$

Consider now the function

$$\phi(a,t) = x_1(a,t) - \bar{x}(a,t) = -x_0\frac{ak}{b^2}e^{-\frac{b}{a}t} + \frac{a}{b}\dot{x}_0\left[e^{-\frac{k}{b}t} - e^{-\frac{b}{a}t}\right] \tag{128.10}$$

This function represents the difference between the approximate solution $x_1(t)$ of [128.1] in the neighborhood of the point of degeneration, where a is very small, and the solution $\overline{x}(t)$ of a completely degenerated equation [128.1] of the first order. The function $\phi(t)$ approaches zero uniformly in the interval $0 < t < \infty$ when $a \to 0$.

The expression for the derivative of this function is

$$\dot{\phi}(a,t) = \dot{x}_1(a,t) - \dot{\overline{x}}(a,t) = \left(x_0\frac{k}{b} + \dot{x}_0\right)e^{-\frac{b}{a}t} - \frac{ak}{b^2}\dot{x}_0 e^{-\frac{k}{b}t} \quad [128.11]$$

For very small values of t the function $\dot{\phi} \approx x_0\frac{k}{b} + \dot{x}_0$, and it is impossible to reduce it by reducing the coefficient a. However, for a sufficiently large t, which is supposed to be fixed, one can always find a value of a small enough so that the value of $\dot{\phi}(t)$ is smaller than a given positive number ϵ.

We can express this by saying that whereas the function $\phi(a,t)$, considered as a function of a, approaches zero *uniformly* in the interval $0 < t < \infty$ when $a \to 0$, the function $\dot{\phi}(a,t)$ behaves in a like manner only when the values of t are sufficiently large. For $t = 0$ the convergence of the function $\dot{x}_1(t)$ to the function $\dot{\overline{x}}(t)$ when $a \to 0$ is not uniform. In other words, to a given a, however small, one can always assign a value of $t = t_1$ such that $\dot{\phi} \approx x_0\frac{k}{b} + \dot{x}_0$. Only in a very special case, when $x_0\frac{k}{b} + \dot{x}_0 = 0$, does this non-uniformity of convergence disappear, but this case is of no practical interest.

One can also state that the difference between the approximate solution $x_1(t)$ of a quasi-degenerate system when a is very small and the corresponding solution $\overline{x}(t)$ of a completely degenerate system when $a = 0$ approaches zero in the whole interval $0 < t < \infty$ when $a \to 0$ except in a very small neighborhood around the point $t = 0$; this neighborhood is smaller as a is smaller and in it the difference $\dot{x}_1(t) - \dot{\overline{x}}(t)$ of the slopes of the two curves $x_1(t)$ and $\overline{x}(t)$ cannot be reduced. This means that the function $x_1(t)$ undergoes a quasi-discontinuous jump in this neighborhood.

When the parameter $k \to 0$, the problem is treated in a similar manner. First, for a completely degenerate equation with $k = 0$, Equation [128.1] becomes

$$a\ddot{x} + b\dot{x} = 0 \qquad\qquad [128.12]$$

Integrating it, one obtains

$$a\dot{x} + bx = M \qquad\qquad [128.13]$$

where M is the constant of integration. The value of M is determined by the initial conditions, namely,

$$a\dot{x}_0 + bx_0 = M \qquad\qquad [128.14]$$

The solution of Equation [128.13] is

$$x = \frac{M}{b} + C e^{-\frac{b}{a}t}$$ [128.15]

where C is a constant of integration. One obtains finally

$$\overline{x}(t) = x_0 + \dot{x}_0 \frac{a}{b}\left(1 - e^{-\frac{b}{a}t}\right)$$ [128.16]

If, however, one proceeds with the solution of Equation [128.1] in the neighborhood of its degeneration, where k is very small, the approximate solution is

$$x_1(t) = x_0 e^{-\frac{k}{b}t} + \frac{a}{b}\dot{x}_0\left(1 - e^{-\frac{b}{a}t}\right)$$ [128.17]

By forming the functions

$$\psi(k,t) = x_1(k,t) - \overline{x}(k,t) \quad \text{and} \quad \dot{\psi}(k,t) = \dot{x}_1(k,t) - \dot{\overline{x}}(k,t) \quad [128.18]$$

one ascertains by an argument similar to that given in connection with the functions $\phi(a,t)$ and $\dot{\phi}(a,t)$ that for a sufficiently small k the function $\dot{\psi}(k,t)$ approaches zero when $k \to 0$ uniformly in the interval $0 < t < \infty$, whereas $\psi(k,t)$ approaches zero when $k \to 0$ for all values of t except when $t \to \infty$, for which value $\psi(k,t)$ approaches the value x_0.

129. IDEALIZATIONS IN PHYSICAL PROBLEMS

In applications, idealizations of quasi-degenerate systems as absolutely degenerate systems are frequently made, as was mentioned in Section 127. Thus, for example, the differential equation of the so-called (R,C)-circuit is usually written in the form

$$R\frac{di}{dt} + \frac{1}{C}i = 0$$ [129.1]

where i is the current in the idealized circuit $(L = 0)$. The corresponding quasi-degenerate equation, with L very small, is

$$L\frac{d^2 i}{dt^2} + R\frac{di}{dt} + \frac{1}{C}i = 0$$ [129.2]

With the solution of the absolutely degenerate equation [129.1] designated by $\overline{i}(t)$ and that of the quasi-degenerate equation [129.2] designated by $i_1(t)$, the functions $\overline{i}(t)$ and $i_1(t)$ have the appearance shown in Figure 129.1. For Equation [129.1], with $L = 0$, the current starts from the point A and decays exponentially thereafter. For the quasi-degenerate equation [129.2], with L very small, the current starts from zero, increases very rapidly, and follows the curve $i_1(t)$ which becomes practically identical with the curve $\overline{i}(t)$ after a very short time; this time is shorter as L is smaller. According to the absolutely degenerate equation [129.1], with $L = 0$, the current $\overline{i}(t)$ undergoes a true mathematical discontinuity OA at $t = 0$, whereas the current $i_1(t)$ of the quasi-degenerate equation [129.2], with $L \approx 0$, has a quasi-discontinuity OA' which approaches OA when L approaches zero.

Although these facts are well known if considered independently of the previous history of the system, as in the above discussion, they appear in a somewhat different form in a quasi-discontinuous stationary relaxation oscillation. Thus, for example, the oscillation depicted in Figure 127.4 is governed by the full differential equation of the second order on the analytic branches AB, A'B', ... of the trajectories; these branches are determined in terms of the *two* constants of integration corresponding to the initial conditions represented by the points A and A' of the phase plane. During the jumps BA', B'A'', ... the transition is governed by two differential equations of the first order. Since the solutions of each of these equations are determined by one constant of integration, there appears a relation between the variables $\frac{di}{dt}$ and i_c of the phase plane which does not exist on the analytic branches AB, A'B', ... As a result of this, the jumps must occur along a certain direction in the phase plane.

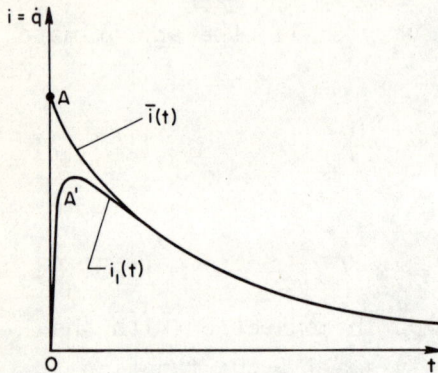

Figure 129.1

Thus the assumption of certain idealizations specified in connection with Figure 127.3 not only permits a discontinuous treatment of the problem but also indicates the direction of the jumps in the phase plane.

It is impossible, however, to proceed beyond this point if one attempts to apply these idealizations to the problem of discontinuous stationary relaxation oscillations. What is lacking in the system of Figure 127.4 is the mechanism by which the phenomenon of "closing" or "opening" the switch is produced *spontaneously by the internal reactions* of the circuit itself.

In order to be able to formulate this condition and thus to complete the discontinuous theory it will be necessary to introduce an *a priori* proposition whose validity is justified only by its agreement with the observed facts. This emphasizes once more the physical nature of this theory as distinguished from the contents of Parts I and II in which the argument was purely analytical.

130. CRITICAL POINTS OF DIFFERENTIAL EQUATIONS; BASIC ASSUMPTION

It was shown that, as a result of certain idealizations, discontinuities appear in the mathematical treatment of physical phenomena which exhibit rapid changes at certain points of their cycles. The use of discontinuities is convenient in some respects but inevitably introduces certain complications. These facts are too well known from the theory of mechanical impacts to need any emphasis here.

It is obvious that similar difficulties are to be expected if a discontinuous treatment of relaxation oscillations is adopted. For example, in an electronic "sweep circuit" some variables change so rapidly at certain points in the cycle that it is natural to attempt to idealize these changes by mathematical discontinuities. Obviously, any attempt to explain these changes on the basis of some kind of impact is difficult because the energy delivered by the external source, a battery, remains constant, and one cannot very well correlate the apparent continuity of the energy input into the system with the quasi-discontinuous changes of some of its variables. Very frequently a slight change of a parameter causes a disappearance of the phenomenon, and vice versa. In some particularly simple circuits in which the effect is known to exist, one succeeds in "explaining" it by a more or less elementary physical argument. In more complicated circuits it is impossible to give an account of what actually happens and, still less, to predict theoretically the existence, or non-existence, of such effects. There exists no analytical theory of these oscillations which would permit a treatment of these phenomena on a uniform basis as was possible for the quasi-linear oscillations with which we were concerned in Parts I, II, and III.

In order to be able to find a solution and to correlate the numerous experimental phenomena on a common basis, it becomes necessary to define terms and to introduce some kind of basic assumption, the value of which is to be justified by its agreement with the observed facts.

Definition: Critical points are the points at which the differential equation describing a phenomenon in a certain domain ceases to describe it.

Basic Assumption: Whenever the representative point following a trajectory of the differential equations describing a phenomenon reaches a critical point, a discontinuity occurs in some variable of the system.

Since, by virtue of the basic assumption, the occurrence of discontinuities depends on the existence of critical points, it is necessary to specify certain criteria by which their existence can be ascertained. In what follows we will encounter two principal criteria.

1. Let us consider a system of differential equations of the form

$$\frac{dx}{dt} = \frac{P(x,y)}{R(x,y)}; \qquad \frac{dy}{dt} = \frac{Q(x,y)}{R(x,y)} \qquad\qquad [130.1]$$

Obviously these differential equations become meaningless and, hence, cease to

describe a physical phenomenon for the points (x_i, y_i) for which $R(x_i, y_i) = 0$.
This equation represents a certain locus of critical points, and by virtue of
the basic assumption a discontinuity occurs each time the representative point
reaches the curve $R(x_i, y_i) = 0$. It is important to note that, as far as the
trajectory is concerned, the passage through a critical point does not in any
way affect its determinateness since R cancels out in the expression $\frac{dy}{dx} = \frac{Q}{P}$.
It is impossible, however, to determine the *motion* on the trajectory in the
neighborhood of a critical point. In this respect the local properties of a
critical point are opposite to those of a singular point where the trajectory
is indeterminate but the motion is determinate.

2. The existence of critical points or of a locus of such points can
sometimes be revealed from the study of trajectories in a certain domain of
the phase plane. A typical example in which this can be done is shown in Figure 130.1. The trajectories arrive at, or
depart from, a certain threshold L from both
sides, as shown. *If no singular points, that
is, postions of equilibrium. exist in a narrow domain surrounding L, one can assert that
the line L is a locus of critical points.*

It is apparent that the trajectories
situated in the regions M and N belong to two
different differential equations. Let us assume that the phenomenon is represented by the
motion of the representative point R on a trajectory T of the region N. Since the singular

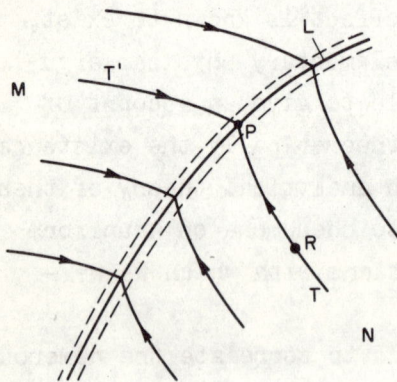

Figure 130.1

points are absent by our assumption, R will reach a point P on L in a finite
time. Having reached this point, the representative point finds itself in a
kind of *analytical impasse* from which there is no normal issue, that is, along
the integral curves. In fact R cannot pass onto the trajectory T' passing
through P nor can it turn back on T since, in both cases, this would be inconsistent with the differential equations prescribing a definite direction on
the trajectories of the two regions M and N. Nor can the representative point
remain at the point P which is not a position of equilibrium. The differential
equations cease to have any meaning at the point P and therefore cease to represent the physical phenomenon. Hence the point P is a critical point, and the
line L is a locus of such points. By our basic assumption the discontinuities
necessarily occur once the representative point has reached some point on L.

We are going to use the basic assumption extensively in the investigation of relaxation oscillations in relatively complicated circuits in
which it is impossible to predict the nature of the phenomenon on a basis of

elementary intuitive reasoning. It is useful to illustrate the application of the basic assumption to the simple example given previously, Figures 127.3 and 127.4. It is apparent that at the instant when the switch is closed, or opened, the differential equation of the second order ceases to describe the phenomenon since the right and the left portions of the circuit, instead of being in series, become in parallel. Hence this instant corresponds to a critical point, and a discontinuity is to be expected as we have ascertained by the elementary argument. The same argument applies to the ball striking the walls. In these two examples the oscillations are of the impulse-excited type, and the application of the basic assumption does not yield anything of interest.

We shall see that in connection with relaxation oscillations proper the basic assumption will be a useful tool by which the possibility of relaxation oscillations can be ascertained.

131. CONDITIONS OF MANDELSTAM

At the end of Section 127 certain idealizations and a choice of variables were specified so as to be able to introduce a discontinuous treatment of certain problems. It was shown that the necessary condition for such a treatment is the degeneracy of differential equations from the second to the first order if the variables $\frac{di}{dt}$ and $\frac{dV}{dt}$ are selected. In the preceding section we have formulated a sufficient condition for the occurrence of a discontinuity on the basis of a certain basic assumption.

There still remains one question to be settled, namely, the determination of the discontinuities once we have ascertained by the assumption that the discontinuity has to occur. Using the terminology of the phase plane, we can specify this last part of the problem as follows. Let us assume that the representative point R has reached a critical point $A(x_1, y_1)$. We may question into which other point $B(x_2, y_2)$ the representative point will jump from the point A. In discussing the solutions [127.3] of Equations [127.2] we have already touched this subject and found that in the very special case considered there the jump is from $A(0,0)$ to $B\left(\frac{E}{r}, \frac{E}{L}\right)$.

L. Mandelstam formulated the conditions of a jump on the basis of certain plausible assumptions regarding the continuity of energy during the infinitely short time interval of the discontinuity. It is to be noted that these conditions of Mandelstam are useful for relaxation oscillations and not for impulse-excited oscillations for reasons which will appear later. The argument of Mandelstam is based on the continuity of the functions $i(t)$, the current through an inductance L, and $V(t)$, the voltage across the capacitor, as was previously mentioned in connection with the expressions [127.3] representing solutions of the degenerate equations of the first order. Since

$i(t)$ and $V(t)$ are continuous, clearly the electromagnetic energy $\frac{Li^2}{2}$ stored in an inductance and the electrostatic energy stored in a capacitor are also continuous functions of time. One obtains the conditions of Mandelstam by writing

$$\Delta i\Big|_{t_0-0}^{t_0+0} = 0; \qquad \Delta V\Big|_{t_0-0}^{t_0+0} = 0 \qquad [131.1]$$

where $(t_0 - 0,\ t_0 + 0)$ is the infinitely small time interval during which the discontinuity occurs. The important point to be noted in connection with these conditions is that they are applicable to an infinitely small time interval and to circuits with finite dissipative parameters. The first restriction is trivial and is nothing but the expression of a continuity of functions $i(t)$ and $V(t)$. As to the second, it requires an additional remark. One could formulate the following case in which the conditions of Mandelstam apparently do not hold. Let us assume that a charged capacitor is suddenly short-circuited so that its energy $\frac{CV^2}{2}$ disappears instantly; this seems to contradict the second condition [131.1] of Mandelstam. The fallacy of this reasoning lies in the fact that the only way in which the energy can disappear suddenly is to be totally converted into heat. But in order that this may occur, a finite dissipative parameter must be present. If, however, such a dissipative parameter exists in the circuit, there exists also a finite time constant so that the disappearance of the charge, and, hence, of the energy, cannot be instantaneous, and it is sufficient to define a small time interval consistent with the time constant of the circuit to ensure the validity of the conditions of Mandelstam.

The usefulness of the conditions of Mandelstam is limited only to relaxation oscillations proper. In fact, in impulse-excited oscillations the idealization employed is of an entirely different kind, and it is assumed that the energy exchanges between the system and an external source occur instantaneously. Summing up the result of this and of the preceding sections, it can be stated that the basic assumption and the conditions of Mandelstam are useful in studies of relaxation oscillations but are unnecessary for impulse-excited oscillations.

132. REMARKS CONCERNING SYSTEMS OF DEGENERATE DIFFERENTIAL EQUATIONS

In Section 3 it was mentioned that a differential equation of the second order can always be represented by a system of two differential equations of the first order if a new variable $y = \frac{dx}{dt}$ is introduced. Likewise, a differential equation of the nth order can be reduced to a system of n differential equations of the first order by introducing the variables $\frac{dx}{dt} = y_1$, $\frac{dy_1}{dt} = y_2, \cdots$.

With degenerate differential equations the situation is somewhat different. Thus a completely degenerate equation of the second order is, in fact, a differential equation of the first order. As a result of this, the phase space, instead of being two-dimensional, that is, a phase plane, becomes uni-dimensional, that is, a phase line. Moreover, instead of analytic trajectories, piecewise analytic trajectories become possible.

A system of two differential equations of the second order can generally be reduced to a system of four differential equations of the first order, which means a system of the fourth order. If, however, each of the original differential equations of the second order degenerates into one equation of the first order, the system of the fourth order reduces to one equation of the second order, and its solutions can be represented by trajectories in a phase plane. This resultant equation of the second order, however, represents the result of degeneration of the system of the fourth order. We can express this by saying that we have a *doubly degenerate* system. Since each of the two differential equations of the first order admits discontinuous solutions, the doubly degenerate system of the second order will also possess certain discontinuous stretches in its phase plane so that its trajectories, in general, will be composed of certain analytic arcs joined by these stretches. Under certain conditions a doubly degenerate system of the second order may degenerate into a single differential equation of the first order; we can call such a case a *triply degenerate* system. We shall encounter one such system in what follows. In a triply degenerate system one differential equation of the first order represents the result of the degeneration of the system of the fourth order.

Although the use of degenerate equations extends the application of topological methods to a series of important practical cases which could not otherwise be represented in a phase plane, it should be noted that piecewise analytic trajectories of this kind "closed" by discontinuous stretches do not exhibit the features common to the regular analytic trajectories studied in Part I. We shall encounter, for example, systems in which no singularities exist inside such "closed" trajectories; in some other systems such trajectories include singularities alternating in the course of time between a focal, or nodal, point and a saddle point. Moreover, certain difficulties arise in the formulation of conditions for stability of such degenerate systems, as will be specified in Chapter XXV. These peculiarities are, of course, to be expected. They reflect to some extent the fact that the discontinuous theory of relaxation oscillations is based on certain idealizations; this fact makes it difficult to compare it directly with classical methods making use of analytic functions. The principal usefulness of this theory at present is that it permits obtaining satisfactory qualitative information in a great majority of important practical problems whose solutions are beyond the reach of existing analytical methods.

CHAPTER XXI

DEGENERATE SYSTEMS WITH ONE DEGREE OF FREEDOM

133. PERIODIC SOLUTIONS OF DEGENERATE SYSTEMS OF THE FIRST ORDER
      A differential equation of the first order

$$\frac{dx}{dt} = f(x) \qquad\qquad [133.1]$$

obviously does not possess continuous analytic periodic solutions. Moreover,
one can assert that if the function $f(x)$ is single-valued, no continuous, although not necessarily analytic, periodic solutions are possible. In fact,
in order that *some* sort of periodicity may exist, it is necessary that the
system traverse the same line $x = x_1$ with two oppositely directed velocities;
this, however, is impossible if $f(x)$ is single-valued. In the example illustrated by Figure 127.2b, we saw that the "closed" periodic trajectory ABCDA
is characterized by the fact that the function $f(x) = \pm v_0$ is actually double-
valued. It so happens that, in the example referred to, the function $f(x)$ is
a constant. It is easy, however, to waive this restriction by assuming that
the plane on which the ball rolls, instead of being horizontal, rises toward
the right wall. Then the trajectory will be a trapezoid ABCDA, as shown in
Figure 133.1. One could imagine
still other cases by assuming that,
instead of rolling on a plane, the
ball rolls on some kind of cylindrical surface whose generating lines
are parallel to the $\dot{x}$-axis. In this
case the trajectory would be formed
by stretches AB and CD of analytic
arcs "closed" by the discontinuous
stretches BC and DA.

        The change from one branch
of the function $f(x)$ to the other one
generally occurs at critical points
and is discontinuous. Very frequently

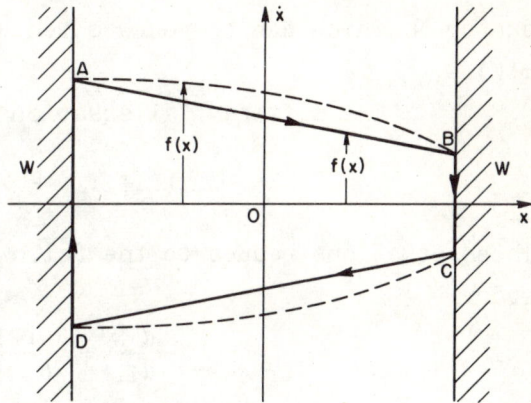

Figure 133.1

this is equivalent to saying that the phenomenon is governed by two distinct
differential equations during its cycle. During one fraction of the cycle
the phenomenon is described by one differential equation and during the other
fraction by the other equation. The change from one differential equation to
the other occurs at the critical points. In the example illustrated by Figure
133.1 the function $f(x)$ happens to have branches which are symmetrical with
respect to the x-axis. This is not always so, as will be shown later. We will
now illustrate this matter by the following two well-known examples.

134. RELAXATION OSCILLATIONS IN A CIRCUIT CONTAINING A GASEOUS CONDUCTOR

In view of the fact that this subject has been explored, we shall omit the familiar details and will endeavor primarily to show the application of the discontinuous theory in order to prepare the groundwork for more complicated cases beyond the reach of elementary theory.

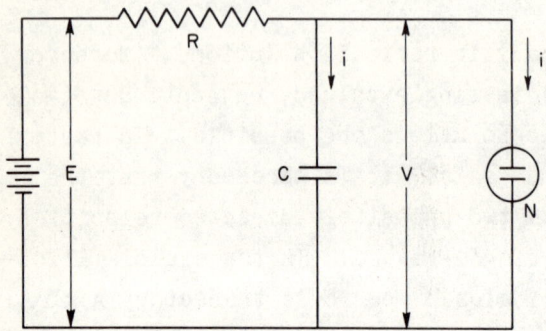

Figure 134.1

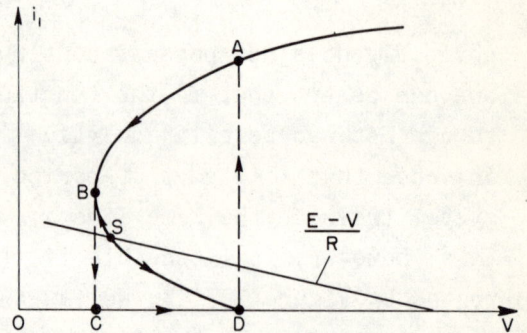

Figure 134.2

Figure 134.1 shows a circuit with the usual notations and with the positive directions as indicated; N is a gaseous conductor, such as a neon tube.

Figure 134.2 represents the characteristic* ABD of the gaseous conductor N, which can be represented by a non-linear empirical relation $i_1 = \phi(V)$.

The differential equations of the circuit obviously are

$$R(i + i_1) + V = E; \quad i = C\frac{dV}{dt} \qquad [134.1]$$

These equations reduce to the following differential equation of the first order

$$\frac{dV}{dt} = \frac{1}{RC}\Big[E - V - R\phi(V)\Big] \qquad [134.2]$$

This equation is valid only when the discharge exists; during its extinction $i_1 = \phi(V) = 0$, and we have

$$\frac{dV}{dt} = \frac{1}{RC}(E - V) \qquad [134.3]$$

Since we know that the phenomenon is characterized by alternate striking and extinction of the discharge, it is apparent that it is represented

---

* In order to avoid any misunderstanding, we shall use the term *characteristic* in the engineering sense, that is, to designate a certain experimental curve connecting the values of certain physical quantities, such as current i_1 through the non-linear conductor *N* and voltage *V* across it. We will reserve the term *trajectory* to mean an *integral curve* of a differential equation, as we have done previously.

alternately by two distinct differential equations, [134.2] and [134.3].
Since these differential equations are of the first order, only one constant
of integration is involved in their solutions. But as there are two dynamic
variables $i_1 = \phi(V)$ and V, it is apparent that there must exist a definite
relation between these variables, as has been mentioned in connection with
Equation [128.3]. During the time intervals when the discharge exists, this
relation is obviously the characteristic ABD.

Since the phase space is uni-dimensional for this system, it is apparent that during the intervals when the discharge exists the characteristic
appears as the *phase line* and during the intervals of extinction the phase
line is the V-axis. Aside from these phase lines, the plane is not involved.

As is well known from elementary theory, the points of equilibrium
are given by the points of intersection of the characteristic and the straight
line $i = \dfrac{E - V}{R}$. On the upper branch AB of the characteristic the equilibrium
is stable; on the lower branch BD it is unstable, as is easy to ascertain by
an elementary procedure. The case when the straight line $i = \dfrac{E - V}{R}$ cuts the
upper branch of the characteristic is obviously of no interest from the standpoint of oscillations. We shall confine our attention, therefore, to the case
when the resistance R has been adjusted to a value at which the straight line
and the characteristic intersect at some point S situated on the lower unstable branch BD.

Assume that we start the investigation of the phenomenon at the instant when the discharge has just appeared; this instant is represented by the
point A in Figure 134.2. Since $\dfrac{dV}{dt} < 0$ on the upper branch in this case, the
representative point will move from A to B on the upper branch. The arrows on
the characteristic, which, as was just explained, is also the phase line, indicate the positive directions consistent with the differential equation. It
follows, therefore, that having reached the point B, the representative point
finds itself in a situation which was specified in connection with Figure
130.1, so that the point B is a critical point of the differential equation
[134.2], and by our basic assumption we can assert that a jump must occur at
this point. In order to determine the character of the jump we have to apply
the condition of Mandelstam. The only form of stored energy is the electrostatic energy $\dfrac{CV^2}{2}$ stored in the capacitor. Thus the condition of the jump is

$$\Delta V \Big|_{t_0 - 0}^{t_0 + 0} = 0$$

which means that "during" the jump the voltage V across the capacitor remains
constant, that is, the jump occurs parallel to the i_1-axis along the stretch
BC. The process of extinction is thus "explained" on the basis of the discontinuous theory.

Beginning with the point C, Equation [134.3] describes the process of charging the capacitor with no discharge. During that time interval the representative point moves along the V-axis with a finite velocity until the point D is reached. Here the discharge strikes again, and the representative point is transferred discontinuously to the point A, after which the cycle is repeated. Since at the point D Equation [134.3] ceases to represent the phenomenon, we conclude that D is also a critical point.

It is thus seen that the familiar phenomenon of relaxation oscillations of a circuit containing a gaseous conductor can be treated consistently on the basis of the discontinuous theory and can be represented by a piecewise analytic cycle ABCDA formed by two analytic branches AB and CD "closed" by the discontinuous stretches BC and DA. We note also certain differences between the discontinuous oscillations just studied and the continuous oscillations treated by the classical theory in Part I. The closed trajectory ABCDA is not of a limit-cycle type in that the phenomenon jumps, so to say, directly into its cycle without a gradual asymptotic spiraling around it. This cycle resembles in all respects a similar cycle shown in Figures 127.2b and 133.1 describing the idealized behavior of a ball undergoing reflections from constraining walls.

So far, study of such oscillations does not reveal anything new, and the main purpose of this discussion is to illustrate the application of the discontinuous theory of relaxation oscillations to a familiar phenomenon generally treated by elementary methods. As we proceed further, the usefulness of this theory will become more manifest. In the example treated in the following section, for instance, it would be relatively difficult to apply the semi-intuitive physical argument. In still further examples it would be altogether impossible.

135. RC-MULTIVIBRATOR

As a second example of a system which can be described by one differential equation of the first order, we shall investigate the so-called RC-multivibrator circuit shown in Figure 135.1. The electron tube V_2 is a nonlinear conductor characterized by the equation $I_a = \phi(e_g)$. The tube V_1 appears here merely as a linear amplifier amplifying the potential difference ri, the feed-back voltage, between the points B and D and applying the amplified voltage $e_g = kri$ to the grid of V_2, k being the amplification factor of V_1. The circuit is idealized in the customary manner, that is, the effects of the parasitic inductance, the grid current, and the anode reaction are neglected.

The differential equations of the circuit with the positive directions shown are

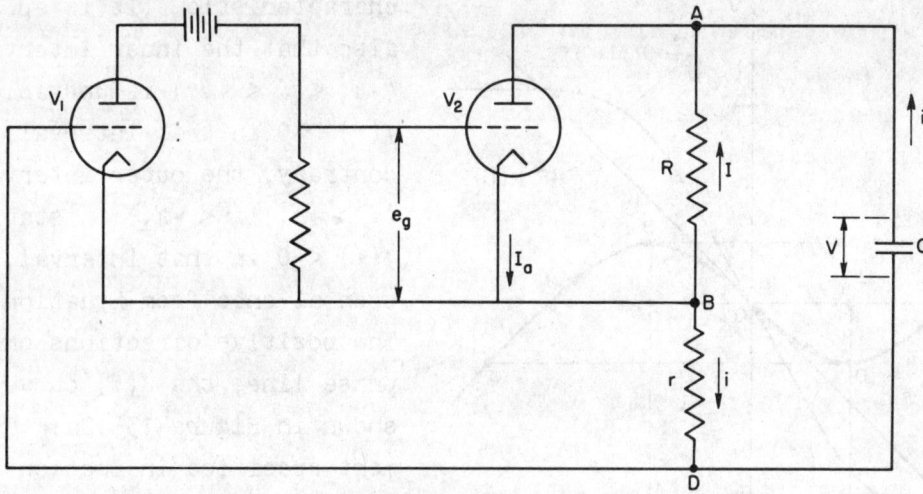

Figure 135.1

$$(R + r)i + V = R\phi(kri); \qquad i = C\frac{dV}{dt} \qquad\qquad [135.1]$$

These equations reduce to the equation

$$\left[krR\phi'(kri) - (R + r)\right]\frac{di}{dt} = \frac{1}{C}i \qquad\qquad [135.2]$$

The critical point $i = i_1$ is given by the equation

$$f(i_1) = \left[krR\phi'(kri_1) - (R + r)\right] = 0 \qquad\qquad [135.3]$$

where $\phi'(kri_1)$ designates the slope of the characteristic at the point $i = i_1$. One can also apply the argument given in connection with Figure 130.1. For this purpose the graphical procedure shown in Figures 135.2a and b will be useful. Figure 135.2a shows the characteristic $I_a = \phi(kri)$ of V_2 multiplied by a constant factor R. The tube V_2 is supposed to be biased at a point O in the middle of the rectilinear part of its characteristic. From the usual form of the characteristic $\phi(kri)$ it is apparent that its slope $\frac{d\phi}{di} = \phi'$ is maximum when $i = 0$ and approaches zero monotonically as $|i| \to \infty$. Let $\phi'(0) = S$ and assume that $RS > R + r$, without which, obviously, no self-excitation is possible. The curve $V(i)$ represents the function $R\phi(kri) - (R + r)i$. The curve shown in Figure 135.2b is the slope curve of the function $R\phi(kri)$ multiplied by a constant factor kr and referred to the axis M'N'. It is apparent that if this curve is referred to the MN-axis parallel to M'N' and at a distance $(R + r)$ from the origin O, the ordinates $f(i)$ of this curve represent the left-hand term of the expression [135.3]. Hence, the points P and Q are critical points, and by transferring these points on the diagram of Figure 135.2a one obtains the critical points B and D situated on the $V(i)$-curve and symmetrical with respect to the origin under the assumed idealization of the

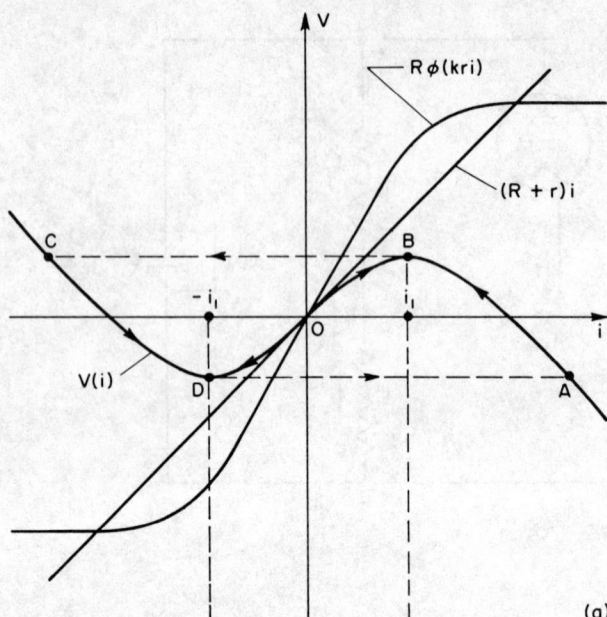

(a)

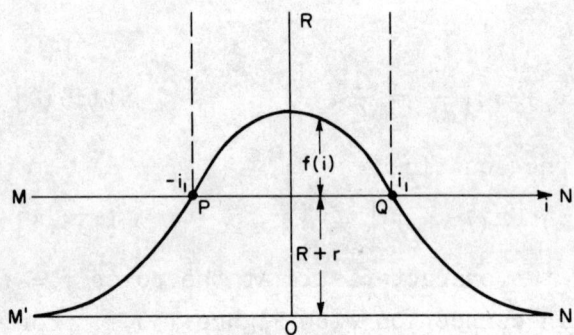

(b)

Figure 135.2

characteristic. It is apparent also that the inner interval $(-i_1 < i < +i_1)$ is unstable since $f(i) > 0$ in that interval. On the contrary, the outer interval $(i > +i_1; i < -i_1)$ is stable since $f(i) < 0$ in that interval, as is seen at once from Equation [135.2]. The positive directions on the phase line, the $V(i)$ curve, are shown in Figure 135.2a. The argument specified in Section 130 is therefore applicable. Thus, for example, when the representative point has reached the point B on the stretch AB, it has to jump discontinuously, and the second condition of Mandelstam specifies that the jump must occur parallel to the i-axis, since in such a case the energy stored in the capacitor does not change during the jump. The discontinuous stretch BC so traversed ends at the point C. Here the phenomenon is again governed by the differential equation, and the analytic stretch CD is traversed with a finite velocity. At the point D another jump occurs along the stretch DA, so that a closed piecewise analytic cycle ABCDA results. The phenomenon therefore follows a pattern substantially the same as that which has previously been investigated in connection with the ball striking the walls and also with the neon-tube oscillator. The difference between the neon-tube circuit and the multivibrator circuit is that for the former the phenomenon is described alternately by two separate differential equations [134.2] and [134.3], whereas for the latter the phenomenon is governed by only one differential equation [135.2]. Because of the symmetry of the curve $V(i)$ and that of the critical points, however, the closed cycle is obtained with the origin as the center of symmetry.

404

136. SYSTEM WITH ONE DEGREE OF FREEDOM DESCRIBABLE BY TWO DIFFERENTIAL EQUATIONS OF THE FIRST ORDER

The systems with one degree of freedom so far considered could be expressed by one differential equation of the first order. Chaikin and Lochakow (14) have investigated an interesting case when a dynamical system with one degree of freedom is describable by *two* differential equations of the second order possessing critical points. We shall outline briefly the principal features of the relaxation oscillations appearing in this case.

The fact that the system of differential equations is now of the second order will account for the representation of the phenomenon in the phase plane instead of its uni-dimensional representation by a phase line, as in previous cases. It will be shown that the discontinuous theory permits establishing the principal features of the phenomenon, although a direct intuitive argument, such as is applicable in the simple systems of Sections 133, 134, and 135, is insufficient here.

The circuit investigated by Chaikin and Lochakow is shown in Figure 136.1. It is observed that the only difference between this circuit and that shown in Figure 135.1 is that here the inductance L replaces the resistance R of the circuit of Figure 135.1. It will be shown now that the behavior of this circuit exhibits features entirely different from those of the circuit of Figure 135.1.

Using the previous notations, we obtain, by Kirchhoff's laws,

$$I_a = \phi(kri) = I + i; \qquad L\frac{dI}{dt} - ri - \frac{1}{C}\int i\,dt = 0 \qquad [136.1]$$

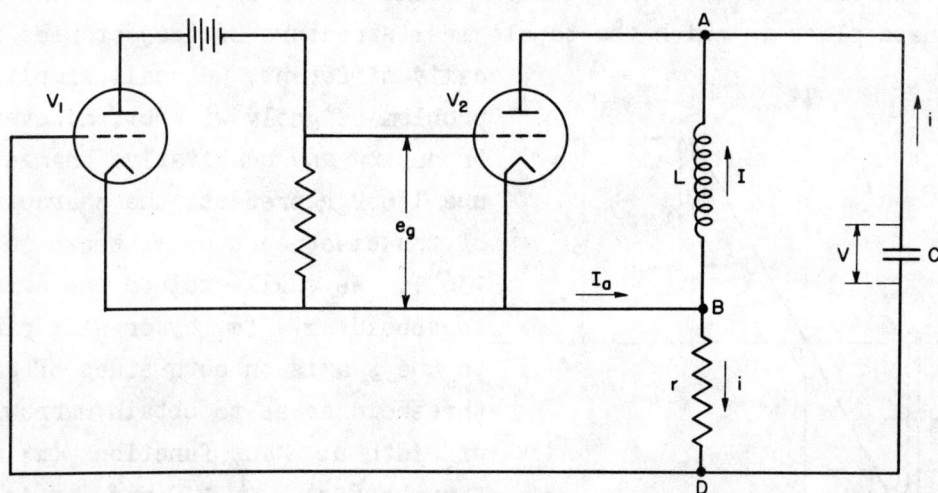

Figure 136.1

Introducing the variables $x = kri$ and $y = \dfrac{dI}{dt}$ and differentiating these equations, one gets

$$\frac{dx}{dt} = \frac{y}{\psi(x)}; \qquad \frac{dy}{dt} = \frac{x}{krLC} + \frac{1}{kL}\frac{y}{\psi(x)} \qquad [136.2]$$

where

$$\psi(x) = \phi'(x) - \frac{1}{kr} \qquad [136.3]$$

The phase trajectories are given by the equation

$$\frac{dy}{dx} = \frac{x\psi(x)}{krLCy} + \frac{1}{kL} \qquad [136.4]$$

The point $x = y = 0$ is clearly a singular point. It is apparent from the form of the characteristic of electron tubes that the function $\psi(x)$ decreases monotonically from a positive value $\psi(0) = S - \dfrac{1}{kr}$ to a negative value $\psi(x) = -\dfrac{1}{kr}$ when $|x| \to \infty$. Hence there exist two roots $x = \pm x_1$, for which both $\dfrac{dx}{dt}$ and $\dfrac{dy}{dt}$ become infinite. According to our definition, these roots $x = \pm x_1$ are the *critical points* of the system [136.2]. In the phase plane the values $x = \pm x_1$ determine two *critical thresholds*; that is, they are loci of the critical points of this system. It is to be noted that at these thresholds the tangent to the phase trajectories

$$\left(\frac{dy}{dx}\right)_{x = \pm x_1} = \frac{1}{kL} \qquad [136.5]$$

is determinate. It is impossible, however, to determine the *motion* of the representative point since the differential equations become meaningless at these points.

In order to show that these thresholds $x = \pm x_1$ separate the regions of the phase plane in which the topological structure of trajectories is radically different, we shall simplify the problem slightly without, however, introducing any qualitative changes. Figure 136.2 represents the characteristic of the electron tube V_2 shown in Figure 136.1. We shall exclude the critical thresholds $x = \pm x_1$ by drawing parallels to the y-axis on both sides of each threshold so as to obtain narrow strips of width Δx. The function $\psi(x)$ will then be $S(x) - \dfrac{1}{kr} > 0$ and $-\dfrac{1}{kr}$ in the inner and outer intervals, respectively. This will cause no qualitative changes but will change slightly the form of the

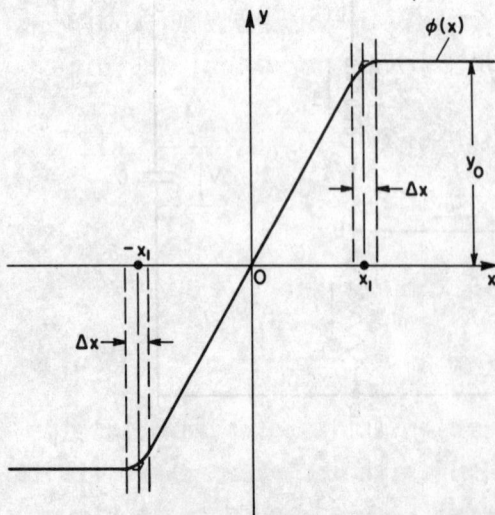

Figure 136.2

trajectories in the neighborhood of the strips; see Section 9, Part I. Since the equations then become linear, the standard procedure, see Section 18, Part I, shows that the origin O appears as a saddle point for the trajectories of the inner interval $(-x_1 < x < +x_1)$ and as either a focal point (if $r < 2\sqrt{\frac{L}{C}}$) or a nodal point (if $r > 2\sqrt{\frac{L}{C}}$) in the outer interval $(x < -x_1; \ x > +x_1)$. We shall assume the existence of a focal point in the outer interval since this is commonly encountered in applications.

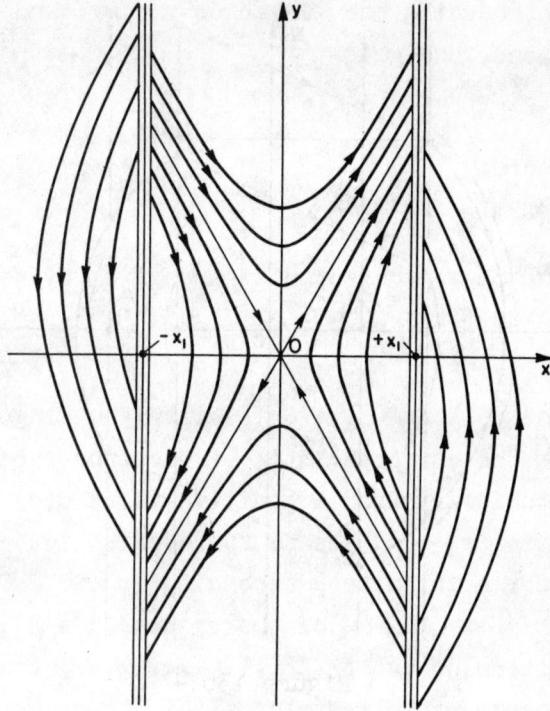

Figure 136.3

The picture of trajectories in this case is shown in Figure 136.3. A continuum of hyperbolic trajectories corresponding to the saddle point fills the inner interval, and a continuum of spirals corresponding to the focal point appears in the outer interval. By an elementary discussion of the sign of $\frac{dy}{dx}$ in Equation [136.4] for different quadrants of both intervals, it can be ascertained that the positive directions on the trajectories are oriented as shown by the arrows. It is apparent that these thresholds $x = \pm x_1$ are loci of critical points, and discontinuities occur whenever the representative point following a trajectory reaches one of the lines $x = \pm x_1$. Since the differential equations become meaningless at the critical points, the determination of discontinuities is made by the conditions [131.1] of Mandelstam, which, in this case, are

$$\Delta I \Big|_{t_0 - 0}^{t_0 + 0} = \int_{t_0 - 0}^{t_0 + 0} y \, dt = 0; \qquad \Delta V \Big|_{t_0 - 0}^{t_0 + 0} = \frac{1}{krC} \int_{t_0 - 0}^{t_0 + 0} x \, dt = 0 \quad [136.6]$$

Applying these conditions to Equations [136.1], one obtains

$$\phi(x_1) - \frac{x_1}{kr} = \phi(x_2) - \frac{x_2}{kr}; \qquad y_1 - y_2 = \frac{x_1 - x_2}{kL} \qquad [136.7]$$

where x_2 and y_2 are the coordinates of the representative point immediately after the discontinuity. Since the function $\phi(x)$ is an empirical curve, it is preferable to plot first the function $\theta(x) = \phi(x) - \frac{x}{kr}$ as was done in Figure 135.2a. One obtains for $\theta(x)$ a curve similar to the curve $V(i)$ of Figure

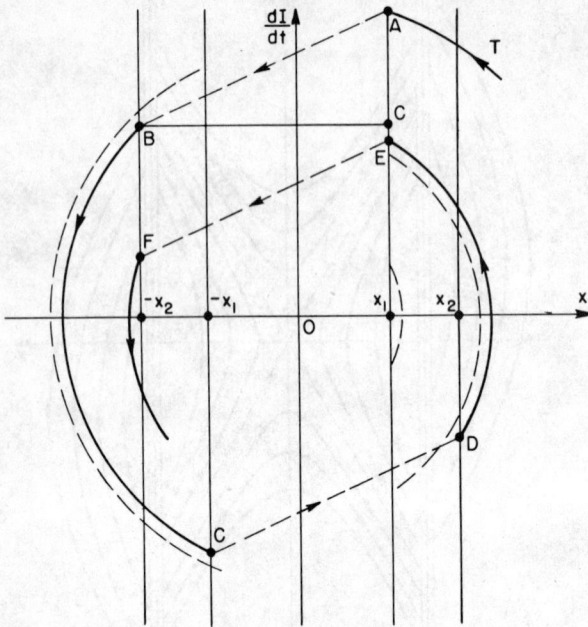

Figure 136.4

135.2a. By expressing the condition $\theta(x_1) = \theta(x_2)$, one can find x_2 if x_1 is given. We omit this graphical construction and merely mention that for characteristics of electron tubes commonly encountered the jump occurs from $+x_1$ to $-x_2$ (with $|x_2| > |x_1|$) and from $-x_1$ to $+x_2$. When x_2 is known, the second equation [136.7] permits determining y_2 for given x_1 and y_1.

The representation of such a quasi-discontinuous oscillation in the phase plane of the variables (x, y) is shown in Figure 136.4. It is noted that the jump from (x_1, y_1) to (x_2, y_2) is the same for all trajectories. Assume that the representative point, following a trajectory T of the outer interval, has reached a critical point A of coordinates (x_1, y_1). The second equation [136.7] then permits determining the "direction" of the jump AB in the phase plane. At the point B another spiral trajectory begins which encounters at C another critical point resulting in the jump CD, and so on. It can be shown, although we omit the proof, that after one turn of the radius vector the piecewise analytic spiral ABCDE will approach the origin, which means that the point E is below the point A if the latter is sufficiently distant from the origin O. If, however, one applies the same reasoning to a point A' near the x-axis on the critical line $x = \pm x_1$, one finds, on the contrary, that E' is above A'. Thus the large spirals shrink and the small ones grow with each turn of the radius vector. Hence there exists one and only one piecewise analytic spiral for which the points A and E coincide so that the trajectory becomes closed. Such a closed trajectory may be termed a *piecewise analytic limit cycle*, and it is stable. One notes the difference between such a trajectory and the piecewise analytic cycles described in Sections 133, 134, and 135, which are not of the *limit-cycle* type. The difference is due to the fact that the present phenomenon is expressible by *two* differential equations of the first order and is represented in the *phase plane*, whereas in the sections mentioned above it was determined by *one* differential equation of the first order and was represented by *phase lines* without involving any other points of the phase plane.

Another remarkable feature of
this analysis is that the unstable hyperbolic trajectories of the inner interval
do not appear at all in this representation
because that interval is traversed discontinuously. Experiments made by Chaikin and
Lochakow corroborate these theoretical conclusions. In their experiments a cathode-
ray oscillograph was adapted to record the
phase trajectories of the system, as was
explained in connection with Figure 24.7,
Part I. The record has the appearance shown
in Figure 136.5. There are two spiral arcs
BC and DE corresponding to a relatively slow

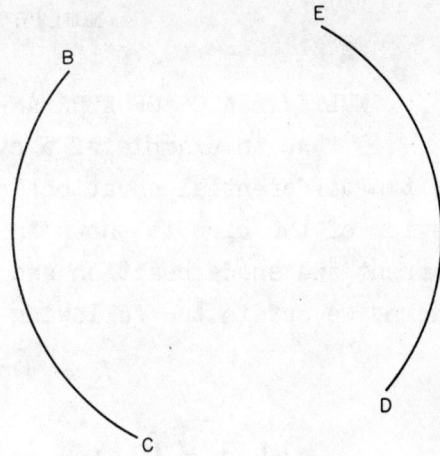

Figure 136.5

motion of the electronic beam on the analytic trajectories of the outer interval. The quasi-discontinuous jumps EB and CD remain unrecorded because of the
much higher speed of the beam in the region of the inner interval. It seems
logical to assume that when the phenomenon starts from rest, *one* hyperbolic
trajectory of the inner interval is actually traversed, but once the first
critical point has been reached, the phenomenon begins to "skip" the inner interval and continues to do so thereafter.

Once the essential features of this phenomenon have been ascertained
by this method, it is easy to give a corresponding physical interpretation.
The fact that the jumps occur obliquely in the phase plane of the variables
(x, y) means that at these instants the voltage $L \dfrac{dI}{dt}$ across the inductance and
the current $i = C \dfrac{dV}{dt}$ in the capacitor undergo quasi-discontinuities, although
the current I through the inductance and the voltage V across the capacitor
remain continuous. In other words, the functions $I(t)$ and $V(t)$ are continuous
but are not analytic at the jumps in the sense that they have discontinuous
first derivatives. This is in agreement with the elementary theory of an impulsive excitation of the idealized (L,R)- and (R,C)-circuits. It is apparent,
however, that mere knowledge of these well-known facts would be entirely insufficient for the purpose of establishing a qualitative picture of a complicated phenomenon of this nature if no general method, such as that offered by
the discontinuous theory, were available.

137. MULTIVIBRATOR OF ABRAHAM-BLOCH*

As an example of a system with two degrees of freedom describable by two differential equations of the first order we shall investigate the behavior of the circuit shown in Figure 137.1. Neglecting the effect of grid current and anode reaction and using the notations and positive directions shown, we obtain the following equations:

$$I_1 = I_{a1} + i_1; \qquad I_2 = I_{a2} + i_2$$

$$RI_1 + \frac{1}{C}\int i_1\, dt + ri_1 = E; \qquad RI_2 + \frac{1}{C}\int i_2\, dt + ri_2 = E \qquad [137.1]$$

$$I_{a1} = \phi(e_{g1}) = \phi(ri_2); \qquad I_{a2} = \phi(e_{g2}) = \phi(ri_1)$$

where $I_a = \phi(e_g)$ is the non-linear characteristic of the electron tubes V_1 and V_2. Differentiating the second group of equations [137.1] and making use of the other two groups, we obtain the following system of differential equations:

$$(R + r)\frac{di_1}{dt} + \frac{1}{C}i_1 + Rr\phi'(ri_2)\frac{di_2}{dt} = 0$$

$$\qquad [137.2]$$

$$Rr\phi'(ri_1)\frac{di_1}{dt} + (R + r)\frac{di_2}{dt} + \frac{1}{C}i_2 = 0$$

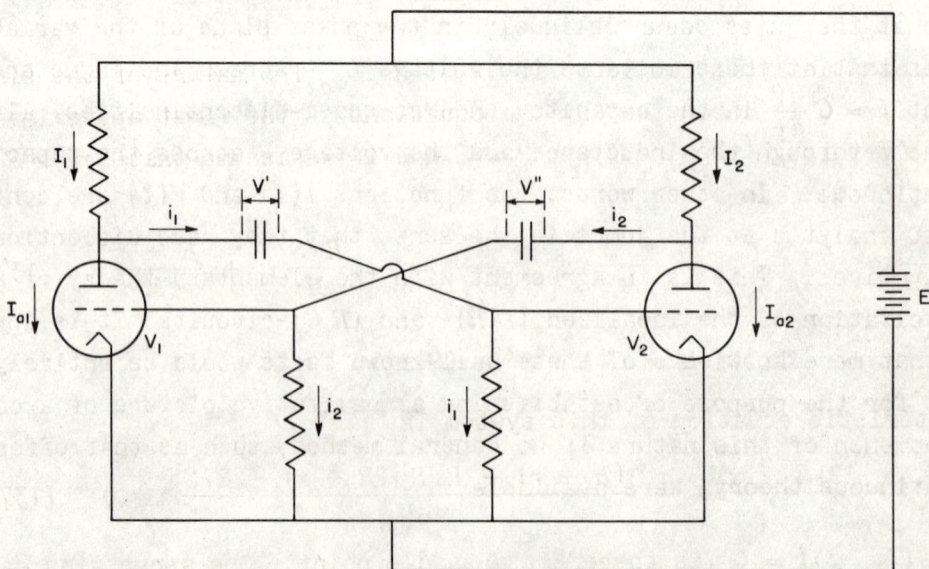

Figure 137.1

---

* This device is described in Reference (15).

This system reduces to the following equations:

$$\frac{di_1}{dt} = \frac{(R + r)\dfrac{i_1}{C} - Rr\phi'(ri_2)\dfrac{i_2}{C}}{R^2 r^2 \phi'(ri_1)\phi'(ri_2) - (R + r)^2}$$

$$\frac{di_2}{dt} = \frac{(R + r)\dfrac{i_2}{C} - Rr\phi'(ri_1)\dfrac{i_1}{C}}{R^2 r^2 \phi'(ri_1)\phi'(ri_2) - (R + r)^2}$$

[137.3]

which are of the form

$$\frac{di_1}{dt} = \frac{P(i_1, i_2)}{U(i_1, i_2)}; \qquad \frac{di_2}{dt} = \frac{Q(i_1, i_2)}{U(i_1, i_2)}$$

[137.4]

One notes the symmetry of Equations [137.3] with respect to the variables i_1 and i_2; this symmetry is due, of course, to the symmetry of the circuit.

The phase trajectories in the (i_1, i_2)-plane are given by the equation

$$\frac{di_2}{di_1} = \frac{Q(i_1, i_2)}{P(i_1, i_2)}$$

[137.5]

From the explicit values of the functions P and Q, Equations [137.3], one observes that the origin $i_1 = i_2 = 0$ is a singular point, that is, an equilibrium point of the circuit.

We first inquire whether closed analytic trajectories are possible in the system. Applying the negative criterion of Bendixson, see Section 25, one ascertains that

$$\frac{dP}{di_1} + \frac{dQ}{di_2} = \frac{2(R + r)}{C} = \text{constant}$$

[137.6]

Hence no closed analytic trajectories exist here. The nature of the singular point $i_1 = i_2 = 0$ is determined by the equations of the first approximation. If we let $\phi'(ri_1)_{i_1 = 0} = \phi'(ri_2)_{i_2 = 0} = S$ and if we assume that $RrS > R + r$, Equations [137.3] become

$$\frac{di_1}{dt} = \frac{R + r}{M} i_1 - \frac{RrS}{M} i_2; \qquad \frac{di_2}{dt} = -\frac{RrS}{M} i_1 + \frac{R + r}{M} i_2 \quad [137.7]$$

where

$$M = C[R^2 r^2 S^2 - (R + r)^2] > 0$$

The characteristic equation of this system is

$$\lambda^2 - \frac{2(R + r)}{M}\lambda + \frac{[(R + r) + RrS][(R + r) - RrS]}{M^2} = 0 \quad [137.8]$$

The origin $(i_1 = i_2 = 0)$ is therefore a saddle point. One ascertains easily that, when $RrS < R + r$, the origin is a stable nodal point, but this case is of no interest from the standpoint of relaxation oscillations. We will assume the existence of a saddle point. Since, initially, $RrS > R + r$ and the origin is unstable, the variables i_1 and i_2 begin to increase. On the other hand, from the form of the characteristic $I_a = \phi(ri)$, we know, see Section 135, that $|\phi'(ri)| \to 0$ when $i \to \infty$. The function

$$U(i_1, i_2) = C[R^2 r^2 \phi'(ri_1)\phi'(ri_2) - (R + r)^2] \qquad [137.9]$$

which is initially positive, decreases monotonically when i_1 and i_2 increase and is negative when i_1 and i_2 are very large and are equal. Hence there are certainly some values of i_1 and i_2 for which $U = 0$. This means that the system [137.3] has critical points so that by virtue of the basic assumption, Section 130, discontinuities must occur at these points. The expression $U(i_1, i_2) = 0$ defines a certain curve Γ_1 in the plane of the variables i_1 and i_2. In order to simplify the notation, let us designate by x_1 and y_1 the values of i_1 and i_2, respectively, situated on the curve Γ_1 shown in Figure 137.2. The equation of this curve is then

$$R^2 r^2 \phi'(rx_1)\phi'(ry_1) - (R + r)^2 = 0 \qquad [137.10]$$

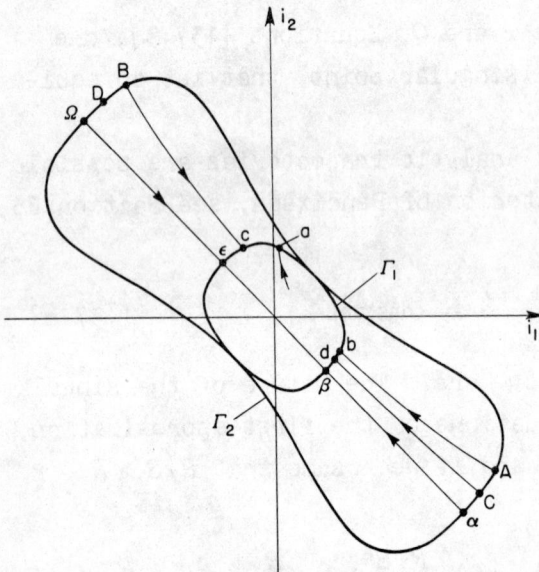

Figure 137.2

From the form of the functions $\phi'(rx_1)$ and $\phi'(ry_1)$, approximating the slope to the characteristic $I_a = \phi(e_g)$ of the electron tube, one ascertains that the curve Γ_1 is a symmetrical closed curve with the origin at its center and has the form shown in Figure 137.2. As soon as the representative point following a trajectory has reached a point (x_1, y_1) on the curve Γ_1, a jump must occur, and the point (x_2, y_2) into which the representative point jumps is determined by the conditions of Mandelstam which we now propose to apply. Since the only form of stored energy in this case is purely electrostatic, namely, the energy stored in capacitors, the conditions of Mandelstam require that the potential differences V' and V'' across the capacitors remain constant during the discontinuity. This gives the conditions

$$V' = E - R\phi(ri_2) - (R + r)i_1; \quad V'' = E - R\phi(ri_1) - (R + r)i_2 \quad [137.11]$$

If we designate now the terminal coordinates of the jump by (x_2, y_2), the conditions of Mandelstam obviously are

$$R\phi(ry_1) - (R + r)x_1 = R\phi(ry_2) - (R + r)x_2$$

$$R\phi(rx_1) - (R + r)y_1 = R\phi(rx_2) - (R + r)y_2 \qquad [137.12]$$

In these notations (x_1, y_1) represents the critical point on the curve Γ_1 from which the representative point is transferred discontinuously to some other point (x_2, y_2) determined by these equations. Since there is generally a one-to-one correspondence between the points (x_1, y_1) and (x_2, y_2), we conclude that the locus of the points (x_2, y_2) is another curve Γ_2 which is also a closed curve symmetrical with respect to both variables i_1 and i_2 since the circuit is entirely symmetrical.

The phase-plane representation of the behavior of the Abraham-Bloch multivibrator can then be described as follows. Assume that the representative point has reached a critical point a on the curve Γ_1. From this point it jumps into a *corresponding point* A on the curve Γ_2. At the point A begins a stretch of a continuous analytic trajectory Ab. The point b is another critical point where another jump bB occurs. At B a second continuous trajectory begins which ends at another critical point c, from which a new jump cC takes place; at C a continuous stretch Cd begins which ends at d, and so on.

By a more detailed analysis of such piecewise analytic trajectories interrupted by discontinuities, it can be shown that the transient behavior of the Abraham-Bloch multivibrator approaches a stationary symmetrical state, which is oriented along the bisector of the i_1- and i_2-axes and which consists of a continuous stretch $\alpha\beta$ followed by a jump $\beta\Omega$, then by another continuous trajectory $\Omega\epsilon$ followed by another jump $\epsilon\alpha$ which closes the "cycle." In this case, the cycle is uni-dimensional, that is, it is the phase line $\Omega\alpha$.

It is apparent that if, instead of assuming the asymmetry of the initial conditions as we did, only a steady-state condition was aimed at, a simplification could be made in the differential equations by introducing the conditions of symmetry, that is, $i_1 = -i_2$ and $\phi'(ri_1) = -\phi'(ri_2)$. With this simplification, one obtains a single differential equation of the first order, namely,

$$\frac{di}{dt} = \frac{(R + r) + Rr\phi'(ri)}{R^2 r^2 [\phi'(ri)]^2 - (R + r)^2} \frac{i}{C} \qquad [137.13]$$

which reduces to the form

$$[Rr\phi'(ri) - (R + r)]\frac{di}{dt} = \frac{i}{C} \qquad [137.14]$$

This is identical with Equation [135.2], the equation of an asymmetrical relaxation oscillation. We conclude, therefore, that the transient behavior of the Abraham-Bloch multivibrator is represented by a doubly degenerate system. As far as the stationary condition described by one differential equation

[137.14] of the first order is concerned, the multivibrator is represented by a triply degenerate system, to use the terminology of Section 132.

138. HEEGNER'S CIRCUIT; ANALYTIC TRAJECTORIES

As a second example of a doubly degenerate system, we shall investigate the so-called Heegner circuit (16) shown in Figure 138.1, which is the same as the circuit of an asymmetrical RC relaxation oscillation shown in Figure 135.1, the only difference being that there is now an additional capacitor C_2 shunting the resistor R. We propose to show now that the addition of the capacitor C_2 radically modifies the behavior of the circuit. It would be impossible to see this without the criteria of Section 130.

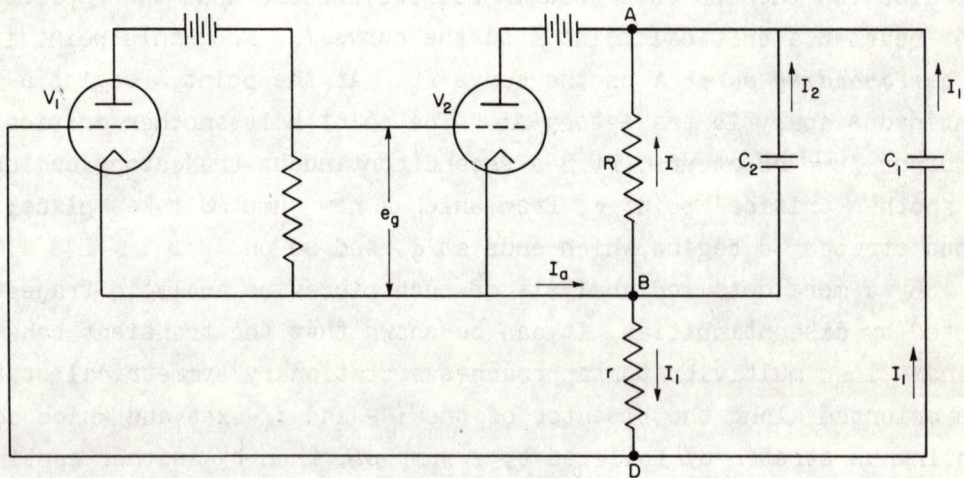

Figure 138.1

With the positive directions indicated by arrows, the application of Kirchhoff's laws gives

$$I_a = I + I_1 + I_2; \qquad I_1 = C_1 \frac{d}{dt}(RI - rI_1); \qquad I_2 = C_2 R \frac{dI}{dt} \quad [138.1]$$

Putting $I_a = \phi(krI_1)$, as we have previously, and eliminating I, we obtain the following system of the second order:

$$\frac{dI_1}{dt} = -\frac{1}{rC_1}I_1 + \frac{1}{rC_2}I_2$$

$$\frac{dI_2}{dt} = \frac{R - Rrk\phi'(krI_1)}{RrC_1}I_1 - \frac{R + r - Rrk\phi'(krI_1)}{RrC_2}I_2 \qquad [138.2]$$

It is observed that this system of differential equations has no critical points, and hence no discontinuities are to be expected. The only singular point is $I_1 = I_2 = 0$. Noting that $\phi'(0) = S$ is a maximum and that the function $|\phi'(krI_1)| \to 0$ when $|I_1| \to \infty$, the characteristic equation of the system

[138.2] is

$$\lambda^2 + \left[\frac{C_2}{C_1} + \frac{R + r - RrkS}{R} \right] \frac{1}{rC_2} \lambda + \frac{1}{RrC_1C_2} = 0 \qquad [138.3]$$

It is noted that the singularity here is *not* a saddle point. Hence, it is either a nodal point, if the roots λ_1 and λ_2 are real, or a focal point, if they are conjugate complex. In both cases the singularity is unstable if

$$\frac{R + r - RrkS}{R} \geqq \frac{C_2}{C_1} \qquad [138.4]$$

If the singularity is unstable, self-excitation from rest is possible. By approximating the experimental function $I_a = \phi(krI_1)$ by a polynomial and by applying the bifurcation theory, it is possible to establish the existence of a stable limit cycle. We shall omit this calculation since the fact that the Heegner circuit is capable of producing continuous self-excited oscillations is well known.

Although the Heegner circuit does not produce quasi-discontinuous relaxation oscillations, it is mentioned here as an example of the difficulties which appear if an analysis is attempted on the basis of a more or less intuitive physical argument. In the meantime, this circuit provides an additional example for testing the validity of the basic assumption.

139. TRANSITION BETWEEN CONTINUOUS AND DISCONTINUOUS SOLUTIONS OF DEGENERATE SYSTEMS

On the basis of the preceding argument, one might ask whether a gradual modification of a given dynamical system, for example, an electric circuit, might cause a transition from continuous performance to quasi-discontinuous performance, or vice versa. It will now be shown that such a transition is indeed possible and that its mathematical formulation can be reduced to the question of the appearance, or disappearance, of critical points as a result of the variation of a certain parameter in the differential equations. In order to show this, let us consider a slightly modified Heegner circuit such as that shown in Figure 139.1. The modification in question is that the capacitor C_2, instead of being connected to the point B, is now connected by an adjustable sliding contact to some point E along the resistor r, as shown. Let r_1 be the resistance between the points B and E and r_2 be that between E and D, where $r_1 + r_2 = r$ and $r_1/r = \beta$. Proceeding as we did in Section 138, we obtain the following system of equations:

$$\frac{dI_1}{dt} = - \frac{1}{(1 - \beta)rC_1} I_1 + \frac{1}{(1 - \beta)rC_2} I_2$$

$$[139.1]$$

$$\frac{dI_2}{dt} = \frac{[\beta r + R - rR\phi'kr(I_1 + \beta I_2)]\dfrac{I_1}{C_1} - [r + R - rR\phi'kr(I_1 + \beta I_2)]\dfrac{I_2}{C_2}}{(1 - \beta)[R + \beta r - \beta rR\phi'kr(I_1 + \beta I_2)]}$$

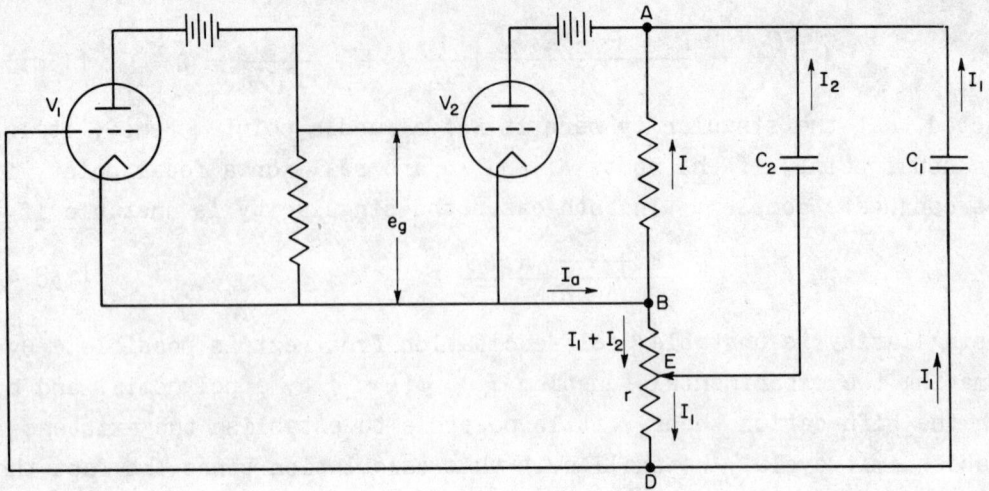

Figure 139.1

It is apparent that for $\beta = 1$, that is, $r_1 = r$, the circuit reduces to that shown in Figure 135.1 where a discontinuous performance occurs. For $\beta = 0$ and $r_1 = 0$, we have Heegner's circuit, which produces continuous oscillations. For some intermediate value of β, the co-factor of $(1 - \beta)$ in the denominator of the second equation [139.1] may vanish, which means that the otherwise con-

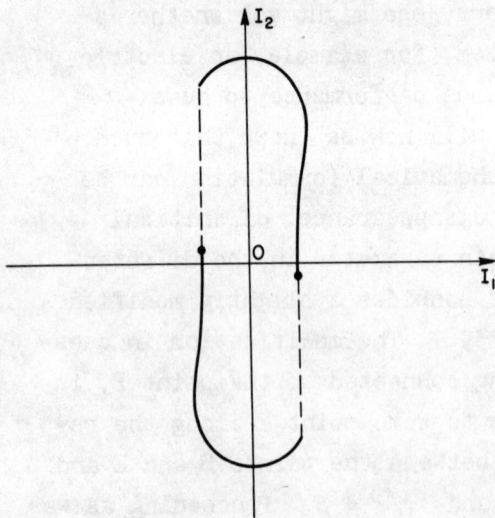

Figure 139.2

tinuous oscillation will undergo a discontinuous jump parallel to the I_2-axis as shown by the broken lines in Figure 139.2. This generally occurs when the system [139.1] is characterized by a saddle point, and the transition range is at the point where an unstable focal point degenerates into a saddle point, see Figure 18.1.

We shall not enter into a further study of these complicated and relatively unexplored phenomena. It is sufficient to emphasize once more that their apparent complexity is related to the appearance, or disappearance, of critical points in the differential equations.

CHAPTER XXIII

MECHANICAL RELAXATION OSCILLATIONS

140. INTRODUCTORY REMARKS

To date, mechanical relaxation oscillations have been studied less than electrical ones. As was mentioned in the introduction to this report, which appears in Part I, two principal reasons account for this. First, the determination of the parameters of a mechanical system is generally more complicated than the determination of the parameters of an electric circuit. Secondly, mechanical relaxation oscillations always appear as undesirable parasitic phenomena, and the endeavor of engineers is directed toward their elimination rather than their study. These phenomena generally take the form of "jarring" motions resulting from dry friction, misalignment of machinery, and similar factors. Whether any useful applications of these effects can be found is difficult to say. Very likely this state of affairs will continue until the laws of friction, which usually account for the appearance of such effects, are better understood and can be controlled with a prescribed degree of reliability. For the time being, the whole subject of mechanical relaxation oscillations is purely academic.

In addition to mechanical relaxation oscillations proper, of which we will indicate examples in Sections 141 and 142, there exists a class of oscillations maintained by periodically timed impacts. These oscillations also exhibit quasi-discontinuous behavior describable by piecewise analytic trajectories. These impact-maintained oscillations can hardly be considered to be of a *relaxation* type, although very frequently, and perhaps improperly, they are classified as such. Typical examples of these systems are clocks and quenched spark oscillators, in which the energy of a linear dissipative dynamical system is increased periodically in a quasi-discontinuous manner by special timing. We shall leave the investigation of impulse-excited systems to a later chapter and will investigate here a simple mechanical system of a pure relaxation type.

Let us consider a non-linear differential equation of the form

$$m\ddot{x} + kx = -F(\dot{x}) = -\mu f(\dot{x}) \qquad [140.1]$$

where $F(\dot{x})$ is a certain non-linear function of velocity which we shall identify with friction. If μ is small, Equation [140.1] is of a quasi-linear type and can be discussed by the standard methods of Part II. More specifically, for particular forms of the function $f(x)$ self-excitation may occur, and the oscillation may approach a stable limit cycle, as was studied in Part I in connection with Froude's pendulum; see Section 8.

When μ is large, Equation [140.1] cannot be solved by existing analytical methods, and at present the only guide to its solution is the qualitative analysis of Liénard;* see Section 36. We know from his analysis that the
periodic trajectory of the differential equation when μ is large generally
consists of two pairs of branches. On one pair of branches the motion of the
representative point is slow and the displacements are large, so the system
remains for a relatively large fraction of its relaxation period in that region. On the other pair of branches, however, the motion is very rapid. This
phase of the motion is of very short duration so that, in spite of the large
values of velocity and acceleration prevailing during these short fractions of
the cycle, the coordinate has no time to change appreciably. Liénard's analysis fails, however, to determine the "corners" connecting these branches in a
closed analytic curve; thus a rigorous analytic solution is still lacking.

The mechanical relaxation oscillations caused by friction exhibit
the familiar picture previously studied. In fact, there are time intervals
when the slow motion becomes a state of rest, followed by an interval of exceedingly rapid motion, followed by another period of rest, and so on. We are
thus confronted with a special type of relaxation oscillation appearing as a
kind of "jarring" motion.

141. QUALITATIVE ASPECTS OF A MECHANICAL RELAXATION OSCILLATION

Since a condition of degeneration, as previously shown, is essential
for the appearance of quasi-discontinuous solutions of a differential equation
of the second order and since we are trying to approximate the relaxation
process by a motion in conformity with the Liénard analysis, we must consider
a mechanical system with a very small mass.

Under this assumption, the motion of the system is determined mainly
by the balance between the restoring force kx and the friction force $\mu f(\dot{x})$.
When this balance is momentarily lost at a certain instant of the cycle, the
acceleration and the velocity of the system may suddenly reach very large values since, by our assumption, the mass is very small.

When $m = 0$, Equation [140.1] degenerates into the equation

$$F(\dot{x}) = - kx \qquad [141.1]$$

which describes the pair of branches of the Liénard cycle on which the system
remains a relatively long time and the coordinate changes appreciably. The
balance between the restoring force and the friction force takes place on
these branches. Differentiating this equation, one has

* Recent research (12) of J.A. Shohat gave hope of bridging this gap, but these efforts have been
interrupted by his untimely death.

$$F'(\dot{x})\ddot{x} = -k\dot{x} \qquad [141.2]$$

If the function $F(\dot{x})$ is such that $F'(\dot{x}) < 0$ in a certain region, Equation [141.2] shows that this region is unstable. If at a certain point in this region $F'(\dot{x}) \approx 0$, the acceleration $\ddot{x}$ may acquire a very large value so that a new balance of forces will appear in which the term $m\ddot{x}$ will play a role in spite of the assumed smallness of the mass m. We thus reach the conclusion that this condition characterizes the second pair of branches of the Liénard cycle which are traversed in a very short time. During this phase of the cycle the acceleration is very large and the velocity varies in a quasi-discontinuous manner by a finite quantity, but the coordinate does not change appreciably because of the short duration of this phase.

The qualitative aspect of the motion in this case is similar in all respects to that which occurs when a ball strikes a wall. However, the underlying dynamical facts are different. For a mechanical impact, the quasi-discontinuities in velocity and acceleration described above are due to an external force, the reaction of constraint when the ball strikes the wall. In Equations [141.1] and [141.2] these discontinuities appear as a result of the disappearance of the balance of forces expressed by Equation [141.1] and are due to the assumed peculiarities of the function $F(\dot{x})$.

The preceding argument can be condensed somewhat by putting $\dot{x} = y$ in Equation [141.2], which gives

$$\frac{dy}{dt} = -\frac{ky}{F'(y)} \qquad [141.3]$$

It is apparent that this equation has a critical point when $F'(y) = 0$ and, hence, ceases to describe the phenomenon at that point. In order to determine the discontinuity by which we idealize the quasi-discontinuity of the physical problem, we must again apply the condition of Mandelstam. In the idealized case, $m = 0$; hence, the kinetic energy is zero so that the total energy is the potential energy, which is a function of the coordinate x. From the condition of Mandelstam we infer, therefore, that the function $x(t)$ is continuous although it has a discontinuous second derivative, as is to be expected. The situation is thus similar to that which we have studied in Chapter XXI in connection with electrical relaxation oscillations. It also resembles the results obtained in the theory of mechanical impacts, with the difference, however, that the quasi-discontinuity here arises from the existence of a critical point in the differential equation and is not due to external impulsive excitation as it is for a mechanical impact where the energy also changes abruptly.

142. MECHANICAL RELAXATION OSCILLATIONS CAUSED BY NON-LINEAR FRICTION

Since Equation [141.2] has a critical point for $F'(\dot{x}) = 0$, we conclude that relaxation oscillations are possible in a system of this kind whenever the friction force considered as a function of the velocity $\dot{x}$ possesses extremum values. Moreover, the general condition specified in Section 133, that is, that $F(\dot{x})$ should be a two-valued function of x, must also be fulfilled.

In practice, these theoretical conditions are frequently encountered. Thus, when a shaft rotates in a bearing, Sommerfeld (17) has indicated that the friction force goes through a minimum for a speed v_1 given by the equation

$$v_1 = \frac{1}{15.1} \frac{\delta^2 P}{\lambda r^2} \qquad [142.1]$$

where P is the pressure,

λ is the coefficient of viscosity of the lubricant,

r is the radius of the shaft, and

δ is the thickness of the oil film.

Chaikin and Kaidanowski (18) have investigated mechanical relaxation oscillations by the device described in the following paragraphs.

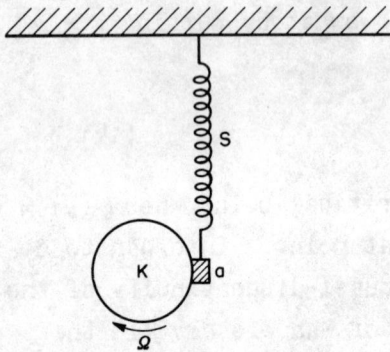

Figure 142.1

A relatively small mass a forming a Prony brake engaged frictionally a rotating shaft K, as shown in Figure 142.1. The mass a was centralized in a definite position by a rather strong spring S. A definite friction force was secured by means of another spring not shown, pressing a against the shaft K.

The differential equation of motion of a, neglecting its mass (which results in the degeneration of the equation to the first order), is

$$r\left(F\left[(\Omega - \dot{\phi})r\right]\right) = c\phi \qquad [142.2]$$

where $F(v) = F[(\Omega - \dot{\phi})r]$ is the friction force, a non-linear function of the relative peripheral velocity $v = (\Omega - \dot{\phi})r$,

Ω is the angular velocity of the shaft K,

$\dot{\phi}$ is the angular velocity of a for small departures ϕ, and

c is a constant depending on the spring's strength.

The approximate form of the function $F(v)$ is shown in Figure 142.2. It is noted that the tangent to this characteristic is horizontal at the point $B(v = 0)$. When $v = 0$, a moves together with K, and $\dot{\phi} = \Omega$. When a is not moving, $\phi = 0$ and $v = v_0 = \Omega r$. To the right of the point $v = v_0$ the mass a and

the shaft K move in the same direction; to the left of $v = v_0$ they
move in opposite directions. Because
of the constraining spring S no continuous motion of a is possible;
there may, however, be a position of
equilibrium for which $\dot{\phi} = 0$. As long
as $v = 0$, that is, $\dot{\phi} = \Omega$, the spring
S is gradually stretched, and the
friction force F is a static force
which may have any value whatever
provided $F \leqq F_1$, where F_1 is the

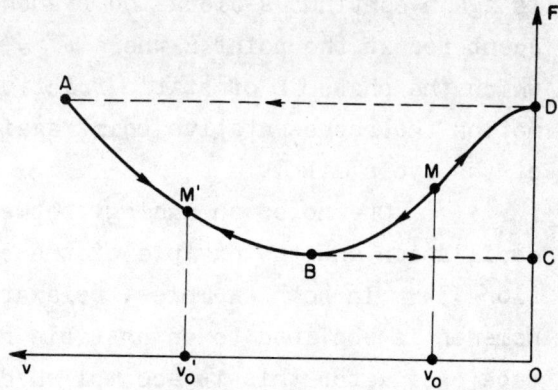

Figure 142.2

limit of static friction. When a is moved by the amount ϕ_1, for which $c\phi_1 = F_1 r$, the limit of static friction is reached. During this phase ($v = 0$) of
the phenomenon, the representative point moves along the axis of F until it
reaches the point D, the limit of static friction.

Differentiating Equation [142.2], we have

$$- r^2 F'[(\Omega - \dot{\phi})r]\ddot{\phi} = c\dot{\phi} \qquad\qquad [142.3]$$

where F' designates $\frac{dF}{d\dot{\phi}}$. It is seen that $F' < 0$ when $\dot{\phi}$ and $\ddot{\phi}$ have the same
signs, and $F' > 0$ when they have opposite signs. Moreover, for $v = v_0$ the
quantity $\dot{\phi}$ goes through zero and changes its sign. If the speed Ω of the shaft
is relatively small, the point M will be on the part BD of the dynamical characteristic of friction which may be considered here as the *phase line* of the
process, see Section 134. On the part BD of the phase line, $F' < 0$, so that
$\dot{\phi}$ and $\ddot{\phi}$ have the same sign; this part of the phase line is therefore unstable,
as shown by the arrows. It follows, therefore, that when the representative
point has reached the point D during the "static friction period" CD of the
process, it cannot pass onto the dynamic characteristic DBA. We conclude
that the point D is a critical point.

One can illustrate this also by putting $\dot{\phi} = y$ in Equation [142.3],
which gives

$$\frac{dy}{dt} = - \frac{cy}{r^2 F'[(\Omega - y)r]}$$

From this expression it follows that $\frac{dy}{dt} = \ddot{\phi} = \infty$ at the point D
since $F'[(\Omega - \dot{\phi})r] = 0$ at this point. At D, the representative point undergoes a discontinuity, the direction of which is parallel to the v-axis because
here the discontinuity occurs at a constant potential energy, as required by
the condition of Mandelstam. The jump terminates at the point A where the
characteristic is met, and the subsequent motion of the representative point

is again continuous along the branch BC until another critical point is encountered at the point B where $F' = 0$. Here another jump DA occurs, after which the phase CD of static friction begins anew; during that phase of the motion the representative point again moves continuously along the branch CD of the cycle DABCD.

One notes an analogy between this example of a mechanical relaxation oscillation and the example of the relaxation oscillation of a neon tube, Section 134. In both examples, relaxation oscillations are possible if the phenomenon is confined to an unstable region of the characteristic. In the neon-tube oscillator this is accomplished by adjusting the resistance so that the straight line $\frac{E - V}{R}$ cuts the non-linear characteristic, the phase line of the process, on its unstable branch. With the brake described in this section, a similar effect is obtained by running the shaft K at a relatively slow speed Ω so as to have the point M in Figure 142.2 in the region where $F' < 0$. There are no relaxation oscillations in a neon-tube circuit if the line $\frac{E - V}{R}$ intersects the characteristic on its upper stable branch, see Figure 134.2; likewise, no mechanical relaxation oscillations are observed, see Figure 142.2, if the angular velocity Ω of the shaft is large enough so that the point M' corresponding to $v_0' = \Omega r$ is on the stable branch CD of the friction characteristic. The piecewise analytic cycles ABCDA in both Figures 134.2 and 142.2 are indicated by the corresponding letters. Thus, for example, the branch CD corresponds to the period when the capacitor is charged (Figure 134.2) and to the period when the static friction force F increases with no slipping between a and K (Figure 142.1). Branch AB in both examples corresponds to continuous trajectories of a non-linear differential equation. In both figures the discontinuous stretches DA and BC are determined by the condition of Mandelstam, and so on. Plotted in the (ϕ, t)-plane, the curves of the mechanical relaxation oscillations observed by Chaikin and Kaidanowski have a typical "saw-tooth" appearance, see Figure 142.3, characterizing electrical relaxation oscillations of a similar nature.

This discussion emphasizes the features which all relaxation oscillations have in common.

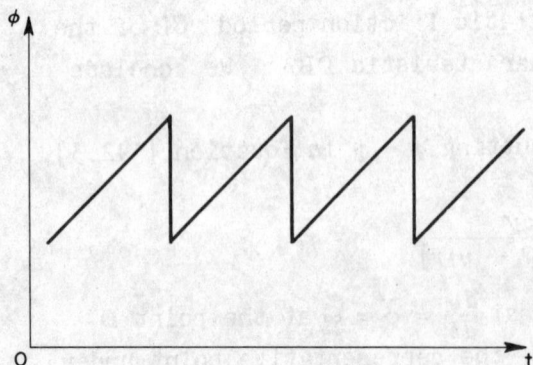

Figure 142.3

CHAPTER XXIV

OSCILLATIONS MAINTAINED BY PERIODIC IMPULSES

143. INTRODUCTORY REMARKS

We have defined "relaxation oscillations" as stationary self-excited oscillations exhibiting quasi-discontinuities at some points of their cycle. One of the fundamental properties of these oscillations is that their stationary state does not depend on the initial conditions of the system. In that respect they resemble the continuous oscillations of the limit-cycle type studied in Chapter IV with the difference, however, that because of the existence of discontinuous stretches their properties are different from those of continuous oscillations.

As a somewhat different type of oscillation appear the so-called *impulse-excited oscillations*. In some respects these oscillations resemble relaxation oscillations as defined above; in some other respects they differ from them.

The feature common to both types of oscillations is that they can be represented in a phase plane by piecewise analytic trajectories. For both types, also, the stationary state does not depend on initial conditions; moreover, the stationary trajectories of both are "closed" by discontinuous stretches.

The essential difference between these two types of oscillations lies in the physical process during the quasi-discontinuous rapid changes, idealized as mathematical discontinuities. In the pure relaxation oscillations with which we have been concerned in preceding chapters of Part IV, the energy stored in the system during the quasi-discontinuous interval does not change appreciably. This results in an idealized picture of these phenomena with an assumption that the energy *does not change* in the interval ($t_0 - 0$, $t_0 + 0$). Moreover, the existence of these discontinuities, as we saw, was formally reduced to that of the critical points in the differential equations describing the system.

For the impulse-excited oscillations which we are going to investigate in this chapter, a difference exists, in that the discontinuous stretches in the representation of the phenomenon by phase trajectories correspond precisely to the impulsive changes of the energy of the system.

In the investigation of relaxation oscillations proper, we had to rely mostly on the theory of electric circuits. We shall begin the study of impulse-excited oscillations by investigating the behavior of a mechanical device known for centuries, the clock.

144. ELEMENTARY THEORY OF THE CLOCK

A clock is a mechanical device consisting of three principal elements:

1.   An oscillatory dissipative system, for example, an ordinary pendulum, a torsional pendulum with a hair spring, etc.

2.   A source of energy, for example, a weight, a main spring, etc., which has to be replenished periodically ("winding" the clock).

3.   An escapement connecting periodically the first and second elements.

The purpose of the escapement is to release periodically the energy stored in the second element in the form of an impulse and to apply this impulse to the first element at an appropriate instant of the oscillation.

Since the instant at which the impulse is released by the escapement is uniquely determined by the motion of the system, the system is *autonomous* in the sense that all three elements, 1, 2, and 3, of the mechanism are connected so as to form a single unit, just as a thermionic generator forms a single autonomous unit comprising an oscillating circuit, a battery, and an electron tube with its grid control circuit. We shall see later that it is possible to arrange the operation of an electron-tube circuit so that it resembles the performance of a clock, but in general the mode of operation of a clock differs in other respects from that of the thermionic oscillators commonly used.

The escapement communicates to the oscillatory system periodically timed impulses which we shall first idealize as instantaneous and of a constant value a. Let v_1 be the velocity of the system immediately after the first impulse, from which instant we wish to study the motion. If we assume that the system is a linear dissipative one with a decrement d per cycle, the velocity v_2' immediately before the second impulse will be $v_2' = v_1 e^{-d}$. Immediately after the second impulse, the velocity will be $v_2 = v_2' + a = v_1 e^{-d} + a$, where a is the impulsive increment of the velocity, and so on for subsequent impulses. A stationary state will be reached when, beginning with a certain number n of impulses, $v_n \approx v_{n+1} \approx v_{n+2} \approx \cdots \approx v_0$, which gives

$$v_0 = \frac{a}{1 - e^{-d}} \qquad [144.1]$$

The representation of the process in the phase plane is shown in Figure 144.1, where one spiral trajectory S of the system is indicated. As was shown in Section 5, these spirals form a continuous family so that through every ordinary point of the phase plane passes one and only one such spiral. Let us designate as u the segment AB of the $\dot{x}$-axis. This intercept represents

the change of the initial radius vector
OA after one revolution 2π. From the
properties of the logarithmic spiral it
is apparent that the intercept u, considered as a function of r_0 = OA, is a
monotonic function $u(r_0)$. Since the
spirals S form a continuous family, it
is also obvious that the function $u(r_0)$
is a continuous monotonically increasing function of the radius vector r. On
the other hand, by our hypothesis, the
impulsive changes of the velocity v due
to the operation of the escapement are
constant and hence are represented by
constant jumps a along the $\dot{x}$-axis. It

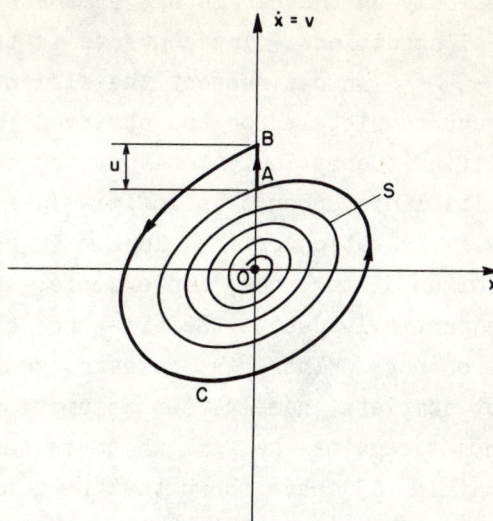

Figure 144.1

follows, therefore, that a steady-state condition will be attained when a radius vector r_0 = OA is reached for which $u(r_0) = a$. This stationary condition
is represented by a piecewise analytic cycle BCAB shown in Figure 144.1 by a
heavy line; this cycle consists of a convergent spiral BCA (since, by our
assumption, the system is dissipative) "closed" by a discontinuous jump AB
representing the impulsive increase of the velocity v caused by the impact.
It is also clear that such a stationary piecewise analytic cycle BCAB is of
a *stable limit-cycle* type in the sense that, if one starts from the relatively
small values of the initial radius vector r_0 = OA, the value of a is initially
greater than the corresponding value of the intercept $u(r_0)$ in this region of
the phase plane. Physically this means that the energy communicated by the
impulse is greater than the amount of energy which the system is able to dis-
sipate during one cycle 2π, which will result in the fact that the subsequent
radius vectors r_0 = OA will grow initially. If, on the contrary, the initial
velocity of the system is sufficiently great, the dissipation of energy per
cycle is greater than the impulsive increments communicated by the escapement
so that the spirals will gradually shrink. The stable condition is reached
when the impulsive increments a are just equal to the intercepts $u(r_0)$ in a
particular region. In view of the continuity and the monotonic character of
the function $u(r_0)$, it is clear that there exists one and only one piecewise
analytic limit cycle BCAB of the clock and it is stable. This elementary
discussion accounts for the fact that the clock's performance is of a *limit-
cycle* type and as such does not depend on initial conditions, see Chapter IV;
in other words, the ultimate performance of a clock does not depend on how
it has been started. Once it is started the operation of the clock depends

entirely on the parameters of the system and has nothing to do with the initial conditions. The converse is true for a mathematical pendulum.

In one respect the elementary theory discussed above fails to account completely for the observed facts. For, if a clock is wound, this simplified theory indicates that the clock should start by itself even if the initial disturbance is infinitely small. In other words, it predicts a *soft* self-excitation of the clock. In reality, unless a clock is given a certain minimum disturbance, for example, shaking, it will not start. This threshold is partially due to the existence of Coulomb friction not taken into consideration here. There is, however, another reason why the elementary theory is not complete, namely, our assumption that the jump a in velocity caused by the impact remains the same whatever the velocity of the system. Andronow and Chaikin (13) have shown that by a slight refinement of the preceding theory it is possible to explain better the observed facts.

Let us assume that the change of kinetic energy during the impact remains constant, that is,

$$\frac{mv_1^2}{2} - \frac{mv_0^2}{2} = \text{constant}$$

In the phase-plane representation this is equivalent to the condition

$$y_1^2 - y_0^2 = h^2 \qquad [144.2]$$

where h is a constant determined by the properties of the escapement and y_0 and y_1 are the values of the radius vector immediately before and immediately after the impact. It follows, therefore, that the jump a in the phase plane, instead of being constant as was originally assumed, is now given by the equation

$$a = \sqrt{y_0^2 + h^2} - y_0 \qquad [144.3]$$

that is, it decreases with increasing velocity y_0 according to a hyperbolic law, as shown in Figure 144.2.

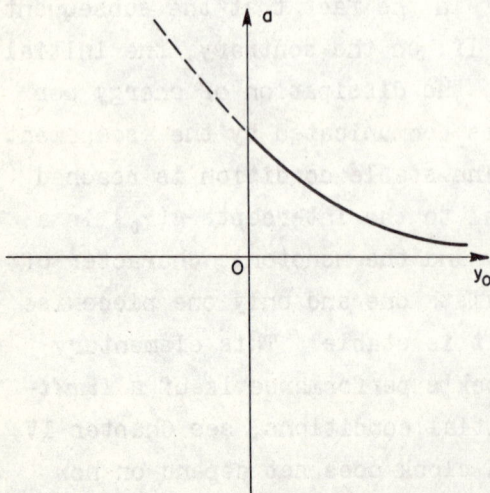

Figure 144.2

This refinement of the theory, although it leads to conclusions concerning the existence of a stable piecewise analytic limit cycle which are similar to those obtained by the original simplified theory, is not yet sufficient to explain the fact that a clock is a system with a *hard* self-excitation.

In order to extend the theory still further it is necessary to investigate how Coulomb friction manifests itself in the representation of motion by phase trajectories.

145. PHASE TRAJECTORIES IN THE PRESENCE OF COULOMB FRICTION

The customary idealization of Coulomb, or dry, friction consists in assuming that the friction force f_0 remains constant during the motion and changes its sign with a change of the direction of motion, as shown in Figure 145.1.

The motion of a system with one degree of freedom in the presence of Coulomb friction cannot be described by one differential equation but requires two equations, one for $\dot{x} < 0$ and the other for $\dot{x} > 0$, namely,

$$m\ddot{x} + kx = + f_0; \qquad m\ddot{x} + kx = - f_0 \qquad [145.1]$$

Putting $\frac{k}{m} = \omega_0^2$ and $|f_0| = a\omega_0^2$, these two equations are

$$\ddot{x} + \omega_0^2 x = + a\omega_0^2 \qquad \text{when} \ \dot{x} < 0$$
$$\ddot{x} + \omega_0^2 x = - a\omega_0^2 \qquad \text{when} \ \dot{x} > 0 \qquad [145.2]$$

Introducing the variables $x_1 = x - a$ for the first equation [145.2] and $x_2 = x + a$ for the second, one obtains two equations, namely,

$$\ddot{x}_1 + \omega_0^2 x_1 = 0 \qquad \text{when} \ \dot{x} < 0$$
$$\ddot{x}_2 + \omega_0^2 x_2 = 0 \qquad \text{when} \ \dot{x} > 0 \qquad [145.3]$$

These equations are obviously identical, with the difference, however, that the center of oscillation is displaced from $+a$ to $-a$, and vice versa, each time $\dot{x}$ changes its sign. It is to be noted that $\dot{x}$ itself does not enter into the equations of motion. The "change of equations" occurs at the instant when $\dot{x} = 0$. In the (x,t)-plane such a motion can be represented by the curve shown in Figure 145.2. Assume that initially the system has been deviated to the right $(x_{01} > 0)$ and then released with an initial velocity $\dot{x}_{01} = 0$. The system will then move to the left $(\dot{x} < 0)$. As was just mentioned, this is a sinusoidal motion with respect to the axis t_1 displaced a distance $+a$ from

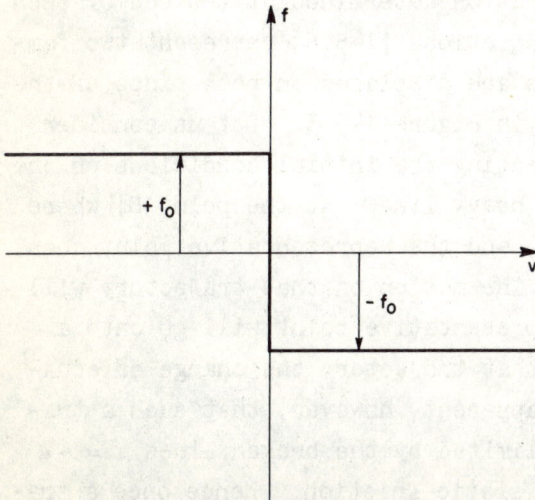

Figure 145.1

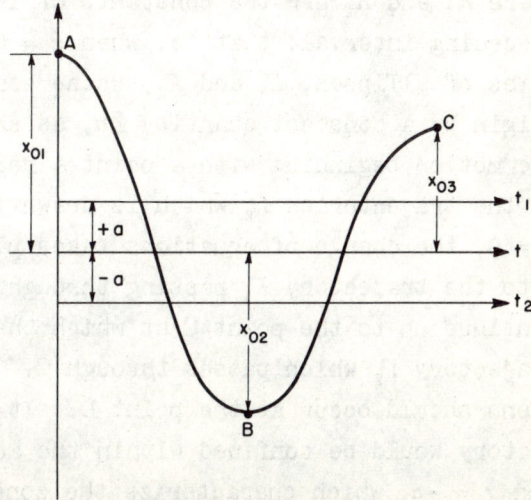

Figure 145.2

the t-axis. At the point B the velocity $\dot{x}$ is equal to zero, and the amplitude is $|x_{02}| = |x_{01} - 2a|$ *with respect to the* t*-axis.* At the point B the change of equations takes place, and the "acting abscissa axis" is now t_2 displaced a distance $-a$ from the t-axis. With respect to the t_2-axis, the motion is again sinusoidal, so that the point C (at which $\dot{x} = 0$) is at the same distance from the t_2-axis as the point B was originally. With respect to the t-axis, however, the amplitude of the point C is $x_{03} = x_{02} - 2a$. It is seen that with respect to the t-axis the amplitudes decrease in an *arithmetic progression* with the constant difference $2a$. The motion stops after a certain number of swings. The time interval between two consecutive maximums (A and C in Figure 145.2) is the same as for a harmonic oscillator, as follows from the preceding discussion. It is to be noted again that the curve ABC$\cdots$ is a piecewise analytic curve which loses its analyticity at the points A, B, C, $\cdots$, at which there is a discontinuity in the second derivative.

The representation of such a motion by phase trajectories is obtained if we observe that each of the equations [145.3] is represented by an elliptic trajectory around the vortex point, see Section 1.

If we let $\frac{dx}{dt} = y$, Equations [145.3] become

$$\frac{dy}{dx} = -\frac{\omega_0^2(x - a)}{y} \qquad \text{when } y < 0$$

$$\frac{dy}{dx} = -\frac{\omega_0^2(x + a)}{y} \qquad \text{when } y > 0$$

[145.4]

Integrating these equations, one gets

$$\frac{(x - a)^2}{R_1^2} + \frac{y^2}{R_1^2 \omega_0^2} = 1 \qquad \text{when } y < 0$$

$$\frac{(x + a)^2}{R_2^2} + \frac{y^2}{R_2^2 \omega_0^2} = 1 \qquad \text{when } y > 0$$

[145.5]

where R_1 and R_2 are the constants of integration determined at the end of each preceding interval, that is, when $\dot{x} = 0$. Equations [145.5] represent two families of ellipses, Γ_1 and Γ_2, whose centers are displaced on both sides of the origin by a constant quantity $\pm a$, as shown in Figure 145.3. Let us consider the motion beginning with a point A representing the initial conditions on one of the trajectories Γ_2 which is drawn in a heavy line. At the point B, where $y = 0$, the change of equations takes place, and the representative point goes onto the trajectory Γ_1 passing through B. The motion on that trajectory will continue up to the point C at which the representative point will go onto a trajectory Γ_2 which passes through C. On that trajectory the change of equations should occur at the point D. It is apparent, however, that such a trajectory would be confined within the zone limited by the broken lines $x = +a$ and $x = -a$, which characterize the zone of static friction. Hence once a trajectory is reached which does not emerge from that zone, the motion ceases.

It is thus seen that idealized
Coulomb friction is capable of being represented by piecewise analytic trajectories formed by elliptic arcs of the two
families Γ_1 and Γ_2 with centers symmetrically displaced by a constant quantity a
on both sides of the origin O. The junction points of the arcs are situated on
the x-axis. At these points the curve has
a continuous first, but a discontinuous
second, derivative as may be expected
from the fact that the friction force
changes discontinuously at these points.
Instead of having a point of equilibrium,
systems possessing Coulomb friction have

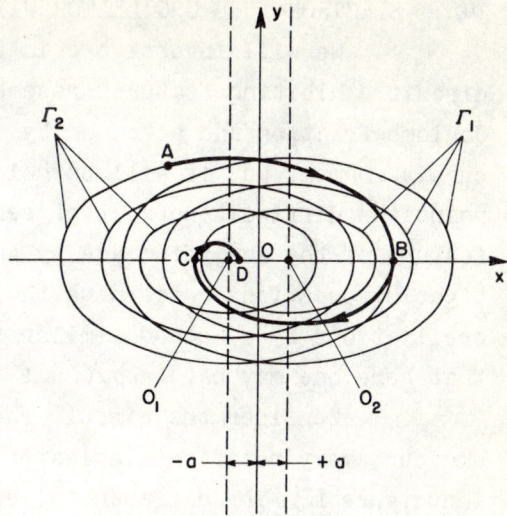

Figure 145.3

a *line of equilibrium* O_1O_2, which means that any point on the segment O_1O_2 is
a point of equilibrium and that the segment O_1O_2 itself is the zone of *static
friction*.

Making use of these conclusions regarding the form of trajectories
in the presence of Coulomb friction, Andronow and Chaikin have further elabo-
ated the theory of the clock. We shall omit the details of their theory and
will merely indicate their argument as well as their final conclusions.

By introducing "angular time" $\tau = \omega_0 t$, as we did on a number of occasions, Equations [145.3] can be reduced to the form

$$\frac{d^2x_1}{d\tau^2} + x_1 = 0 \qquad \text{when } \dot{x} < 0$$

$$\frac{d^2x_2}{d\tau^2} + x_2 = 0 \qquad \text{when } \dot{x} > 0$$

[145.6]

The trajectories of these equations are two families C_1 and C_2 of concentric
circles whose centers are displaced on the x-axis on both sides of the origin
by a fixed quantity a. By reproducing the preceding argument and by expressing
the condition that the ultimate trajectory always emerges from the "dead zone"
of static friction, these authors show that, if the trajectory is to emerge
ultimately from the dead zone, the impulsive change of kinetic energy h^2 must
be equal to or greater than $16f_0^2$, where f_0 is the Coulomb force. This means
that a clock is a mechanism with a *hard* self-excitation. In other words, unless the condition stated above concerning the relation between h^2 and $16f_0^2$
is satisfied, a clock will not start. If, however, this condition is satisfied, the clock will start and will approach its piecewise analytic limit
cycle irrespective of any other aspects of the initial conditions.

146. ELECTRON-TUBE OSCILLATOR WITH QUASI-DISCONTINUOUS GRID CONTROL

We will investigate in this section the behavior of an electron-tube circuit exhibiting features resembling those of a mechanical system possessing Coulomb friction and acted on by impulses. The analogy, as we shall see, is purely formal, but it will be helpful in approaching from a somewhat new viewpoint the difficult subject of self-excited oscillations. The interesting feature of the analysis made by Andronow and Chaikin is that it permits investigating questions concerning the establishment and stability of self-excited oscillations by a method similar to that used in the preceding section, except that here one may have *negative Coulomb friction* maintaining the oscillations.

Consider the circuit shown in Figure 146.1 with positive directions and customary notations indicated. The symbol x designates the current in the inductance L. The differential equation of the circuit is

$$L\frac{dx}{dt} + Rx + \frac{1}{C}\int (x - I_a)\, dt = 0 \qquad [146.1]$$

Differentiating and rearranging, we obtain

$$L\ddot{x} + R\dot{x} + \frac{1}{C}x = \frac{1}{C}f(e_g) \qquad [146.2]$$

where $I_a = f(e_g)$ is the non-linear characteristic of the electron tube. We will consider a peculiar performance of this circuit, namely, the one which appears when the coefficient of mutual inductance M is made very large. As a result of this, the amplitude $|e_g|$ of the grid-voltage variation will also be large; this will cause the electron tube to act more or less as a switch operating between the points A, when $I_a = 0$, and B, when $I_a = I_s$, where I_s is the saturation plate current. It is apparent that when the grid potential varies between the limits $\pm e_g$, as shown in Figure 146.2, the interval A_1B_1 corresponding to the variations $\pm e_{g1}$, which are instrumental in causing the plate current to vary, is small in comparison with the total interval AB, and it is possible to idealize the performance as a discontinuous characteristic such as

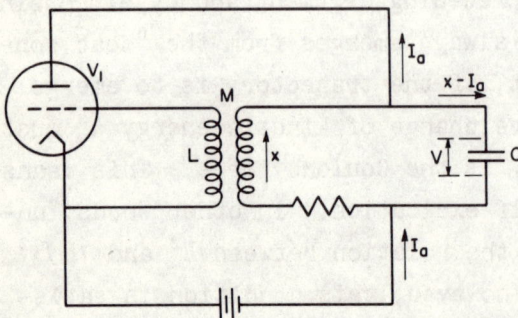

Figure 146.1

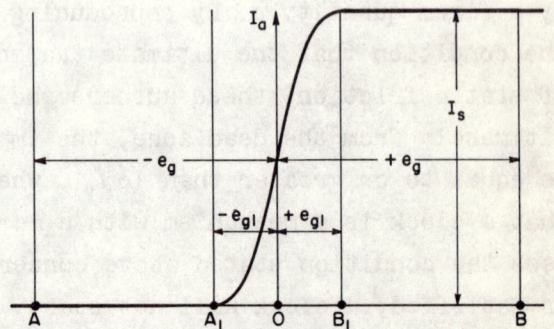

Figure 146.2

that shown in Figure 145.1. Instead of being described by one non-linear differential equation [146.2], the phenomenon will be described alternately by two linear differential equations

$$\ddot{x} + 2h\dot{x} + \omega_0^2 x = 0 ; \qquad \ddot{x} + 2h\dot{x} + \omega_0^2 x = \omega_0^2 I_s \qquad [146.3]$$

where $2h = \frac{R}{L}$, $\omega_0^2 = \frac{1}{LC}$, and $\omega_0^2 I_s = \frac{1}{LC} f(+e_g)$. It is obvious that the change from one equation to the other occurs at the point where $\dot{x}$ changes its sign.

We shall assume that the connections are made so that $M > 0$, $e_g > 0$ when $\dot{x} < 0$, and $e_g < 0$ when $\dot{x} > 0$. We shall investigate the second alternative later.

In view of our idealization, the anode current I_a will undergo discontinuities in the neighborhood of $\dot{x} = 0$. These discontinuities have to pass through the capacitor branch of the oscillating circuit since in the inductive branch no discontinuities of current are possible. However, the discontinuities $L\frac{dx}{dt}$ in the voltage across the inductance are possible. We conclude, therefore, that the quantities which are capable of varying discontinuously are I_a in the capacitor branch and $L\frac{dx}{dt}$ across the inductance. The quantity x remains continuous. Another continuous quantity is the voltage V across the capacitor, as was mentioned in Section 131.

It is noted that the change from one differential equation to the other, mentioned above, resembles the situation which we have already encountered in connection with Equations [145.2] describing the behavior of a system possessing Coulomb friction, and may follow a similar argument. We can write the second equation [146.3] as

$$\ddot{\bar{x}} + 2h\dot{\bar{x}} + \omega_0^2 \bar{x} = 0 \qquad [146.4]$$

where $\bar{x} = x - I_s$. In this form the first equation [146.3] and Equation [146.4] are two linear differential equations possessing focal points on the t-axis at a distance I_s from each other. We can, therefore, repeat the argument used in connection with Figure 145.2. Let us consider the phenomenon from the instant when the amplitude is x_1 and the electron-tube switch is off, which corresponds to the first equation [146.3]. During the first half-cycle the original amplitude x_1, see Figure 146.3, will be reduced by damping and will become x_2. It is noted that $x_2 < x_1$ if referred to the t-axis. At the point B the electron-tube current jumps suddenly to the value I_s and, as we saw, the new abscissa axis is now t_1, displaced above the t-axis by the quantity I_s. With respect to this t_1-axis, the initial amplitude is now $\bar{x}_2 = x_2 + I_s$ and although during the following half-cycle the amplitude is again reduced with respect to this axis because of the dissipation of energy, the position of the point C with respect to the t-axis may be at a higher level than that of A if

432

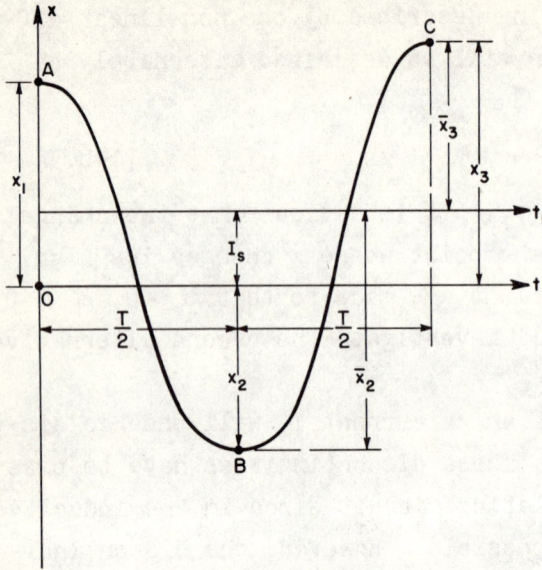

Figure 146.3

I_s is large enough. Beginning with
the point C, we can resume the same
argument which we used at the point
A, and so on.

It is seen that, because of
this quasi-discontinuous timing of
the electronic switch, the amplitudes
in the oscillating circuit may grow,
thus outweighing the effect of the
dissipation of energy. It is easy to
express this condition mathematically. If one designates by x the amplitudes referred to the t-axis and by
$\overline{x}$ those referred to the t_1-axis, one
has

$$x_2 = x_1 e^{-\frac{hT}{2}}; \qquad \overline{x}_2 = x_1 e^{-\frac{hT}{2}} + I_s$$

$$\overline{x}_3 = \overline{x}_2 e^{-\frac{hT}{2}} = x_1 e^{-\frac{2hT}{2}} + I_s e^{-\frac{hT}{2}}; \qquad x_3 = \overline{x}_3 + I_s = x_1 e^{-\frac{2hT}{2}} + I_s e^{-\frac{hT}{2}} + I_s$$

$$\cdots\cdots\cdots$$

If the amplitude reaches a stationary value, $x_3 = x_1 = x_0$, which gives

$$x_0 = \frac{I_s(1 + e^{-\frac{hT}{2}})}{1 - e^{-hT}} = \frac{I_s}{1 - e^{-\frac{hT}{2}}} \qquad [146.5]$$

This shows that a stationary amplitude x_0 is determined solely by the properties of the circuit and is independent of the initial conditions.

The question of the stability of these oscillations can be investigated graphically by comparing their subsequent amplitudes. For instance, take
the relation between x_1 and x_3, namely,

$$x_3 = x_1 e^{-hT} + I_s(1 + e^{-\frac{hT}{2}}) \qquad [146.6]$$

In the (x_1, x_3)-plane, see Figure 146.4, this relation is a straight line with
a slope $\tan \alpha = e^{-hT}$, and an intercept $I_s(1 + e^{-\frac{hT}{2}}) = A$. On the other hand,
if the oscillation is stationary, $x_1 = x_3$, which represents the bisector of
the angle between the x_1- and x_3-axes. The point M of intersection of these
lines determines the stationary amplitude x_0. If the initial amplitude x_1'
is not stationary, the subsequent amplitude will be x_3' and the corrected amplitude will be x_3' on the x_1-axis to which the following amplitude x_5' will
correspond on the x_3-axis, and its corrected value on the x_1-axis will be x_5'.

By the interplay of the subsequent
corrections it is seen that any
non-stationary amplitude tends to
approach the stationary value x_0.
This argument is also valid when
the initial non-stationary amplitude is larger than the stationary
amplitude x_0. Hence the stationary
amplitude is *stable*. It should be
noted that if we reverse the connection of the coils, the displacement of the x_1-axis with respect
to the x-axis by the quantity I_s
will occur in a direction opposite
to that shown in Figure 146.3.
This will result in a *reduction* of
the subsequent amplitudes similar
to that found in connection with

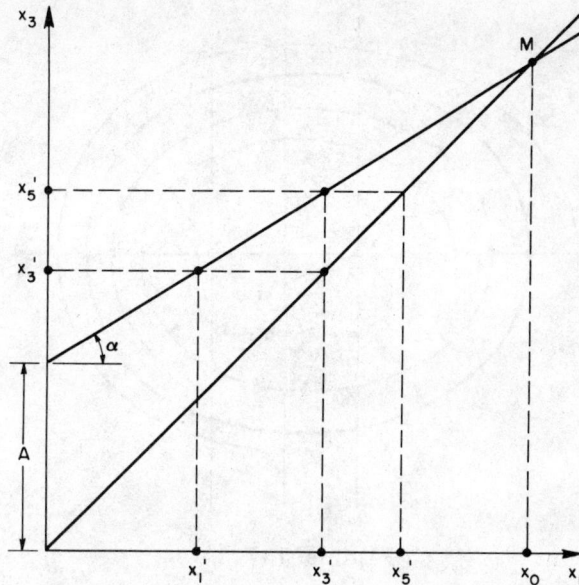

Figure 146.4

Figure 145.2 illustrating the action of Coulomb friction. Viewed from this
standpoint, the circuit behaves as if it had a kind of *negative Coulomb damping* when $M > 0$ and a *positive Coulomb damping* when $M < 0$. The self-excitation
of the circuit occurs when the circuit is characterized by *negative Coulomb
damping*.

147. PHASE TRAJECTORIES OF AN IMPULSE-EXCITED OSCILLATOR

The property of negative Coulomb damping of the circuit investigated
in the preceding section becomes still more striking if we analyze the phase
trajectories of the system [146.3] which we write in the form

$$\ddot{x} + 2h\dot{x} + \omega_0^2 x = 0$$
$$\ddot{x}_1 + 2h\dot{x}_1 + \omega_0^2 x_1 = 0$$

[147.1]

where $x_1 = x - I_s$. Since each of these equations describes a damped oscillator, each is represented by a spiral trajectory approaching a stable focal
point; see Section 5. The focal points of these equations are separated by a
constant distance I_s along the x-axis in the $(x,\dot{x})$ phase plane. Figure 147.1
shows the phase diagram of the motion corresponding to Equations [147.1].
Point O is the focal point of the first equation [147.1], and $\overline{O}$ that of the
second equation. Let us start from a certain arbitrary initial condition,
represented, for instance, by a point 1 on the negative abscissa axis. Through
Point 1 passes the spiral trajectory 1m2 having O as its focal point and representing the first equation [147.1]. At the point 2 the "change of equations"

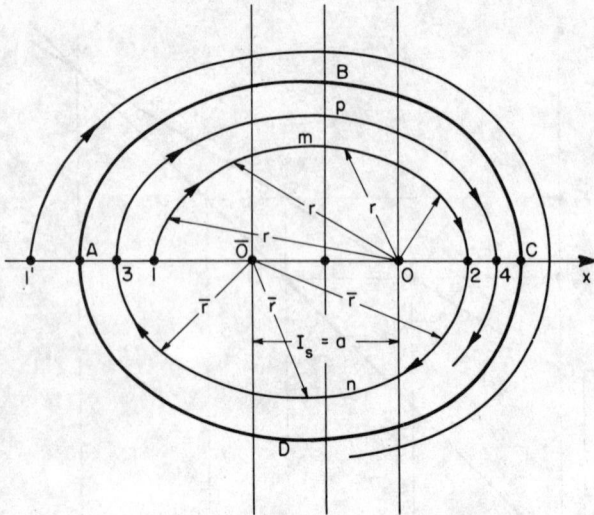

Figure 147.1

occurs, and the phenomenon is now governed by the second equation [147.1] having its focal point at $\overline{O}$. The second stretch of the spiral trajectory $2n3$ ends at the point 3, where the first equation begins to describe the phenomenon again; this arc of the spiral trajectory $3p4$ ends at the point 4, and so on. It can be shown that the piecewise analytic trajectory $1m2n3p4\cdots$ ultimately approaches a closed curve ABCDA formed by two spiral arcs, ABC with O as its focal point and CDA with $\overline{O}$ as its focal point. One obtains a similar conclusion if, instead of starting with a point 1, one starts with a point 1' exterior to the closed curve ABCDA and repeats the argument. We shall designate by r the radius vectors with respect to the focal point O when the representative point moves on the upper spiral arcs, and by $\overline{r}$ the radius vectors with a focal point at $\overline{O}$ when the representative point moves on the lower arcs. For the subsequent radius vectors along the x-axis, we have the following obvious relations:

$$r_2 = r_1 e^{-\frac{\pi h}{\omega}}; \quad \overline{r}_3 = \overline{r}_2 e^{-\frac{\pi h}{\omega}} = (r_2 + a)e^{-\frac{\pi h}{\omega}} = (r_1 e^{-\frac{\pi h}{\omega}} + a)e^{-\frac{\pi h}{\omega}}; \cdots$$

One obtains easily the following general expressions:

$$r_k = a\left[1 + e^{-\frac{\pi h}{\omega}} + e^{-\frac{2\pi h}{\omega}} + \cdots + e^{-(k-2)\frac{\pi h}{\omega}}\right] + r_1 e^{-(k-1)\frac{\pi h}{\omega}}; \quad \overline{r}_k = r_k - a$$

$$[147.2]$$

$$\overline{r}_s = a\left[1 + e^{-\frac{\pi h}{\omega}} + \cdots + e^{-(s-2)\frac{\pi h}{\omega}}\right] + r_1 e^{-(s-1)\frac{\pi h}{\omega}}; \quad r_s = \overline{r}_s - a$$

where k is an odd integer and s is an even integer. If k and s increase indefinitely, that is, if the number of turns of the piecewise analytic spiral $1m2n3p4\cdots$ increases indefinitely, the spiral approaches the closed curve ABCDA, previously mentioned, in the manner specified in Section 22. One sees this immediately from the expressions given above for r_k and $\overline{r}_s$ when $k \to \infty$ and $s \to \infty$, namely,

$$\lim_{k \to \infty} (r_k) = \frac{a}{1 - e^{-\frac{\pi h}{\omega}}} = \lim_{s \to \infty} (\overline{r}_s) \qquad [147.3]$$

The conclusions remain exactly the same if one repeats the argument for a piecewise analytic spiral $1'm'2'n'3'p'\cdots$ starting at a relatively distant point $1'$.

It is thus apparent that the closed curve ABCDA formed by the two arcs of the logarithmic spirals is a *piecewise analytic limit cycle* which the oscillation approaches as $t \to \infty$. Moreover, this limit cycle is *stable*. It is useful to emphasize once more that this limit cycle characterizing stationary periodic motion is determined exclusively by the constant parameters $a = I_s$, h, and ω of the oscillatory system and is entirely independent of initial conditions. This is an essential property of self-excited oscillations, as was pointed out in Section 22.

It is also worth mentioning that we have obtained these results of the classical theory by replacing the actual non-linear equation [146.2] by a system [147.1] of two alternating linear differential equations. Such a procedure becomes possible only after we have idealized the relatively complicated non-linear characteristic, shown in Figure 146.2, as a discontinuous step-function like that shown in Figure 145.1. In connection with this it may be useful to recall the statement made in Section 3 that the really important difference between linear and non-linear systems is their behavior *in the large* and that *local properties* are of relatively minor importance. This argument is a typical example of a situation of this kind where a certain idealization of the local properties of trajectories does not change their properties in the large and merely simplifies a problem which would otherwise be extremely complex.

CHAPTER XXV

EFFECT OF PARASITIC PARAMETERS ON STATIONARY STATES OF DYNAMICAL SYSTEMS

148. PARASITIC PARAMETERS

The study of relaxation oscillations in the preceding sections was made under the assumption of certain simplifying idealizations which resulted in degenerate equations instead of complete ones containing both *oscillatory* parameters (L and C in electrical problems and m and k in mechanical ones).

Although the advantages of such simplifications, as we saw, are numerous and the results obtained in this manner are generally found to be in agreement with experimental facts, the introduction of these simplifying assumptions is not without theoretical difficulties and, in some cases, which we will analyze here, may lead to certain complications. In spite of the fact that such cases appear generally as rare exceptions, it is important to analyze this matter in greater detail now that we are acquainted with the general method, at least in its present scope.

One of the principal difficulties, noted on several occasions, is the inconsistency between the number of integration constants appearing in a degenerate problem and that in the corresponding non-degenerate one. Thus, for example, if the non-degenerate problem involves a differential equation of the second order, two constants of integration are necessary to determine the solution; these constants appear as certain definite physical "initial conditions." In the corresponding degenerate problem, where the differential equation is of the first order, one constant of integration is sufficient to determine a solution. If, however, there still exist two physical factors to which some initial values can be assigned, these factors cannot have entirely arbitrary values but must readjust themselves eventually so that a definite relation exists between them, as was explained in Section 128. The discontinuous theory of relaxation oscillations *ignores* this rather delicate passage from the solutions of one form to those of the other form, just as the classical theory of mechanical impacts ignores the unknown dynamics of the collision process. Both theories follow a somewhat similar argument, namely, the rapidly changing motion is idealized during a very short time interval as a mathematical discontinuity occurring in the *infinitely short* time interval ($t - 0$, $t + 0$), and the loss of information resulting from intentionally overlooking the dynamics of the process is supplemented by *additional physical information* which permits solution of the problem *in the large* although certain *local* details are inevitably lost in such a procedure. In the theory of mechanical impacts this additional physical information is provided by the theorems of momentum and kinetic energy as well as by defining a certain empirical *coefficient of restitution* characterizing the instantaneous dissipation of energy during the impact; likewise, in the discontinuous theory of relaxation oscillations this additional information appears in the form of the conditions of Mandelstam.

The use of the concepts "infinitely short time interval," "infinitely large acceleration," and so on, instead of the more correct terms "very short time interval," "very large acceleration," and so on, while convenient for the description of a phenomenon *in the large*, is sometimes capable of introducing serious errors in a theoretical argument and of leading to conclusions at variance with experimental facts.

Thus, for instance, in dealing with an idealized (*L,R*)-circuit, we describe its behavior by the equation

$$L\frac{di}{dt} + Ri = E(t) \qquad [148.1]$$

This equation describes the phenomenon with adequate accuracy in a range sufficient for practical purposes (on the scale, say, of milliseconds). If, however, the behavior of the same circuit is studied in a different range (say, on the scale of microseconds), this equation may not give a correct answer. In fact, any resistor or inductance coil inevitably has a small *parasitic capacity* C_p, and if we take this capacity into account a more correct equation will be

$$RLC_p\frac{d^2i_1}{dt^2} + L\frac{di_1}{dt} + Ri_1 = E(t) \qquad [148.2]$$

It was shown in Section 128 that under certain conditions the solutions $i(t)$ and $i_1(t)$ of Equations [148.1] and [148.2] may have entirely different features locally, although in the large these solutions are practically indistinguishable. For that reason an electrical engineer would prefer to use the simpler equation [148.1] rather than the more complicated one [148.2]. These facts are too well known to need further emphasis here. However, they are frequently very troublesome. Thus, for instance, a student attempting to investigate the behavior of a simple circuit by means of a cathode-ray oscillograph, instead of observing the pattern of curves in accordance with his differential equation, usually observes what is commonly called "hash," that is, a far more complicated pattern of numerous harmonics with cross modulation, and so on. The reason for this is that too many parasitic parameters have been neglected in forming the differential equation, and consequently the true differential equation is far more complicated than the assumed one.

In most practical cases such discrepancies are not very serious. However, in some special instances, analyzed in what follows, difficulties may arise which lead to paradoxes already noted by certain authors (19) (20).

A further remark may be useful. Consider the differential equation of an (L,R,C)-circuit,

$$L\ddot{q} + R\dot{q} + \frac{1}{C}q = 0 \qquad [148.3]$$

and assume that L is very small. If L is neglected, one has a differential equation of the first order. The expression "L is very small" is, however, rather indefinite in the sense that it is not important to know that L is small but rather that the consideration of the problem is restricted to the range in which the term $L\ddot{q}$ is negligible compared with the other two terms. Still more confusing is the effect of the degeneration when $C \to 0$, which leads to a meaningless result. If, however, we make $C \to \infty$, at the limit we obtain

$$L\frac{di}{dt} + Ri = 0 \qquad [148.4]$$

which is an absolutely degenerate equation of an idealized (L,R)-circuit. Here the degeneration occurs not because a parameter is small but because it is *large*. This confusion disappears if, instead of the parameter C, the capacity, we use the *elastance* $k = \frac{1}{C}$ as a parameter. It is convenient, for this reason, to consider parameters as parasitic if they are small or if the corresponding terms in the differential equation are small. The first condition is merely a definition, whereas the second condition specifies the range in which a small parameter can be neglected.

149. INFLUENCE OF PARASITIC PARAMETERS ON THE STATE OF EQUILIBRIUM OF A DYNAMICAL SYSTEM

Consider a system with several degrees of freedom expressible by the differential equation

$$a_0 x^{(n)} + a_1 x^{(n-1)} + \cdots + a_{n-2}\ddot{x} + a_{n-1}\dot{x} + a_n x = 0 \qquad [149.1]$$

where $x^{(n)} = \frac{d^n x}{dt^n}$, and so on. The corresponding characteristic equation is

$$a_0\lambda^n + a_1\lambda^{n-1} + \cdots + a_{n-2}\lambda^2 + a_{n-1}\lambda + a_n = 0 \qquad [149.2]$$

The equilibrium is stable if the real parts of the roots of [149.2] are negative, which can be ascertained by the well-known criteria of Routh-Hurwitz. As was previously stated, we never know the exact form of the differential equations in a physical problem because of a number of parasitic parameters either entirely unknown or known only approximately.

Let us assume that Equation [149.1] is a degenerate one derived from some other equation describing more correctly the behavior of the system by taking into account a parasitic parameter α. There are two ways in which this parasitic parameter may appear, depending on whether it is of the "inductance" type or of the "elastance" type.

If it is of the inductance type, the non-degenerate equation will be

$$\alpha x^{(n+1)} + a_0 x^{(n)} + a_1 x^{(n-1)} + \cdots + a_{n-1}\dot{x} + a_n x = 0 \qquad [149.3]$$

If it is of the elastance type, it will be

$$a_0 x^{(n)} + a_1 x^{(n-1)} + \cdots + a_{n-1}\dot{x} + a_n x + \alpha \int x\, dt = 0 \qquad [149.4]$$

Differentiating this equation, we get

$$a_0 x^{(n+1)} + a_1 x^{(n)} + \cdots + a_{n-1}\ddot{x} + a_n \dot{x} + \alpha x = 0 \qquad [149.5]$$

For both types of parasitic parameter the order of the original differential equation has been raised by one unit. The corresponding characteristic equations are

$$\alpha \lambda^{n+1} + a_0 \lambda^n + a_1 \lambda^{n-1} + \cdots + a_{n-1}\lambda + a_n = 0 \qquad [149.6]$$

$$a_0 \lambda^{n+1} + a_1 \lambda^n + a_2 \lambda^{n-1} + \cdots + a_n \lambda + \alpha = 0 \qquad [149.7]$$

They now have $(n+1)$ roots, whereas the original characteristic equation [149.2] had only n roots. Since α is small, by our assumption, the old n roots change but little owing to the appearance of the new root, and we may neglect this change. The matter hinges, therefore, on the new root λ_{n+1}.

We can write Equation [149.2], in terms of its roots, as

$$a_0(\lambda - \lambda_1)(\lambda - \lambda_2) \cdots (\lambda - \lambda_n) = 0 \qquad [149.8]$$

The new characteristic equation [149.6] of the "parasitic inductance" type can accordingly be written as

$$\alpha(\lambda - \lambda_1)(\lambda - \lambda_2) \cdots (\lambda - \lambda_n)(\lambda - \lambda_{n+1}) = \frac{\alpha}{a_0}\Big[a_0\lambda^n +$$

$$+ a_1\lambda^{n-1} + \cdots + a_{n-1}\lambda + a_n\Big](\lambda - \lambda_{n+1}) \qquad [149.9]$$

Expanding the right-hand side of this equation and identifying it with Equation [149.6], we get

$$\lambda_{n+1} = -\frac{a_0}{\alpha} \qquad [149.10]$$

Applying a similar argument to Equation [149.7], we obtain

$$\lambda_{n+1} = -\frac{\alpha}{a_n} \qquad [149.11]$$

The sign of the new root λ_{n+1} indicates its effect on the stability of equilibrium. The general integral of the new system is

$$x = C_1 e^{\lambda_1 t} + C_2 e^{\lambda_2 t} + \cdots + C_n e^{\lambda_n t} + C_{n+1} e^{\lambda_{n+1} t} \qquad [149.12]$$

If the conditions of stability for the original degenerate equation [149.1] are fulfilled, the stability of the new equation [149.3] or [149.5] will depend solely on the new root λ_{n+1}. If this root is *stable*, that is, if its real part is negative, the equilibrium will still be stable. If, however, the root λ_{n+1} is unstable, the non-degenerate system will be unstable although the corresponding degenerate system is stable. For a complete discussion, one must apply the Routh-Hurwitz criteria, as usual.

In practical problems the existence of parasitic parameters is generally unknown; still less known is the magnitude of such parameters. For these reasons in a complicated physical problem one is never certain about the actual conditions of stability. This is why one occasionally observes somewhat puzzling departures from theoretical predictions based on a simplified study of a system expressed in terms of differential equations with known parameters.

Conclusions obtained from the simple discussion given above may appear to some extent paradoxical. Thus, for instance, if the parasitic parameter is of the "inductance" type, see Equation [149.10], the new root λ_{n+1} is larger as the parasitic parameter α is smaller. If, however, it is of the "elastance" type, see Equation [149.11], the magnitude of the root λ_{n+1} is proportional to α.

The rather erratic "floating" of a system around its theoretical position of equilibrium can sometimes be traced to the effects of parasitic parameters, as we shall see from a few typical examples in the following sections.

150. EFFECT OF PARASITIC PARAMETERS ON STABILITY OF AN ELECTRIC ARC

The question of the stability of an electric arc was the subject of considerable controversy in the past (19) (20). In Section 21 this matter was investigated in detail by means of Liapounoff's equations of the first approximation on the basis of a differential equation with finite parameters L, C, and ρ. The behavior of the arc is far more complex if some of these parameters are small, a condition which results in a degenerate form of the differential equation describing the process.

Using the notation of Section 21, we recall that the differential equations are

$$L\frac{di}{dt} = V - \psi(i); \qquad C\frac{dV}{dt} = \frac{E - V - Ri}{R} \qquad [150.1]$$

where i is the arc current, V is the potential difference across the capacitor, and $\psi(i) = V_a$ is the non-linear characteristic of the arc, see Figure 150.1. As was explained in Section 21, there are either three equilibrium

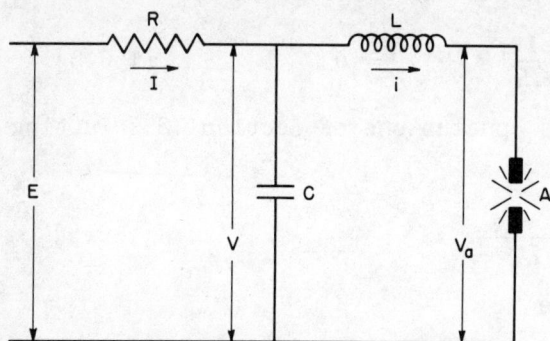

Figure 150.1

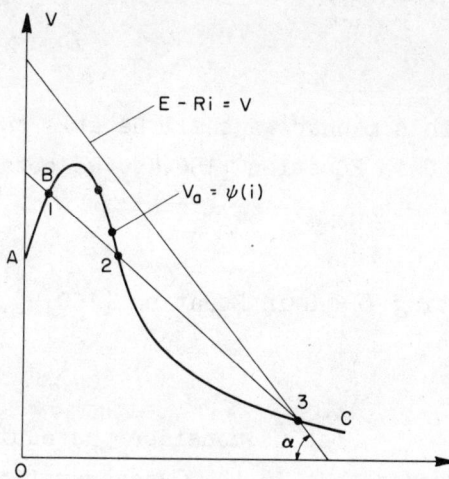

Figure 150.2

points (Points 1, 2, and 3) or one such
point (Point 3), as shown in Figure
150.2, depending on the orientation of
the straight line $E - Ri$ with respect to the characteristic $\psi(i)$.

It was shown that for small departures, v of voltage and j of arc
current, from the corresponding equilibrium values, the equations of the
first approximation are

$$\frac{dv}{dt} = -\frac{v}{RC} - \frac{j}{C}; \qquad \frac{dj}{dt} = \frac{v}{L} - j\frac{\rho}{L} \qquad [150.2]$$

where $\rho = \psi'(i_0)$ is the slope of the tangent to the characteristic $\psi(i_0)$ at
the point $i = i_0$. The characteristic equation of the system is

$$\lambda^2 + \left(\frac{1}{RC} + \frac{\rho}{L}\right)\lambda + \frac{1}{LC}\left(1 + \frac{\rho}{R}\right) = 0 \qquad [150.3]$$

When there are three points of equilibrium, it is observed that Point 1 corresponds to $\rho = \psi'(i_0) > 0$. This point is always stable because the real parts
of the roots of Equation [150.3] are negative. It is, therefore, either a
stable nodal, or a stable focal, point according to whether the roots are real
or conjugate complex. At Point 2 the equilibrium is unstable because $\rho < 0$
and, moreover, $|\rho| > R$. This point, therefore, is a saddle point. Point 3 is
a point of stable equilibrium because, although at this point $\rho < 0$, $|\rho| < R$.

Having recalled these conclusions of Section 21, we propose to investigate now what happens to these various conditions of equilibrium when
the system undergoes a degeneration, that is, when one of the two *oscillatory
parameters* L and C approaches zero. We may distinguish two cases of degeneration, namely, C-degeneration when $C \to 0$ and L-degeneration when $L \to 0$.

In order to investigate the C-degeneration, it is convenient to
write Equation [150.3] as

$$C\lambda^2 + \left(\frac{1}{R} + \frac{C\rho}{L}\right)\lambda + \frac{1}{LR}(R + \rho) = 0 \qquad [150.4]$$

For the investigation of the *L*-degeneration we will write it as

$$L\lambda^2 + \left(\frac{L}{RC} + \rho\right)\lambda + \frac{1}{CR}(R + \rho) = 0 \qquad [150.5]$$

In this manner we shall be able to use the conclusions of Section 128. Putting *C* = 0 in Equation [150.4], we obtain

$$\lambda = -\frac{R + \rho}{L} \qquad [150.6]$$

Putting *L* = 0 in Equation [150.5], we have

$$\lambda = -\frac{1}{CR\rho}(R + \rho) \qquad [150.7]$$

Let us consider the equilibrium at Point 2 of Figure 150.2. It is observed that in the *C*-degeneration this point is still unstable. In the *L*-degeneration, it is stable. A considerable controversy existed on this subject in the technical literature before this question was completely understood. The following explanation was suggested by S. Chaikin (20) (21).

Let us consider the characteristic equation

$$a\lambda^2 + b\lambda + c = 0 \qquad [150.8]$$

with *a* > 0 and *c* < 0, which characterizes a saddle point; see Section 18. We can define saddle points as *positive* when *b* > 0 and as *negative* when *b* < 0. In the case of *a*-degeneration, a positive saddle point gives rise to a positive root and, hence, to unstable equilibrium. If, however, the saddle point is negative, the degenerate system has stable equilibrium at this point. Thus the *a*-degeneration reverses the stability at Point 2 of Figure 150.2. Since in both cases Point 2 corresponds to a saddle point of the system, we conclude that the only way to obtain stability under this condition is to have the representative point follow a stable separatrix.* If, however, it follows the stable separatrix, there exists a fixed relation between *x* and *y* = $\dot{x}$ in the phase plane. But this is precisely what happens in a degenerate system described by a differential equation of the first order, see Equation [128.3]. The condition of degeneration thus *imposes* this singular trajectory, the only one which is stable in the neighborhood of a saddle point. In this case, therefore, a threshold exists similar to that which exists for the asymptotic motion of a pendulum approaching a point of unstable equilibrium, see Section 4, Case 3; such a case is never obtained in practice since there exist no absolutely degenerate systems, that is, systems in which *a* = 0.

---

* Only in a purely theoretical case when the motion of the representative point takes place along the stable separatrix or asymptote of a saddle point, may the latter be considered as a *stable* singularity. If the actual motion of the representative point occurs in the neighborhood of this theoretical motion, it may appear that the saddle point is a stable singularity, at least for a limited time. In view of this, one could characterize the saddle point as an *almost unstable* singularity.

For practical purposes, if precautions are made to reduce the parasitic parameter to a very low value, the representative point will follow a
trajectory very closely to the stable separatrix so that one has the impression that the phenomenon would ultimately "settle" at Point 2 as if it were a
point of stable equilibrium. In reality, sooner or later the representative
point will depart from this point as a result of accidental disturbances.

By a similar argument one finds that Point 3 of stable equilibrium
for a non-degenerate system may become unstable in the case of L-degeneration,
as follows from Equation [150.1] in which $\rho < 0$ and $|\rho| < R$.

Point 1 is stable both for the non-degenerate and the degenerate
systems. It is thus seen that the assumption of absolute degeneration may
lead to conclusions at variance with experimental facts as far as the question of stability is concerned.

151. EFFECT OF PARASITIC PARAMETERS ON STABILITY OF RELAXATION OSCILLATIONS

As another example of the same sort, we shall investigate the behavior of the circuit shown in Figure 135.1, taking into account the presence of
the small parasitic inductances L and L' shown in Figure 151.1. Kirchhoff's
equations for this circuit are

$$I + i = I_a; \qquad L\frac{dI}{dt} + RI - ri - L_1\frac{di}{dt} - \frac{1}{C}\int i\,dt = 0 \qquad [151.1]$$

Moreover, $I_a = \phi(kri)$ as before. Elimination of I_a and I between
these equations results in the equations

$$\frac{di}{dt} = \frac{R\phi(kri) - (R + r)i - V}{L + L' - Lkr\phi'(kri)}; \qquad \frac{dV}{dt} = \frac{i}{C} \qquad [151.2]$$

The conditions of equilibrium are obviously $i = 0$ and $R\phi(0) - V = 0$. On the

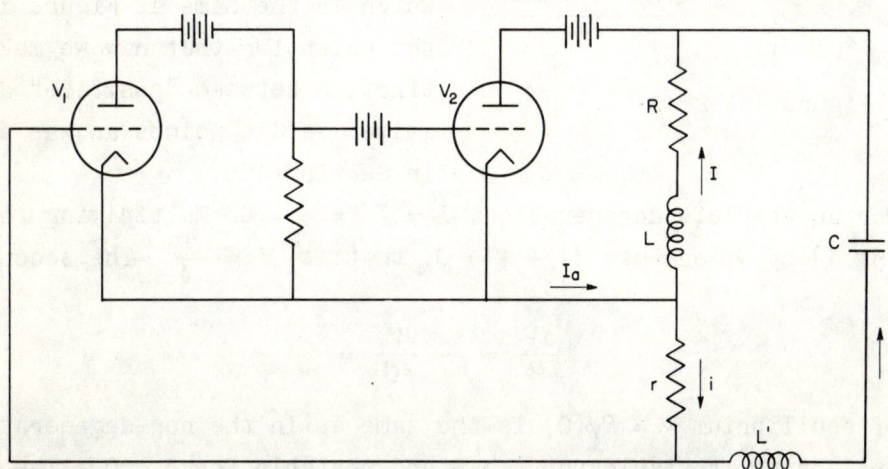

Figure 151.1

other hand, for small departures from equilibrium, we can write

$$\phi(kri) = \phi(0) + kri\phi'(0) + \cdots$$

Limiting the expansion to the first term and noting that $\phi'(0) = S$, the Liapounoff equations of the first approximation are

$$\frac{di}{dt} = -\frac{\delta}{\gamma}i - \frac{V}{\gamma}; \quad \frac{dV}{dt} = \frac{i}{C} \qquad [151.3]$$

where

$$\delta = r + R(1 - Skr) \quad \text{and} \quad \gamma = L' + L(1 - Skr) \qquad [151.4]$$

The characteristic equation of the system [151.3] is

$$\lambda^2 + \frac{\delta}{\gamma}\lambda + \frac{1}{\gamma C} = 0 \qquad [151.5]$$

and its roots are

$$\lambda_{1,2} = \frac{-\delta \pm \sqrt{\delta^2 - \frac{4\gamma}{C}}}{2\gamma} \qquad [151.6]$$

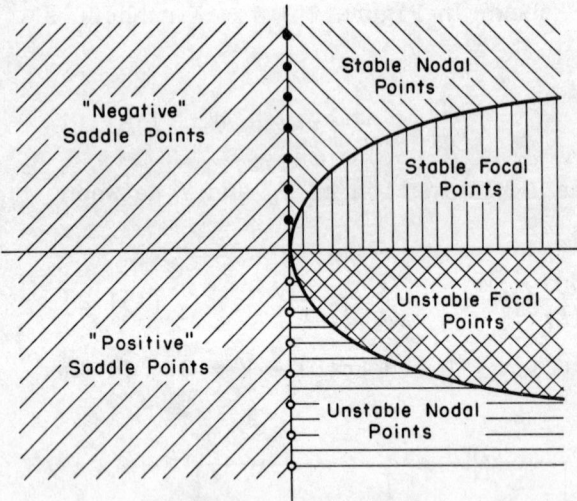

Figure 151.2

For $\gamma < 0$ the roots are real and of opposite sign; hence, the singularity is a saddle point. For $\gamma > 0$, the singularity is either a nodal point or a focal point, depending on whether the roots are real or conjugate complex. If they are conjugate complex, with $\delta > 0$, the singularity is stable; with $\delta < 0$, it is unstable. The distribution of singularities is shown in Figure 151.2, which is the same as Figure 18.1 with the exception that now we make a distinction between "positive" and "negative" saddle points as was explained in Section 150.

For an absolute degeneration, $L = L' = \gamma = 0$. Multiplying the first equation [151.3] by γ, one has $\delta i + V = 0$, that is, $i = -\frac{V}{\delta}$. The second equation gives

$$\frac{dV}{dt} = -\frac{V}{\delta C} \qquad [151.7]$$

The point of equilibrium $V = R\phi(0)$ is the same as in the non-degenerate system. The equilibrium is stable for $\delta > 0$ and unstable for $\delta < 0$. The points of stable equilibrium are indicated by solid points on the positive axis of ordinates and those of unstable equilibrium by circles on the negative axis of ordinates. It is seen that the region of stable equilibrium is localized in the region of "negative" saddle points and that of unstable equilibrium in the region of "positive" ones. It was shown, however, in the preceding section that such stability is of theoretical interest only, because it is impossible in practice to prescribe the initial conditions accurately enough to make the representative point follow the stable separatrix, just as it is impossible to impart to a pendulum a velocity just sufficient to produce an asymptotic motion. Moreover, no physical system is completely degenerate, but is only quasi-degenerate.

The situation is still further complicated by the fact that stability conditions are influenced not only by the existence of parasitic parameters but also by their *relative importance*. In order to show this, assume, for instance, that $L \neq 0$, $L' = 0$, $1 - Skr < 0$, but R is sufficiently small to render $\delta = r + R(1 - Skr)$ positive. In such a case the equilibrium is unstable for any value of L, however small, because the real part of the roots is positive, that is, $\delta > 0$ and $\gamma < 0$. In a degenerate system, where $L = L' = 0$, the equilibrium is stable, however, as follows from Equation [151.7]. Since any physical system is only quasi-degenerate, we conclude that the equilibrium is unstable in this case.

If we consider now the second case, when $L' \neq 0$, the situation is different. Let us assume, as previously, that $1 - Skr < 0$. It is obvious that, by giving L' a suitable value, the quantity $\gamma = L' + L(1 - Skr)$ can be made positive and since $\delta = r + R(1 - Skr)$ is also positive, as previously assumed, it follows from Equation [151.6] that the equilibrium is stable. Hence, the equilibrium which was unstable for $L \neq 0$, $L' = 0$ becomes stable for $L = 0$, $L' \neq 0$. Thus the change from stability to instability depends here on the ratio L/L' of the parasitic parameters.

Since in practice one is seldom sure of the existence of parasitic parameters, much less of their relative values, the predetermination of stability conditions for a circuit of this kind becomes altogether meaningless. It is likely that floating, erratic excitation and similar phenomena still little explored can be explained on this basis.

To sum up the results of this analysis, it can be stated that, in general, the effect of parasitic parameters is negligible in practice unless the system happens to be in the neighborhood of a branch point of equilibrium. If the system is in such a neighborhood, even a small "cause" may exert an appreciable "effect" on the system, and its behavior then becomes entirely unpredictable.

REFERENCES

(1) "On Relaxation Oscillations," by B. Van der Pol, Philosophical Magazine, 7th Series, Vol. 2, November 1926.

(2) "Über Relaxationschwingungen" (On Relaxation Oscillations), by B. Van der Pol, Zeitschrift für Hochfrequenztechnik, Vol. 28, 1926, and Vol. 29, 1927.

(3) "Über Kippschwingungen insbesondere bei Elektronenröhren" (On Sweep Oscillations in Electron Tubes), by E. Friedländer, Archiv für Elektrotechnik, Vol. 17, No. 1, September 1926, and Vol. 18, No. 2, October 1926.

(4) "Reissdiagramme von Senderröhren" (Graphical Diagram for Transmitting Tubes), by H. Rukop, Zeitschrift für Technische Physik, Vol. 5, 1924.

(5) "Eine neue Schaltung zur Erzeugung von Schwingungen mit linearem Spannungsverlauf" (New Wiring Connection for Generating Oscillations with Linear Voltage Curvature), by G. Frühauf, Archiv für Elektrotechnik, Vol. 21, No. 5, February 1929.

(6) "Zur Theorie des rückgekoppelten Röhrensenders" (On the Theory of Regenerative Coupled Vacuum Tube), by F. Kirschstein, Zeitschrift für Hochfrequenztechnik, Vol. 33, No. 6, June 1929.

(7) "Über Schwingungszeugung mittels eines Elektronröhrensystems bei welchem die Kapazität von untergeordneter Bedeutung ist" (On the Excitation of Oscillations by Means of a Vacuum-Tube System in Which Capacity Is of Subordinate Importance), by K. Heegner and I. Watanabe, Zeitschrift für Hochfrequenztechnik, Vol. 34, No. 2, August 1929.

(8) "Über symmetrische Kippschwingungen und ihre Synchronisierung" (On Symmetrical Relaxation Oscillations and Their Synchronization), by H.E. Hollmann, Elektrische Nachrichtentechnik, Vol. 8, No. 10, October 1931.

(9) "On the Theory of the Frühauf Circuit," by L.P. Cholodenko, Journal of Technical Physics, USSR, (Russian), Vol. 5, 1935.

(10) "Les systemes autoentretenues et les oscillations de relaxation" (Self-Excited Systems and Relaxation Oscillations), by Ph. LeCorbeiller, Hermann, Paris, 1931.

(11) "On the Existence of Periodic Solutions of Second Order Differential Equations," by N. Levinson, Journal of Mathematics and Physics, Vol. 22, 1943.

(12) "On Van der Pol's and Related Non-Linear Differential Equations," by J.A. Shohat, Journal of Applied Physics, Vol. 15, 1944.

(13) "Theory of Oscillations," by A. Andronow and S. Chaikin, Moscow, (Russian), 1937.

(14) "Oscillations discontinues" (Discontinuous Oscillations), by S. Chaikin and L. Lochakow, Journal of Technical Physics, USSR, (Russian), Vol. 5, 1935.

(15) "Mesure en valeur absolue des périodes des oscillations électriques de haute fréquence" (Absolute Value of Periods of High-Frequency Electric Oscillations), by H. Abraham and E. Bloch, Annales de Physique, Vol. 12, No. 9, 1919.

(16) "Über Schwingungszeugung mittels eines Elektronröhrensystems welche Selbstinduction nicht erhalten" (On the Excitation of Oscillations by Means of an Electron-Tube System without Self-Induction), by K. Heegner, Zeitschrift für Hochfrequenztechnik, Vol. 29, 1927.

(17) "Zur hydrodynamischen Theorie der Schmiermittelreibung" (On the Hydrodynamic Theory of Lubricating-Oil Friction), by A. Sommerfeld, Zeitschrift für Mathematik und Physik, Vol. 50, 1904.

(18) "Mechanical Relaxation Oscillations," by S. Chaikin and N. Kaidanowsky, Journal of Technical Physics, USSR, (Russian), Vol. 3, 1933.

(19) "Warum kehren sich die für den Lichtbogen gültigen Stabilitätsbedingungen bei Elektronenröhren um?" (Why Do the Conditions of Stability Valid for an Electric Arc Light Reverse in Electron Tubes?), by H. Barkhausen, Physikalische Zeitschrift, Vol. 27, No. 2, February 1926.

(20) "Über Stabilitätsbedingungen und ihre Abhängigkeit von Steuerorganen" (On Stability Conditions as Functions of Control Elements), by E. Friedländer, Physikalische Zeitschrift, Vol. 27, 1926.

(21) "Effect of Small Parameters on the Stationary State of a Dynamical System," by S. Chaikin, Journal of Technical Physics, USSR, (Russian), Vol. 5, 1935.

Bogoliuboff, 2-3,67,135,137,181,210,234 (*see also*
Kryloff and Bogoliuboff)
method of equivalent linearization of, 137,209,
233
notation of, 254,263
quasi-linear theory of, 4,234,244,249,258,331,
342
theory of first approximation of, 183,186-188,
209,258,289,323
treatise of, 251,288,303

Boltzmann, theory of, 5

Bowshewerow, 73

Branch point
of equilibrium, 3,42,48,55,60,82,165,445
of limit cycles, 88

Brillouin, M., 355

Canonical equation, 45

Canonical form, 329
of linear equations, 42-44
of non-linear system,52

Cartan, E. and H., 105,181

Cartan-Liénard, conditions of, 182

Cauchy's theorem
of existence for solution of differential
equation, 2,9
of existence of linear differential equation, 2
of phase trajectories, 11,14
of uniqueness, 24

Chaikin, E., 351

Chaikin, S., 3-4,75,135,137,381,383,405,409,420,
422,426,429-430,442

Change of equations, 427-428,433

Characteristic equation, 14,18,42,44-45,47,57-58,
102,114,120,138,173,179,311,313,318,329,345,
347,358,389,411,414,438-439,441-442,444
for transient state of quasi-linear system, 264
of linear circuit, 269
of non-linear system, 268

Characteristic exponents, 83-85,154-155,329

Characteristic parameter, 323

Classification of singularities, 42,47

Clock
elementary theory of, 424-426
limit cycles in, 67-68
self-excitation of, 426,429
theory of, 429

Coalescence
of equilibrium points, 33
of frequencies, 279,341,351
of limit cycles, 72-73,166
of singular points, 127,349-350
of singularities, 29,34,36-37,39

Coefficient of restitution, 383,437

Combination frequencies, 273-274,278-279,286,
290,296,301

Combination harmonics, 273-274,276,286,294

Combination oscillations, 295

Combination tones, definition of, 272

Complex admittance, 253,256

Complex amplitudes, 254
method of, 251-252,255-256,258-259,262

Complex impedance, 253,256

Conditional stability, range of, 61

Conservative system, 7,23,25,38,40,42,106,128,161,
185,189,224,267,362,375-376
cylindrical phase trajectories of, 118-119
equilibrium of, 40
motion of, 42
oscillations of, 214
periodic motion in, 62-63
points of equilibrium in, 34

Constant linear parameter, 317

Constant parameter, 201,252,370,435
linear dissipative system with, 258

Continuum
of circles, 326
of closed curves, 62,119
of closed trajectories, 12-13,62,140-141
of phase trajectories, 62,128,407

Coulomb damping, 195
negative, 433
positive, 433

Coulomb friction, 426-427,429-431,433
existence of, 426
negative, 430
phase trajectories in presence of, 427-429

Coupled electronic oscillators, stability of, 158

Coupled frequencies, 265,278

Coupling
autoparametric non-linear, 375
between degrees of freedom, 253,270
critical value of, 340
inductive, 260
lack of, 254
non-linear,375

Coupling factor, 253

Criteria
for existence
of critical point, 393-394
of focal point, 13
of limit cycle, 75-77
of nodal point, 13
of saddle point, 13
of Bendixson, 75,77-79,105,345,411
application of, 79-82
of Kaufmann for stability, 61
of Liapounoff for stability, 48-49,311-312
application of, 49-55
of Poincaré, 105,165
of Poincaré-Liapounoff for stability, 311-312
of Routh-Hurwitz for stability, 156,438,440
of stability, 22-23,33,333
applied to non-linear system, 3,55
of equilibrium, 60-61
of singularities, 47

Critical damping, 371

Critical points, 31,38,102,395,399,401-406,408-409,
412-415,419-423
criteria for existence of, 393-394
locus of, 394,406-407
of differential equations, 392-395
theory of, 130

453

Equitime interval, 367

Equivalent Balance of Energy, Principle of, 181, 233,236-238

Equivalent linear equation, 235-236

Equivalent linear impedance, 281

Equivalent linear system, 236,281,286

Equivalent linearization
  for multiperiodic systems, 274-278
  method of, 137,233-236,269,279,288,297,314
    applied to steady state of quasi-linear sys-
      tem, 258-262
    applied to transient state of quasi-linear
      system, 262-267
    examples of application of, 239-245
    in quasi-linear systems with several fre-
      quencies, 285-288
    principle of, 239,258,275,277,309

Equivalent linearized equation, 244

Equivalent linearized system, 314
  self-excitation of, 278

Equivalent parameter, 236-239,241,281-283,297,
    310,314,316-317
  critical value of, 234,278
  definition of, 234-235,286
  determination of, 233-236
  non-linear, 277
  of multiperiodic system, 275

Euler's identity, 251

Exchange of stability, 34,38

Excitation
  asynchronous, 234,295,298
  autoparametric, 355-356,374-377
    condition for, 374
  autoperiodic, 297-298,305
  external, 289,335-336,340
    absence of, 337-344
    system with, 289
  external periodic, 249,289,294,313,317,320,335,
    342,376
    of quasi-linear systems, 289-300
    system with, 323
  heteroparametric, 355-356,360,363,373-374
    conditions of, 356,371
    dependence on frequency and phase of parameter
      variation, 365-369
    of dissipative system, 369-371
    principal features of, 367-369
  heteroperiodic, 298,355-356
    absence of, 299
  non-resonant external, of quasi-linear system,
    294-295
  parametric, 4,249,308-313,355-377
    definition of, 308
    of critically damped or overdamped circuit,
      371
  periodic non-resonant, 289-292

Existence
  of autoperiodic oscillation, 295-300
  of closed trajectories, 21,108-113,129
  of critical point, criteria for, 393-394
  of focal point, criteria for, 13
  of limit cycles, 99,181-182,198,200-203,224-
    229,348
    condition for, 169,173,176,179,199,207,227
    criteria for, 75-77
    proof of, 79

Existence - *continued*
  of nodal point, criteria for, 13
  of periodic solution, 105-115,121,144-145,220,224
    condition for, 136,152
    geometrical analysis of, 105-115
    in non-conservative system, 224-229
    proof of, 105
  of principal solution, 333
    conditions for, 335
  of saddle point, criterion for, 13
  of self-excited oscillations, 181

Expansions of Poincaré, 141

External excitation, 289,335-336,340
  absence of, 337-344
  non-resonant, 294-295
  system with, 289

External frequency, 307,341,348,351,353-354

External periodic excitation, 249,289,294,313,317,
    320,335,342,376
  of quasi-linear systems, 289-300
  system with, 323

Externally applied frequency, 336,340

Faraday-Maxwell theory, 124

Fleming, 5

Floquet, theorem of, 357

Focal point, 16,18,22,69-70,75-77,79,101-103,114,
    120,123,125,127,347,349,386,388,397,407,
    415-416,431,433-434,441,444
  criterion of existence of, 13
  definition of, 13
  motion in neighborhood of, 13
  stability of, 47-48,57-60,88-89,91-92,97,99,
    165-166,175-177,202
  stable, 13,202
  unstable, 13,311

Fractional-order resonance, 301,303,305-309,373

Franck, A., 6

Frequency
  acoustic entrainment of, 342,351-352
  autoperiodic, 297-299,325,342,349
  coalescence of, 279,341,351
  combination, 273-274,278-279,286,290,296,301
  correction, 174,193,217-219,240
  coupled, 265,278
  demultiplication, 272-273
  demultiplication network, 352
  entrainment of, *see* Entrainment of frequency
  enternal, 307,341,348,351,353-354
  externally applied, 336,340
  harmonics of, 296
  heteroperiodic, 297-301,348-349
  of pendulum, 342
  of quasi-linear oscillation, 217
  of ripple, 363,365,367-368
  of self-excited non-linear system, 265
  of self-excited oscillations, 261
  of subharmonic oscillation, 336
  of thermionic generator, 158-159
  synchronization of, 352,354

Friction
  Coulomb, 426-427,429-431,433
    existence of, 426
    negative, 430
    phase trajectories in presence of, 427-429